ALGEBRA 1

Solution Key

A Beka Book® Pensacola, FL 32523-9100
an affiliated ministry of PENSACOLA CHRISTIAN COLLEGE®

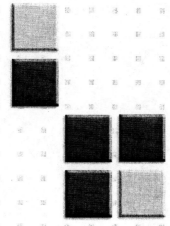

***Algebra 1* Solution Key**
Second Edition

A Beka Book, a Christian textbook ministry affiliated with Pensacola Christian College, is designed to meet the need for Christian textbooks and teaching aids. The purpose of this publishing ministry is to help Christian schools reach children and young people for the Lord and train them in the Christian way of life.

UNIT 1 — Introduction to Algebra

Exercises 1.1   Pages 1-3

1. 110
2. 15¢
3. 15 oz.
4. 16; 4
5. The product of b and c; The product of 2, b, and c; 12; 18
6. 40
7. 2; 6
8. 2; 4
9. 4;3
   $\frac{5a}{6}$ or $\frac{5}{6}a$
   $\frac{3x}{8}$ or $\frac{3}{8}x$
10. x+y; 10
11. 1900
12. 175 days
13. 13,000
14. 132 oranges
15. 70; 45
16. 19; 54
17. 6500
18. 10; 14 - a; 17; 14 + y
19. 5c
20. t + 2
21. p - 10
22. $\frac{d}{10}$; 10d
23. 2m
24. $\frac{c}{2}$
25. 8 and 10; x - 1 and x + 1; a - 1 and a + 1
26. y - 2 and y + 2; y - 1 and y + 1

Exercises 1.2   Page 4

1. (a) x + 5 = 18 (b) x + 8 = 15 (c) x + 7 = 22 (d) x + 2 = 12
   (e) x + 6 = 25 (f) 4x = 28 (g) 5x = 35 (h) x + 50 = 180
   (i) x + 60 = 120 (j) 2x + 1 = 21 (k) 3x - 1 = 20 (l) x - 7 = 8
   (m) $\frac{3}{4}x = 18$ or $\frac{3x}{4} = 18$
2. Twelve decreased by a number is five.
3. b; m + 2 = 28
4. Seventeen more than a number is thirty-five.
5. Five times a number is thirty-five.
6. Five more than a number is eighteen.
7. $\frac{3}{4}x = 20$ or $\frac{3x}{4} = 20$
8. $\frac{1}{2}x = 16$

Exercises 1.3   Pages 5-6

1. $x = 10$ 2. $n = 16$ 3. $w = 3$ 4. $y = 3$

5. Two more than three times what number is eleven? $b = 3$

6. One less than twice what number is thirteen? $a = 7$

7. Three increased by what number is seventeen? $x = 14$

8. What number decreased by five is fifteen? $x = 20$

9. Eighteen is three times what number? $x = 6$

10. Nine times what number is forty-five? $r = 5$

11. Three more than twice what number is fifteen? $x = 6$

12. Four less than what number is eight? $x = 12$

13. Four more than five times what number is twenty-four? $a = 4$

14. One less than four times what number is fifteen? $a = 4$

15. One half of what number is three? $x = 6$

16. One more than one half of what number is eleven? $x = 20$

17. Two thirds of what number is ten? $z = 15$

18. Three fourths of what number is twelve? $r = 16$

19. Twenty decreased by what number equals sixteen? $x = 4$

20. One increased by twice what number is seventeen? $x = 8$

21. Eighteen equals what number increased by five? $x = 13$

22. Sixteen decreased by what number is two? $x = 14$

23. Five increased by twice what number is twenty-five? $m = 10$

24. Three less than four times what number is twenty-nine? $x = 8$

25. The sum of two thirds of what number and one third of the number is eight? $x = 8$

26. Twenty-six is one more than five times what number? $a = 5$

27. Four increased by twice what number is twenty-four? $x = 10$

28. Six equals what number divided by 100? $x = 600$

Exercises 1.4a Page 7

1.
$$x + 5 = 8$$
$$x + 5 - 5 = 8 - 5$$
$$x = 3$$

2.
$$y + 7 = 12$$
$$y + 7 - 7 = 12 - 7$$
$$y = 5$$

3.
$$z + 9 = 16$$
$$z + 9 - 9 = 16 - 9$$
$$z = 7$$

4.
$$a + 12 = 15$$
$$a + 12 - 12 = 15 - 12$$
$$a = 3$$

5.
$$30 = m + 5$$
$$30 - 5 = m + 5 - 5$$
$$25 = m$$

6.
$$10 = x + 4$$
$$10 - 4 = x + 4 - 4$$
$$6 = x$$

7.
$$12 = c + 2$$
$$12 - 2 = c + 2 - 2$$
$$10 = c$$

8.
$$x + 1.5 = 4.5$$
$$x + 1.5 - 1.5 = 4.5 - 1.5$$
$$x = 3$$

9.
$$x + 4.1 = 10.1$$
$$x + 4.1 - 4.1 = 10.1 - 4.1$$
$$x = 6$$

10.
$$x + .03 = 7.25$$
$$x + .03 - .03 = 7.25 - .03$$
$$x = 7.22$$

Exercises 1.4b Page 7

1.
$$2x = 10$$
$$\frac{2x}{2} = \frac{10}{2}$$
$$x = 5$$

2.
$$4x = 12$$
$$\frac{4x}{4} = \frac{12}{4}$$
$$x = 3$$

3.
$$2r = 26$$
$$\frac{2r}{2} = \frac{26}{2}$$
$$r = 13$$

4.
$$4a = 18$$
$$\frac{4a}{4} = \frac{18}{4}$$
$$a = \frac{9}{2}$$

5.
$$8 = 2y$$
$$\frac{8}{2} = \frac{2y}{2}$$
$$4 = y$$

6.
$$42 = 10b$$
$$\frac{42}{10} = \frac{10b}{10}$$
$$\frac{21}{5} = b$$

7.
$$3.0 = 1.5n$$
$$\frac{3.0}{1.5} = \frac{1.5n}{1.5}$$
$$2 = n$$

8.
$$4.5 = 1.5c$$
$$\frac{4.5}{1.5} = \frac{1.5c}{1.5}$$
$$3 = c$$

Exercises 1.4c Page 8

1.
$$x - 49 = 78$$
$$x - 49 + 49 = 78 + 49$$
$$x = 127$$

2.
$$x - \frac{3}{4} = \frac{1}{3}$$
$$x - \frac{3}{4} + \frac{3}{4} = \frac{1}{3} + \frac{3}{4}$$
$$x = \frac{13}{12}$$

3.
$$c - 279 = 402$$
$$c - 279 + 279 = 402 + 279$$
$$c = 681$$

4.
$$m - 22 = 49$$
$$m - 22 + 22 = 49 + 22$$
$$m = 71$$

5.
$$p - 5\tfrac{1}{2} = 6\tfrac{1}{5}$$
$$p - 5\tfrac{1}{2} + 5\tfrac{1}{2} = 6\tfrac{1}{5} + 5\tfrac{1}{2}$$
$$p = 11\tfrac{7}{10}$$

6.
$$t - 2005 = 4416$$
$$t - 2005 + 2005 = 4416 + 2005$$
$$t = 6421$$

7.
$$y - 15 = 6\tfrac{1}{7}$$
$$y - 15 + 15 = 6\tfrac{1}{7} + 15$$
$$y = 21\tfrac{1}{7}$$

8.
$$z - 4.06 = 9.4$$
$$z - 4.06 + 4.06 = 9.4 + 4.06$$
$$z = 13.46$$

9.
$$a - .0029 = 50.03$$
$$a - .0029 + .0029 = 50.03 + .0029$$
$$a = 50.0329$$

Exercises 1.4d   Page 9

1. addition axiom
2. addition axiom
3. subtraction axiom
4. multiplication axiom
5. division axiom

6.
$$\frac{x}{2} = 3$$
$$2\left(\frac{x}{2}\right) = 2\cdot 3$$
$$x = 6$$

7.
$$\frac{a}{6} = 3$$
$$6\left(\frac{a}{6}\right) = 6\cdot 3$$
$$a = 18$$

8.
$$\frac{n}{4} = 2.5$$
$$4\left(\frac{n}{4}\right) = 4(2.5)$$
$$n = 10$$

9.
$$\frac{n}{5} = 2$$
$$5\left(\frac{n}{5}\right) = 5(2)$$
$$n = 10$$

10.
$$\frac{1}{2}s = 1.6$$
$$2\left(\frac{1}{2}s\right) = 2(1.6)$$
$$s = 3.2$$

11.
$$\frac{1}{5}a = 3.1$$
$$5\left(\frac{1}{5}a\right) = 5(3.1)$$
$$a = 15.5$$

Exercises 1.5   Pages 10-11

1.
$$a + 6 = 10$$
$$a + 6 - 6 = 10 - 6$$
$$a = 4$$

2.
$$3x = 18$$
$$\frac{3x}{3} = \frac{18}{3}$$
$$x = 6$$

3.
$$36 = 4m$$
$$\frac{36}{4} = \frac{4m}{4}$$
$$9 = m$$

4.
$$2y + 3y = 45$$
$$5y = 45$$
$$\frac{5y}{5} = \frac{45}{5}$$
$$y = 9$$

5. $$\begin{aligned} 40 &= 5x + 4x + x \\ 40 &= 10x \\ \frac{40}{10} &= \frac{10x}{10} \\ 4 &= x \end{aligned}$$

6. $$\begin{aligned} x - 2 &= 8 \\ x - 2 + 2 &= 8 + 2 \\ x &= 10 \end{aligned}$$

7. $$\begin{aligned} \frac{x}{2} &= 3 \\ 2\cdot\frac{x}{2} &= 2\cdot 3 \\ x &= 6 \end{aligned}$$

8. $$\begin{aligned} \frac{x}{3} &= 5 \\ 3\cdot\frac{x}{3} &= 3\cdot 5 \\ x &= 15 \end{aligned}$$

9. $$\begin{aligned} 56 + z &= 98 \\ 56 - 56 + z &= 98 - 56 \\ z &= 42 \end{aligned}$$

10. $$\begin{aligned} 29 &= 2a - 11 \\ 29 + 11 &= 2a - 11 + 11 \\ 40 &= 2a \\ \frac{40}{2} &= \frac{2a}{2} \\ 20 &= a \end{aligned}$$

11. $$\begin{aligned} \frac{2}{3}x &= 12 \\ \frac{3}{2}\left(\frac{2}{3}x\right) &= \frac{3}{2}(12) \\ x &= 18 \end{aligned}$$
or
$$\begin{aligned} \frac{2}{3}x &= 12 \\ 3\left(\frac{2}{3}x\right) &= 3(12) \\ 2x &= 36 \\ \frac{2x}{2} &= \frac{36}{2} \\ x &= 18 \end{aligned}$$

12. $$\begin{aligned} 8a - 3 &= 29 \\ 8a - 3 + 3 &= 29 + 3 \\ 8a &= 32 \\ \frac{8a}{8} &= \frac{32}{8} \\ a &= 4 \end{aligned}$$

13. $$\begin{aligned} 16 &= 2y + 9 \\ 16 - 9 &= 2y + 9 - 9 \\ 7 &= 2y \\ \frac{7}{2} &= \frac{2y}{2} \\ \frac{7}{2} &= y \end{aligned}$$

14. $$\begin{aligned} 6t + 9 &= 27 \\ 6t + 9 - 9 &= 27 - 9 \\ 6t &= 18 \\ \frac{6t}{6} &= \frac{18}{6} \\ t &= 3 \end{aligned}$$

15. $$\begin{aligned} 13 &= 4m - 7 \\ 13 + 7 &= 4m - 7 + 7 \\ 20 &= 4m \\ \frac{20}{4} &= \frac{4m}{4} \\ 5 &= m \end{aligned}$$

16. $$\begin{aligned} 2.5 &= \frac{1}{2}x \\ 2(2.5) &= 2\left(\frac{1}{2}x\right) \\ 5 &= x \end{aligned}$$

17. $$\begin{aligned} 27 &= 6s - 9 \\ 27 + 9 &= 6s - 9 + 9 \\ 36 &= 6s \\ \frac{36}{6} &= \frac{6s}{6} \\ 6 &= s \end{aligned}$$

18. $$\begin{aligned} 2\tfrac{1}{2}x &= 10 \\ \frac{5}{2}x &= 10 \\ \frac{2}{5}\left(\frac{5}{2}x\right) &= \frac{2}{5}(10) \\ x &= 4 \end{aligned}$$
or
$$\begin{aligned} 2\tfrac{1}{2}x &= 10 \\ \frac{5}{2}x &= 10 \\ 2\left(\frac{5}{2}x\right) &= 2\cdot 10 \\ 5x &= 20 \\ \frac{5x}{5} &= \frac{20}{5} \\ x &= 4 \end{aligned}$$

19.
$$\begin{aligned} 6b + b - 2 &= 12 \\ 7b - 2 &= 12 \\ 7b - 2 + 2 &= 12 + 2 \\ 7b &= 14 \\ \frac{7b}{7} &= \frac{14}{7} \\ b &= 2 \end{aligned}$$

20.
$$\begin{aligned} 8y + 11 &= 51 \\ 8y + 11 - 11 &= 51 - 11 \\ 8y &= 40 \\ \frac{8y}{8} &= \frac{40}{8} \\ y &= 5 \end{aligned}$$

21.
$$\begin{aligned} 3x - x - 5 &= 15 \\ 2x - 5 &= 15 \\ 2x - 5 + 5 &= 15 + 5 \\ 2x &= 20 \\ \frac{2x}{2} &= \frac{20}{2} \\ x &= 10 \end{aligned}$$

22.
$$\begin{aligned} 5m + 2m - 6 &= 50 \\ 7m - 6 &= 50 \\ 7m - 6 + 6 &= 50 + 6 \\ 7m &= 56 \\ \frac{7m}{7} &= \frac{56}{7} \\ m &= 8 \end{aligned}$$

23.
$$\begin{aligned} 6a + 2a - 1 &= 15 \\ 8a - 1 &= 15 \\ 8a - 1 + 1 &= 15 + 1 \\ 8a &= 16 \\ \frac{8a}{8} &= \frac{16}{8} \\ a &= 2 \end{aligned}$$

24.
$$\begin{aligned} 5x - 11 &= 19 \\ 5x - 11 + 11 &= 19 + 11 \\ 5x &= 30 \\ \frac{5x}{5} &= \frac{30}{5} \\ x &= 6 \end{aligned}$$

25.
$$\begin{aligned} 35 &= 8n + 15 \\ 35 - 15 &= 8n + 15 - 15 \\ 20 &= 8n \\ \frac{20}{8} &= \frac{8n}{8} \\ \frac{5}{2} &= n \end{aligned}$$

26.
$$\begin{aligned} 4s + 2\tfrac{1}{2} &= 6\tfrac{1}{2} \\ 4s + 2.5 &= 6.5 \\ 4s + 2.5 - 2.5 &= 6.5 - 2.5 \\ 4s &= 4 \\ \frac{4s}{4} &= \frac{4}{4} \\ s &= 1 \end{aligned}$$

27.
$$\begin{aligned} 2\tfrac{1}{3}s + \tfrac{2}{3}s &= 6 \\ 3s &= 6 \\ \frac{3s}{3} &= \frac{6}{3} \\ s &= 2 \end{aligned}$$

28.
$$\begin{aligned} 5.2y - 3.2y &= 4 \\ 2y &= 4 \\ \frac{2y}{2} &= \frac{4}{2} \\ y &= 2 \end{aligned}$$

29.
$$\begin{aligned} 1\tfrac{1}{2}y - 1 &= 2 \\ 1.5y - 1 + 1 &= 2 + 1 \\ 1.5y &= 3 \\ \frac{1.5y}{1.5} &= \frac{3}{1.5} \\ y &= 2 \end{aligned}$$

or

$$\begin{aligned} 1\tfrac{1}{2}y - 1 &= 2 \\ 1\tfrac{1}{2}y - 1 + 1 &= 2 + 1 \\ 1\tfrac{1}{2}y &= 3 \\ \tfrac{3}{2}y &= 3 \\ \tfrac{2}{3}(\tfrac{3}{2}y) &= \tfrac{2}{3}(3) \\ y &= 2 \end{aligned}$$

30.
$$\begin{aligned} 1.5x + 1.0x &= 7.5 \\ 2.5x &= 7.5 \\ \frac{2.5x}{2.5} &= \frac{7.5}{2.5} \\ x &= 3 \end{aligned}$$

NOTE: In many problems, the answer may be reached by more than one route. The principle students must follow is this: WHATEVER IS DONE TO ONE SIDE OF THE EQUATION MUST BE DONE TO THE OTHER SIDE.

Exercises 1.6 Pages 11-12
(The check is left to the teacher.)

1. $3x = 12$
$\frac{3x}{3} = \frac{12}{3}$
$x = 4$

2. $6 = x + 2$
$6 - 2 = x + 2 - 2$
$4 = x$

3. $a - 2 = 5$
$a - 2 + 2 = 5 + 2$
$a = 7$

4. $10 = x + 2$
$10 - 2 = x + 2 - 2$
$8 = x$

5. $3x + 2 = 8$
$3x + 2 - 2 = 8 - 2$
$3x = 6$
$\frac{3x}{3} = \frac{6}{3}$
$x = 2$

6. $5x + 6 = 21$
$5x + 6 - 6 = 21 - 6$
$5x = 15$
$\frac{5x}{5} = \frac{15}{5}$
$x = 3$

7. $4y - 3 = 13$
$4y - 3 + 3 = 13 + 3$
$4y = 16$
$\frac{4y}{4} = \frac{16}{4}$
$y = 4$

8. $\frac{2}{3}y = 10$
$\frac{3}{2}(\frac{2}{3}y) = \frac{3}{2}(10)$
$y = 15$

9. $\frac{4}{5}a = 20$
$\frac{5}{4}(\frac{4}{5}a) = \frac{5}{4}(20)$
$a = 25$

10. $3n - 2 + 7 = 8$
$3n + 5 = 8$
$3n + 5 - 5 = 8 - 5$
$3n = 3$
$\frac{3n}{3} = \frac{3}{3}$
$n = 1$

11. $2p + \frac{1}{3} = \frac{7}{3}$
$2p + \frac{1}{3} - \frac{1}{3} = \frac{7}{3} - \frac{1}{3}$
$2p = 2$
$\frac{2p}{2} = \frac{2}{2}$
$p = 1$

12. $5n + \frac{1}{2} = 10\frac{1}{2}$
$5n + \frac{1}{2} - \frac{1}{2} = 10\frac{1}{2} - \frac{1}{2}$
$5n = 10$
$\frac{5n}{5} = \frac{10}{5}$
$n = 2$

13. $8x - \frac{1}{4} = 7\frac{3}{4}$
$8x - \frac{1}{4} + \frac{1}{4} = 7\frac{3}{4} + \frac{1}{4}$
$8x = 8$
$\frac{8x}{8} = \frac{8}{8}$
$x = 1$

14. $\frac{3}{4}a = 15$
$\frac{4}{3}(\frac{3}{4}a) = \frac{4}{3}(15)$
$a = 20$

15. $7n + 1.3 = 22.3$
$7n + 1.3 - 1.3 = 22.3 - 1.3$
$7n = 21$
$\frac{7n}{7} = \frac{21}{7}$
$n = 3$

16. $3y + 2.5 - 1.5 = 13$
$3y + 1 = 13$
$3y + 1 - 1 = 13 - 1$
$3y = 12$
$\frac{3y}{3} = \frac{12}{3}$
$y = 4$

Exercises 1.7 Pages 12-13

1. $6(\$.90) = \$5.40$;
   $6c$

2. $70 \cdot 3 = 210$ miles;
   $70 \cdot 4 = 280$ miles;
   $70h$ miles

3. $\frac{\$.72}{4} = \$.18$; $5(\$.18) = \$.90$;
   $\$.18n$

4. $m + n$

5. $\frac{m}{3}$; $\frac{t}{3}$; $\frac{2t}{3}$ or $\frac{2}{3}t$

6. $x - s = 2$
   $x = 2 + s$

7.
$$\begin{aligned} 1 - n &= d \\ 1 - n + n &= d + n \\ 1 &= d + n \\ 1 - d &= d - d + n \\ 1 - d &= n \end{aligned}$$

8. $c - 7$; $c + 10$

9. $300 - n$

10. $v + v + 15 = 2v + 15$

11. $2n$; $2n + 5$

12. $4n$; $n + 4n = 5n$; $5n = 30$
$$\frac{5n}{5} = \frac{30}{5}$$
$$n = 6$$
$4n = 24$ boys

13. x in April; $4x$ in March

14. x sold by brother; $\frac{x}{2}$ by Joshua

or $2x$ by brother; x by Joshua

15. $5w$; $P = 2w + 2(5w)$
$$P = 2w + 10w$$
$$P = 12w$$

16. $4s$; $4s = 48$

Exercises 1.8 Pages 13-17

1. See page 13 in text.

2.
   1. let x = the smaller number, 29
   2. $3x$ = the larger number, 87

   sum of parts = sum of parts

   3. $(x) + (3x) = 116$
   4. $4x = 116$
$$\frac{4x}{4} = \frac{116}{4}$$
$$x = 29$$
   5. $29 + 87 = 116$ ✓

3.
1. let x = the smaller number, 18
2. $3x$ = the larger number, 54

sum of parts = sum of parts

3. $(x) + (3x) = 72$
4. $4x = 72$

$\frac{4x}{4} = \frac{72}{4}$

$x = 18$

5. $18 + 54 = 72$ ✓

4.
1. let x = the number, 36
2. $\frac{1}{2}x$ = $\frac{1}{2}$ of the number, 18

sum of parts = sum of parts

3. $(x) + (\frac{1}{2}x) = 54$
4. $\frac{3}{2}x = 54$

$\frac{2}{3}(\frac{3}{2}x) = \frac{2}{3}(54)$

$x = 36$

5. $36 + 18 = 54$ ✓

5.
1. let x = the number, 105
2. $\frac{1}{5}x$ = $\frac{1}{5}$ of the number, 21

difference of parts = difference of parts

3. $(x) - (\frac{1}{5}x) = 84$
4. $\frac{4}{5}x = 84$

$\frac{5}{4}(\frac{4}{5}x) = \frac{5}{4}(84)$

$x = 105$

5. $105 - 21 = 84$ ✓

6.-7. See page 14 in text.

8.
1. let w = width, 1/4"
2. $3w$ = length, 3/4"

perimeter = perimeter

3. $2w + 2(3w) = 2$
4. $2w + 6w = 2$

$8w = 2$

$\frac{8w}{8} = \frac{2}{8}$

$w = \frac{1}{4}$

5. $\frac{1}{4} + \frac{1}{4} + \frac{3}{4} + \frac{3}{4} = \frac{8}{4} = 2$ ✓

9.
1. let x = width, 15"
2. $x + 4$ = length, 19"

perimeter = perimeter

3. $2(x) + 2(x+4) = 68$
4. $2x + 2x + 8 = 68$

$4x + 8 = 68$

$4x + 8 - 8 = 68 - 8$

$4x = 60$

$\frac{4x}{4} = \frac{60}{4}$

$x = 15$

5. $15 + 15 + 19 + 19 = 68$ ✓

10.
1. let n = the number of weeks in which Susan and Katie will have the same amount of money, 12
2. $2n$ = amount of Susan's deposit each week

n = amount of Katie's deposit each week

Susan's amount in n weeks = Katie's amount in n weeks

3. $48 + 2n = 60 + n$
4. $48 + 2n - n = 60 + n - n$

$48 + n = 60$

$48 - 48 + n = 60 - 48$

$n = 12$

5. $48 + 24 = 72$ Susan's amount; $60 + 12 = 72$ Katie's amount ✓

11. See page 15 in text.

12.
1. let x = shipment for home ports (millions), 10
2. $4x$ = shipment for foreign ports (millions), 40

total loaded = total loaded

3. $x + 4x = 50$
4. $5x = 50$

$$\frac{5x}{5} \quad \frac{50}{5}$$

$$x = 10$$

5. 10
+40
50 ✓

13.
1. let x = faculty score, 2
2. $2x$ = students score, 4

total runs scored = total runs scored   4 to 2

3. $(x) + (2x) = 6$
4. $3x = 6$

$$\frac{3x}{3} = \frac{6}{3}$$

$$x = 2$$

5. 4
+2
6 ✓

14.
1. let x = equal angles, 62.5^0
2. sum of angles = sum of angles
3. $(x) + (x) + (55) = 180$
4. $2x + 55 = 180$

$$2x + 55 - 55 = 180 - 55$$

$$2x = 125$$

$$\frac{2x}{2} = \frac{125}{2}$$

$$x = 62.5$$

5. 62.5
62.5
+55
180 ✓

15.
1. let x = distance in morning, 105 miles
2. $3x$ = distance in afternoon, 315 miles

total distance = total distance

3. $(x) + (3x) = 420$
4. $4x = 420$

$$\frac{4x}{4} \quad \frac{420}{4}$$

$$x = 105$$

5. 105
+315
420 ✓

16.
1. let x = cost of Nathan's radio, \$25
2. $4x$ = cost of John's radio, \$100

cost of both sets = cost of both sets

3. $(x) + (4x) = 125$
4. $5x = 125$

$$\frac{5x}{5} = \frac{125}{5}$$

$$x = 25$$

5. 25
+100
125 ✓

17\. 1. let x = number of seniors, 48
2\. x + 48 = number of freshmen, 96

total freshmen and seniors = total freshmen and seniors

3\. $(x) + (x + 48) = 144$

4\. $2x + 48 - 48 = 144 - 48$

$$2x = 96$$

$$\frac{2x}{2} = \frac{96}{2}$$

$$x = 48$$

5\.
```
  48
 +96
 144 ✓
```

18\. 1. let x = number of games lost, 4
2\. 4x = number of games won, 16

16 wins
4 losses

total games played = total games played

3\. $(x) + (4x) = 20$

4\. $5x = 20$

$$\frac{5x}{5} = \frac{20}{5}$$

$$x = 4$$

5\.
```
   4
 +16
  20 ✓
```

19\. 1. let x = amount from advertising, \$181
2\. 2x = amount from tickets, \$362

amount received = amount received

3\. $(x) + (2x) = 543$

4\. $3x = 543$

$$\frac{3x}{3} = \frac{543}{3}$$

$$x = 181$$

5\.
```
  181
 +362
  543 ✓
```

20\. 1. let x = length of side, 9"
2\. ----

perimeter = perimeter

3\. $4s = 36$

4\. $\frac{4s}{4} = \frac{36}{4}$

$$s = 9$$

5\.
```
  9
  9
  9
 +9
 36 ✓
```

21\. 1. let c = length of side **c**, 8"
2\. 2c = lengths of sides **a** and **b**, 16"

perimeter = perimeter

3\. $(c) + (2c) + (2c) = 40$

4\. $5c = 40$

$$\frac{5c}{5} = \frac{40}{5}$$

$$c = 8$$

5\.
```
   8
  16
 +16
  40 ✓
```

22\. 1. let w = width, 8"
2\. 2w = length, 16"

perimeter = perimeter

3\. $2w + 2(2w) = 48$

4\. $2w + 4w = 48$

$$6w = 48$$

$$\frac{6w}{6} = \frac{48}{6}$$

$$w = 8$$

5\.
```
   8
   8
  16
 +16
  48 ✓
```

23\. 1. let p = third part, 3
2\. 2p = second part, 6
4p = first part, 12

sum of parts = sum of parts

3\. $p + 2p + 4p = 21$

4\. $7p = 21$

$$\frac{7p}{7} = \frac{21}{7}$$

$$p = 3$$

5\.
```
   6
  12
 + 3
  21 ✓
```

24. 1. let x = sales by second boy, 10
2. $2x$ = sales by first boy, 20
$3x$ = sales by third boy, 30
total sold = total sold
3. $(2x) + (x) + (3x) = 60$
4. $6x = 60$
$\frac{6x}{6} = \frac{60}{6}$
$x = 10$
5. 20
10
+30
60 ✓

25. 1. let x = length of first side, 12"
2. $x + 4$ = length of second side, 16"
$x - 3$ = length of third side, 9"
perimeter = perimeter
3. $(x) + (x + 4) + (x - 3) = 37$
4. $3x + 1 = 37$
$3x + 1 - 1 = 37 - 1$
$3x = 36$
$\frac{3x}{3} \quad \frac{36}{3}$
$x = 12$
5. 12
16
+ 9
37 ✓

26. 1. let x = wages of each helper, $60
2. $4x$ = wages of plumber, $240
total wages = total wages
3. $(x) + (x) + (4x) = 360$
4. $6x = 360$
$\frac{6x}{6} = \frac{360}{6}$
$x = 60$
5. 60
60
+240
360 ✓

27. 1. let s = cost of saddle, $360
2. $3s$ = cost of pony, $1080
cost of both = cost of both
3. $(3s) + (s) = 1440$
4. $4s = 1440$
$\frac{4s}{4} = \frac{1440}{4}$
$s = 360$
5. 360
+1040
1440 ✓

28. 1. let x = one part of 92, 69
2. $\frac{1}{3}x$ = other part of 92, 23
sum of parts = sum of parts
3. $(x) + (\frac{1}{3}x) = 92$
4. $\frac{4}{3}x = 92$
$\frac{3}{4}(\frac{4}{3}x) = \frac{3}{4}(92)$
$x = 69$
5. 69
+23
92 ✓

29. 1. let x = number of skaters, 1000
2. $3x$ = number of spectators, 3000
total at rink = total at rink
3. $(x) + (3x) = 4000$
4. $4x = 4000$
$\frac{4x}{4} \quad \frac{4000}{4}$
$x = 1000$
5. 1000
+ 3000
4000 ✓

30.
1. let x = length of first side, 9"
2. x + 3 = length of second side, 12"
x + 5 = length of third side, 14"
perimeter = perimeter
3. (x) + (x + 3) + (x + 5) = 35
4. 3x + 8 = 35
3x + 8 - 8 = 35 - 8
3x = 27
$\frac{3x}{3} = \frac{27}{3}$
x = 9
5. 9
12
+14
35 ✓

31.
1. let x = degrees in equal angle, 55°
2. x + 15 = degrees in third angle, 70°
sum of angles = sum of angles
3. (x) + (x) + (x + 15) = 180
4. 3x + 15 = 180
3x + 15 - 15 = 180 - 15
3x = 165
$\frac{3x}{3} = \frac{165}{3}$
x = 55
5. 55
55
+70
180 ✓

32.
1. let x = cost/dozen cheaper balls, $16.20
2. x + 3 = cost/dozen expensive balls, $19.20
total cost = total cost
3. (x) + (x + 3) = 35.40
4. 2x + 3 = 35.40
2x + 3 - 3 = 35.40 - 3
2x = 32.40
$\frac{2x}{2} \quad \frac{32.40}{2}$
x = 16.20
5. 16.20
+19.20
35.40 ✓

33.
1. let x = number of rainy days, 8
2. x + 11 = number of cloudy days, 19
x + 14 = number of clear days, 22
total days = total days
3. (x) + (x + 11) + (x + 14) = 7(7)
4. 3x + 25 = 49
3x + 25 - 25 = 49 - 25
3x = 24
$\frac{3x}{3} = \frac{24}{3}$
x = 8
5. 8
19
+22
49 ✓

34.
1. let x = number of girls, 18
2. 2x - 12 = number of boys, 24
class total = class total
3. (x) + (2x - 12) = 42
4. 3x - 12 = 42
3x - 12 + 12 = 42 + 12
3x = 54
$\frac{3x}{3} \quad \frac{54}{3}$
x = 18
5. 18
+24
42 ✓

35.
1. let x = size of audience, 198
2. $\frac{1}{3}x + 18$ = outside guests
guests = guests
3. $\frac{1}{3}x + 18 = 84$
4. $\frac{1}{3}x + 18 - 18 = 84 - 18$
$\frac{1}{3}x = 66$
$3(\frac{1}{3}x) = 3(66)$
x = 198
5. 66
+18
84 ✓

36. 1. let x = amount earned first day, $21
2. x + 6.25 = amount earned second day
x + 12.50 = amount earned third day
three days earnings = three days earnings
3. $(x) + (x + 6.25) + (x + 12.50) = 81.75$
4. $3x + 18.75 = 81.75$

$$3x + 18.75 - 18.75 = 81.75 - 18.75$$
$$3x = 63$$
$$\frac{3x}{3} = \frac{63}{3}$$
$$x = 21$$

5.
$$\begin{array}{r} 21.00 \\ 27.25 \\ +33.50 \\ \hline 81.75 \end{array} \checkmark$$

37. 1. let x = first week, 4
2. 2x = second week, 8
4x = third week, 16
8x = fourth week, 32
fourth week = fourth week
3. $8x = 32$
4. $\frac{8x}{8} = \frac{32}{8}$

$$x = 4$$

5.
$$\begin{array}{r} 8 \\ \times 4 \\ \hline 32 \end{array} \checkmark$$

38. 1. let x = first week, 6
2. 2x = second week, 12
4x = third week, 24
8x = fourth week, 48
total earnings = total earnings
3. $(x) + (2x) + (4x) + (8x) = 90$
4. $15x = 90$

$$\frac{15x}{15} = \frac{90}{15}$$
$$x = 6$$

5.
$$\begin{array}{r} 6 \\ 12 \\ 24 \\ +48 \\ \hline 90 \end{array} \checkmark$$

39. 1. let x = the number, 13
2. 2x + 9 = twice a number increased by 9

3. $2x + 9 = 35$
4. $2x + 9 - 9 = 35 - 9$

$$2x = 26$$
$$\frac{2x}{2} = \frac{26}{2}$$
$$x = 13$$

5.
$$\begin{array}{r} 13 \\ \times 2 \\ \hline 26 \\ +9 \\ \hline 35 \end{array} \checkmark$$

TEST A   Pages 17-18

I.

1. $51 - y$

2. $n + 2$; $n - 1$

3. $3y$; $y - 6$; $3y + 5$; $(y + 8) + (3y + 8) = 4y + 16$

4. $26 + s$; $g - 26$

II. The check is left for the teacher.

1. $$\begin{aligned} 3x &= 15 \\ \frac{3x}{3} &= \frac{15}{3} \\ x &= 5 \end{aligned}$$

2. $$\begin{aligned} \frac{1}{2}x &= 30 \\ 2(\frac{1}{2}x) &= 2(30) \\ x &= 60 \end{aligned}$$

3. $$\begin{aligned} \frac{2}{3}x &= 12 \\ \frac{3}{2}(\frac{2}{3}x) &= \frac{3}{2}(12) \\ x &= 18 \end{aligned}$$

4. $$\begin{aligned} 6 + y &= 19 \\ 6 + y - 6 &= 19 - 6 \\ y &= 13 \end{aligned}$$

5. $$\begin{aligned} z - 7 &= 12 \\ z - 7 + 7 &= 12 + 7 \\ z &= 19 \end{aligned}$$

6. $$\begin{aligned} 6a + 2 &= 20 \\ 6a + 2 - 2 &= 20 - 2 \\ 6a &= 18 \\ \frac{6a}{6} &= \frac{18}{6} \\ a &= 3 \end{aligned}$$

7. $$\begin{aligned} 3y - 5 &= 7 \\ 3y - 5 + 5 &= 7 + 5 \\ 3y &= 12 \\ \frac{3y}{3} &= \frac{12}{3} \\ y &= 4 \end{aligned}$$

8. $$\begin{aligned} 11x - 8x - 8 &= 10 \\ 3x - 8 &= 10 \\ 3x - 8 + 8 &= 10 + 8 \\ 3x &= 18 \\ \frac{3x}{3} &= \frac{18}{3} \\ x &= 6 \end{aligned}$$

III.

1. let x = length of shorter room
   $x + 6$ = length of longer room
   length of room = length of room
   $(x) + (x + 6) = 38$

2. let $4x$ = original price
   x = amount of reduction
   selling price = selling price
   $4x - x = 48$

3. let x = number sold by Carol
   $4x$ = number sold by Tom
   total magazines sold = total magazines sold
   $(x) + (4x) = 35$

4. let x = length of one side
   $x + 3$ = length of second side
   $2x$ = length of third side
   perimeter of triangle = perimeter of triangle
   $(x) + (x + 3) + (2x) = 27$

TEST B   Pages 18

I.

1. $30 - x$

2. $e - 2$; $e + 1$

3. $g - 14$; $s + 14$

4. $2m$; $m - 7$; $2m + 11$; $(m + 5) + (2m + 5) = 3m + 10$

II. The check is left for the teacher.

1. $5x = 30$
$$\frac{5x}{5} = \frac{30}{5}$$
$$x = 6$$

2. $\frac{1}{3}x = 8$
$$3(\frac{1}{3}x) = 3(8)$$
$$x = 24$$

3. $\frac{3}{4}y = 12$
$$\frac{4}{3}(\frac{3}{4}y) = \frac{4}{3}(12)$$
$$y = 16$$

4. $a + 11 = 17$
$$a + 11 - 11 = 17 - 11$$
$$a = 6$$

5. $b - 8 = 4$
$$b - 8 + 8 = 4 + 8$$
$$b = 12$$

6. $8z + 5 = 29$
$$8z + 5 - 5 = 29 - 5$$
$$8z = 24$$
$$\frac{8z}{8} = \frac{24}{8}$$
$$z = 3$$

7. $5x - 2 = 8$
$$5x - 2 + 2 = 8 + 2$$
$$5x = 10$$
$$\frac{5x}{5} = \frac{10}{5}$$
$$x = 2$$

8. $9x - 5x - 11 = 17$
$$4x - 11 = 17$$
$$4x - 11 + 11 = 17 + 11$$
$$4x = 28$$
$$\frac{4x}{4} = \frac{28}{4}$$
$$x = 7$$

III.

1. let x = number of peanut butter
x - 18 = number of oatmeal
total cookies baked = total cookies baked
(x) + (x - 18) = 112

2. let x = earnings of younger
3x = earnings of older
total earned = total earned
(x) + (3x) = 75

3. let x = Greg's age
6x = Father's age
sum of ages = sum of ages
(x) + (6x) = 42

4. let w = width of rectangle
4w = length of rectangle
perimeter = perimeter
2w + 2(4w) = 65

TEST C Page 19

1. 1. let x = number of bus drivers, 3
2. 5x = number of parents, 15
15x = number of boys, 45
15x - 12 = number of girls, 33
total riders = total riders
3. (x) + (5x) + (15x) + (15x - 12) = 96
4. $36x - 12 = 96$
$$36x - 12 + 12 = 96 + 12$$
$$36x = 108$$
$$\frac{36x}{36} = \frac{108}{36}$$
$$x = 3$$

5.
```
  3
 15
 45
+33
---
 96 ✓
```

2\. 1. let x = distance Michelle walks, 1/4 mile
2\. 3x = distance Charity walks, 3/4 mile
distance = distance
3\. $3x - x = \frac{1}{2}$
4\. $2x = \frac{1}{2}$
$\frac{2x}{2} = \frac{1}{2} \cdot \frac{1}{2}$
$x = \frac{1}{4}$
5\. $\frac{3}{4} - \frac{1}{4} = \frac{1}{2}$ ✓

3\. 1. let x = amount Sam earned, \$18
2\. 2x - 3 = amount David earned, \$33
total earned = total earned
3\. $(x) + (2x - 3) = 51$
4\. $3x - 3 = 51$
$3x - 3 + 3 = 51 + 3$
$3x = 54$
$\frac{3x}{3} = \frac{54}{3}$
$x = 18$
5\. \$18
+33
\$51 ✓

4\. 1. let x = number of A's, 6
2\. x + 7 = number of B's, 13
3x = number of C's, 18
x - 1 = number of D's, 5
total pupils = total pupils
3\. $(x) + (x + 7) + (3x) + (x - 1) = 42$
4\. $6x + 6 = 42$
$6x + 6 - 6 = 42 - 6$
$6x = 36$
$\frac{6x}{6} = \frac{36}{6}$
$x = 6$
5\. 6
13
18
+ 5
42 ✓

5\. 1. let x = number of rainy days, 19
2\. 3x + 8 = number of clear days, 65
total days = total days
3\. $(x) + (3x + 8) = 12(7)$
4\. $4x + 8 = 84$
$4x + 8 - 8 = 84 - 8$
$4x = 76$
$\frac{4x}{4} = \frac{76}{4}$
$x = 19$
5\. 19
+65
84 ✓

6\. 1. let x = number of essays, 5
2\. 2x + 8 = number of novels, 18
total books = total books
3\. $(x) + (2x + 8) + 5 = 28$
4\. $3x + 13 = 28$
$3x + 13 - 13 = 28 - 13$
$3x = 15$
$\frac{3x}{3} = \frac{15}{3}$
$x = 5$
5\. 5
5
+18
28 ✓

7\. 1. let x = number of tens, 10
2\. 2x = number of fives, 20
$\frac{1}{2}x$ = number of twenties, 5
value of bills = value of bills
3\. $10x + 5(2x) + 20(\frac{1}{2}x) = 300$
4\. $10x + 10x + 10x = 300$
$30x = 300$
$\frac{30x}{30} = \frac{300}{30}$
$x = 10$
5\. 100
100
+100
300 ✓

8. 1. let x = miles by boat, 6

2. 12x = miles by train, 72

x - 4 = miles by bus, 2

total miles = total miles

3. $(x) + (12x) + (x - 4) = 80$

4.
$$14x - 4 = 80$$
$$14x - 4 + 4 = 80 + 4$$
$$14x = 84$$
$$\frac{14x}{14} = \frac{84}{14}$$
$$x = 6$$

5.
$$\begin{array}{r} 6 \\ 72 \\ +2 \\ \hline 80 \end{array} \checkmark$$

UNIT 2 — The Nature of Algebraic Numbers

Exercises 2.1 Page 21

1. 2
2. 3
3. 1.5
4. $\frac{1}{2}$
5. $\frac{3}{4}$
6. .8

Exercises 2.2a Page 22

1. $p = 2a + 2b$
   $p = 2 \times 4 + 2 \times 6$
   $p = 8 + 12$
   $p = 20$ inches

2. $p = 2a + 2b$
   $p = 2 \times 3 + 2 \times 5$
   $p = 6 + 10$
   $p = 16$ feet

3. $p = 2a + 2b$
   $p = 2 \times 10 + 2 \times 15$
   $p = 20 + 30$
   $p = 50$ meters

4. $p = 2a + 2b$
   $p = 2 \times 5 + 2 \times 7$
   $p = 10 + 14$
   $p = 24$ yards

5. $p = 2a + 2b$
   $p = 2 \times 1\frac{1}{2} + 2 \times 2\frac{1}{2}$
   $p = 3 + 5$
   $p = 8$ inches

6. $p = 2a + 2b$
   $p = 2 \times 2\frac{1}{4} + 2 \times 3\frac{1}{4}$
   $p = 4\frac{1}{2} + 6\frac{1}{2}$
   $p = 11$ feet

7. $p = 2a + 2b$
   $p = 2 \times 1.1 + 2 \times 4.1$
   $p = 2.2 + 8.2$
   $p = 10.4$ inches

8. $p = 2a + 2b$
   $p = 2 \times 2 + 2 \times 4$
   $p = 4 + 8$
   $p = 12$ feet

9. $p = 2a + 2b$
   $p = 2 \times 3 + 2 \times 6$
   $p = 6 + 12$
   $p = 18$ inches

10. $p = 2a + 2b$
    $p = 2 \times 4 + 2 \times 8$
    $p = 8 + 16$
    $p = 24$ meters

Exercises 2.2b Pages 22-23

1. $p = a + b + c$
   $p = 2 + 3 + 4$
   $p = 9$ inches

2. $p = a + b + c$
   $p = 5 + 6 + 3$
   $p = 14$ feet

3. $p = a + b + c$
   $p = 12 + 10 + 8$
   $p = 30$ meters

4. $p = a + b + c$
   $p = 15 + 13 + 11$
   $p = 39$ yards

5. $p = a + b + c$
   $p = 1\frac{1}{2} + 2\frac{1}{2} + 3$
   $p = 7$ inches

6. $p = a + b + c$
   $p = 3.1 + 4.1 + 2.1$
   $p = 9.3$ feet

7. $p = a + b + c$
   $p = 8 + 9 + 10$
   $p = 27$ inches

8. $p = a + b + c$
   $p = 12.1 + 13.1 + 10.1$
   $p = 35.3$ meters

9. $p = a + b + c$
   $p = 6\frac{1}{3} + 7\frac{1}{3} + 8\frac{1}{3}$
   $p = 22$ yards

10. (a) monomial (b) trinomial (c) binomial
    (d) binomial (e) trinomial (f) binomial

Exercises 2.3 Page 23

1. 6a
2. 14x
3. 7x
4. 0
5. 2a + 4b
6. 8x + y
7. 5s + 5t
8. 4c

Exercises 2.4 Page 24

1. 10 x 6 = 60 square inches; 8 x 4 = 32 square feet
2. Multiply the base by the altitude; the product of the altitude and the base
3. 8 x 3 = 24; What is the value of the area when the altitude is 8 and the base is 3?
4. 9 x 7 = 63 square feet
5. 100; 2
6. 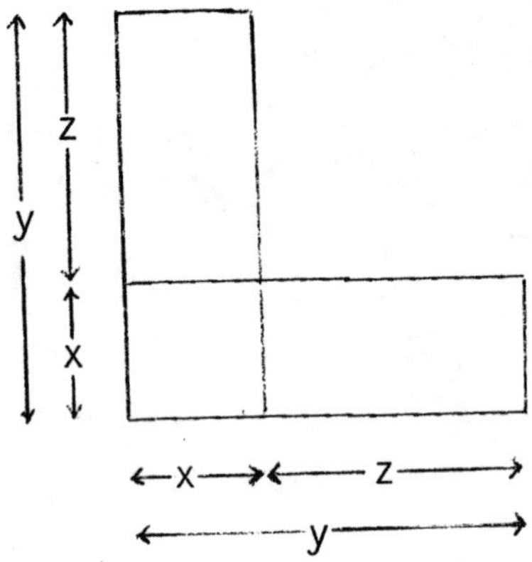

Since area equals base times height, the area of the vertical rectangle is xy, and the area of the horizontal rectangle is yx. Since the two rectangles are congruent, the areas are equal.

Show that ab = ba in the same manner.

7. 5 x 0 = 0
8. 1 x 1 x 2 = 2
9. 0 x 1 x 2 = 0
10. 3 x 0 x 5 = 0

Exercises 2.5 Page 25

1. $n^2 = 8^2 = 64$; $n^2 = 6^2 = 36$; $n^2 = 5^2 = 25$; $n^2 = (1.5)^2 = 2.25$; $n^2 = 10^2 = 100$
2. $5n^2 = 5 \times 2^2 = 5 \times 4 = 20$; $(5n)^2 = 5n \times 5n = 25n^2$
3. 2 in each one
4. 5 x 5 x 5 = 125 cubic inches
5. s is the number of blocks long, s^2 is the number of blocks in one layer, and there are s layers; so $s^2 \cdot s = s^3$
6. $4^3 = 4 \times 4 \times 4 = 64$ cubic feet; $3^3 = 3 \times 3 \times 3 = 27$ cubic inches; $10^3 = 10 \times 10 \times 10 = 1000$ cubic yards

7. An exponent tells how many times to use a number as a factor while a coefficient is a single factor.

8.

$5x^3$	coefficient 5	exponent 3
$3a^2b^4$	coefficient 3	exponent of a is 2, of b is 4
$4m^3n^5$	coefficient 4	exponent of m is 3, of n is 5
$8a^2b^2c^2$	coefficient 8	exponent of a, b, and c is 2
$10x^3y^2z^4$	coefficient 10	exponent of x is 3, of y is 2, of z is 4

<u>Review</u> Pages 26-27

1. 8 divided by 4
2. w divided by v
3. m divided by n
4. the product of a and b divided by the product of 3 and x
5. the sum of a divided by b and r divided by s
6. a minus r divided by the sum of b and s
7. 5 + 2; x + y
8. 9 - 6; m - n
9. 3 x 4 and $3 \cdot 4$; r x s, $r \cdot s$, and rs
10. 8 ÷ 5 and $\frac{8}{5}$; p ÷ q and $\frac{p}{q}$
11. 5d + 2c
12. $ab - 2 \cdot 4$
13. 3mn
14. $\frac{v - w}{cd}$
15. Answer in text
16. Answer in text
17. (a - b)(5m + 2)
18. $\frac{a(a + b)}{b(a - b)}$

<u>Exercises 2.7</u> Pages 27-29

1. x to the 6th power
   $x \cdot x \cdot x \cdot x \cdot x \cdot x$
2. y to the 4th power
   $y \cdot y \cdot y \cdot y$
3. z to the 8th power
   $z \cdot z \cdot z \cdot z \cdot z \cdot z \cdot z \cdot z$
4. x squared, y squared
   $x \cdot x \cdot y \cdot y$
5. a cubed, b cubed
   $a \cdot a \cdot a \cdot b \cdot b \cdot b$
6. r squared, s squared
   $r \cdot r \cdot s \cdot s$
7. 3, w squared, z
   $3 \cdot w \cdot w \cdot z$
8. 4, p cubed, 9 to the fifth
   $4 \cdot p \cdot p \cdot p \cdot q \cdot q \cdot q \cdot q \cdot q$
9. 2, m cubed, n squared
   $2 \cdot m \cdot m \cdot m \cdot n \cdot n$
10. 9 a, b cubed, c squared, d to the fourth
    $9 \cdot a \cdot b \cdot b \cdot b \cdot c \cdot c \cdot d \cdot d \cdot d \cdot d$
11. 5, p squared, q cubed, s to the fourth, t to the fifth
    $5 \cdot p \cdot p \cdot q \cdot q \cdot q \cdot s \cdot s \cdot s \cdot s \cdot t \cdot t \cdot t \cdot t \cdot t$

12. 7, m to the seventh, n to the fourth, x cubed, y
$7 \cdot m \cdot m \cdot m \cdot m \cdot m \cdot m \cdot m \cdot n \cdot n \cdot n \cdot n \cdot x \cdot x \cdot x \cdot y$

13. 2^2 14. 3^3 15. 5^4 16. $3a^3$ 17. $8\ell^3$

18. $9r^3s^2$ 19. 2^3x^2 20. $7z^4$ 21. $3a^2b^3$ 22. 3; a; 3a

23. 5 numerical; a literal; g literal; $\frac{1}{2}g$ mixed

24. a and x 25. 3, m, n, 3m, 3n, mn 26. x and x^2

27. 5, r, s, 5r, 5s, rs, $5r^2$, $5s^2$, r^2s^2, $5r^2s$, $5rs^2$, 5rs, r^2s, s^2r

28. 6, 3, 2, n, 3n, 2n 29. 15, 5, 3, z, 15z, 5z, 3z, z^2, $5z^2$, $3z^2$

*30. p, q, r, s, pq, pr, ps, qr, qs, rs, pqr, pqs, qrs, prs

*31. 24, v, t, 24v, 24t, vt, 2, 2v, 2t, 2vt, 3, 3v, 3t, 3vt, 4, 4v, 4t, 4vt, 6, 6v, 6t, 6vt, 8, 8v, 8t, 8vt, 12, 12v, 12t, 12vt

32. (1) Binomials: $3ax + 2y^2$; $2a + 3b$; $3x + 2b$
(2) Trinomials: $2x^2y - xy + a^2x^2$
(3) Monomials: 2ax; $3x^2y$
(4) Polynomials: All may be considered polynomials.

(5) Similar Terms: 2ax, 3ax, and -4ax
$2y^2$ and $-y^2$
$3x^2y$ and $2x^2y$
a^2x^2 and $3a^2x^2$
2a, 6a, and 3a
3b and 2b
2d and d

(6) Dissimilar Terms: -xy; 3x; -c; $-c^2$; and $-2a^2$

33.
$$\begin{aligned} 3 \times 4 \div 2 \times 3 &= 12 \div 2 \times 3 \\ &= 6 \times 3 \\ &= 18 \end{aligned}$$

34. (a)
$$\begin{aligned} 3 - 2 - 1 + 8 - 3 + 4 &= 1 - 1 + 8 - 3 + 4 \\ &= 0 + 8 - 3 + 4 \\ &= 8 - 3 + 4 \\ &= 5 + 4 \\ &= 9 \end{aligned}$$

(b)
$$\begin{aligned} 5 + 1 - 4 + 3 - 2 + 6 &= 6 - 4 + 3 - 2 + 6 \\ &= 2 + 3 - 2 + 6 \\ &= 5 - 2 + 6 \\ &= 3 + 6 \\ &= 9 \end{aligned}$$

35. $7 + 10 - 6 \div 3 \times 4$
$= 7 + 10 - 2 \times 4$
$= 7 + 10 - 8$
$= 17 - 8$
$= 9$

36. $5 \times 10 - 7$
$= 50 - 7$
$= 43$

37. $5 \times (10 - 7)$
$= 5 \times 3$
$= 15$

38. $2 \times 5 + 3 \times 4$
$= 10 + 3 \times 4$
$= 10 + 12$
$= 22$

39. $(25 - 13) \div 4 \times 2$
$= 12 \div 4 \times 2$
$= 3 \times 2$
$= 6$

40. $16 - 2 \times 2 \times 12 \div 4$
$= 16 - 4 \times 12 \div 4$
$= 16 - 48 \div 4$
$= 16 - 12$
$= 4$

41. $6 + 2 \times 8 - 4 \div 2$
$= 6 + 16 - 4 \div 2$
$= 6 + 16 - 2$
$= 22 - 2$
$= 20$

42. $(6 + 2) \times 8 - 4 \div 2$
$= 8 \times 8 - 4 \div 2$
$= 64 - 4 \div 2$
$= 64 - 2$
$= 62$

43. $(6 + 2 \times 8 - 4) \div 2$
$= (6 + 16 - 4) \div 2$
$= (22 - 4) \div 2$
$= 18 \div 2$
$= 9$

44. $6 + 2 \times (8 - 4) \div 2$
$= 6 + 2 \times 4 \div 2$
$= 6 + 8 \div 2$
$= 6 + 4$
$= 10$

45. $6 + 2 \times (8 - 4 \div 2)$
$= 6 + 2 \times (8 - 2)$
$= 6 + 2 \times 6$
$= 6 + 12$
$= 18$

46. Two x square plus y square;
$2 \cdot x \cdot x + y \cdot y$

47. Three x minus four y;
$3 \cdot x - 4 \cdot y$

48. Four a b minus c cube;
$4 \cdot a \cdot b - c \cdot c \cdot c$

49. Three, x square plus two y minus three z;
$3 \cdot x \cdot x + 2 \cdot y - 3 \cdot z$

50. a square, x square minus three xy plus two z square;
$a \cdot a \cdot x \cdot x - 3 \cdot x \cdot y + 2 \cdot z \cdot z$

51. Five, b square, y plus x square, y square plus five c, z square;
$5 \cdot b \cdot b \cdot y + x \cdot x \cdot y \cdot y + 5 \cdot c \cdot z \cdot z$

52. $5a + 3x^2$

53. $3b - 2a^5$

54. $ab(a - c)$

55. $\frac{3x}{5(a + b + c)}$

56. $7xy + 3z^3$

57. $mn - 6m^2$

58. $a^5(b + c)$

59. $12a^2 - 5b^3$

60. $\frac{8ab}{4c^7}$

61. $a^2 + b^2 - 2ab$

Exercises 2.8 Page 30

1. $10a$
$= 10\cdot 5$
$= 50$

2. $2ab$
$= 2\cdot 5\cdot 3$
$= 10\cdot 3$
$= 30$

3. $3cm$
$= 3\cdot 10\cdot 4$
$= 30\cdot 4$
$= 120$

4. $6bc$
$= 6\cdot 3\cdot 10$
$= 18\cdot 10$
$= 180$

5. $5m^2$
$= 5\cdot 4^2$
$= 5(4\cdot 4)$
$= 5\cdot 16$
$= 80$

6. $2a^2b$
$= 2\cdot 5^2\cdot 3$
$= 2\cdot 25\cdot 3$
$= 50\cdot 3$
$= 150$

7. $3bm^3$
$= 3\cdot 3\cdot 4^3$
$= 3\cdot 3\cdot (4\cdot 4\cdot 4)$
$= 3\cdot 3\cdot 64$
$= 9\cdot 64$
$= 576$

8. $4a^3b$
$= 4\cdot 5^3\cdot 3$
$= 4\cdot (5\cdot 5\cdot 5)\cdot 3$
$= 4\cdot 125\cdot 3$
$= 500\cdot 3$
$= 1500$

9. am^4
$= 5\cdot 4^4$
$= 5\cdot (4\cdot 4\cdot 4\cdot 4)$
$= 5\cdot 256$
$= 1280$

10. $(ab)^2$
$= (5\cdot 3)^2$
$= 15^2$
$= 15\cdot 15$
$= 225$

11. a^2b^2
$= 5^2\cdot 3^2$
$= (5\cdot 5)\cdot (3\cdot 3)$
$= 25.9$
$= 225$

12. $a^b c$
$= 5^3\cdot 10$
$= (5\cdot 5\cdot 5)\cdot 10$
$= 125\cdot 10$
$= 1250$

13. $\frac{1}{3}ab^2$
$= \frac{1}{3}\cdot 5\cdot 3^2$
$= \frac{1}{3}\cdot 5\cdot (3\cdot 3)$
$= \frac{1}{\cancel{3}}\cdot 5\cdot \overset{3}{\cancel{9}}$
$= 15$

14. $\frac{1}{2}bm$
$= \frac{1}{\cancel{2}}\cdot 3\cdot \overset{2}{\cancel{4}}$
$= 6$

15. $\frac{1}{5}abc$
$= \frac{1}{\cancel{5}}\cdot \cancel{5}\cdot 3\cdot 10$
$= 1\cdot 3\cdot 10$
$= 3\cdot 10$
$= 30$

16. $3b^2cm^2$
$= 3\cdot 3^2\cdot 10\cdot 4^2$
$= 3\cdot (3\cdot 3)\cdot 10\cdot (4\cdot 4)$
$= 3\cdot 9\cdot 10\cdot 16$
$= 27\cdot 10\cdot 16$
$= 270\cdot 16$
$= 4320$

17. $3m^2n^2$
$= 3\cdot 0^2\cdot 4^2$
$= 3\cdot (0\cdot 0)\cdot (4\cdot 4)$
$= 3\cdot 0\cdot 16$
$= 0$

18. $7b^2r$
$= 7\cdot 2^2\cdot 0$
$= 0$

19. $\dfrac{3a^2b}{5b}$

$= \dfrac{3\cdot 4^2\cdot 2}{5\cdot 2}$

$= \dfrac{48}{5}$ or 9 3/5

20. $3s^b b^a$
$= 3\cdot 5^2\cdot 2^4$
$= 3\cdot (5\cdot 5)\cdot (2\cdot 2\cdot 2\cdot 2)$
$= 3\cdot 25\cdot 16$
$= 75\cdot 16$
$= 1200$

Key to Unit 2, page 30

21. $\dfrac{a^2bs}{abs^2}$

$= \dfrac{4^2 \cdot 2 \cdot 5}{4 \cdot 2 \cdot 5^2}$

$= \dfrac{(4 \cdot 4) \cdot 2 \cdot 5}{4 \cdot 2 \cdot (5 \cdot 5)}$

$= \dfrac{4}{5}$

22. $\frac{3}{8}a^3br$

$= \frac{3}{8} \cdot 4^3 \cdot 2 \cdot 0$

$= 0$

23. $2^a b^3 s^2 r^4$

$= 2^4 \cdot 2^3 \cdot 5^2 \cdot 0^4$

$= 0$

24. See page 30 in text.

25. $2x + 3x$
$= 2 \cdot 2 + 3 \cdot 2$
$= 4 + 6$
$= 10$
and
$5x$
$= 5 \cdot 2$
$= 10$

$2x + 3x$
$= 2 \cdot 3 + 3 \cdot 3$
$= 6 + 9$
$= 15$
and
$5x$
$= 5 \cdot 3$
$= 15$

Answers vary for the third question.

26. $m(a + b)$
$= 5(4 + 3)$
$= 5 \cdot 7$
$= 35$

$ma + mb$
$= 5 \cdot 4 + 5 \cdot 3$
$= 20 + 15$
$= 35$

Answers vary for the second question.

27. $(a - b)^2$
$= (4 - 2)^2$
$= 2^2$
$= 4$

$a^2 - 2ab + b^2$
$= 4^2 - 2 \cdot 4 \cdot 2 + 2^2$
$= (4 \cdot 4) - 2 \cdot 4 \cdot 2 + (2 \cdot 2)$
$= 16 - 2 \cdot 4 \cdot 2 + 4$
$= 16 - 8 \cdot 2 + 4$
$= 16 - 16 + 4$
$= 0 + 4$
$= 4$

Answers vary for the second question.

28. $a^2 + b^2$
$= 5^2 + 3^2$
$= 25 + 9$
$= 34$

29. $(a + b)^2$
$= (5 + 3)^2$
$= 8^2$
$= 64$

30. $n^5 - 1$
$= 1^5 - 1$
$= (1 \cdot 1 \cdot 1 \cdot 1 \cdot 1) - 1$
$= 1 - 1$
$= 0$

31. $(b - 1)^5$
$= (3 - 1)^5$
$= 2^5$
$= 2 \cdot 2 \cdot 2 \cdot 2 \cdot 2$
$= 4 \cdot 2 \cdot 2 \cdot 2$
$= 8 \cdot 2 \cdot 2$
$= 16 \cdot 2$
$= 32$

32. $ab - bn + mb^2 \div (3mn^2)$
$= 5 \cdot 3 - 3 \cdot 1 + 4 \cdot 3^2 \div (3 \cdot 4 \cdot 1^2)$
$= 5 \cdot 3 - 3 \cdot 1 + 4 \cdot 9 \div (3 \cdot 4 \cdot 1)$
$= 15 - 3 + 36 \div 12$
$= 15 - 3 + 3$
$= 12 + 3$
$= 15$

33. $(ab - bn + mb^2) \div (3\ mn^2)$
$= (5 \cdot 3 - 3 \cdot 1 + 4 \cdot 3^2) \div (3 \cdot 4 \cdot 1^2)$
$= (5 \cdot 3 - 3 \cdot 1 + 4 \cdot 9) \div (3 \cdot 4 \cdot 1)$
$= (15 - 3 + 36) \div (3 \cdot 4 \cdot 1)$
$= 48 \div 12$
$= 4$

Review Pages 31-32

1. Monomial
$6t$
$= 6 \cdot 10$
$= 60$

2. Monomial
$7t$
$= 7 \cdot 10$
$= 70$

3. Binomial-Polynomial
$9t + 9$
$= 9 \cdot 10 + 9$
$= 90 + 9$
$= 99$

4. Monomial
t^2
$= 10^2$
$= 10 \cdot 10$
$= 100$

5. Trinomial-Polynomial
$t^2 + 2t + 1$
$= 10^2 + 2 \cdot 10 + 1$
$= 100 + 20 + 1$
$= 121$

6. Trinomial-Polynomial
$3t^2 + 6t + 5$
$= 3 \cdot 10^2 + 6 \cdot 10 + 5$
$= 3 \cdot 100 + 6 \cdot 10 + 5$
$= 300 + 60 + 5$
$= 365$

7. Monomial
t^3
$= 10^3$
$= 10 \cdot 10 \cdot 10$
$= 100 \cdot 10$
$= 1000$

8. Polynomial
$t^3 + 2t^2 + 5t + 4$
$= 10^3 + 2 \cdot 10^2 + 5 \cdot 10 + 4$
$= 1000 + 2 \cdot 100 + 5 \cdot 10 + 4$
$= 1000 + 200 + 50 + 4$
$= 1254$

9. Polynomial
$5t^3 + 3t^2 + 8t + 6$
$= 5 \cdot 10^3 + 3 \cdot 10^2 + 8 \cdot 10 + 6$
$= 5 \cdot 1000 + 3 \cdot 100 + 8 \cdot 10 + 6$
$= 5000 + 300 + 80 + 6$
$= 5386$

10. (a) $25 = 20 + 5$
$= 2 \cdot 10 + 5$
$= 2t + 5$

$523 = 500 + 20 + 3$
$= 5 \cdot 100 + 2 \cdot 10 + 3$
$= 5 \cdot 10^2 + 2 \cdot 10 + 3$
$= 5t^2 + 2t + 3$

$4867 = 4000 + 800 + 60 + 7$
$= 4 \cdot 1000 + 8 \cdot 100 + 6 \cdot 10 + 7$
$= 4 \cdot 10^3 + 8 \cdot 10^2 + 6 \cdot 10 + 7$
$= 4t^3 + 8t^2 + 6t + 7$

(b) $732 = 700 + 30 + 2$
$= 7 \cdot 100 + 3 \cdot 10 + 2$
$= 7 \cdot 10^2 + 3 \cdot 10 + 2$
$= 7t^2 + 3t + 2$

$893 = 800 + 90 + 3$
$= 8 \cdot 100 + 9 \cdot 10 + 3$
$= 8 \cdot 10^2 + 9 \cdot 10 + 3$
$= 8t^2 + 9t + 3$

11. (a) two times a; a times a

(b)

when $a = 1$	$2a = 2 \cdot 1 = 2$	$a^2 = 1 \cdot 1 = 1$
when $a = 2$	$2a = 2 \cdot 2 = 4$	$a^2 = 2 \cdot 2 = 4$
when $a = 3$	$2a = 2 \cdot 3 = 6$	$a^2 = 3 \cdot 3 = 9$
when $a = \frac{1}{2}$	$2a = 2 \cdot \frac{1}{2} = 1$	$a^2 = \frac{1}{2} \cdot \frac{1}{2} = \frac{1}{4}$
when $a = \frac{1}{3}$	$2a = 2 \cdot \frac{1}{3} = \frac{2}{3}$	$a^2 = \frac{1}{3} \cdot \frac{1}{3} = \frac{1}{9}$

(c) 2; 0

12. $2^3 = 2\cdot2\cdot2 = 8$
$3^2 = 3\cdot3 = 9$

3^2 is greater

$4^2 = 4\cdot4 = 16$
$2^4 = 2\cdot2\cdot2\cdot2 = 16$

$4^2 = 2^4$

$2^5 = 2\cdot2\cdot2\cdot2\cdot2 = 32$
$5^2 = 5\cdot5 = 25$

2^5 is greater

$2^3 = 2\cdot2\cdot2 = 8$
$2^2 = 2\cdot2 = 4$

2^3 is greater

$(\frac{1}{2})^3 = \frac{1}{2}\cdot\frac{1}{2}\cdot\frac{1}{2} = \frac{1}{8}$
$(\frac{1}{2})^2 = \frac{1}{2}\cdot\frac{1}{2} = \frac{1}{4}$

$(\frac{1}{2})^2$ is greater

$1^3 = 1\cdot1\cdot1 = 1$
$1^2 = 1\cdot1 = 1$

$1^3 = 1^2$

13. decreased; increased

14. $3x = 3\cdot1 = 3$

$4x^2 = 4\cdot1\cdot1 = 4$

$6x^3 = 6\cdot1\cdot1\cdot1 = 6$

$8x^5 - 4x^4 + 2x^3 - x + 5$
$= 8\cdot1^5 - 4\cdot1^4 + 2\cdot1^3 - 1 + 5$
$= 8\cdot1 - 4\cdot1 + 2\cdot1 - 1 + 5$
$= 8 - 4 + 2 - 1 + 5$
$= 10$

1; 2; 3; 5, 4, 3, and 1

15. 2, 1, $\frac{1}{2}$, b, $3b^2$, a^2b^3

16. Answers will vary.

17. Multiply together n factors of a
$\underbrace{a\cdot a\cdot a\cdot \ldots\ldots a}_{n \text{ factors}}$

18. $6ab = 6\cdot5\cdot4 = 30\cdot4 = 120$

$2cd = 2\cdot3\cdot2 = 6\cdot2 = 12$

$4nbd = 4\cdot3\cdot4\cdot2 = 12\cdot4\cdot2 = 48\cdot2 = 96$

$\frac{1}{2}ea = \frac{1}{2}\cdot1\cdot5 = \frac{1}{2}\cdot5 = \frac{5}{2}$

$nd^{n+1} = 3\cdot2^{3+1} = 3\cdot2^4 = 3\cdot16 = 48$

19. $3a^2b = 3\cdot5^2\cdot4 = 3\cdot25\cdot4 = 75\cdot4 = 300$

$3ab^2 = 3\cdot5\cdot4^2 = 3\cdot5\cdot16 = 15\cdot16 = 240$

$3(ab)^2 = 3\cdot(5\cdot4)^2 = 3\cdot20^2 = 3\cdot400 = 1200$

$d^2n^3 = 2^2\cdot3^3 = 4\cdot27 = 108$

$(dn)^3 = (2\cdot3)^3 = 6^3 = 216$

$d^{n-2} = 2^{3-2} = 2^1 = 2$

20. $a + b \div d - n \div e = 5 + 4 \div 2 - 3 \div 1$
$= 5 + 2 - 3$
$= 4$

21. $a(b-d)+a-n\div c = 5(4-2)+5-3\div 3$
$= 5\cdot 2+5-1$
$= 10+5-1$
$= 14$

22. $10\div d+3\div n-e = 10\div 2+3\div 3-1$
$= 5+1-1$
$= 5$

23. $10\div(d+3)+ac\div n = 10\div(2+3)+5\cdot 3\div 3$
$= 10\div 5+5\cdot 3\div 3$
$= 2+15\div 3$
$= 2+5$
$= 7$

24. $c^5+c^4+2c^3-2c^2-3c+3 = 3^5+3^4+2\cdot 3^3-2\cdot 3^2-3\cdot 3+3$
$= 243+81+2\cdot 27-2\cdot 9-9+3$
$= 243+81+54-18-9+3$
$= 354$

25. $a^4+b^5-c^2-d^2+e^6 = 5^4+4^5-3^2-2^2+1^6$
$= 625+1024-9-4+1$
$= 1637$

26. $d^7+d^6+3d^5-5d^4+2d^3-4d^2+8d-1$

$= 2^7+2^6+3\cdot 2^5-5\cdot 2^4+2\cdot 2^3-4\cdot 2^2+8\cdot 2-1$
$= 128+64+3\cdot 32-5\cdot 16+2\cdot 8-4\cdot 4+8\cdot 2-1$
$= 128+64+96-80+16-16+16-1$
$= 223$

27. $12x = 72$
$\frac{12x}{12} = \frac{72}{12}$
$x = 6$

28. $3n = 21$
$\frac{3n}{3} = \frac{21}{3}$
$n = 7$

29. $n+3n = 40$
$4n = 40$
$\frac{4n}{4} = \frac{40}{4}$
$n = 10$

30. $6n-4n = 13$
$2n = 13$
$\frac{2n}{2} = \frac{13}{2}$
$n = \frac{13}{2}$

31. $4a = 1280$
$\frac{4a}{4} = \frac{1280}{4}$
$a = 320$

32. $2n-\frac{1}{3}n = 24$
$1\frac{2}{3}n = 24$
$\frac{5}{3}n = 24$
$\frac{3}{5}\cdot\frac{5}{3}n = 24\cdot\frac{3}{5}$
$n = \frac{72}{5}$

33. $m+2m = 18$
$3m = 18$
$\frac{3m}{3} = \frac{18}{3}$
$m = 6$

34. $5-d+x$

35. $5-\frac{c}{100}x$

Time Tests   Pages 32-33

(A)

1.
$$\begin{aligned} &2x^2 - 3xy \\ &= 2\cdot 3^2 = 3\cdot 3\cdot 2 \\ &= 2\cdot 9 = 3\cdot 3\cdot 2 \\ &= 18 - 9\cdot 2 \\ &= 18 - 18 \\ &= 0 \end{aligned}$$

2.
$$\begin{aligned} &3mn + nm^2 \\ &= 3\cdot 4\cdot 3 + 3\cdot 4^2 \\ &= 3\cdot 4\cdot 3 + 3\cdot 16 \\ &= 36 + 48 \\ &= 84 \end{aligned}$$

3.
$$\begin{aligned} &ab^2 - 2ab \\ &= 3\cdot 2^2 - 2\cdot 3\cdot 2 \\ &= 3\cdot 4 - 2\cdot 3\cdot 2 \\ &= 12 - 6\cdot 2 \\ &= 12 - 12 \\ &= 0 \end{aligned}$$

4.
$$\begin{aligned} &\frac{x^2}{2} + \frac{4xy}{5} \\ &= \frac{2^2}{2} + \frac{4\cdot 2\cdot 5}{5} \\ &= \frac{4}{2} + \frac{40}{5} \\ &= 2 + 8 \\ &= 10 \end{aligned}$$

5.
$$\begin{aligned} &a^2 + 3a^2b \\ &= 2^2 + 3\cdot 2^2\cdot 4 \\ &= 4 + 3\cdot 4\cdot 4 \\ &= 4 + 48 \\ &= 52 \end{aligned}$$

6.
$$\begin{aligned} &5a^2 - 2ac \\ &= 5\cdot 2^2 - 2\cdot 2\cdot 3 \\ &= 5\cdot 4 - 2\cdot 2\cdot 3 \\ &= 20 - 12 \\ &= 8 \end{aligned}$$

7.
$$\begin{aligned} &3ab + a^2b \\ &= 3\cdot 2\cdot 3 + 2^2\cdot 3 \\ &= 3\cdot 2\cdot 3 + 4\cdot 3 \\ &= 18 + 12 \\ &= 30 \end{aligned}$$

8.
$$\begin{aligned} &5x^2 - y^2 \\ &= 5\cdot 3^2 - 5^2 \\ &= 5\cdot 9 - 25 \\ &= 45 - 25 \\ &= 20 \end{aligned}$$

9.
$$\begin{aligned} &\frac{a^2}{3} + \frac{4ay}{6} \\ &= \frac{3^2}{3} + \frac{4\cdot 3\cdot 4}{6} \\ &= \frac{9}{3} + \frac{48}{6} \\ &= 3 + 8 \\ &= 11 \end{aligned}$$

10.
$$\begin{aligned} &r^2 + s^2 \\ &= 5^2 + 3^2 \\ &= 25 + 9 \\ &= 34 \end{aligned}$$

11.
$$\begin{aligned} &4x^2 - 2xy \\ &= 4\cdot 2^2 - 2\cdot 2\cdot 3 \\ &= 4\cdot 4 - 2\cdot 2\cdot 3 \\ &= 16 - 12 \\ &= 4 \end{aligned}$$

12.
$$\begin{aligned} &ab^2 + 2ab \\ &= 4\cdot 3^2 + 2\cdot 4\cdot 3 \\ &= 4\cdot 9 + 2\cdot 4\cdot 3 \\ &= 36 + 24 \\ &= 60 \end{aligned}$$

13.
$$\begin{aligned} &cd^2 - 3cd \\ &= 3\cdot 4^2 - 3\cdot 3\cdot 4 \\ &= 3\cdot 16 - 3\cdot 3\cdot 4 \\ &= 48 - 36 \\ &= 12 \end{aligned}$$

14.
$$\begin{aligned} &(x + y)^2 \\ &= (5 + 3)^2 \\ &= 8^2 \\ &= 64 \end{aligned}$$

15.
$$\begin{aligned} &3rs - 2s^2 \\ &= 3\cdot 4\cdot 5 - 2\cdot 5^2 \\ &= 3\cdot 4\cdot 5 - 2\cdot 25 \\ &= 60 - 50 \\ &= 10 \end{aligned}$$

(B)

1. $7a^2 + 7$ 2. $4x + y$ 3. $2x^3 + 6y$ 4. $5x^2 + 2$

5. $3xy + 21$ 6. $11a^2 + 9b$ 7. $11x^2 + 20x$ 8. $2x + 3$

9. $17b^2 + 7$ 10. $19ab + 8c$ 11. $6a + 6b^3$ 12. $18r + 19$

13. $9a^3 + 1$ 14. $5a$

Test A   Page 34

I

1. $3pq$ 2. $xy - m^2$ 3. $(x - y)(3y + 4)$ 4. $\frac{3x}{y^2}$ 5. $a + 2b$

II

1. $5x^3$ 2. m^4s^2 3. $6a^2b^3$

III

Answers will vary.

IV

1. $3xy - 2mn$
$= 3\cdot3\cdot2 - 2\cdot4\cdot1$
$= 18 - 8$
$= 10$

2. $\frac{m^2}{4y} + \frac{ax}{7m}$
$= \frac{4^2}{4\cdot2} + \frac{0\cdot3}{7\cdot4}$
$= \frac{16}{8} + 0$
$= 2$

3. xy^3
$= 3\cdot2^3$
$= 3\cdot8$
$= 24$

4. $x^3 + y^2$
$= 3^3 + 2^2$
$= 27 + 4$
$= 31$

5. $m + xy - m \div y$
$= 4 + 3\cdot2 - 4 \div 2$
$= 4 + 6 - 2$
$= 8$

6. $(y + m)^2$
$= (2 + 4)^2$
$= 6^2$
$= 36$

7. $(m - n)(x + y)$
$= (4 - 1)(3 + 2)$
$= 3\cdot5$
$= 15$

V

1. $3a^2 + 2a + 1$ 2. $6x + 4y + 8z$ 3. $6ab + 9$ 4. 0

TEST B   Pages 34-35

I

1. $b^3 + c^2$ 2. $5a\cdot2c$ or $10ac$ 3. $(3a - 7)(2a + 5)$ 4. $\frac{b^2}{xy}$ 5. $p - 2q$

II

1. $3a^3$ 2. b^2d^4 3. $4a^3bc^2$

III

1.-3. Answers will vary.   4. binomial

IV

1. 7×5

2. $8 - 3 \times 2 + 24 \div 2$
$= 8 - 6 + 12$
$= 14$

V

1. $3ab + 5cd$
$= 3\cdot0\cdot1 + 5\cdot2\cdot3$
$= 0 + 30$
$= 30$

2. $\frac{d^3}{b + c}$
$= \frac{3^3}{1 + 2}$
$= \frac{27}{3}$
$= 9$

3. $d^2 - c^2$
$= 3^2 - 2^2$
$= 9 - 4$
$= 5$

4. $(a + e)^2$
$= (0 + 4)^2$
$= 4^2$
$= 16$

5. $(e - b)(c + d)$
$= (4 - 1)(2 + 3)$
$= 3 \cdot 5$
$= 15$

6. $3b^2c$
$= 3 \cdot 1^2 \cdot 2$
$= 3 \cdot 1 \cdot 2$
$= 6$

VI

1. $4x^2 + 4x + 4$
2. 0
3. $4mn + 11$
4. $9a + 3b$

TEST C Page 36

1. "a squared" or "a to the second power"
"a cubed" or "a to the third power"

2. "a to the fourth"

3. a^2 gives the area of a square of side a
a^3 gives the volume of a cube of edge a

4. $5^2 - 2 \cdot 5 = 25 - 2 \cdot 5$
$= 25 - 10$
$= 15$

5. $a^2 = 3a$ $\quad 3^2 = 3 \cdot 3$
$a = 3$ $\quad 0^2 = 3 \cdot 0$
$a = 0$

6. $2a^2 + 4ab + 3b^2 + 2b^3$
$= 2 \cdot 2^2 + 4 \cdot 2 \cdot 3 + 3 \cdot 3^2 + 2 \cdot 3^3$
$= 2 \cdot 4 + 4 \cdot 2 \cdot 3 + 3 \cdot 9 + 2 \cdot 27$
$= 8 + 24 + 27 + 54$
$= 113$

7. $3a^2 + 8ab + b^2 - 6ab + 5b^2 - a^2 - 3b^2 + 2ab + 2b^3$
$= 3 \cdot 2^2 + 8 \cdot 2 \cdot 3 + 3^2 - 6 \cdot 2 \cdot 3 + 5 \cdot 3^2 - 2^2 - 3 \cdot 3^2 + 2 \cdot 2 \cdot 3 + 2 \cdot 3^3$
$= 3 \cdot 4 + 8 \cdot 2 \cdot 3 + 9 - 6 \cdot 2 \cdot 3 + 5 \cdot 9 - 4 - 3 \cdot 9 + 2 \cdot 2 \cdot 3 + 2 \cdot 27$
$= 12 + 48 + 9 - 36 + 45 - 4 - 27 + 12 + 54$
$= 113$
They are the same.

8. The first method

9. $8 + 6 \div 2 - 3 \times 2 + 7 = 14 \div 2 - 3 \times 2 + 7$
$= 7 - 3 \times 2 + 7$
$= 4 \times 2 + 7$
$= 8 + 7$
$= 15$

10. $8 + 6 \div 2 - 3 \times 2 + 7 = 8 + 3 - 6 + 7$
$= 12$

11. They are different.
Everybody will
get the same result.

12. Left to right

13. Left to right

14. 1. let x = the first Sunday
2. $x + 7$ = the second Sunday
$x + 14$ = the third Sunday
$x + 21$ = the fourth Sunday

3. $(x) + (x + 7) + (x + 14) + (x + 21) = 66$
4.
$$4x + 42 = 66$$
$$4x + 42 - 42 = 66 - 42$$
$$4x = 24$$
$$\frac{4x}{4} = \frac{24}{4}$$
$$x = 6$$

5.
$$\begin{array}{r} 6 \\ 13 \\ 20 \\ +27 \\ \hline 66 \end{array}$$ ✓

15. 1. let x = miles walked before supper
2. $x - 2.5$ = miles walked after supper
3. $(x) + (x - 2.5) = 7$
4.
$$2x - 2.5 = 7$$
$$2x - 2.5 + 2.5 = 7 + 2.5$$
$$2x = 9.5$$
$$\frac{2x}{2} = \frac{9.5}{2}$$
$$x = 4.75$$

5.
$$\begin{array}{r} 4.75 \\ +2.25 \\ \hline 7.00 \end{array}$$ ✓

Exercises 3.2a   Page 40

1. January $12,000; February $16,000; March $30,000; April $25,000; May $27,000
2. January; March
3. $16,000 - $12,000 = $4000
4. $30,000 - $25,000 = $5000
5. $25,000 - $12,000 = $13,000
6. $27,000 - $16,000 = $11,000
   May is $11,000 greater.

Exercises 3.2b   Page 41

1. Relative proportion of the dimension of a graph to the corresponding objects represented
2. Same width, same width; same width
3. Numerical or chronological order; easier to read
4. Lower left corner; yes, begin with a number larger than zero
5. Below the graph; tells what information is represented by the graph
6. Make measurements carefully; draw straight lines; put numbers on lines not between them; other answers possible

Exercises 3.3   Page 42

1.

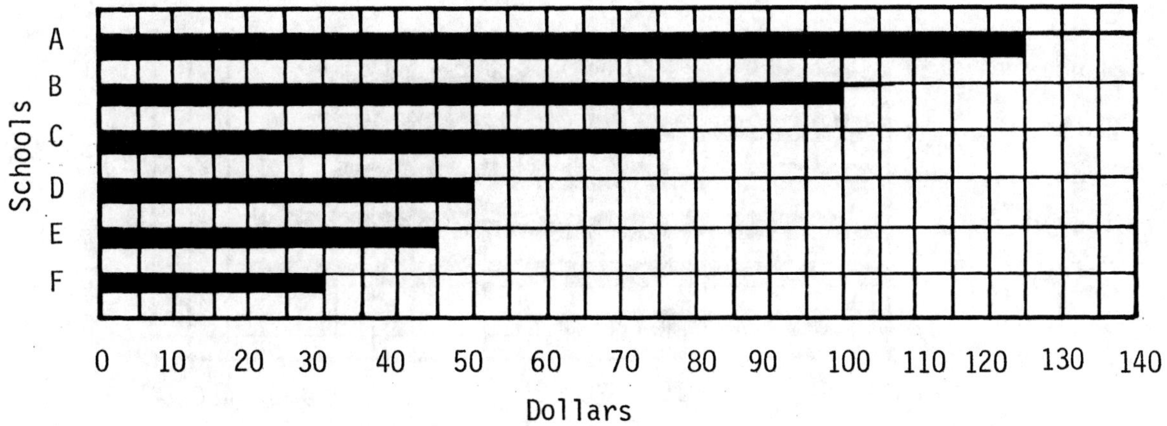

School Donations to Junior Red Cross

Key to Unit 3, page 42

2.

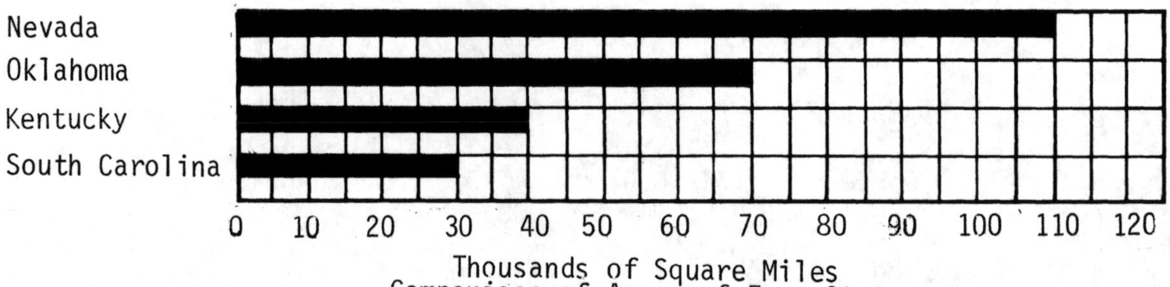

Comparison of Areas of Four States

3.

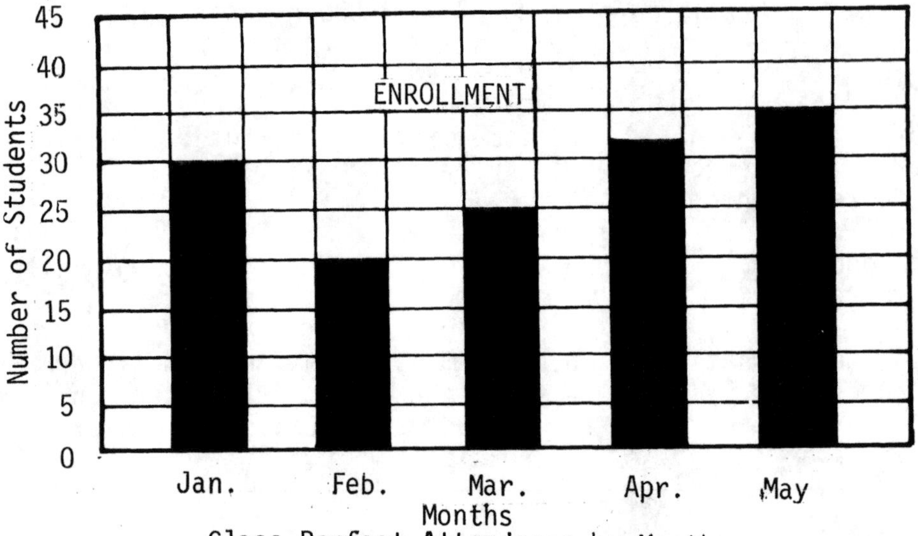

Class Perfect Attendance by Months

4.

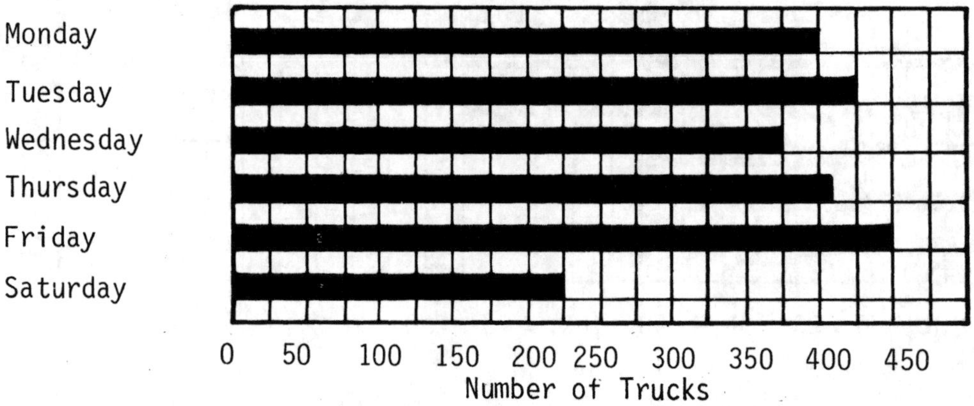

Trucks Manufactured by Day of the Week

5.

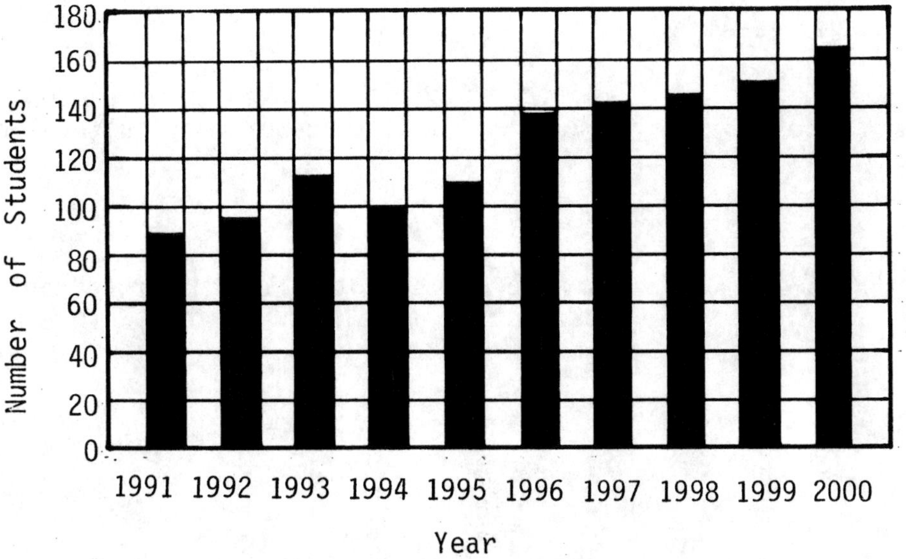

Freshman Class Growth over Ten Years

6.

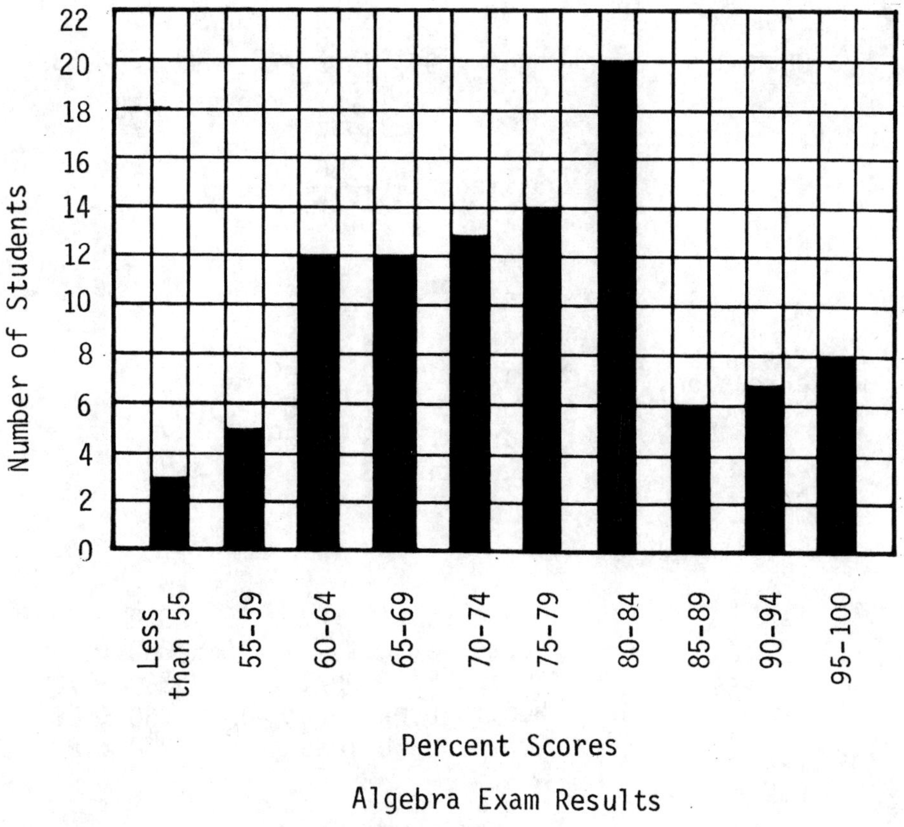

Algebra Exam Results

Exercises 3.4 Pages 43-44

1. 81% - 7% = 74%

74% more of the total exports were manufactured goods than were agricultural products.

2. 9% - 5% = 4%

4% more of the total Ford Motor Company production were Mercurys than were Lincolns.

3.

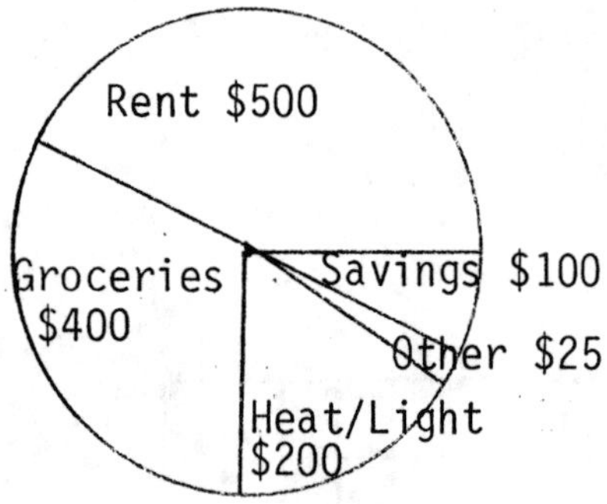

Family Monthly Expenditures

$\frac{100}{1225} = .0816$

$.0816 \times 360^{\circ} \approx 29.38^{\circ}$

Rent $\frac{500}{1225} = 5 \times 29.38 \approx 147^{\circ}$

Groceries $\frac{400}{1225} = 4 \times 29.38 \approx 118^{\circ}$

Heat/Light $\frac{200}{1225} = 2 \times 29.38 \approx 59^{\circ}$

Other $\frac{25}{1225} = \frac{29.38}{4} \approx 7^{\circ}$

Savings $\frac{100}{1225} = 29^{\circ}$

4.

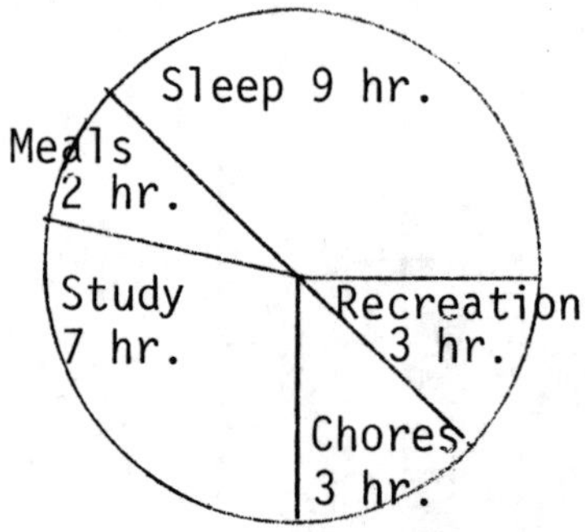

Edgar Jerome's Daily Time Budget

$\frac{360}{24} = 15^{\circ}$

Sleep $9 \times 15^{\circ} = 135^{\circ}$
Meals $2 \times 15^{\circ} = 30^{\circ}$
Study $7 \times 15^{\circ} = 105^{\circ}$
Chores $3 \times 15^{\circ} = 45^{\circ}$
Recreation $3 \times 15^{\circ} = 45^{\circ}$

5.

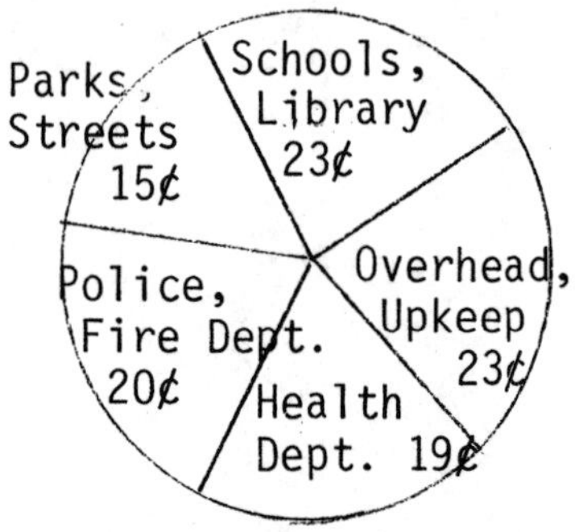

Malta City Expenditures per Dollar

Schools, Library $.23 \times 360 \approx 83^{\circ}$
Parks, Streets $.15 \times 360 \approx 54^{\circ}$
Police, Fire Dept. $.20 \times 360 \approx 72^{\circ}$
Health Department $.19 \times 360 \approx 68^{\circ}$
Overhead, Upkeep $.23 \times 360 \approx 83^{\circ}$

Exercises 3.5   Pages 44-45

1. July; October - November

2. 9^0; 10^0; 1^0; 8^0; 6^0; 2 P.M.

3.

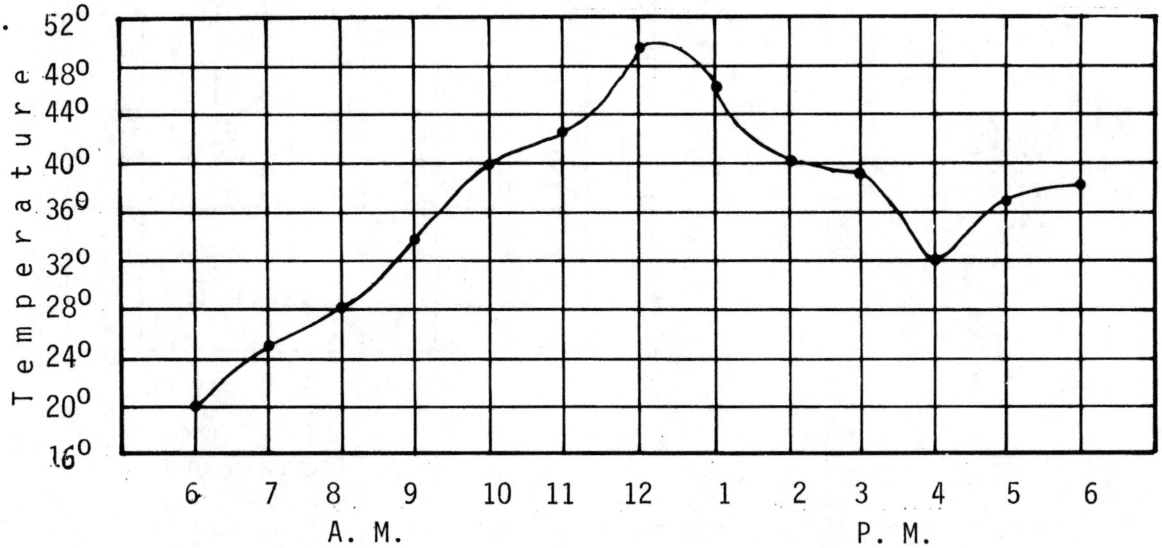

Hourly Daytime Temperatures

4.

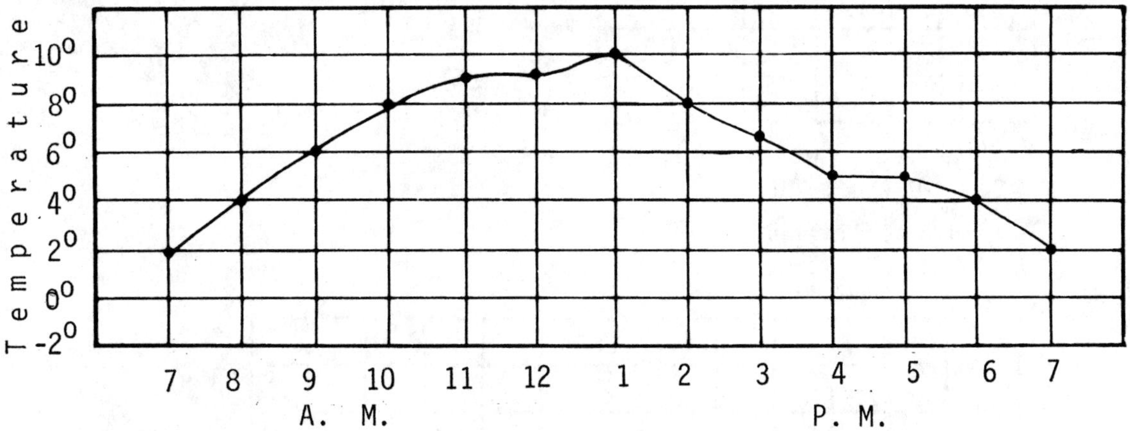

Hourly Daytime Temperatures

5.

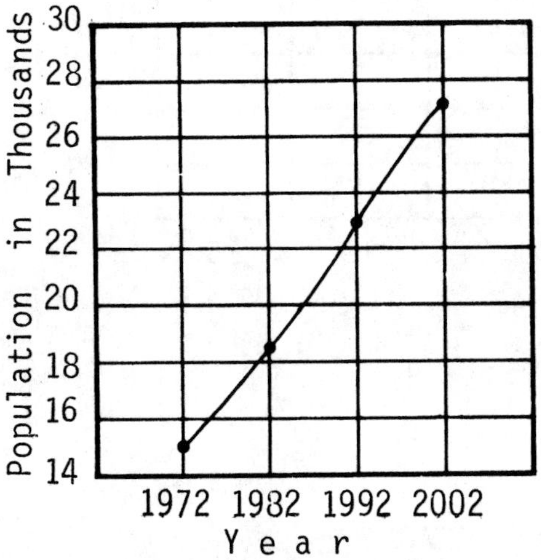

Population Growth

1979 ≈ 17,500
1986 ≈ 20,500
1998 ≈ 26,000

20,000   1985
25,000   1996

Exercises 3.6 Pages 46-47

1. May $16.50
   June $13
   July $11.75
   August $13.75
   September $13
   October $13.50
   November $11.50
   December $11

2.

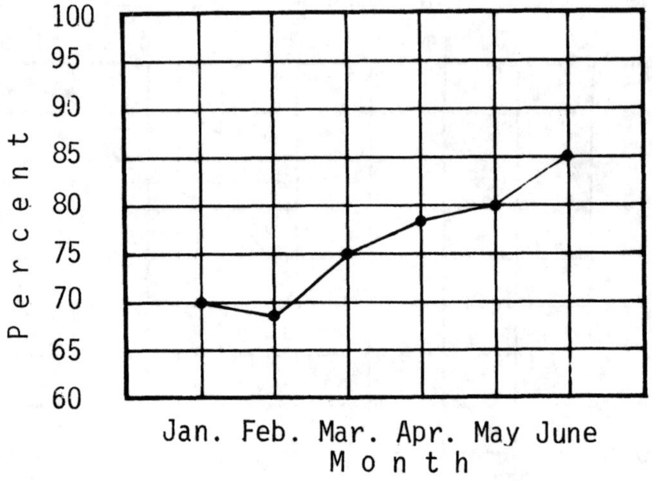

Monthly Algebra Scores

3.

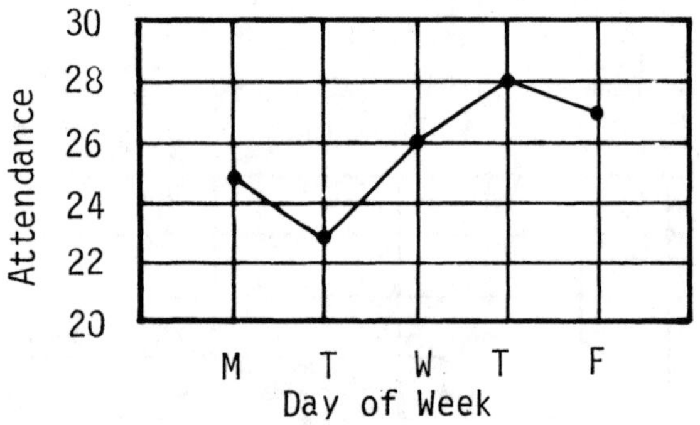

Class Attendance

4. a)

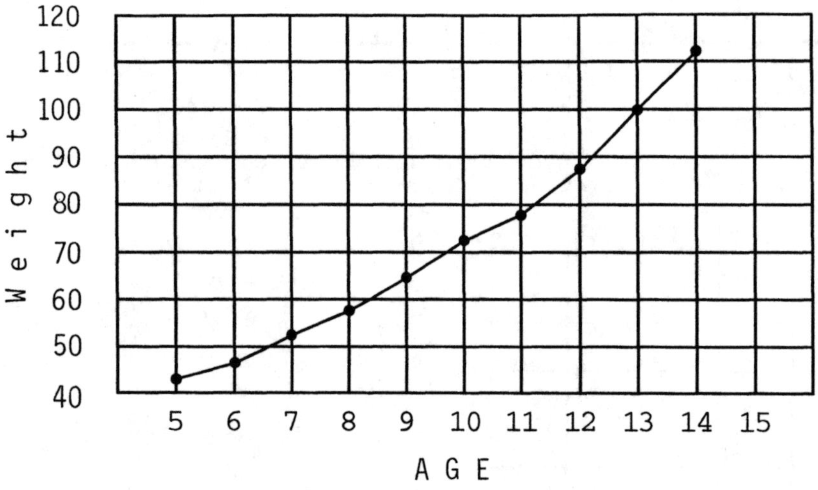

Age-Weight Comparison

b) 11.8 yr.

c) approximately 124 lb. (Answers may vary.)

5.

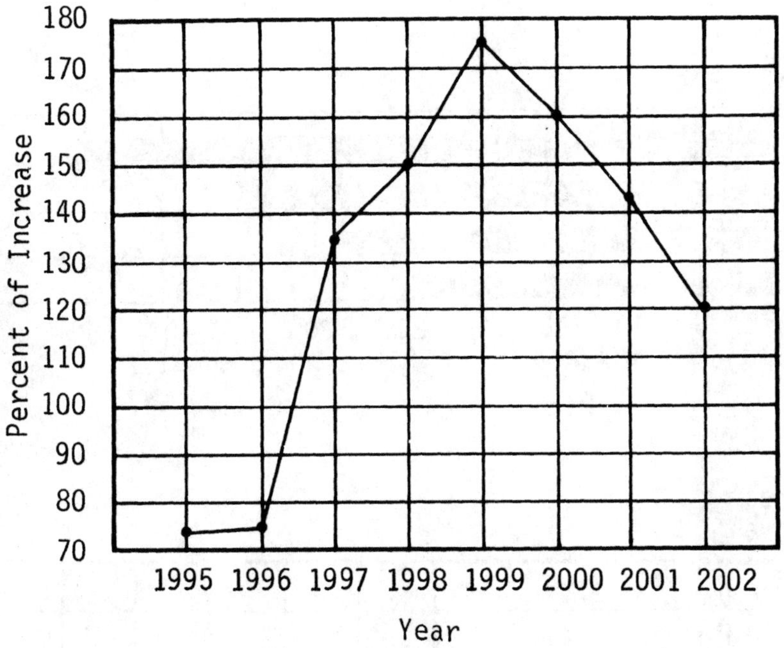

Percent Increase in Labor Costs

6.

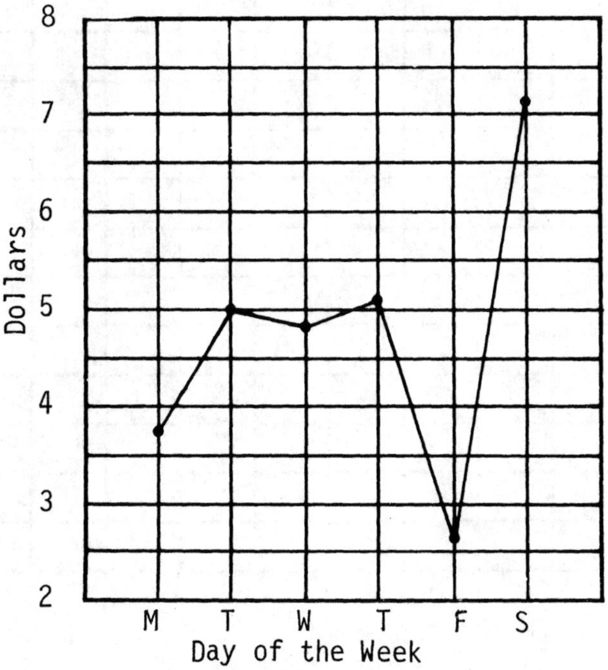

Daily Earnings

7. Out-of-class project; graphs will vary.

8. Answers will vary. Generally,
   1. When comparing data from different sources
   2. When the relationship of parts to the whole is to be emphasized and all values are recorded at the same time
   3. When gradual or continuous changes are depicted

Review Pages 47-49

1.

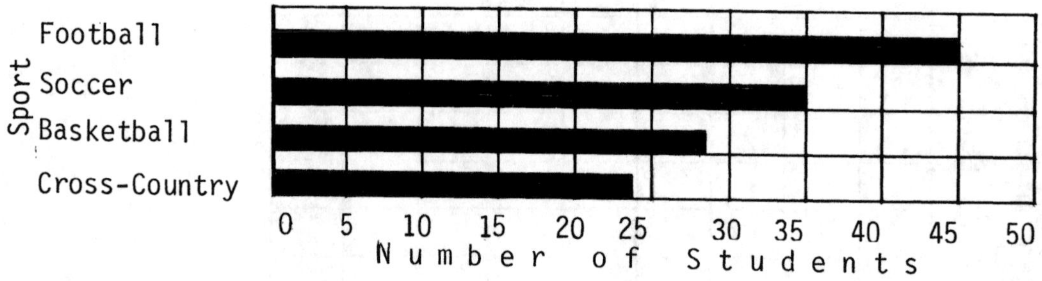

City High School Sports Tryouts

2.

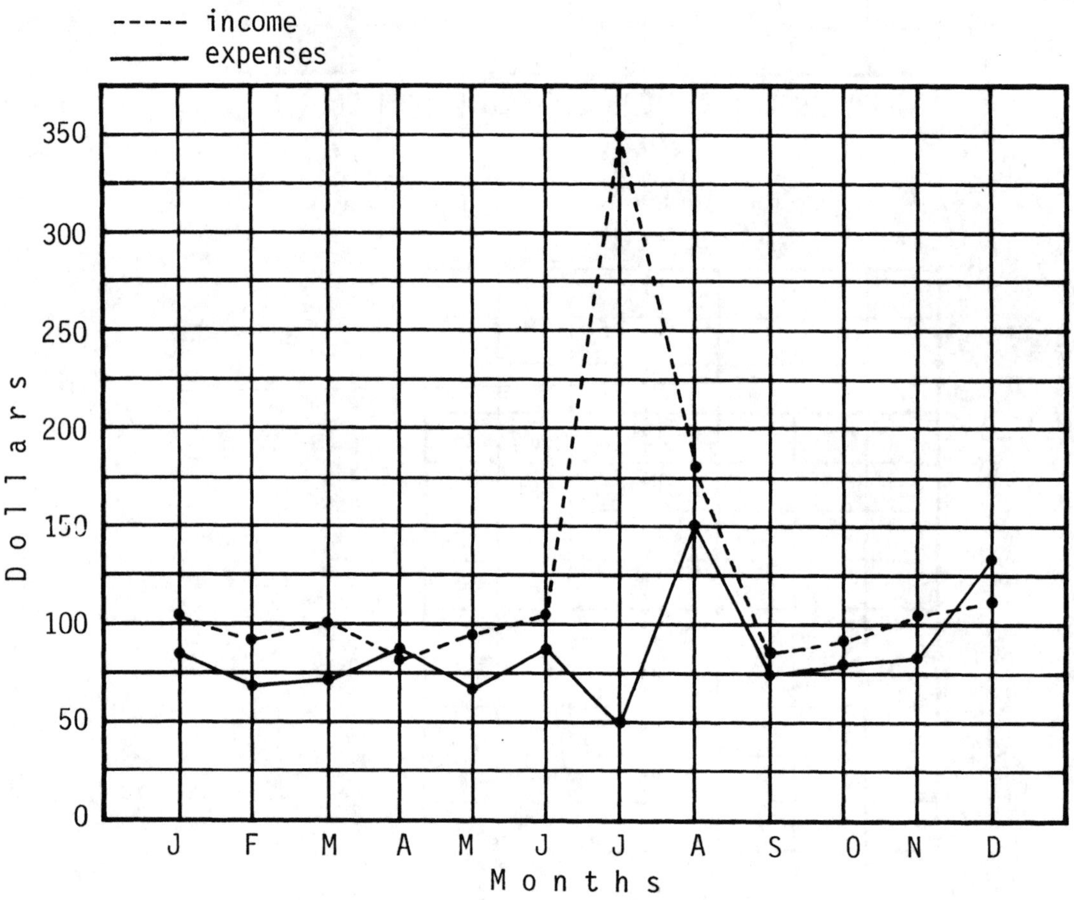

Year's Income and Expenses

a) Expenses exceeded income in April.

b) By increased income

3.

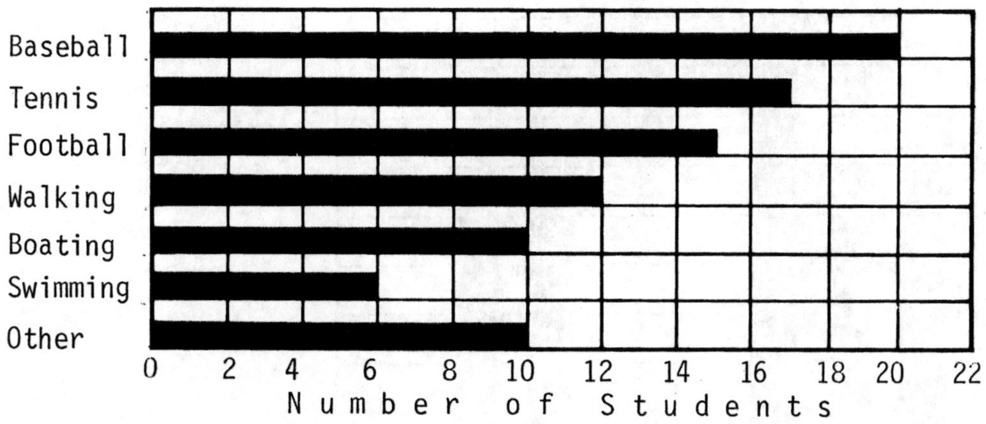

Senior Class Athletic Preference

4.

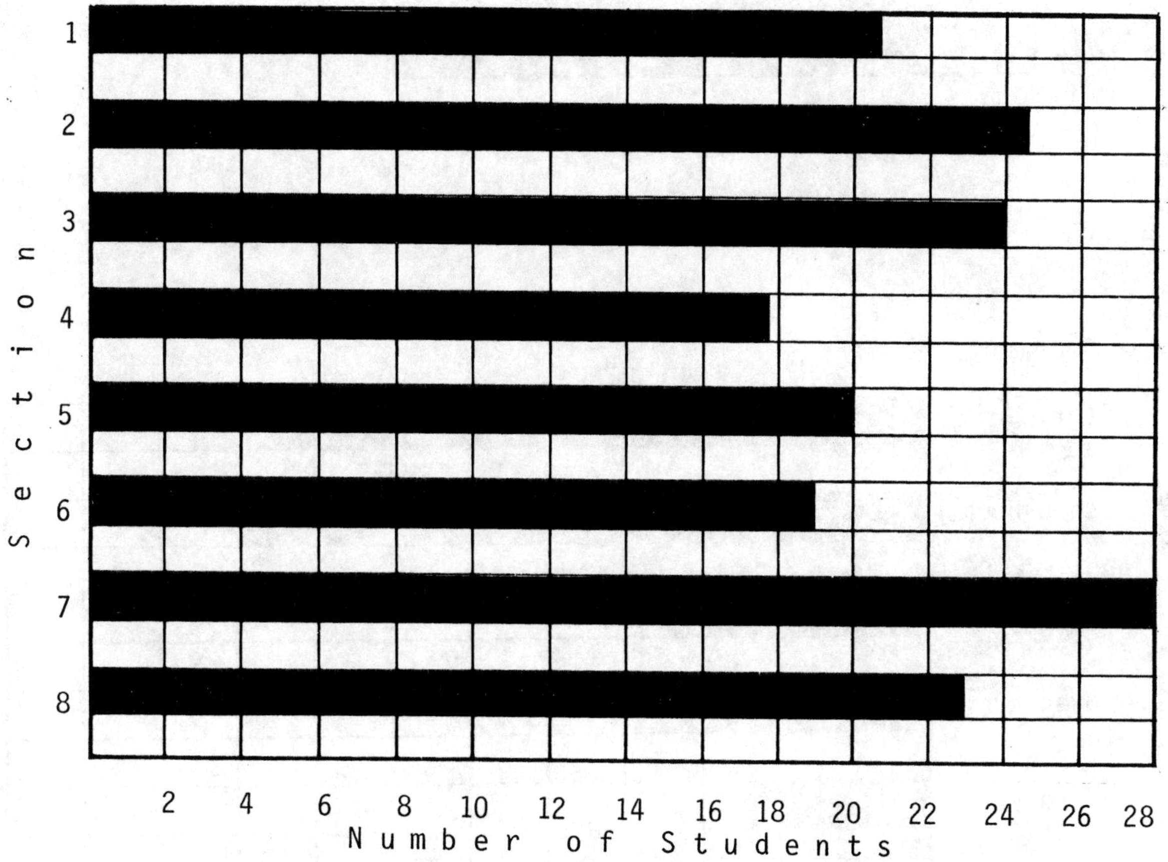

Algebra Enrollment by Section

5.

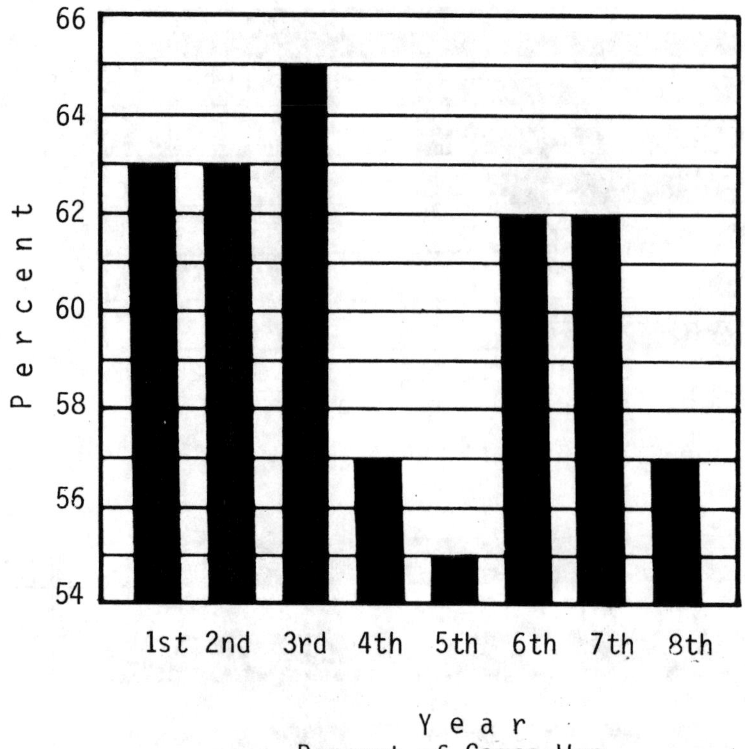

Percent of Games Won

6.

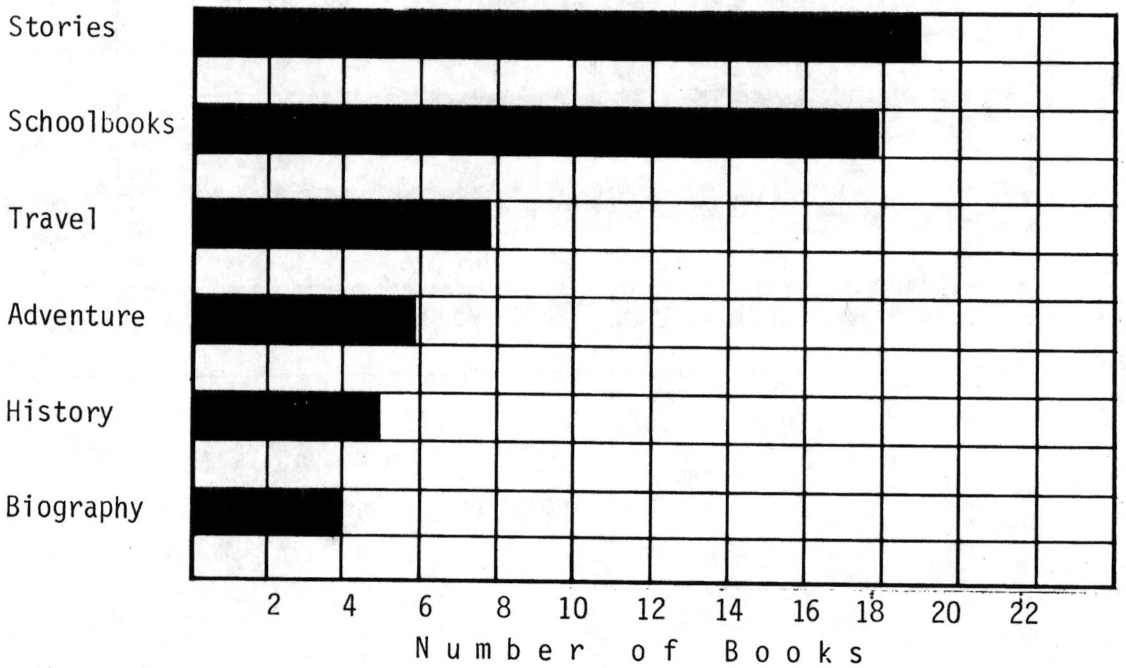

Books by Subject

7.

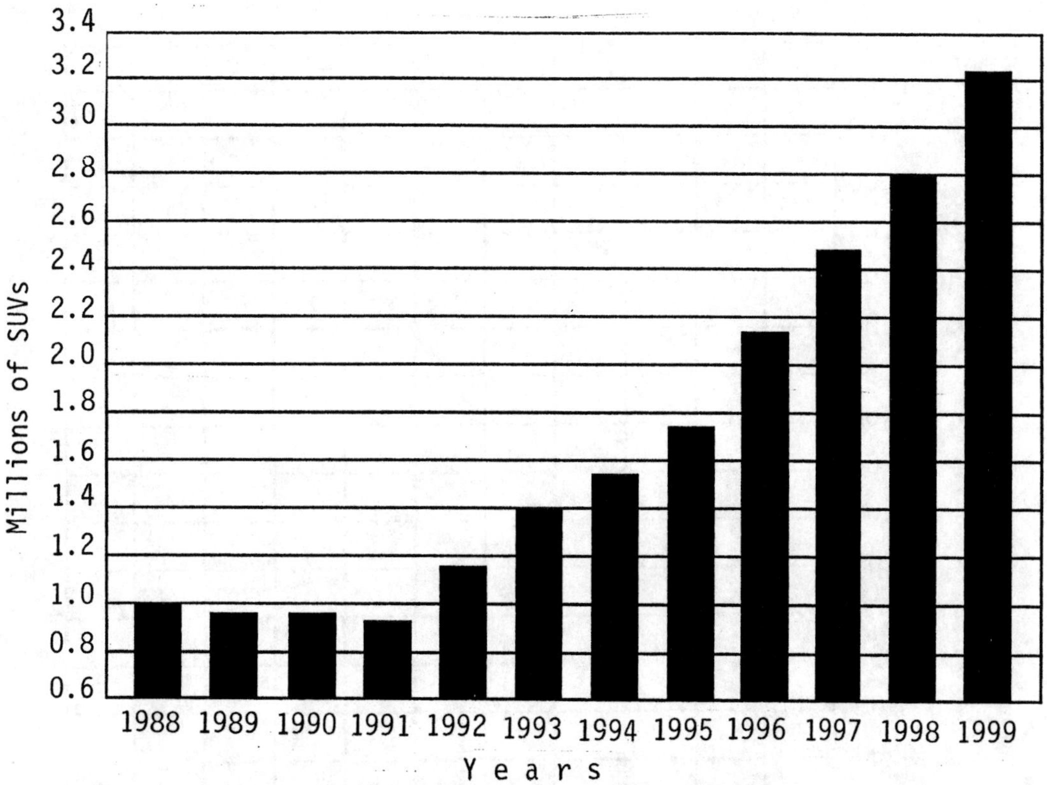

U.S. SUV Sales 1988-1999

8.

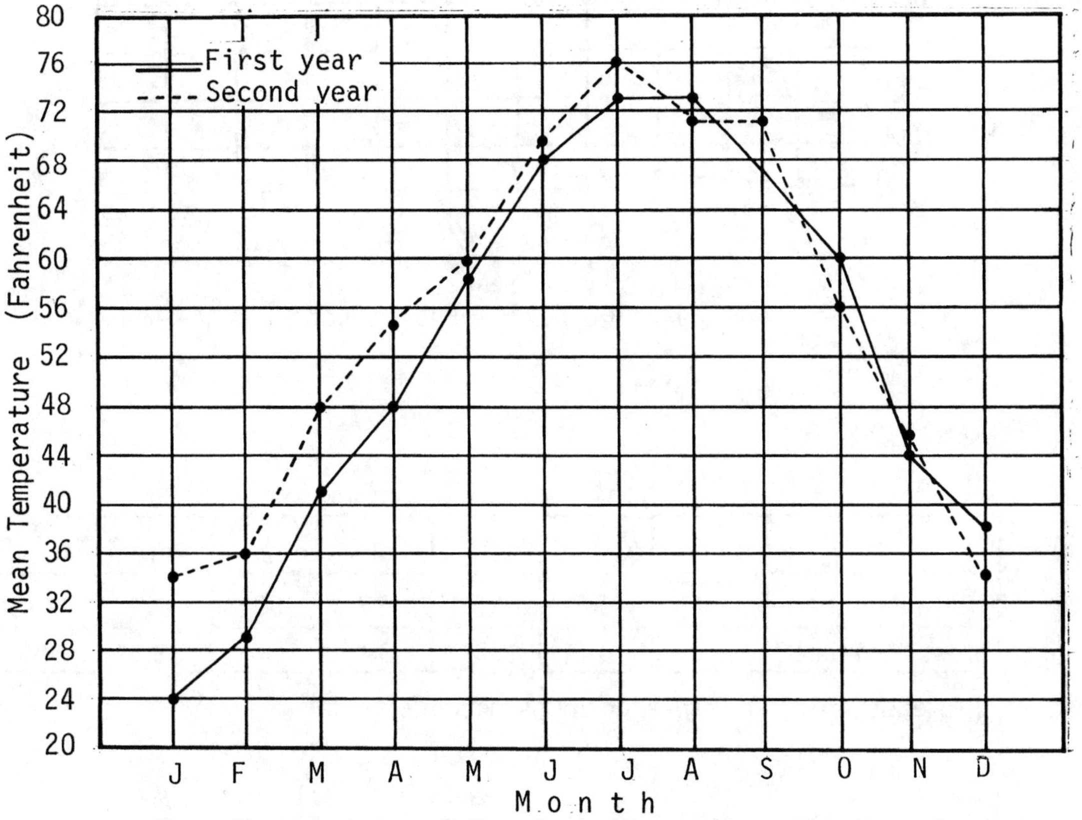

Mean Temperature of New York City over a Two-Year Period

9. a)

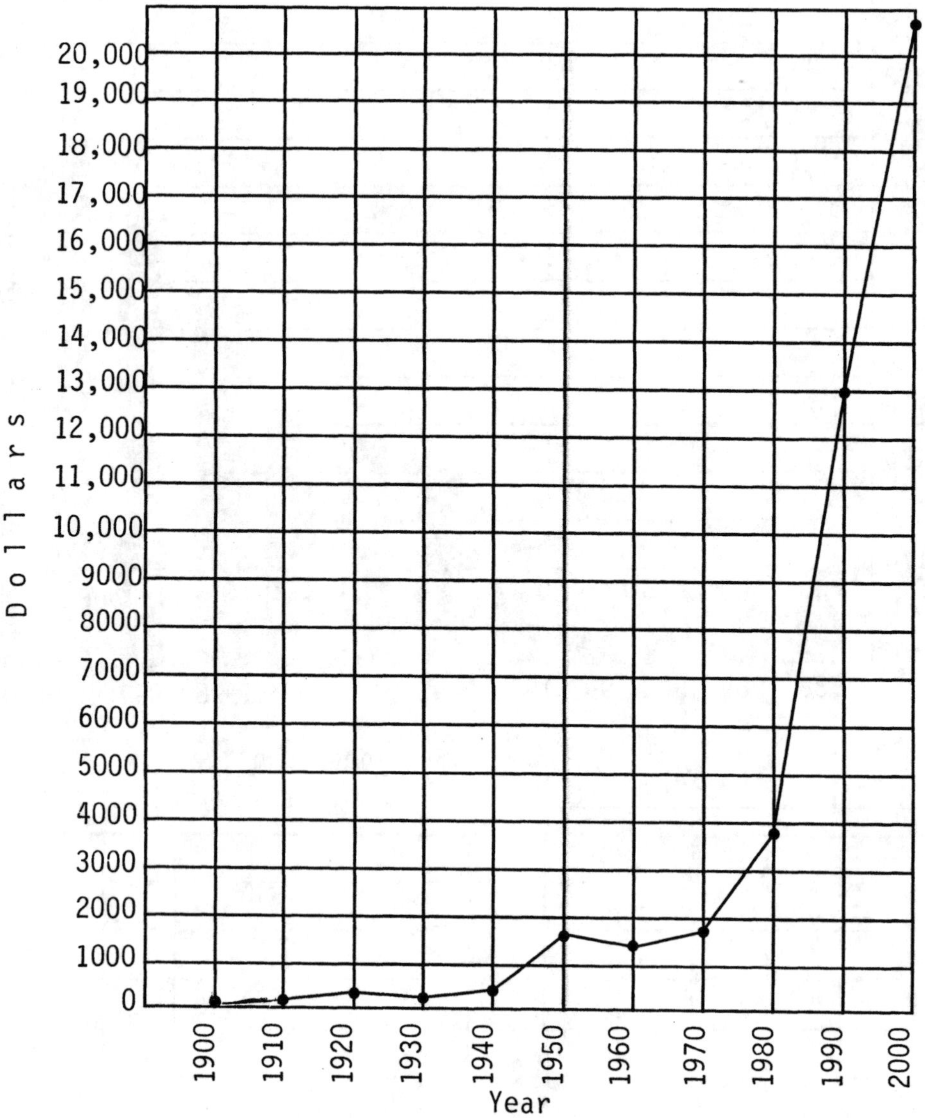

U.S. per Capita Public Debt

b) 1980 to 1990

10. a)

	Aug 23	Aug 24	Aug 25	Aug 26	Aug 27	Aug 28	Aug 29	Aug 30
North Latitude	56°	56°	55°	53°	50°	47°	44°	43°
West Longitude	7.5°	14°	23°	34°	45°	52.5°	63°	72°

(Note: departure and arrival positions included.)

b) By graph
Aug 26 to Aug 27

53° - 50° = 3° latitude
45° - 34° = 11° longitude

11.

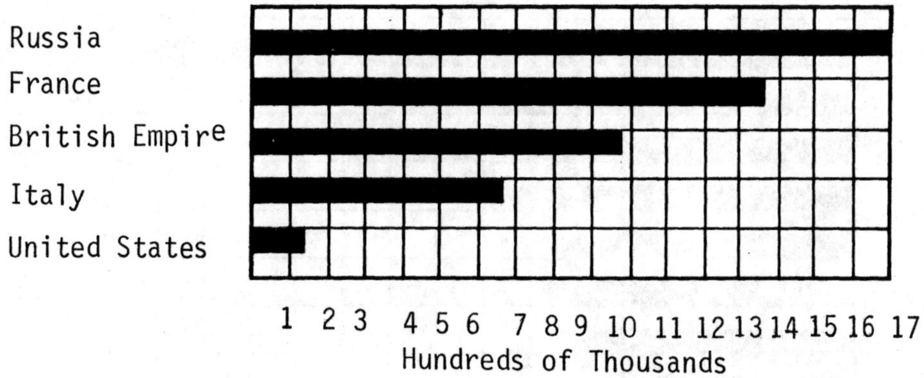

Men Killed in World War I

12. a)

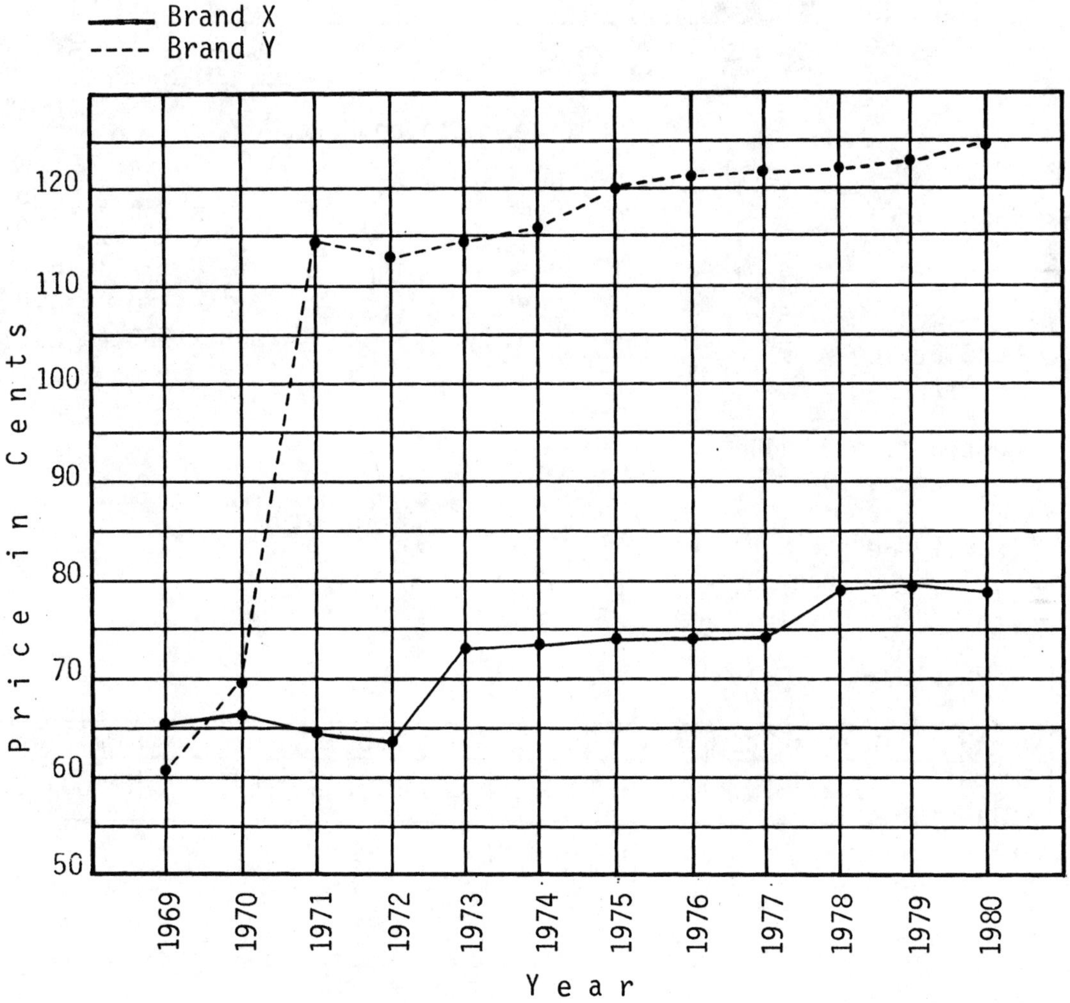

Brand X and Brand Y Price Comparison

b) Brand Y

13.

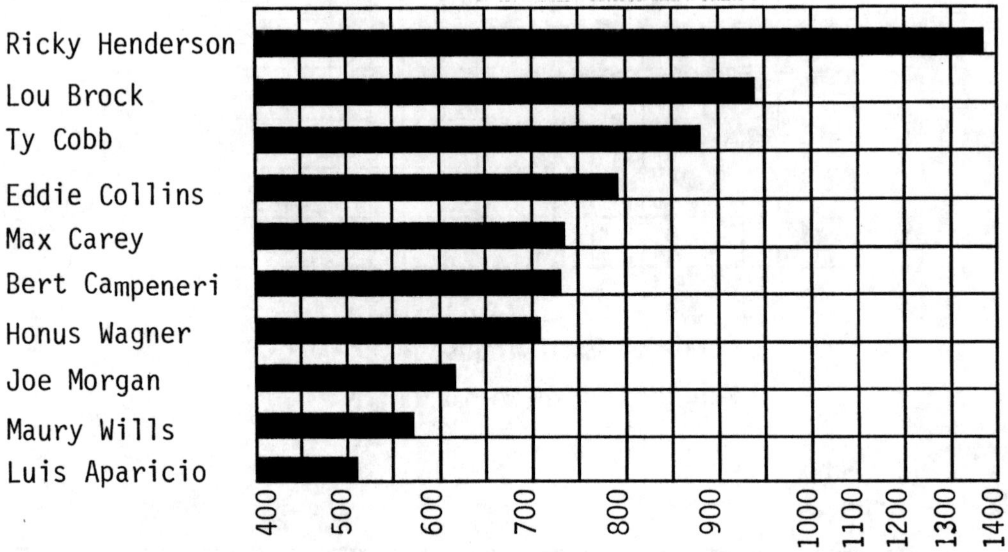

Career Stolen Bases

14.

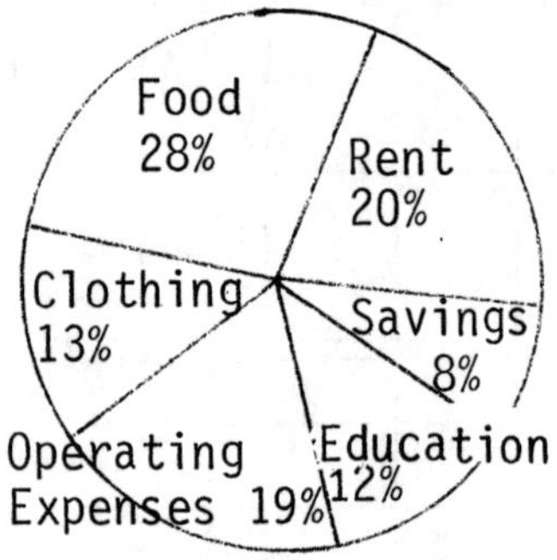

Family Budget Expenses
by Percent

Rent	.20 x 360 =	72°
Food	.28 x 360 =	101°
Clothing	.13 x 360 =	47°
Operating Expenses	.19 x 360 =	68°
Education	.12 x 360 =	43°
Savings	.08 x 360 =	29°

Test A   Page 50

1.

Month	Sept	Oct	Nov	Dec	Jan	Feb	Mar	Apr	May	June
Amount Collected	$2.25	$2.75	$3.00	$1.50	$2.00	$2.25	$1.25	$2.00	$5.00	$2.50

The election was probably held in May.

2. a)

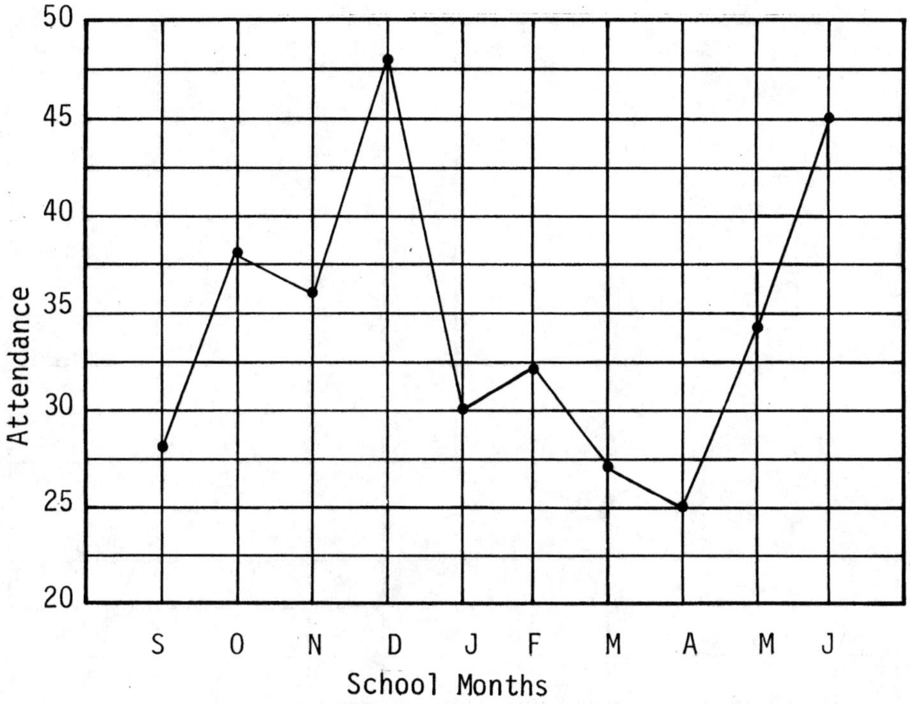

Drama Club Meetings Attendance

b) By the increased attendance

c) In June

Test B Pages 50 -51

1.

Range of Grade	51-60	61-70	71-80	81-90	91-100
Number of Students	2	6	5	12	10

22 students made above 80

2. a)

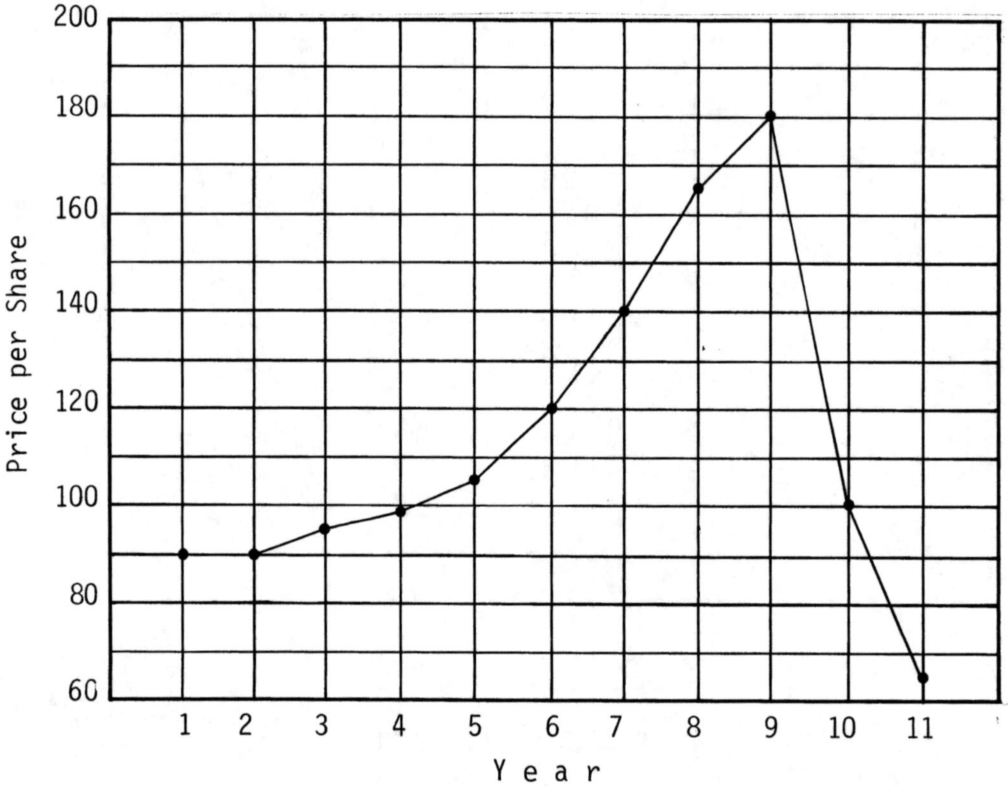

Price of a Certain Stock

b) In the ninth year

3. Temperature changes continuously.

Test C   Pages 51-53

1.

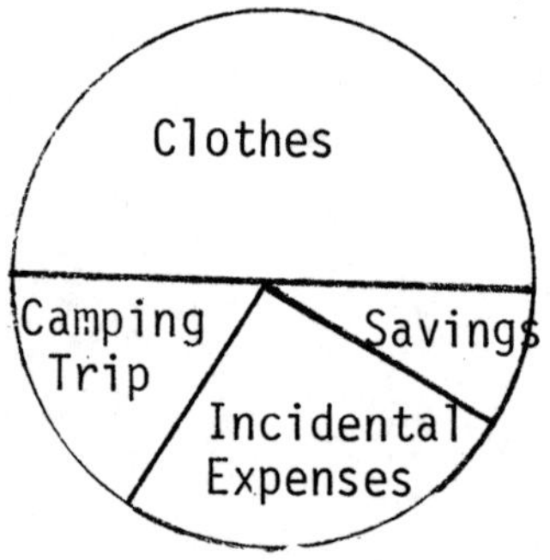

Clothes $\frac{1}{2} \times 360 = 180^{o}$

Camping Trip $\frac{1}{6} \times 360 = 60^{o}$

Incidental Expenses $\frac{1}{4} \times 360 = \underline{90^{o}}$

330°

Savings $360^{o} - 330^{o} = 30^{o}$

2. a)

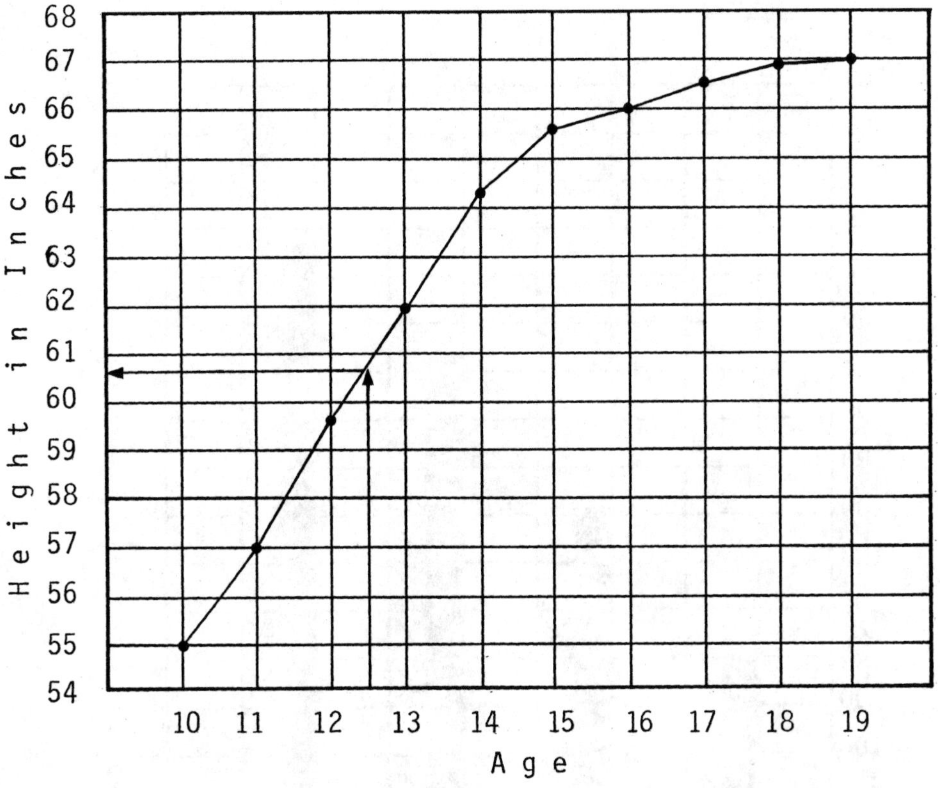

Height on Successive Birthdays

b) 60.6 inches

3.

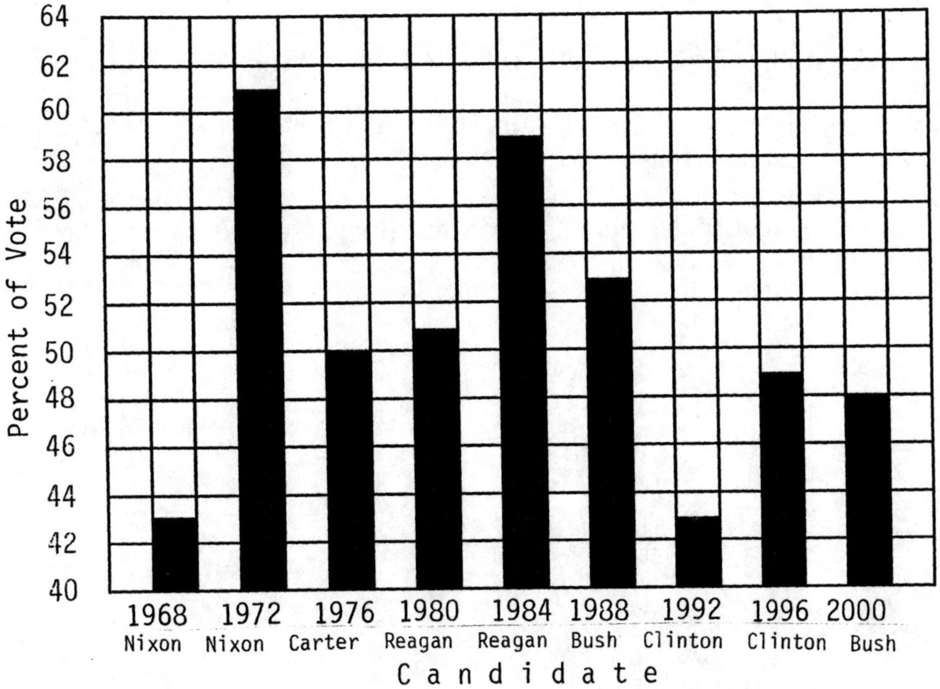

Winning Percent of Vote in Nine Presidential Elections

4. 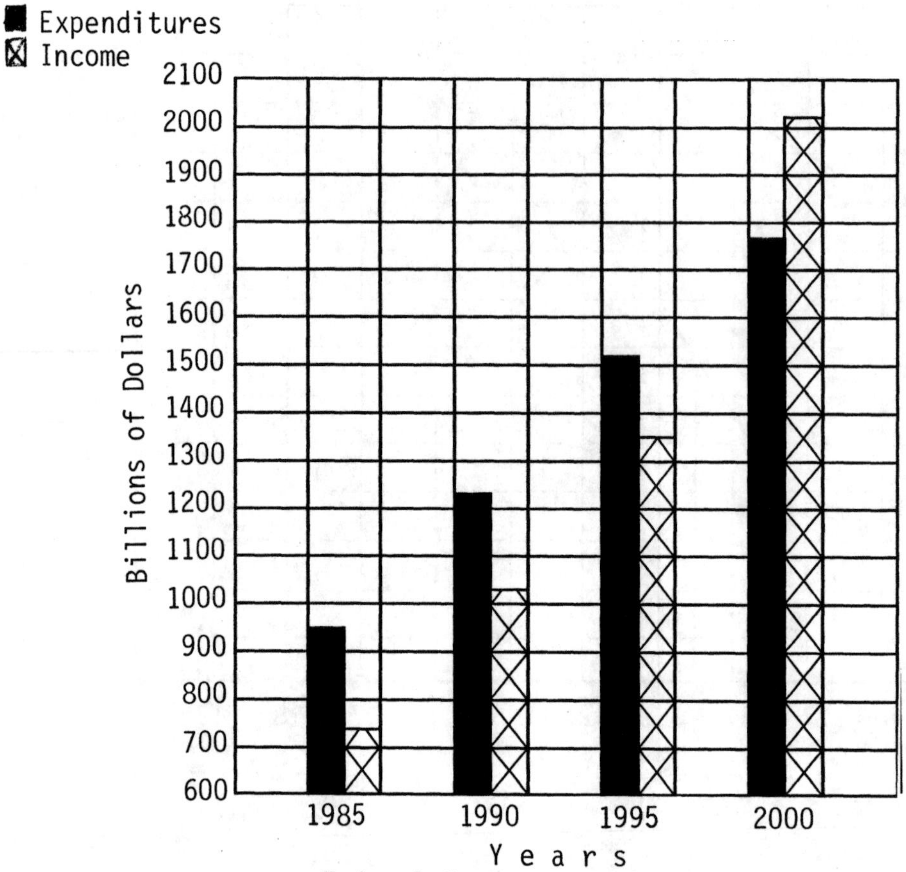

Federal Income and Expenditures

5. a) Increase in revenue was not affected by national events.

   b) Yes; percent related to the whole best shown with a circle graph; Yes, areas are proportional to the totals.

   c) The second should be about twice as large as the first; no

   d) Operating expenses; gross earnings

UNIT 4 — Formulas

Exercises 4.3 Pages 56-59

1. The interest is found by multiplying \$100 by .0875 times the number of years.

2. $i = (100)(.0875)t$
   $i = 8.75t$

3. $i = 100(.065)t$
   $i = 6.5t$

4. To find interest, multiply the amount of the principal by the interest rate as a decimal and the time in years.

5. Multiply the amount earned per hour by the number of hours worked.

   Marcus: $\frac{12.60}{2} = 6.30$ per hour $w = 6.30h$

   Russell: $w = 5.45h$

6. The amount of an investment which includes both the principal and the interest earned on it is found by multiplying the principal by one more than the product of the annual interest rate and the time in years.

7. $a = p(1+rt)$
   $a = 1000[1+(.09)2]$
   $a = 1000(1+.18)$
   $a = 1000(1.18)$
   $a = \$1180$

8. $a = p(1+rt)$
   $a = 1000[1+(.07)(3)]$
   $a = 1000[1+.21]$
   $a = 1000(1.21)$
   $a = \$1210$

9. $a = p(1+rt)$
   $a = 500[1+(.0625)(4)]$
   $a = 500[1+.25]$
   $a = 500(1.25)$
   $a = \$625$

10. $c = 3.45 + .79(w-2)$ where c is the cost and w the weight in pounds

11. $c = .35w + 3.42$

12. $c = 1.18w + .27$
    $c = 1.18(5) + .27$
    $c = 5.90 + .27$
    $c = \$6.17$

13. $c = 1.18w + .27$
    $c = 1.18(6) + .27$
    $c = 7.08 + .27$
    $c = \$7.35$

    $c = 1.18w + .27$
    $c = 1.18(2) + .27$
    $c = 2.36 + .27$
    $c = \$2.63$

    $c = 1.18w + .27$
    $c = 1.18(10) + .27$
    $c = 11.80 + .27$
    $c = \$12.07$

14. $p = 4s$

15. $p = 4s$
    $p = 4(5) = 20$ in.

    $p = 4s$
    $p = 4(6) = 24$ ft.

16. $p = 4s$
    $p = 4(5) = 20$ in.

    $p = 4s$
    $p = 4(6) = 24$ ft.

    $p = 4s$
    $p = 4(8) = 32$ yd.

    $p = 4s$
    $p = 4(4\frac{3}{4})$
    $p = 4(\frac{19}{4}) = 19$ in.

17. $A = s^2$

18. $A = s^2$
    $A = 2^2$
    $A = 4$ sq. in.

    $A = s^2$
    $A = 3^2$
    $A = 9$ sq. ft.

    $A = s^2$
    $A = (2\frac{1}{2})^2$
    $A = (2.5)^2$
    $A = 6.25$ sq. ft.

19. $p = 2a + 2b$

20. $p = 2a + 2b$
    $p = 2(10) + 2(5)$
    $p = 20 + 10$
    $p = 30$ in.

21. $p = 2a + 2b$
    $p = 2(8) + 2(3)$
    $p = 16 + 6$
    $p = 22$ units

    $p = 2a + 2b$
    $p = 2(6) + 2(1)$
    $p = 12 + 2$
    $p = 14$ in.

22. $V = e^3$

23. $V = e^3$
    $V = 2^3$
    $V = 8$ cu. in.

    $V = e^3$
    $V = 3^3$
    $V = 27$ cu. in.

    $V = e^3$
    $V = 5^3$
    $V = 125$ cu. in.

    $V = e^3$
    $V = 6^3$
    $V = 216$ cu. ft.

24. $A = ab$

25. $A = \frac{1}{2}ab$

26. The area of a trapezoid is the product of one half the altitude and the sum of the bases.

27. $V = lwh$

28. $V = lwh$
    $V = 6(4)(10)$
    $V = 240$ cu. units

    The volume of a rectangular solid is the product of its length, width, and height.

29. let E be the sum of the edges
    $E = 12e$

30. (a) $C = \pi d$ (b) $A = \pi r^2$ (c) $A = s^2$

    (d) $V = lwh$ (e) $V = \frac{1}{3}\pi r^2 h$ (f) $c^2 = a^2 + b^2$

Exercises 4.7   Page 62

1.

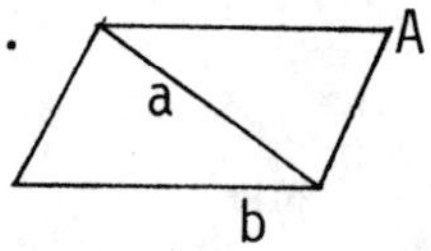

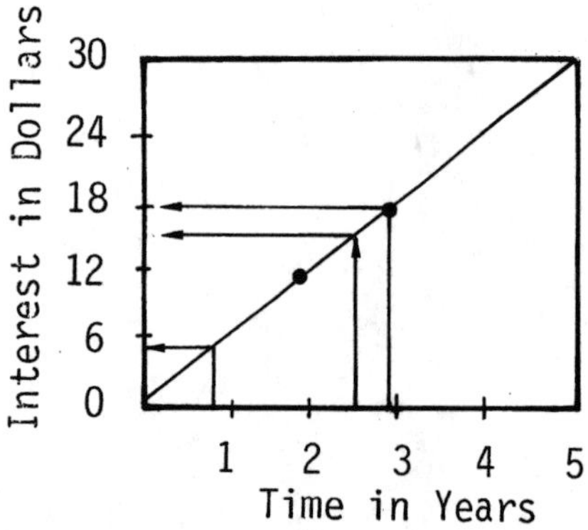

Interest for 2½ years: $15
            3 years: $18
            9 months: $ 4.50
            5 years: $30

2. i = prt

$i = 100(.06)(2.5)$	$i = 100(.06)(3)$	$i = 100(.06)(\frac{9}{12})$	$i = 100(.06)(5)$
$i = 6(2.5)$	$i = 6(3)$	$i = 6(\frac{9}{12})$	$i = 6(5)$
$i = \$15$	$i = \$18$	$i = \$4.50$	$i = \$30$

3. The number of dollars received is the product of the hourly wage \$6 and the number of hours worked.

An additional amount of \$10 is added to the product.

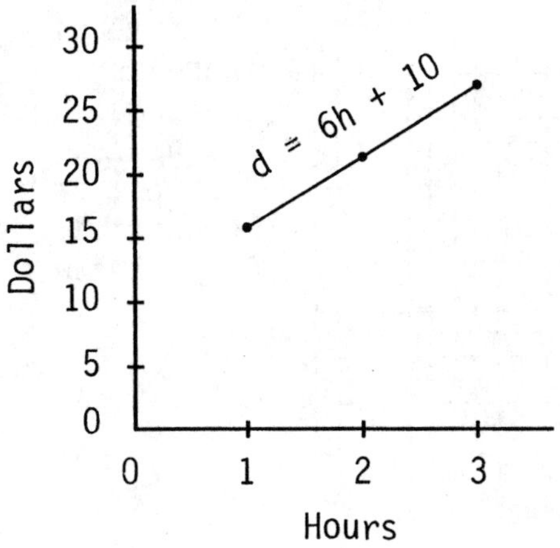

4.

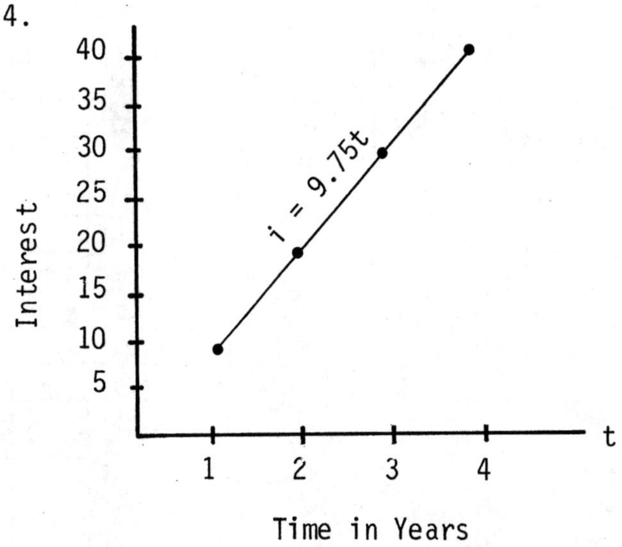

(Problems will vary.)

5. (a) $d = 150t$

(b)

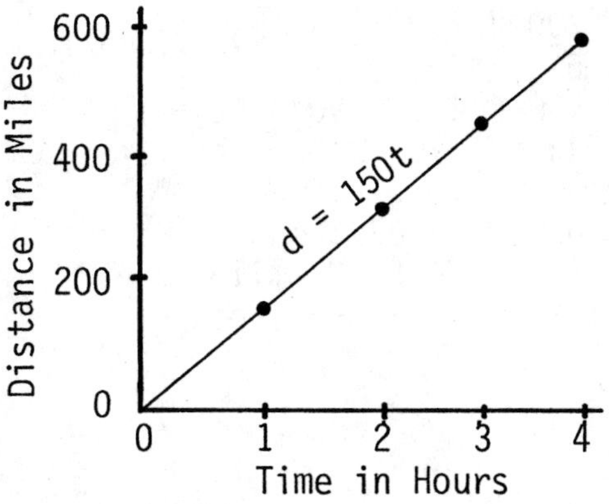

6. To find Fahrenheit temperature from Celsius temperature, multiply the Celsius reading by 9/5 and add 32°.

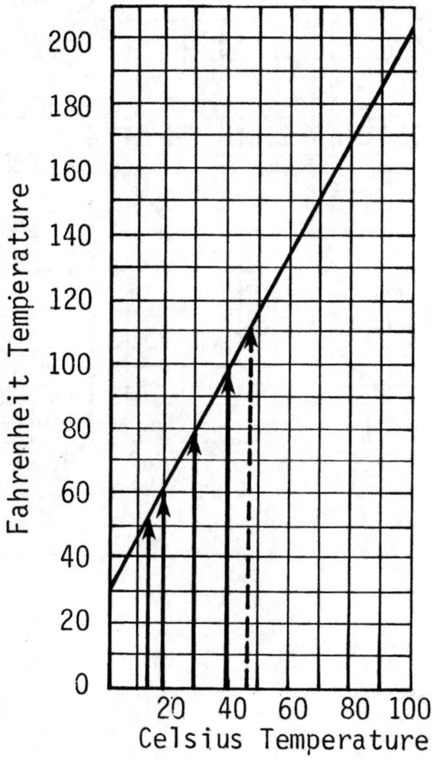

7.

C	F
15°	59°
20°	68°
30°	86°
40°	104°
45°	113°

Exercises 4.8   Pages 63-64

1.

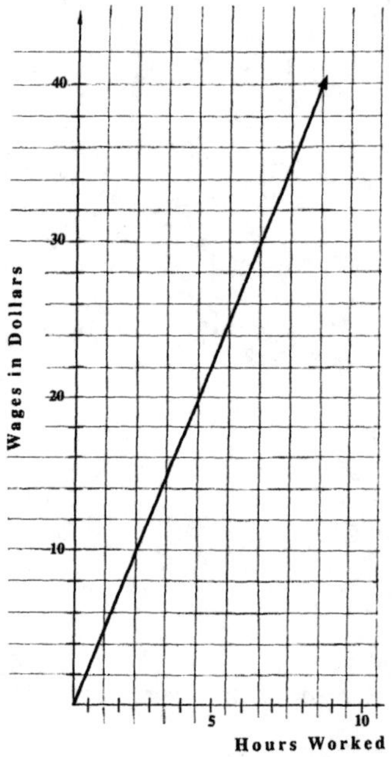

2. 2 hours
   5 hours
   8 hours

3. $6
   $8.50
   $16

4. 22 units

5.

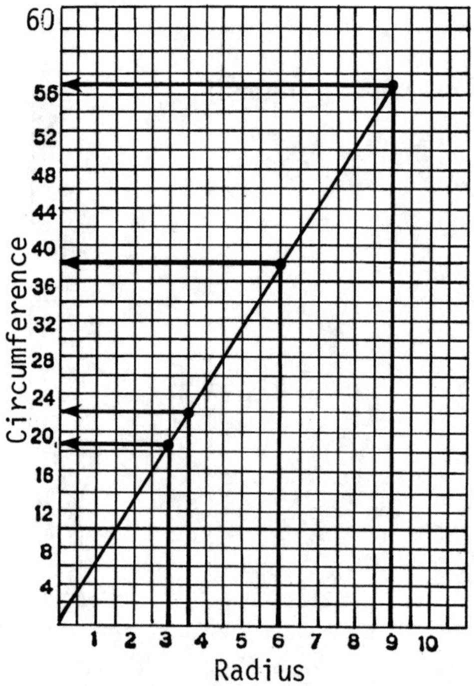

The point (3.5,22) lies on the line.

C=19 when r=3
C=38 when r=6
C=57 when r=9

The rate of increase is the same. When r doubles, C doubles; and when r triples, C triples.

6.

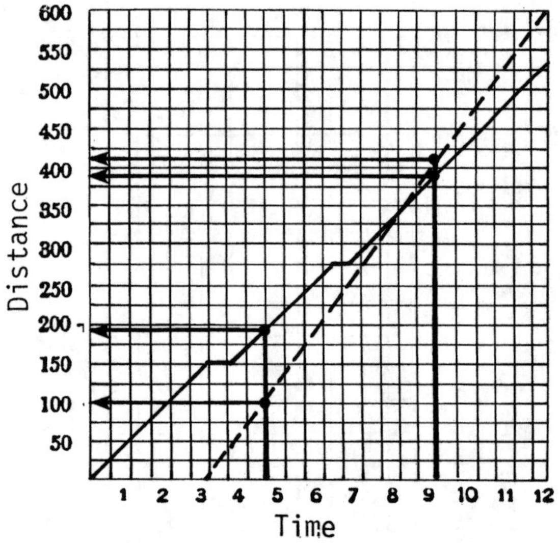

Note: The answers will vary slightly as they are taken from the graph.

$$\text{rate} = \frac{200}{6-3} = \frac{200}{3} = 67 \text{ miles/hour}$$

190 - 100 = 90 miles
405 - 390 = 15 miles

Exact answers: 67.5 mph
86.25 miles
17.5 miles

Exercises 4.9   Page 65

1.
$F = \frac{9}{5}C + 32^o$
$F = \frac{9}{5}(0) + 32$
$F = 32^o$

$F = \frac{9}{5}C + 32^o$
$F = \frac{9}{5}(90) + 32$
$F = 162 + 32$
$F = 194^o$

$F = \frac{9}{5}C + 32^o$
$F = \frac{9}{5}(60) + 32$
$F = 108 + 32$
$F = 140^o$

2.
$C = \frac{5}{9}(F - 32^o)$
$C = \frac{5}{9}(50 - 32)$
$C = \frac{5}{9}(18)$
$C = 10^o$

$C = \frac{5}{9}(F - 32^o)$
$C = \frac{5}{9}(68 - 32)$
$C = \frac{5}{9}(36)$
$C = 20^o$

$C = \frac{5}{9}(F - 32^o)$
$C = \frac{5}{9}(95 - 32)$
$C = \frac{5}{9}(63)$
$C = 35^o$

3. $d = rt$
$d = 85(12)$
$d = 1020$ miles

4.
$r = \frac{d}{t}$
$r = 20 \div \frac{1}{2}$
$r = 20(2)$
$r = 40$ mi. per hr.

$r = \frac{d}{t}$
$r = \frac{2}{3} \div 3\frac{1}{3}$
$r = \frac{2}{3} \div \frac{10}{3}$
$r = \frac{2}{3} \cdot \frac{3}{10}$
$r = \frac{2}{10}$
$r = .2$ mi. per min.

5. $V = \ell wh$
$V = 12(10)(14)$
$V = 120(14)$
$V = 1680$ cu. ft.

6. $A = \pi r^2$
$A = 3.14(5.1)^2$
$A = 3.14(26.01)$
$A = 81.7$ sq. ft. (nearest tenth)

$A = \pi r^2$
$A = 3.14(5^2)$
$A = 3.14(25)$
$A = 78.5$ sq. ft.

$A = \pi r^2$
$A = 3.14(10^2)$
$A = 3.14(100)$
$A = 314$ sq. yd.

7. $C = 40 + 3(16-10)$
$C = 40 + 3(6)$
$C = 40 + 18$
$C = \$.58$

8. $i = 250(.05)(2)$
$i = 250(.1)$
$i = \$25$

9. $d = vt$
$d = 180(3)$
$d = 540$ ft.

10. $C = 2\pi r$
$C = 2(\frac{22}{7})(3.5)$
$C = 7(\frac{22}{7})$
$C = 22$ units

$C = 2\pi r$
$110 = 2(\frac{22}{7})r$
$110 = \frac{44}{7} r$
$110(\frac{7}{44}) = r$
$17.5 = r$

$C = 2\pi r$
$330 = 2(\frac{22}{7})r$
$330 = \frac{44}{7}r$
$330(\frac{7}{44}) = r$
$52.5 = r$

Exercises 4.10 Page 66

1. $i = prt$

$$\frac{i}{pr} = \frac{prt}{pr}$$

$$\frac{i}{pr} = t$$

2.(a) $V = \ell wh$

$$\frac{V}{\ell w} = \frac{\ell wh}{\ell w}$$

$$\frac{V}{\ell w} = h$$

$V = \ell wh$

$$\frac{V}{\ell h} = \frac{\ell wh}{\ell h}$$

$$\frac{V}{\ell h} = w$$

$V = \ell wh$

$$\frac{V}{wh} = \frac{\ell wh}{wh}$$

$$\frac{V}{wh} = \ell$$

(b) The height of a rectangular solid equals the volume divided by the product of its length and width.

The width of a rectangular solid is equal to its volume divided by the product of its length and height.

The length of a rectangular solid is equal to its volume divided by the product of its width and height.

(c) Answers will vary.

3. (1) Area of a circle; A
(2) Length of a side of a square; s
(3) Area of a trapezoid; A
(4) Altitude of a triangle; h

4. Divide each member of the equation by 2.

5. Divide each member of the equation by the product of p and t.

6. Subtract twice a from each member of the equation; then divide each member by 2.

7. Divide each member by the product of and w.

8. $i = prt$; $V = \ wh$; $A = \frac{h}{2}(b+b')$; $s = \frac{P}{4}$; $h = \frac{2A}{b}$; $A = \pi r^2$; $p = 2a + 2b$

i - interest
p - principal
r - rate
t - time

V - volume
 - length
w - width
h - altitude

A - area
h - altitude
b - one base
b′ - other base

s - side
P - perimeter

h - height
A - area
b - base

A - area
r - radius

P - perimeter
a - height
b - base

9. $t = \frac{i}{pr}$;

$$t = \frac{i}{pr}$$

$$t = \frac{48}{(300)(.08)}$$

$t = 2$ yr.

(a) Gives the amount of interest
(b) Gives the principal needed
(c) Gives the rate of interest
(d) Gives the time

Exercises 4.13 Pages 68-69

1. $A = bh$
$A = 6(4)$
$A = 24$ sq. in.

2. $h = \frac{A}{b}$
$h = \frac{10}{2.0}$
$h = 5.0$ in.

3. $A = bh$
$A = 50(100)$
$A = 5000$ sq. ft.

4. $A = bh$
$A = 10(3.0)$
$A = 30$ sq. ft.

5. $b = \frac{A}{h}$
$b = \frac{12}{2.0}$
$b = 6.0$ ft.

6. $A = s^2$
$A = (4.0)^2$
$A = 16$ sq. in.

7. $A = s^2$
$A = 40^2$
$A = 1600$ sq. yd.

8. $A = \frac{1}{2}bh$
$A = \frac{1}{2}(10)(8.0)$
$A = 5(8.0)$
$A = 40$ sq. in.

9. $A = \frac{1}{2}bh$
$36 = \frac{1}{2}(12)h$
$36 = 6h$
$\frac{36}{6} = \frac{6h}{6}$
$h = 6.0$ in.

10. $A = \frac{1}{2}bh$
$A = \frac{1}{2}(6.250)(7.640)$
$A = 6.250(3.820)$
$A = 23.88$ sq. in.

11. $A = \frac{1}{2}h(b + b')$
$A = \frac{1}{2}(6)(12 + 8)$
$A = 3(20)$
$A = 60$ sq. in.

12. $A = \frac{1}{2}h(b + b')$
$A = \frac{1}{2}(3.20)(4.80 + 3.60)$
$A = A = 1.60(8.40)$
$A = A = 13.4$ sq. ft.

13. $c^2 = a^2 + b^2$
$c^2 = 3^2 + 4^2$
$c^2 = 9 + 16$
$c^2 = 25$
$c = 5$

14. $A = \frac{1}{2}ap$
$A = \frac{1}{2}(5.20)(36.0)$
$A = 2.60(36.0)$
$A = 93.6$ sq. in.

15. $C = \pi d$
$C = \frac{22}{7}(28)$
$C = 88$ in.

16. $C = 2\pi r$
$C = 2(3.14)(15.2)$
$C = 95.5$ in.

Exercises 4.14 Pages 70-71

1. $V = abc$
$V = 5(7)(2)$
$V = 70$ cu. units

2. $V = abc$
$48 = (2)(3)c$
$48 = 6c$
$\frac{48}{6} = \frac{6c}{6}$
8 units $= c$

3. $V = e^3$
$V = 3^3$
$V = 27$ cu. in.

4. $A = 6e^2$
$A = 6(5^2)$
$A = 6(25)$
$A = 150$ sq. in.

5. $V = \frac{1}{3}Bh$
$V = \frac{1}{3}(6^2)(10)$
$V = \frac{1}{3}(36)(10)$
$V = 120$ cu. in.

6. $A = \frac{1}{2}\ell p$
$A = \frac{1}{2}(11)(20)$
$A = \frac{1}{2}(220)$
$A = 110$ sq. in.

7. $A = \frac{1}{2}\ell p$
$A = \frac{1}{2}(12)(18)$
$A = 6(18)$
$A = 108$ sq. in.

8. $A = 2\pi rh$

$A = 2(\frac{22}{7})(6\frac{1}{2})(14)$

$A = \cancel{2}(\frac{22}{\cancel{7}})(\frac{13}{\cancel{2}})(\overset{2}{\cancel{14}})$

$A = (22)(13)(2)$

$A = 572$ sq. in.

(571 if 3.14 used for π)

9. $V = \pi r^2 h$

$V = (3.14)(4)^2(8)$

$V = 3.14(16)(8)$

$V = 402$ cu. in.

10. $A = \pi r$

$A = (3.14)(6.5)(12)$

$A = (3.14)(78)$

$A = 245$ sq. in.

11. $V = \frac{1}{3}\pi r^2 h$

$V = \frac{1}{3}(3.14)(3)^2(18)$

$V = \frac{1}{\cancel{3}}(3.14)(\overset{3}{\cancel{9}})(18)$

$V = 3.14(54)$

$V = 170$ cu. in.

(nearest cu. in.)

12. $A = 4\pi r^2$

$A = 4(\frac{22}{7})(7)^2$

$A = 4(\frac{22}{\cancel{7}})(\overset{7}{\cancel{49}})$

$A = 616$ sq. in.

(615 if 3.14 used for π)

13. $V = \frac{4}{3}\pi r^3$

$V = \frac{4}{3}(\frac{22}{7})(\frac{7}{2})^3$

$V = \frac{4}{3}(\frac{22}{7})(\frac{343}{8})$

$V = \frac{\cancel{4}}{3}(\frac{\overset{11}{\cancel{22}}}{\cancel{7}})(\frac{\overset{49}{\cancel{343}}}{\underset{2}{\cancel{8}}})$

$V = \frac{11(49)}{3}$

$V = 180$ cu. in.

<u>Exercises 4.15</u> Pages 72-73

1. $d = vt$

$\frac{d}{v} = \frac{vt}{v}$

$\frac{d}{v} = t$

$t = \frac{d}{v}$

$t = \frac{100}{9}$

$t = 11\frac{1}{9}$ sec.

2. $d = \frac{1}{2}at^2$

$d = \frac{1}{2}(9.8)(10)^2$

$d = \frac{1}{2}(9.8)(100)$

$d = 4.9(100)$

$d = 490$ m

3. (1) $d = \frac{1}{2}gt^2$

$d = \frac{1}{2}(980)(3)^2$

$d = 490(9)$

$d = 4410$ cm

(2) $d = \frac{1}{2}gt^2$

$d = \frac{1}{2}(32)(\frac{7}{2})^2$

$d = 16(\frac{49}{4})$

$d = 4(49)$

$d = 196$ ft.

4. $M = mv$

$M = 10(50)$

$M = 500\ \frac{kg\cdot m}{sec}$

$M = mv$

$\frac{M}{v} = \frac{mv}{v}$

$\frac{M}{v} = m$

5. $F = \frac{mv}{t}$

$F = \frac{100(30)}{10}$

$F = 300\ \frac{gram\text{-}cm}{sec^2}$

6. $C = \frac{5}{9}(F-32^\circ)$

$C = \frac{5}{9}(68-32)$

$C = \frac{5}{9}(36)$

$C = 20^\circ$

7. $F = \frac{9}{5}C + 32^\circ$

$F = \frac{9}{5}(35) + 32$

$F = 63 + 32$

$F = 95^\circ$

Review Exercises Page 73

1. $A = 2\pi rh$

$A = 2(\frac{22}{7})(\frac{7}{2})(5.5)$

$A = 2(\frac{22}{7})(\frac{7}{2})(5.5)$

$A = 22(5.5)$

$A = 121$ sq. in.

2. $V = \frac{1}{3}Bh$

$V = \frac{1}{3}(5.75)^2(8.25)$

$V = \frac{1}{3}(33.0625)(8.25)$

$V = 11.020833)(8.25)$

$V = 90.92$ cu. in.

3. $d = \frac{1}{2}gt^2$

$d = \frac{1}{2}(32)(5.2)^2$

$d = (16)(27.04)$

$d = 433$ ft.

4. $C = \frac{5}{9}(F-32)$

$C = \frac{5}{9}(72-32)$

$C = \frac{5}{9}(40)$

$C = \frac{200}{9}$

$C = 22^\circ$

5. $A = \frac{1}{2}bh$

$A = .5(4.25)(6.30)$

$A = \quad (4.25)(3.15)$

$A = 13.4$ sq. ft.

Test A   Pages 73-74

I

1. $C = 2\pi r$

2. $V = \frac{1}{6}\pi d^3$

3. $F = \frac{9}{5}C + 32^0$

4. $C = pn$
Where C = cost, p is the price per pound and n the number of pounds.

II

1. $C = 2\pi r$
$C = 2(\frac{22}{7})(35)$
$C = 2(\frac{22}{7})(35)$ (7 and 35 cancelled: 1, 5)
$C = 220$ in.

2. $V = \frac{1}{6}\pi d^3$
$V = \frac{1}{6}(3.14)(3)^3$
$V = \frac{1}{6}(3.14)27$ (6 and 27 cancelled: 2, 9)
$V = \frac{28.26}{2}$
$V = 14.13$ cu. in

3. $F = \frac{9}{5}C + 32^0$
$F = \frac{9}{5}(15) + 32$
$F = 27 + 32$
$F = 59^0$

4. $C = pn$
$C = (2.98)16$
$C = \$47.68$

III

1. $A = \pi r(r + e)$
$A = 3.14(3.75)(3.75 + 6.25)$
$A = 3.14(3.75)(10)$
$A = 117.75$ sq. units

2. $p = \frac{2d^2n}{5}$
$p = \frac{2(3)^2(6)}{5}$
$p = \frac{2(9)(6)}{5}$
$p = \frac{108}{5}$
$p = 21.6$

IV

1.

base	altitude	Area
6	2	6
6	6	18
6	10	30
6	14	42

$A = \frac{1}{2}(6)(2) = 6$ sq. in

$A = \frac{1}{2}(6)(6) = 18$ sq. in.

$A = \frac{1}{2}(6)(10) = 30$ sq. in.

$A = \frac{1}{2}(6)(14) = 42$ sq. in.

2.

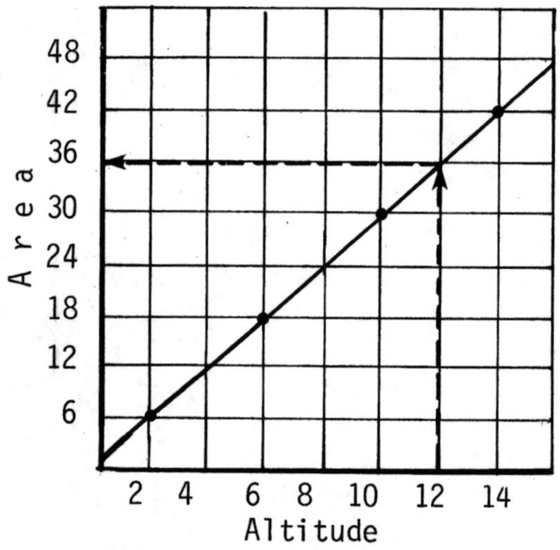

Areas of Triangles of Base Six

3. 36 sq. units

4. $A = \frac{1}{2}bh$
$A = \frac{1}{2}(6)h$
$24 = 3h$
$\frac{24}{3} = \frac{3h}{3}$
$h = 8$ in.

Test B   Pages 74 -75

I

1. $A = \frac{dd'}{2}$ 2. $V = \frac{hs^2}{3}$ 3. $A = p + prt$ 4. $d = rt$

II

1. $A = \frac{dd'}{2}$
$A = \frac{3.5(7.6)}{2}$
$A = \frac{26.6}{2}$
$A = 13.3$ sq. in.

2. $V = \frac{hs^2}{3}$
$V = \frac{7(6)^2}{3}$
$V = \frac{7(36)}{3}$
$V = 7(12)$
$V = 84$ cu. in.

3. $A = p + prt$
$A = 650 + 650(.075)(5)$
$A = 650 + 243.75$
$A = \$893.75$

4. $d = rt$
$d = 50(6.25)$
$d = 312.5$ mi.

III

1. $L = a + d(n-1)$
$L = 6.3 + 3.5(9-1)$
$L = 6.3 + 3.5(8)$
$L = 6.3 + 28$
$L = 34.3$

2. $M = \frac{w\ell^2}{8}$
$M = \frac{14(12)^2}{8}$
$M = \frac{14(144)}{8}$
$M = 14(18)$
$M = 252$

IV

1.

Principal	interest
$ 100	$ 9
400	36
700	63
1,000	90

$i = prt$
$i = (100)(.09)(1) = 9$
$i = (400)(.09)(1) = 36$
$i = (700)(.09)(1) = 63$
$i = (1000)(.09)(1) = 90$

2.

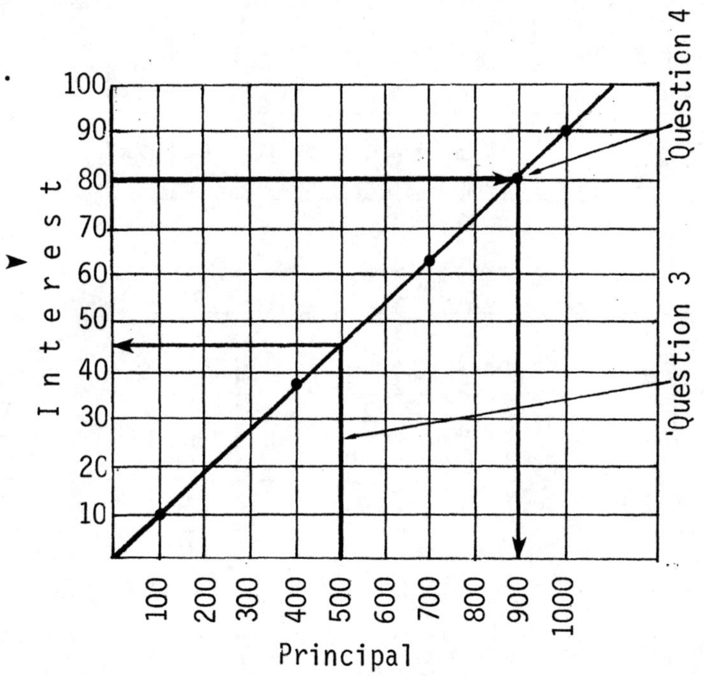

Interest at 9 Percent

3. $45 (from graph)

4. $900 (from graph)

Test C   Pages 75-76

I

1.

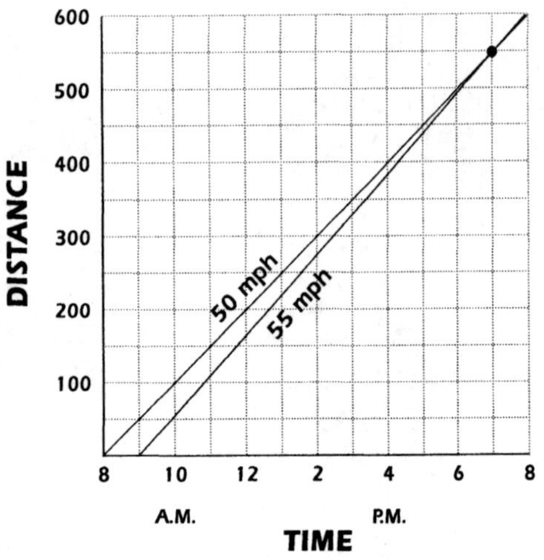

550 miles from home at 7 P.M.

II

1.

Number of Inches in Radius *(r)*	1	2	3	4	5	6
Number of Inches in Circumference *(c)*	2π	4π	6π	8π	10π	12π

2.

Number of Inches in Radius *(r)*	1	2	3	4	5	6
Number of Inches in Area	π	4π	9π	16π	26π	36π

3.

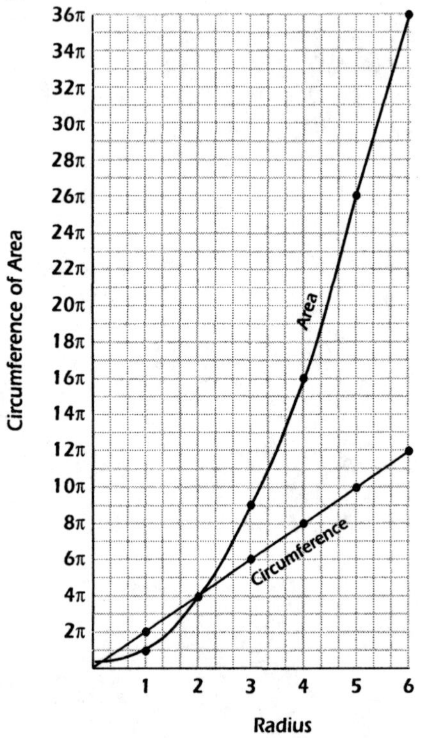

4. (a) increase
   area
   circumference

   (b) two

   (c) 11

   (d) 4.5

III

1.

Number of hours (t)	1	3	5	6	10	15	30
Number of miles per hour (r)	30	10	6	5	3	2	1

2.

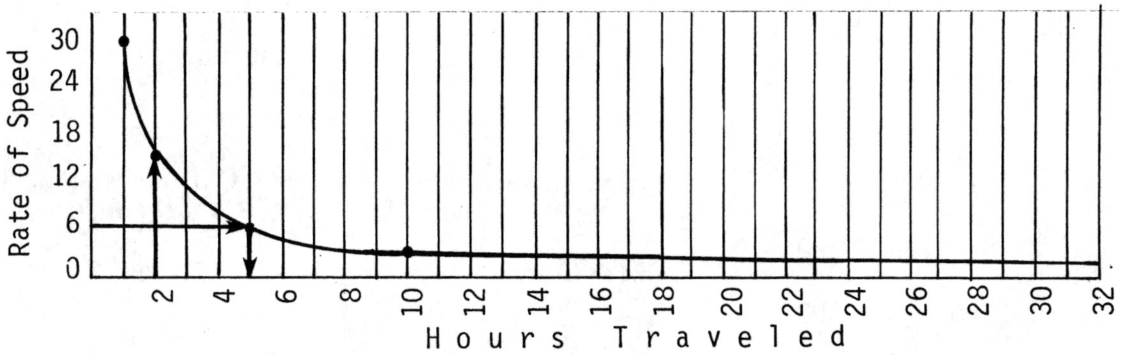

Comparison of Rate and Time to Travel 30 Miles

3.(a) 15 miles per hour (b) 5 hours

IV

1.

s in inches	3	5	6	7	8
A in square inches	9	25	36	49	64

2.

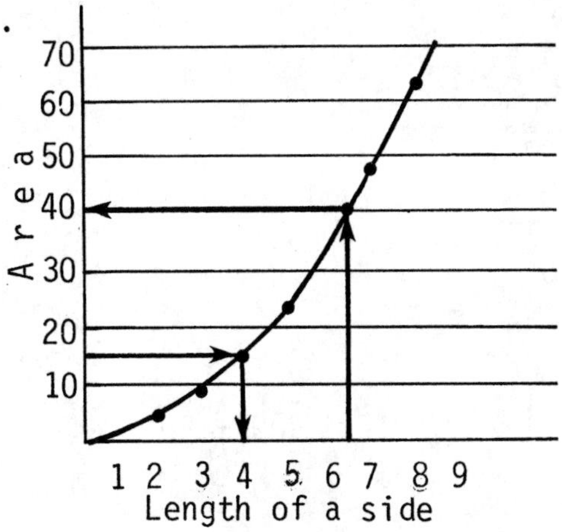

Area of a Square

3.(a)
$A = s^2$
$16 = s^2$
$16 = 4^2$
$s = 4$ in.

(b) 42.25 sq. in.

$A = s^2$
$A = (6.5)^2$
$S = 42.25$ sq. in.

UNIT 5 — Positive and Negative Numbers

Exercises 5.3   Pages 80-81

1. -20

2. 2000 - 100 + 200

3. By subtracting the rate of the current from Michael's rate in still water; 4 + 1 = 5 mph

4.(a) $10 - $2

(b) $120 + $50 - $20

(c) $75,000 - $7,500

5. It pulls upward with a force of 3 ounces; no movement; it pulls downward with a force of 1 ounce.

6. +700 feet above sea level

7. -20° F

Exercises 5.4   Page 82

1. 10   2. -10   3. 0   4. 1   5. -4   6. 3   7. -3

Exercises 5.5   Page 83

1. 10   2. 10   3. 4.1   4. $-15\frac{1}{4}$ 5. -1.6

6. 10   7. 7.4   8. -17.1   9. .6   10. $-3\frac{1}{2}$

11. -7   12. -7   13. -13   14. -6   15. -6

16. 5

17. -100 + 56 = -44
44 B.C.

18. 25 + 5 + 6 + (-8) = 28 yard line;
28 + 13 = 41 yard line
41 + (-5) = 36 yard line;
36 + 11 = 47 yard line

19. 15 + 4 + 5 + (-2) + 30 + (-6) + (-2) + 12 = 56 on the Senior's 44 yard line

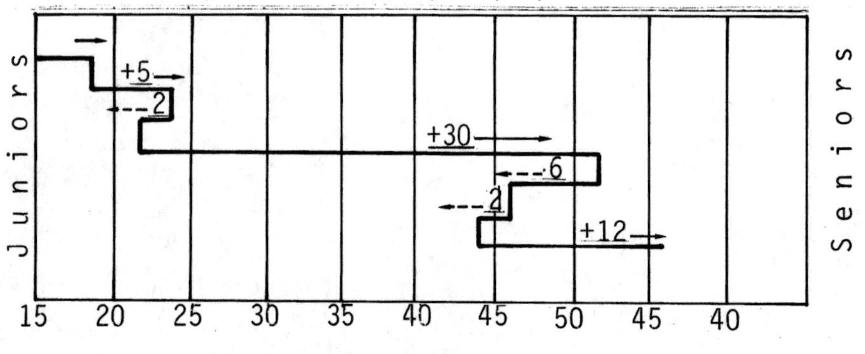

20. 50 + (-10) + 40 + (-30) + 89 = 139 miles

Exercises 5.6 Pages 84-86

1. 3	2. 2	3. 1	4. 0	5. -1	6. -2
7. -3	8. -4	9. -5	10. -7	11. -9	12. -11
13. 4	14. 5	15. 6	16. 7	17. 11	18. 12.1
19. -5	20. -4	21. -3	22. 1	23. 2	24. -23.7
25. 12	26. 7	27. 27.1	28. $20\frac{3}{4}$	29. 48	30. 2
31. 2.7	32. -12.4	33. 16.1	34. -15	35. 0	36. 8
37. -8	38. -13.0	39. -25	40. -1 - 12 = -13		

41. 0 - (-3) = 0 + 3 = 3

42. 14 - (-4) = 14 + 4 = 18

43. -3 - 0 = -3

44. 0 - (-7) = 0 + 7 = 7
7 - (-4) = 7 + 4 = 11
11 + (-2) = 9
9 + (-3) = 6
6 + 7 = 13
13 - 11 = 2
2 + (-6) = -4

45. 3 - (-5) = 3 + 5 = 8
$3 > -5$ by 8 units
$-2 > -5$ by 3 units
$6 > (8-3)$ by 1 unit
$[-2 - (-8)] > [-2 + (-8)]$
by 16 units

46.

Duluth	2 - (-6) = 2 + 6 = 8^0
Helena	-4 - (-12) = -4 + 12 = 8^0
Montreal	18 - (-12) = 18 + 12 = 30^0
New Orleans	56 - 44 = 12^0
New York	42 - 20 = 22^0

47. 32 - (-12) = 32 + 12
= 44^0

48. Duluth and Chicago
Minimum 24 - (-6) = 24 + 6 = 30^0
Maximum 30 - 2 = 28^0
Montreal and New York
Minimum 20 - (-12) = 32^0
Maximum 42 - 18 = 24^0
Helena and New Orleans
Minimum 44 - (-12) = 56^0
Maximum 56 - (-4) = 60^0

49. 105 - (-22) = 105 + 22
= 127 ft.
-127 ft.

Exercises 5.7 Page 88

1. 6; 10; -12; 20; -16; -18; -24
   -6; -10; 12; -20; 16; 18; 24

2.(a) -49.2 (b) 27 (c) -34.02 (d) $-33\frac{3}{4}$ (e) -20

3.(a) 35 (b) -16 (c) -70 (d) 132 (e) -32

4.(a) -50 (b) $-11\frac{1}{4}$ (c) 79.54 (d) $14\frac{2}{9}$ (e) $3\frac{3}{20}$

Exercises 5.8 Pages 88-89

1. -1 2. 36 3. 16 4. 112 5. 36 6. -72 7. -90 8. 98

Exercises 5.9 Pages 89-90

1. 3; -3; 5; -5; 7; -6; -9; 11; -4 2. -3; 3; -5; 5; -7; 6; 9; -11; 4

3. -2 4. -1 5. -3 6. 9 7. -9 8. -5 9. -11

10. -7 11. -4 12. -82 13. 4 14. 1 15. -9 16. -7

17. 9.1 18. -9 19. -20 20. -4 21. 7 22. 9.2

Review Exercises Page 90

1. Numbers larger than zero; numbers smaller than zero

2. Subtraction and direction; 150 miles south; 75 miles north

3. Algebraic numbers include the negative numbers but arithmetic numbers do not.

4. Add its opposite; 12 - (-7) = 12 + 7 = 19. The absolute value of 12 is 12, and the absolute value of -7 is 7.

5. The sign of a product is positive when the factors have like signs and negative when they have unlike signs. The sign of a quotient is positive when the dividend and divisor have like signs and negative when they have unlike signs.

6. positive; negative 7. 7 8. -19 9. -4 10. -8 11. -10 12. 4

13. $12 + 3(2) = 12 + 6 = 18^{\circ}$

$12 + 4(2) + 1(-3) = 12 + 8 + (-3) = 17^{\circ}$

$12 + 4(2) + 4(-3) = 12 + 8 + (-12) = 8^{\circ}$

14. $10^\circ F-(-10^\circ F) = 20^\circ F$
$30^\circ F-(-20^\circ F) = 50^\circ F$

15. 300 - 500 + 400 = $200 gain

16. 3(-3)(-3) = 27

17. 7(-4)(-2) = 56

18. -6(-4)(-9) = -216

19. 18(-6) ÷ (-2) = 54

20. 24(-2) ÷ 2 = -24

21. 9(-2) ÷ (-3) = 6

22. -6(-8) ÷ (-4) = -12

23. -10(-5) ÷ (-2) = -25

24. -12(8) ÷ (-3)(2) = 64

25. 15(-6) ÷ 5(-2) = 36

26. 3 + 5 - 4 + 6 - 1 + 3 + 2 - 5 - 6 + 2 - 3
= 8 - 4 + 6 - 1 + 3 + 2 - 5 - 6 + 2 - 3
= 4 + 6 - 1 + 3 + 2 - 5 - 6 + 2 - 3
= 10 - 1 + 3 + 2 - 5 - 6 + 2 - 3
= 9 + 3 + 2 - 5 - 6 + 2 - 3
= 12 + 2 - 5 - 6 + 2 - 3
= 14 - 5 - 6 + 2 - 3
= 9 - 6 + 2 - 3
= 3 + 2 - 3
= 5 - 3
= 2

27. 8 + 11 - 4 + 6 ÷ (-2)4 = 8 + 11 - 4 + (-3)4
= 8 + 11 - 4 + (-12)
= 19 - 4 + (-12)
= 15 + (-12)
= 3

28. Let credits be positive and debts negative; let income be positive and expenses negative.

29. - 32 + 6 - 10 - 3 + 18 + 7 - 2 = -26 - 10 - 3 + 18 + 7 - 2
= -36 - 3 + 18 + 7 - 2
= -39 + 18 + 7 - 2
= -21 + 7 - 2
= -14 - 2
= -16^0

30. $4ab^2 - 3a^2b = 4(-2)(1)^2 - 3(-2)^2(1) = 4(-2)(1) - 3(4)(1)$
$= -8 - 12$
$= -20$

Test A   Pages 91-92

I

1. Money spent
2. 300 ft. below sea level
3. 8 - 12 + 5 + 3 - 6 - 1 = -3

II

1.(a) -1   (b) -11   (c) 4   (d) 0

2. (a) -3 (b) 4 (c) 15 (d) -23 (e) -7

(f) 5 (g) -22 (h) -18 (i) 19 (j) -9

III

1. (a) 15 (b) -30 (c) -12 (d) 24 (e) 40 (f) -60 (g) -42 (h) 90

2. (a) 4 (b) 9 (c) -4 (d) -4

3. (a) -20 (b) 8 (c) -25 (d) 49 (e) -8 (f) -27

<u>Test B</u> Pages 92 and 93

I

1. Two floors below ground

2. Two more seats were needed .

3. 8 - 5 - 6 + 6 - 7 = - 4
The man is 4 blocks south of his starting point.

II

1. (a) 0 (b) 0 (c) -12

2. (a) -5 (b) 7 (c) 18 (d) -27 (e) 15 (f) 12 (g) -11 (h) -29

(i) 8 (j) -6

III

1. (a) -24 (b) -64 (c) 48 (d) 120 (e) -24 (f) 84

2. (a) 5 (b) -8 (c) -6 (d) -8

3. a) $2(-4) \div 2(7) = -8 \div 2(7)$
$= -4(7)$
$= -28$

b) $9 \div (-3)(-4)5 \div (-10)$
$= -3(-4)5 \div (-10)$
$= 12(5) \div (-10)$
$= 60 \div (-10)$
$= -6$

c) 16 d) -16 e) -27 f) -8

<u>Test C</u> Page 93

I

1. $(ab)^3 = [1(-2)]^3 = (-2)^3 = -8$

2. $a^3b = 1^3(-2) = 1(-2) = -2$

3. $ab^3 = 1(-2)^3 = 1(-8) = -8$

4. $5bde = 5(-2)(-4)(\frac{1}{2}) = -10(-4)(\frac{1}{2})$
$= 40(\frac{1}{2})$
$= 20$

5. $-8bf = -8(-2)(0) = 0$

6. $\frac{-9bd}{8c} = \frac{-9(-2)(-4)}{8(3)} = \frac{-72}{24} = -3$

7. $5b^2 - 2bc - 3c^2 = 5(-2)^2 - 2(-2)(3) - 3(3)^2$
$= 5(4) - 2(-2)(3) - 3(9)$
$= 20 + 12 - 27$
$= 5$

8. $\frac{2c^2 + 3cd + d^2}{b^3 + c^2} = \frac{2(3)^2 + 3(3)(-4) + (-4)^2}{(-2)^3 + 3^2} = \frac{2(9) + 3(3)(-4) + 16}{-8 + 9}$
$= \frac{18 - 36 + 16}{-8 + 9}$
$= \frac{-2}{1}$
$= -2$

9. $bc + 3cd - 2bd + 4bc + 3bd - 7cd - 5bc + 6cd - bd$
$= -2(3)+3(3)(-4)-2(-2)(-4)+4(-2)(3)+3(-2)(-4)-7(3)(-4)-5(-2)(3)+6(3)(-4)-(-2)(-4)$
$= -6 - 36 - 16 - 24 + 24 + 84 + 30 - 72 - 8$
$= -24$

10. $cd^2e - abcf + 8e^2 + b^5 = 3(-4)^2(\frac{1}{2}) - 1(-2)(3)(0) + 8(\frac{1}{2})^2 + (-2)^5$
$= 3(16)(\frac{1}{2}) - 0 + 8(\frac{1}{4}) + (-32)$
$= 24 + 2 + (-32)$
$= -6$

II

1. 1. let x = amount earned by Bradley $12.50
   2. x + 35 = amount earned by Jason $47.50
      x + 35 + 12.50 = amount earned by Sigmund $60.00
      total earnings = total earnings
   3. (x) + (x + 35 + (x + 35 + 12.50) = 120
   4. $3x + 82.50 = 120$
      $3x + 82.50 - 82.50 = 120 - 82.50$
      $3x = 37.50$
      $\frac{3x}{3} = \frac{37.50}{3}$
      x = $12.50
   5. $ 12.50
      47.50
      +60.00
      $120.00 ✓

2. 1. let w = the width 7 inches
   2. 2w - 1 = the length 13 inches
   3. perimeter = perimeter
      $2(2w - 1) + 2w = 40$
   4. $4w - 2 + 2w = 40$
      $6w - 2 = 40$
      $6w - 2 + 2 = 40 + 2$
      $6w = 42$
      $\frac{6w}{6} = \frac{42}{6}$
      $w = 7$
   5. 7
      7
      13
      +13
      40 ✓

3\. 1. let x = the first side <u>7 in.</u>
   2. $x + 2$ = the second side <u>9 in.</u>
   $x - 3$ = the third side <u>4 in.</u>
   3. perimeter = perimeter

$$(x) + (x + 2) + (x - 3) = 20$$

   4.

$$3x - 1 = 20$$
$$3x - 1 + 1 = 20 + 1$$
$$3x = 21$$
$$\frac{3x}{3} = \frac{21}{3}$$
$$x = 7$$

   5.

$$\begin{array}{r} 7 \\ 9 \\ +4 \\ \hline 20 \end{array} \checkmark$$

4\. 1. let x = smaller number <u>8</u>
   2. $7x$ = larger number <u>56</u>
   3. sum of parts = sum of parts

$$(x) + (7x) = 64$$

   4.

$$8x = 64$$
$$\frac{8x}{8} = \frac{64}{8}$$
$$x = 8$$

   5.

$$\begin{array}{r} 8 \\ +56 \\ \hline 64 \end{array} \checkmark$$

5\. 1. let x = the cost of the program <u>\$81</u>
   2. $9x$ = the cost of the computer <u>\$729</u>
   3. total cost = total cost

$$(x) + (9x) = 810$$

   4.

$$10x = 810$$
$$\frac{10x}{10} = \frac{810}{10}$$
$$x = 81$$

   5.

$$\begin{array}{r} 81 \\ +729 \\ \hline 810 \end{array} \checkmark$$

UNIT 6 — Fundamental Operations

Exercises 6.2   Pages 95-96

1. 7; 7 times a number
2. 7 times n; 7n
3. 9a's; 9a
4. 16 c's; 16c
5. 13
6. 13 d's
7. 8
8. 8d
9. Like terms; add their numerical coefficients
10. See page 95 in text.
11. 9
12. 5x
13. 9x
14. -5v
15. 6a
16. 8(a + b)
17. 3a
18. -6y
19. 10mb
20. 8m
21. -7c
22. $-30x^2$
23. 16a
24. 11y
25. 5m
26. ab
27. $-4x^2y^2$
28. 3(x + y) or 3x + 3y
29. $18(a + b)^2$ or $18a^2 + 36ab + 18b^2$
30. See page 96 in text.
31. 2x, 4a, -x, -2a
    = 4a - 2a + 2x - x
    = 2a + x
32. m, -3c, -6m, 4c
    = -3c + 4c + m - 6m
    = c - 5m
33. 4z, -z, -w, +4w
    = -w + 4w + 4z - z
    = 3w + 3z
34. $5r, -\frac{3}{4}t, -2r, -\frac{1}{4}t$
    $= 5r - 2r - \frac{3}{4}t - \frac{1}{4}t$
    $= 3r - t$
35. $\frac{1}{2}p, -\frac{2}{3}q, -\frac{1}{2}p, \frac{1}{6}q$
    $= \frac{1}{2}p - \frac{1}{2}p - \frac{2}{3}q + \frac{1}{6}q$
    $= -\frac{1}{2}q$
36. d, .4b, -.5b, .6
    = .4b - .5b + d + .6
    = -.1b + d + .6
37. $x^2, 2xy, y^2, -3x^2, -4xy, 4y^2$
    $= x^2 - 3x^2 + 2xy - 4xy + y^2 + 4y^2$
    $= -2x^2 - 2xy + 5y^2$
38. $2r^2, rs, 3s^2, -4r^2, +5rs, 6s^2$
    $= 2r^2 - 4r^2 + rs + 5rs + 3s^2 + 6s^2$
    $= -2r^2 + 6rs + 9s^2$
39. $a^3, 3a^2b, -ab^2, b^3, -a^3, -2a^2b, ab^2, 2b^3$
    $= a^3 - a^3 + 3a^2b - 2a^2b - ab^2 + ab^2 + b^3 + 2b^3$
    $= a^2b + 3b^3$

Exercises 6.3   Pages 97-98

1. -3a + 5b
2. 6r + 4s
3. $2x^2 + xy + y^2$

4. $11a^2b - 7ab^2 + 2ac^2 - 9a^2b - 6ab^2 + 4ac^2$
$= 11a^2b - 9a^2b - 7ab^2 - 6ab^2 + 2ac^2 + 4ac^2$
$= 2a^2b - 13ab^2 + 6ac^2$

5. $2a + 2b + 3c + 4b - 4a + 6a - 2c$
$= 2a - 4a + 6a + 2b + 4b + 3c - 2c$
$= 4a + 6b + c$

6. $7w + 4x - 4y - x - 2w + 3y - 3x + 4w$
$= 7w - 2w + 4w + 4x - x - 3x - 4y + 3y$
$= 9w - y$

7. $7\ell - 6m + 3n - 8\ell + 4m + 11n + m - 2\ell$
$= 7\ell - 8\ell - 2\ell - 6m + 4m + m + 3n + 11n$
$= -3\ell - m + 14n$

8. $15r + 6s - 11t + r - 9s + t - 2s + 5r - 2t - r$
$= 15r + r + 5r - r + 6s - 9s - 2s - 11t + t - 2t$
$= 20r - 5s - 12t$

9. $7x - 11y + 4z - 7z + 11x - 4y + 7y - 11z - 4x + y - x - z$
$= 7x + 11x - 4x - x - 11y - 4y + 7y + y + 4z - 7z - 11z - z$
$= 13x - 7y - 15z$

10. $a + 3b + 5c - 6a + d + 4b - 2c - 2b + 5a - d + a - b$
$= a - 6a + 5a + a + 3b + 4b - 2b - b + 5c - 2c + d - d$
$= a + 4b + 3c$

11. $4x^2 - 3xy + 5y^2 + 10xy - 17y^2 - 11x^2 - 5xy + 12x^2 - 2xy$
$= 4x^2 - 11x^2 + 12x^2 - 3xy + 10xy - 5xy - 2xy + 5y^2 - 17y^2$
$= 5x^2 - 12y^2$

12. $2xy - 5y^2 + x^2y^2 - 7xy + 3y^2 - 4x^2y^2 + 5xy + 4y^2 + x^2y^2$
$= x^2y^2 - 4x^2y^2 + x^2y^2 + 2xy - 7xy + 5xy - 5y^2 + 3y^2 + 4y^2$
$= -2x^2y^2 + 2y^2$

13. $2a - 3b + 2b - 3c + 5c - 4a + 10a - 5b + 7b - 3c$
$= 2a - 4a + 10a - 3b + 2b - 5b + 7b - 3c + 5c - 3c$
$= 8a + b - c$

14. $x + y + z + x - y + z + y - z - x + z - x - y + x - z$
$= x + x - x - x + x + y - y + y - y + z + z - z + z - z$
$= x + z$

15. $4x^3 - 2x^2 - 7x + 1 + x^3 + 3x^2 + 5x - 6 + 4x^2 - 8x^3 + 2 - 6x + 2x^3 - 2x^2$
$+ 8x + 4 + 2x^3 - 3x^2 - 2x + 1$
$= 4x^3 + x^3 - 8x^3 + 2x^3 + 2x^3 - 2x^2 + 3x^2 + 4x^2 - 2x^2 - 3x^2 - 7x + 5x$
$-6x + 8x - 2x + 1 - 6 + 2 + 4 + 1$
$= x^3 - 2x + 2$

16. $5x - 3y - 2z + 4y - 2x + 6z + 3a - 2x - 4y + 4b - 2z - 5y + a - 5b + 5y - 6x + 8x + 2y - 5a - 2b + 6x - y - 2z + 4b$

$= 3a + a - 5a + 4b - 5b - 2b + 4b + 5x - 2x - 2x - 6x + 8x + 6x - 3y + 4y - 4y - 5y + 5y + 2y - y - 2z + 6z - 2z - 2z$

$= -a + b + 9x - 2y$

17. $.2x^3 - 4x^2 + x + 2 + .4x^2 - 4x + .4 - x^3 + 3.5x - .6 + 3x^2 + 2x^3 + 1 - .5x + 1.2x^2 + .8x^3$

$= .2x^3 - x^3 + 2x^3 + .8x^3 - 4x^2 + .4x^2 + 3x^2 + 1.2x^2 + x - 4x + 3.5x - .5x + 2 + .4 - .6 + 1$

$= 2x^3 + .6x^2 + 2.8$

Exercises 6.4 Pages 98-99

1. 5; 5 times the number
2. 5 times n; 5n
3. 4 a's; 4a
4. 6 c's; 6c
5. 4 d's; 4d
6. Like terms; subtract their numerical coefficients
7. See page 98 in text.
8. 5
9. 5x
10. 10
11. 10ab
12. $5m^2$
13. 36xy
14. $7ax^2$
15. $21r^2s^3$
16. $2x^2y^2z$
17. 32(a + b) or 32a + 32b
18. 13(x - 4) or 13x - 52
19. n
20. 0
21. 5s
22. 8b
23. 12x
24. 5r
25. 16y
26. 6z
27. 3v
28. 6n
29. 13y
30. 9z

Exercises 6.5 Page 100

1. -t
2. 7x - 4y
3. 3r - 3s
4. $6n^2 - 3n^3$
5. r - 4s
6. $3a^2 - ab - 5b^2$
7. $\begin{array}{r} 5x - 3y + z \\ 2x - y + 8z \\ \hline 3x - 2y - 7z \end{array}$
8. $\begin{array}{r} 3a^2b + b^3 - a^3 \\ 4a^2b + 2b^3 - 8a^3 \\ \hline -a^2b - b^3 + 7a^3 \end{array}$ $= 7a^3 - a^2b - b^3$
9. $\begin{array}{r} 13a^2 + 5b^2 - 4c^2 \\ 8a^2 + 9b^2 + 10c^2 \\ \hline 5a^2 - 4b^2 - 14c^2 \end{array}$

10.
$$\begin{array}{r} 15x - 3y + 2z \\ 3x + 8y - 9z \\ \hline 12x - 11y + 11z \end{array}$$

11.
$$\begin{array}{r} a^2 - ab - b^2 \\ -2a^2 + ab - 2b^2 \\ \hline 3a^2 - 2ab + b^2 \end{array}$$

12.
$$\begin{array}{r} m^2 - mn + n^2 \\ 2m^2 - 3mn + 2n^2 \\ \hline -m^2 + 2mn - n^2 \end{array}$$

13.
$$\begin{array}{r} 4x^2 + 3xy + y^2 \\ 2x^2 - 5xy + 2y^2 \\ \hline 2x^2 + 8xy - y^2 \end{array}$$

14.
$$\begin{array}{r} a^2 + 3ab + b^2 \\ a^2 + 4ab + b^2 \\ \hline -ab \end{array}$$

15.
$$\begin{array}{r} 6x^2 + 4xy - 3y^2 \\ 6x^2 - 3xy + 4y^2 \\ \hline 7xy - 7y^2 \end{array}$$

16.
$$\begin{array}{lr} & 3a^2 - 2ab - b^2 \\ (+) & -2a^2 + 3ab \\ \hline & a^2 + ab - b^2 \\ (-) & a^2 - ab - b^2 \\ \hline & 2ab \end{array}$$

17.
$$\begin{array}{lr} & x - 4y + z \\ (+) & 2x + 3y - 2z \\ \hline & 3x - y - z \end{array}$$

$$\begin{array}{lr} & 3x - y + z \\ (-) & 3x - y - z \\ \hline & 2z \end{array}$$

18.
$$\begin{array}{lr} & m^2n - 2mn^2 \\ (+) & 2m^2n + 2mn^2 - m - n^3 \\ \hline & 3m^2n - m - n^3 \end{array}$$

$$\begin{array}{lr} & m^3 - n^3 \\ (-) & -n^3 + 3m^2n - m \\ \hline & m^3 - 3m^2n + m \end{array}$$

19.
$$\begin{array}{lr} & a^2 + b^2 \\ (+) & 2ab \\ \hline & a^2 + b^2 + 2ab \\ (+) & a^2 - b^2 \\ \hline & 2a^2 + 2ab \\ (+) & a - 2ab + b^2 \\ \hline & 3a^2 + b^2 \end{array}$$

20.
$$\begin{array}{lr} & a^2 + b^2 \\ (-) & 2ab \\ \hline & a^2 + b^2 - 2ab \\ (-) & a^2 - b^2 \\ \hline & 2b^2 - 2ab \\ (+) & a^2 + b^2 - 2ab \\ \hline & a^2 + 3b^2 - 4ab \\ = & a^2 - 4ab + 3b^2 \end{array}$$

21.
$$\begin{array}{lr} & a^2 + b^2 \\ (-) & 2ab \\ \hline & a^2 + b^2 - 2ab \\ (+) & a^2 - b^2 \\ \hline & 2a^2 - 2ab \\ (-) & a^2 + b^2 - 2ab \\ \hline & a^2 - b^2 \end{array}$$

22.
$$\begin{array}{lr} & 2ab \\ (-) & a^2 + b^2 \\ \hline & 2ab - a^2 - b^2 \\ (-) & -2ab + a^2 + b^2 \\ \hline & 4ab - 2a^2 - 2b^2 \\ (+) & a^2 - b^2 \\ \hline & 4ab - a^2 - 3b^2 \\ = & -a^2 + 4ab - 3b^2 \end{array}$$

23. let n = number
$$\begin{aligned} a - n &= b \\ -n &= b - a \\ n &= a - b \end{aligned}$$

24. let n = number
$$\begin{aligned} a + n &= b \\ n &= b - a \end{aligned}$$

Exercises 6.6 Page 102

Students may do some steps mentally as shown on page 102 of the text. The check is left for the teacher.

1.
$$\begin{aligned} 7n + 12 &= 5n + 16 \\ 7n - 5n + 12 &= 5n - 5n + 16 \\ 2n + 12 &= 16 \\ 2n + 12 - 12 &= 16 - 12 \\ 2n &= 4 \\ \frac{2n}{2} &= \frac{4}{2} \\ n &= 2 \end{aligned}$$

2.
$$\begin{aligned} 4r - 11 &= 19 - 2r \\ 4r + 2r - 11 &= 19 - 2r + 2r \\ 6r - 11 &= 19 \\ 6r - 11 + 11 &= 19 + 11 \\ 6r &= 30 \\ \frac{6r}{6} &= \frac{30}{6} \\ r &= 5 \end{aligned}$$

3.
$$\begin{aligned}13x + 4 &= 5x + 12\\ 13x - 5x + 4 &= 5x - 5x + 12\\ 8x + 4 &= 12\\ 8x + 4 - 4 &= 12 - 4\\ 8x &= 8\\ \frac{8x}{8} &= \frac{8}{8}\\ x &= 1\end{aligned}$$

4.
$$\begin{aligned}3s + 14 + 7s &= 78 + 2s\\ 10s + 14 &= 78 + 2s\\ 10s - 2s + 14 &= 78 + 2s - 2s\\ 8s + 14 &= 78\\ 8s + 14 - 14 &= 78 - 14\\ 8s &= 64\\ \frac{8s}{8} &= \frac{64}{8}\\ s &= 8\end{aligned}$$

5.
$$\begin{aligned}9x + 23 + 2x &= 4x + 37\\ 11x + 23 &= 4x + 37\\ 11x - 4x + 23 &= 4x - 4x + 37\\ 7x + 23 &= 37\\ 7x + 23 - 23 &= 37 - 23\\ 7x &= 14\\ \frac{7x}{7} &= \frac{14}{7}\\ x &= 2\end{aligned}$$

6.
$$\begin{aligned}5x - 7 + 15x &= 13x + 14\\ 20x - 7 &= 13x + 14\\ 20x - 13x - 7 &= 13x - 13x + 14\\ 7x - 7 &= 14\\ 7x - 7 + 7 &= 14 + 7\\ 7x &= 21\\ \frac{7x}{7} &= \frac{21}{7}\\ x &= 3\end{aligned}$$

7.
$$\begin{aligned}2(3n - 5) &= 4n + 12\\ 6n - 10 &= 4n + 12\\ 6n - 4n - 10 &= 4n - 4n + 12\\ 2n - 10 &= 12\\ 2n - 10 + 10 &= 12 + 10\\ 2n &= 22\\ \frac{2n}{2} &= \frac{22}{2}\\ n &= 11\end{aligned}$$

8.
$$\begin{aligned}2p - 9 &= 7(2p - 3)\\ 2p - 9 &= 14p - 21\\ 2p - 2p - 9 &= 14p - 2p - 21\\ -9 &= 12p - 21\\ -9 + 21 &= 12p - 21 + 21\\ 12 &= 12p\\ \frac{12}{12} &= \frac{12p}{12}\\ 1 &= p\end{aligned}$$

9.
$$\begin{aligned}22 - 6x &= 40 - 8x\\ 22 - 6x + 8x &= 40 - 8x + 8x\\ 22 + 2x &= 40\\ 22 - 22 + 2x &= 40 - 22\\ 2x &= 18\\ \frac{2x}{2} &= \frac{18}{2}\\ x &= 9\end{aligned}$$

10. See page 102 in text.

11.
$$\begin{aligned}2x - 4 + 6x &= 22 - 15 + 21\\ 8x - 4 &= 28\\ 8x - 4 + 4 &= 28 + 4\\ 8x &= 32\\ \frac{8x}{8} &= \frac{32}{8}\\ x &= 4\end{aligned}$$

12.
$$\begin{aligned}30 + 5x - 32 &= 7x + 12 - 9x\\ 5x - 2 &= -2x + 12\\ 5x + 2x - 2 &= -2x + 2x + 12\\ 7x - 2 &= 12\\ 7x - 2 + 2 &= 12 + 2\\ 7x &= 14\\ \frac{7x}{7} &= \frac{14}{7}\\ x &= 2\end{aligned}$$

13.
$$\begin{aligned}
6x + 5x - 70 &= 5x + 54 - 70\\
11x - 70 &= 5x - 16\\
11x - 5x - 70 &= 5x - 5x - 16\\
6x - 70 &= -16\\
6x - 70 + 70 &= -16 + 70\\
6x &= 54\\
\frac{6x}{6} &= \frac{54}{6}\\
x &= 9
\end{aligned}$$

14.
$$\begin{aligned}
5x + 16 - 6x &= 16 + 25 - 6x\\
-x + 16 &= 41 - 6x\\
-x + 6x + 16 &= 41 - 6x + 6x\\
5x + 16 &= 41\\
5x + 16 - 16 &= 41 - 16\\
5x &= 25\\
\frac{5x}{5} &= \frac{25}{5}\\
x &= 5
\end{aligned}$$

15.
$$\begin{aligned}
9x + 15 - 2x &= 32 + 4x - 11\\
7x + 15 &= 4x + 21\\
7x - 4x + 15 &= 4x - 4x + 21\\
3x + 15 &= 21\\
3x + 15 - 15 &= 21 - 15\\
3x &= 6\\
\frac{3x}{3} &= \frac{6}{3}\\
x &= 2
\end{aligned}$$

16.
$$\begin{aligned}
10x - 39 + 12x - 9x + 42 - 4x &= 42 - 4x\\
9x + 3 &= 42 - 4x\\
9x + 4x + 3 &= 42 - 4x + 4x\\
13x + 3 &= 42\\
13x + 3 - 3 &= 42 - 3\\
13x &= 39\\
\frac{13x}{13} &= \frac{39}{13}\\
x &= 3
\end{aligned}$$

17.
$$\begin{aligned}
16x + 12 - 75 + 2x - 12 - 110 &= 8x - 50 - 25\\
18x - 185 &= 8x - 75\\
18x - 8x - 185 &= 8x - 8x - 75\\
10x - 185 &= -75\\
10x - 185 + 185 &= -75 + 185\\
10x &= 110\\
\frac{10x}{10} &= \frac{110}{10}\\
x &= 11
\end{aligned}$$

18.
$$\begin{aligned}
3x - 18 + 27 + 10x - 11 &= 25 + 4x - 7x + 12 + 3x\\
13x - 2 &= 37\\
13x - 2 + 2 &= 37 + 2\\
13x &= 39\\
\frac{13x}{13} &= \frac{39}{13}\\
x &= 3
\end{aligned}$$

19.
$$\begin{aligned}
18x + 16 &= 8 + 12x + 8 - 13 + 25x - 9 + 100 - 25x\\
18x + 16 &= 94 + 12x\\
18x - 12x + 16 &= 94 + 12x - 12x\\
6x + 16 &= 94\\
6x + 16 - 16 &= 94 - 16\\
6x &= 78\\
\frac{6x}{6} &= \frac{78}{6}\\
x &= 13
\end{aligned}$$

Exercises 6.7 Pages 103-104

1. 1. let p = number of passenger elevators 10,000
   2. p + 2000 = number of freight elevators 12,000
   3. total elevators = total elevators
      (p) + (p + 2000) = 22,000
   4. 2p + 2000 = 22,000
      2p + 2000 - 2000 = 22,000 - 2000
      2p = 20,000
      $\frac{2p}{2} = \frac{20,000}{2}$
      p = 10,000
   5. 10,000 + 12,000 = 22,000 ✓

2. 1. let d = depth below ground 10 ft.
   2. 16d + 2 = height above ground 162 ft.
   3. total height = total height
      (d) + (16d + 2) = 172
   4. 17d + 2 = 172
      17d + 2 - 2 = 172 - 2
      17d = 170
      $\frac{17d}{17} = \frac{170}{17}$
      d = 10
   5. 10 + 162 = 172 ✓

3. 1. let n = the number of unnamed islands 2500
   2. n + 2107 = the number of named islands 4607
   3. total number = total number
      (n) + (n + 2107) = 7107
   4. 2n + 2107 = 7107
      2n + 2107 - 2107 = 7107 - 2107
      2n = 5000
      $\frac{2n}{2} = \frac{5000}{2}$
      n = 2500
   5. 2500 + 4607 = 7107 ✓

4. $\frac{10}{\cancel{11}}(\overset{15}{\cancel{165}}) + 8 = 150 + 8 = 158$ Canadian Falls ✓

5. 1. let k = amount in Katherine's account $400
   2. 3k + 300 = amount in James's account $1500
   3. (k)+(3k + 300)= 1900
   4. 4k + 300= 1900
      4k + 300-300 = 1900- 300
      4k = 1600
      $\frac{4k}{4} = \frac{1600}{4}$
      k = 400
   5. $400 + 1500 = $1900 ✓

6\. 1. let c = the length of the Capitol $751\frac{1}{3}$ ft.

2\. $\frac{1}{2}c + 404\frac{1}{3}$ = length of original Penn Station in New York

3\. station length = station length

$$\frac{1}{2}c + 404\frac{1}{3} = 780$$

4\. $$\frac{1}{2}c + 404\frac{1}{3} - 404\frac{1}{3} = 780 - 404\frac{1}{3}$$

$$\frac{1}{2}c = 375\frac{2}{3}$$

$$\frac{2}{1}\cdot\frac{1}{2}c = \frac{2}{1}\cdot 375\frac{2}{3}$$

$$c = 750\frac{4}{3}$$

$$c = 751\frac{1}{3}$$

5\. $\frac{1}{2}(751\frac{1}{3}) + 404\frac{1}{3} = 780$ ✓

7\. 1. let p = the number of games played 30

2\. $\frac{2}{3}p - 4$ = the number of games won

3\. games won = games won

$$\frac{2}{3}p - 4 = 16$$

4\. $$\frac{2}{3}p - 4 + 4 = 16 + 4$$

$$\frac{2}{3}p = 20$$

$$\frac{3}{2}\cdot\frac{2}{3}p = \frac{3}{2}\cdot 20$$

$$p = 30$$

5\. $\frac{2}{3}(30) - 4 = 16$ ✓

8\. 1. let h = the height of the building 42 ft.

2\. $\frac{2}{3}h + 2$ = length of shadow

$h - 12$ = length of shadow

3\. length of shadow = length of shadow

$$\frac{2}{3}h + 2 = h - 12$$

4\. $$\frac{2}{3}h + 2 - h = h - h - 12$$

$$-\frac{1}{3}h + 2 = -12$$

$$-\frac{1}{3}h + 2 - 2 = -12 - 2$$

$$-\frac{1}{3}h = -14$$

$$-3\cdot -\frac{1}{3}h = -3\cdot -14$$

$$h = 42$$

5\. $\frac{2}{3}(42) + 2 = 30$

$42 - 12 = 30$ ✓

9\. 1. let h = cost of the house <u>$90,000</u>

2\. $\frac{1}{9}h$ = cost of the lot <u>$10,000</u>

$\frac{1}{6}h - 5000$ = cost of the lot

3\. cost of lot = cost of lot

$$\frac{1}{9}h = \frac{1}{6}h - 5000$$

4\.
$$\frac{2}{18}h = \frac{3}{18}h - 5000$$
$$\frac{2}{18}h - \frac{3}{18}h = \frac{3}{18}h - \frac{3}{18}h - 5000$$
$$-\frac{1}{18}h = -5000$$
$$-18(-\frac{1}{18})h = (-18)(-5000)$$
$$h = 90,000$$

5\. $\frac{1}{9}(90,000) = 10,000$ ✓

10\. 1. let ℓ = amount of lettuce sales <u>$5.70</u>

2\. 3ℓ = amount of the spinach sales $17.10

6ℓ = amount of the pea sales $34.20

3\. total sales = total sales

$$(\ell) + (3\ell) + (6\ell) = 57$$
$$10\ell = 57$$
$$\frac{10\ell}{10} = \frac{57}{10}$$
$$\ell = \$5.70$$

5\.
$ 5.70
17.10
+34.20
$57.00 ✓

11\. 1. let x = price of the chair <u>$17</u>

2\. 40 - x = price of the table <u>$23</u>

77 - x = price of the desk <u>$60</u>

3\. cost of table and desk = cost of table and desk

$$(40 - x) + (77 - x) = 83$$

4\.
$$-2x + 117 = 83$$
$$-2x + 117 - 117 = 83 - 117$$
$$-2x = -34$$
$$\frac{-2x}{-2} = \frac{-34}{-2}$$
$$x = 17$$

5\. 17 + 23 = 40
23 + 60 = 83
17 + 60 = 77 ✓

12\. 1. let i = monthly net income <u>$2,000</u>

2\. .25i = amount saved

.25i - 150 = amount given away

3\. amount given away = amount given away

$$.25i - 150 = 350$$

4\.
$$.25i - 150 + 150 = 350 + 150$$
$$.25i = 500$$
$$\frac{.25i}{.25} = \frac{500}{.25}$$
$$i = 2000$$

5\. .25(2000) - 150 = 350 ✓

13. 1. let x = cost of same-price stamps $.62
2. 6x = 3(2x) = cost of third stamp $3.72
3. cost of stamps = cost of stamps
$(x) + (x) + (6x) = 4.96$
4. $8x = 4.96$
$\frac{8x}{8} = \frac{4.96}{8}$
$x = .62$

5. $ .62
.62
+3.72
$4.96 ✓

14. 1. let x = the first consecutive number 11
2. x + 1 = the second consecutive number 12
x + 2 = the third consecutive number 13

3. $3x = (x + 1) + (x + 2) + 8$
4. $3x = 2x + 11$
$3x - 2x = 2x - 2x + 11$
$x = 11$

5. $3(11) = 33$
$(12 + 13) + 8 = 33$ ✓

15. 1. let a = the wage of the apprentice $75
2. 3a = the wage of the plumber $225
a - 50 = the wage of the helper $25
3. price of job = price of job
$(a) + (3a) + (a - 50) = 325$
4. $5a - 50 = 325$
$5a - 50 + 50 = 325 + 50$
$5a = 375$
$\frac{5a}{5} = \frac{375}{5}$
$a = 75$

5. $ 75
225
+ 25
$325 ✓

16. 1. let x = length of the thermometer 20 ft.
2. .8x = length of the tube
3. length of tube = length of tube
$.8x = 16$
4. $\frac{.8x}{.8} = \frac{16}{.8}$
$x = 20$

5. $(.8)(20) = 16$ ✓

17. 1. let n = the number 10
2. $\frac{1}{5}n$ = one fifth of the number
3. sum of parts = sum of parts
$n + \frac{1}{5}n = 12$
4. $\frac{6}{5}n = 12$
$\frac{5}{6} \cdot \frac{6}{5}n = 12 \cdot \frac{5}{6}$
$n = 10$

5. $10 + \frac{1}{5}(10) = 12$ ✓

18. 1. let n = the number <u>21</u>
2.
3. difference = difference

$$2n - \frac{1}{3}n = 35$$

4.

$$\frac{5}{3}n = 35$$

$$\frac{3}{5}\cdot\frac{5}{3}n = 35\cdot\frac{3}{5}$$

$$n = 21$$

5. $2(21) - \frac{1}{3}(21) = 35$ ✓

19. 1. let c = construction cost <u>$4,000,000</u>
2. $2\frac{1}{4}c$ = furnishing cost <u>$9,000,000</u>
3. cost of building = cost of building

$$c + 2\frac{1}{4}c = 13,000,000$$

4.

$$\frac{4}{4}c + \frac{9}{4}c = 13,000,000$$

$$\frac{13}{4}c = 13,000,000$$

$$\frac{4}{13}\cdot\frac{13}{4}c = \frac{4}{13}\cdot 13,000,000$$

$$c = 4,000,000$$

5. $4,000,000 + 2\frac{1}{4}(4,000,000) = 13,000,000$ ✓

20. 1. let i = annual income <u>$6000</u>
2.
3. amount saved = amount saved

$$.30i - 300 = 1500$$

4.

$$.30i - 300 + 300 = 1500 + 300$$

$$.30i = 1800$$

$$\frac{.30i}{.30} = \frac{1800}{.30}$$

$$i = 6000$$

5. $.30(6000) - 300 = 1500$ ✓

<u>Exercises 6.8a</u> Pages 105 - 106

1. $4 + (6 - 3)$
$= 4 + 6 - 3$
$= 10 - 3$
$= 7$

2. $5 + (7 - 1)$
$= 5 + 7 - 1$
$= 12 - 1$
$= 11$

3. $a + (b - 2a)$
$= a + b - 2a$
$= -a + b$

4. $a + (b - c)$
$= a + b - c$

5. $2a + (a - b)$
$= 2a + a - b$
$= 3a - b$

6. $6x + (7x - 2)$
$= 6x + 7x - 2$
$= 13x - 2$

7. $2 + (3 - 1)$
$= 2 + 3 - 1$
$= 5 - 1$
$= 4$

8. $4 + (6 - 5)$
$= 4 + 6 - 5$
$= 10 - 5$
$= 5$

9. $2a + (7a - b)$
$= 2a + 7a - b$
$= 9a - b$

10. $5a - (4a + b)$
$= 5a - 4a - b$
$= a - b$

11. $3 + (6 - 2)$
$= 3 + 6 - 2$
$= 9 - 2$
$= 7$

12. $5a - (7a + 2)$
$= 5a - 7a - 2$
$= -2a - 2$

13. $6x - (2x - 3y)$
$= 6x - 2x + 3y$
$= 4x + 3y$

14. $5x - (7x + 7y)$
$= 5x - 7x - 7y$
$= -2x - 7y$

15. $2x - (x + y)$
$= 2x - x - y$
$= x - y$

16. $x - (y - z)$
$= x - y + z$

17. $x - (-y + z)$
$= x + y - z$

18. $m - n - (-a)$
$= m - n + a$

19. $m - (n - 2a)$
$= m - n + 2a$

20. $5x - (2x + y)$
$= 5x - 2x - y$
$= 3x - y$

21. $a - m + (n - m)$
$= a - m + n - m$
$= a - 2m + n$

22. $5a - 2b - (a - 2b)$
$= 5a - 2b - a + 2b$
$= 4a$

23. $a - (b - c + a) - (c - b)$
$= a - b + c - a - c + b$
$= 0$

24. $2xy + 3y^2 - (x^2 + xy - y^2)$
$= 2xy + 3y^2 - x^2 - xy + y^2$
$= xy + 4y^2 - x^2$
$= -x^2 + xy + 4y^2$

25. $m + (3m - n) - (2n - m + n)$
$= m + 3m - n - 2n + m - n$
$= 5m - 4n$

26. $4x - y - (3x - y) - (2x + 4y)$
$= 4x - y - 3x + y - 2x - 4y$
$= -x - 4y$

27. $(2x^2 - 4xy + y^2) - (x^2 + 2xy - 3y^2)$
$= 2x^2 - 4xy + y^2 - x^2 - 2xy + 3y^2$
$= x^2 - 6xy + 4y^2$

28. $(2a + 3b - 4c) + (a - 3b - 4c)$
$= 2a + 3b - 4c + a - 3b - 4c$
$= 3a - 8c$

29. $b - [x + 4a + (x - 7)]$
$= b - (x + 4a + x - 7)$
$= b - (2x + 4a - 7)$
$= b - 2x - 4a + 7$
$= -4a + b - 2x + 7$

30. $y - [5 - 3b - (7y - 4a)]$
$= y - (5 - 3b - 7y + 4a)$
$= y - 5 + 3b + 7y - 4a$
$= -4a + 3b + 8y - 5$

31. $a - [(7y - 4a - 1) - (a + y)]$
$= a - (7y - 4a - 1 - a - y)$
$= a - (6y - 5a - 1)$
$= 6a - 6y + 1$

32. $3.8a^2 - [5.2a^2 - (a^2 - 3) + 9]$
$= 3.8a^2 - (5.2a^2 - a^2 + 3 + 9)$
$= 3.8a^2 - (4.2a^2 + 12)$
$= 3.8a^2 - 4.2a^2 - 12$
$= -.4a^2 - 12$

33. $= ab - [ab + ac - a - (2a - ac) + 2a - 2ac]$
$= ab - (ab + ac - a - 2a + ac + 2a - 2ac)$
$= ab - (ab - a)$
$= ab - ab + a$
$= a$

34. $4m - [p + 3n + (m + n) + 3 - (6p - 3n - 5m)]$
$= 4m - (p + 3n + m + n + 3 - 6p + 3n + 5m)$
$= 4m - (-5p + 7n + 6m + 3)$
$= 4m + 5p - 7n - 6m - 3$
$= -2m - 7n + 5p - 3$

35. $7.6m^2 - [4.2m^2 - (m^2 - 3) + 7]$
$= 7.6m^2 - (4.2m^2 - m^2 + 3 + 7)$
$= 7.6m^2 - (3.2m^2 + 10)$
$= 7.6m^2 - 3.2m^2 - 10$
$= 4.4m^2 - 10$

Exercises 6.9 Page 107

1. $ax^2 + ab + 2x^2 + 2b$
$= (ax^2 + 2x^2) + (ab + 2b)$

2. $a^3 + 3a^2b + 3ab^2 + b^3$
$= (a^3 + b^3) + (3a^2b + 3ab^2)$

3. $a^2 - b^2 - 2bc - c^2$
$= a^2 - (b^2 + 2bc + c^2)$

4. $a^2 - b^2 + 2bc - c^2$
$= a^2 - (b^2 - 2bc + c^2)$

5. $a^2 + 2ab + b^2 - c^2 + 2cd - d^2$
$= a^2 + 2ab + b^2 - (c^2 - 2cd + d^2)$

6. $a^2 - 2ab + b^2 - c^2 - 2cd - d^2$
$= a^2 - 2ab + b^2 - (c^2 + 2cd + d^2)$

7. $x^3 - x^2 + x - 1 \neq (x^3 - 1) - (x^2 + x)$
$x^3 - x^2 + x - 1 \neq x^3 - 1 - x^2 - x$
$x^3 - x^2 + x - 1 \neq x^3 - x^2 - x - 1$

Removing parentheses changes the signs of every term inside them. The third terms are not equal ($x \neq -x$).

8. $x^2 - y^2 + 2yz - z^2 \neq x^2 - (y^2 + 2yz - z^2)$
$x^2 - y^2 + 2yz - z^2 \neq x^2 - y^2 - 2yz + z^2$

The signs of 2yz and z^2 must be changed when the parentheses are removed.

Algebraic Representation Exercises Pages 108-109

1. $2 + 3$; $x + (-y) + (-z)$
$= x - y - z$

2. $25 - 10$; $25 - n$
$= 15$

3. $9 + 4$; $a + b$
$= 13$

4. $20 - (10 + 4) = 20 - 14 = 6$
$z - (10 + y) = z - 10 - y$

5. $6 + x = 10$
$x = 10 - 6$
$x = 4$

$m + x = 4$
$x = 4 - m$

6. $a - 10$

7. $10 - (a + b + 2)$
$= 10 - a - b - 2$

8. Caleb $x - m$;
Mark $y + m$

9. $40 - x$

10. $2n + 2$ and $2n + 4$;
$2n - 1$ and $2n + 1$

11. $2n + 3$ and $2n + 5$

12. $\frac{n}{d}$; $\frac{n - 2}{d + 3}$

13. $100d - nc$

14. $6t + 8u$

15. $6h + 9t + 5u$

16.
$$\begin{array}{r} h + 2t + 3u \\ 4h + t + 6u \\ \underline{3h + 6t } \\ 8h + 9t + 9u \end{array}$$

$8(100) + 9(10) + 9(1) = 899$
$123 + 416 + 360 = 899$
$899 = 899$

Key to Unit 6, pages 108-111

Review Exercises   Pages 108-109

1. $6a + 7b - 4c - 2a - 4b + 5c$
$= 4a + 3b + c$
$= 4(1) + 3(2) + 3$
$= 4 + 6 + 3$
$= 13$

2. $2x^2 - xy + y^2 - 2xy - 2y^2$
$= 2x^2 - 3xy - y^2$
$= 2(4^2) - 3(4)(5) - 5^2$
$= 2(16) - 60 - 25$
$= 32 - 60 - 25$
$= -53$

3. $2a^2 + 3ab - b^2 - (a^2 - ab - 2b^2)$
$= 2a^2 + 3ab - b^2 - a^2 + ab + 2b^2$
$= a^2 + 4ab + b^2$
$= 1^2 + 4(1)(2) + 2^2$
$= 1 + 8 + 4$
$= 13$

4. $2m - (m-n) - (y + 2z) + (3a + b)$
$= 2m - m + n - y - 2z + 3a + b$
$= m + n - y - 2z + 3a + b$
$= 7 + 8 - 5 - 2(6) + 3(1) + 2$
$= 7 + 8 - 5 - 12 + 3 + 2$
$= 3$

5. $[2a - b - (a + 2b) - 3y - (y - 2z)]$
$= 2a - b - a - 2b - 3y - y + 2z$
$= a - 3b - 4y + 2z$
$= 1 - 3(2) - 4(5) + 2(6)$
$= 1 - 6 - 20 + 12$
$= -13$

6. $(3x - 2y - 4z) - [4x - 2y - (2x - y)]$
$= 3x - 2y - 4z - (4x - 2y - 2x + y)$
$= 3x - 2y - 4z - 4x + 2y + 2x - y$
$= x - y - 4z$
$= 4 - 5 - 4(6)$
$= 4 - 5 - 24$
$= -25$

7. $m^2 - 2mn - (3m^2 + 2mn - n^2)$
$= m^2 - 2mn - 3m^2 - 2mn + n^2$
$= -2m^2 - 4mn + n^2$
$= -2(7)^2 - 4(7)(8) + (8)^2$
$= -2(49) - 4(56) + 64$
$= -98 - 224 + 64$
$= -258$

8. $m^2 - 3mn - n^2 + (4m^2 - 3mn) - (m^2 + n^2)$
$= m^2 - 3mn - n^2 + 4m^2 - 3mn - m^2 - n^2$
$= 4m^2 - 6mn - 2n^2$
$= 4(7)^2 - 6(7)(8) - 2(8)^2$
$= 4(49) - 6(56) - 2(64)$
$= 196 - 336 - 128$
$= -268$

Exercises 6.10   Pages 109-110

1. $21a^2$	2. $-12y^2$	3. $-a^4b^3$	4. $-x^5y^2$
5. $-12xy$	6. $-28x^4$	7. $-27x^2y^3z$	8. $7p^6q^3$
9. $7m^4n$	10. $24a^2w^2$	11. $4abxy$	12. $-3.2c^2d^4z$
13. $-20ab^6cx^7$	14. $-36a^5b^3cd^2$	15. $12x^6y^4z^3$	16. $18a^7b^3c^6$

Exercises 6.11   Pages 110 and 111

1. $4x + 8$	2. $a^2x^3 + axy$	3. $15m^2s^2t^2 + 6st^3$
4. $m^3n + mn^4$	5. $-x^3y - 2x^2y^2 + xy^3$	6. $x^2y^2z + xy^2z^2 + x^2yz^2$
7. $-x^3 - 2x^4 - 6x^5 - 4x^6$	8. $-12x^5 - 18x^4 - 6x^3 - 3x^2$	

9. $ab(6a^2 + a^4 + 1 + 4a^3 + 4a)$
$= ab(a^4 + 4a^3 + 6a^2 + 4a + 1)$
$= a^5b + 4a^4b + 6a^3b + 4a^2b + ab$

10. $.5a(3a + 2.5a^2 + 1)$
$= .5a(2.5a^2 + 3a + 1)$
$= 1.25a^3 + 1.5a^2 + .5a$

11. $\frac{2}{3}x(3x + 1) - \frac{1}{3}x(6x - 2)$
$= 2x^2 + \frac{2}{3}x - 2x^2 + \frac{2}{3}x$
$= \frac{4}{3}x$

12. $1.3a^2b(b - 4) + 2.5ab^2(a - 3)$
$= 1.3a^2b^2 - 5.2a^2b + 2.5a^2b^2 - 7.5ab^2$
$= 3.8a^2b^2 - 5.2a^2b - 7.5ab^2$

13. $6\left(\frac{a^2}{15} - \frac{b^2}{18} + \frac{ab}{10}\right)$
$= 6\left[\left(\frac{5^2}{15}\right) - \frac{3^2}{18} + \frac{5(3)}{10}\right]$
$= 6\left[\left(\frac{25}{15}\right) - \frac{9}{18} + \frac{15}{10}\right]$
$= 6\left(\frac{5}{3} - \frac{1}{2} + \frac{3}{2}\right)$
$= 10 - 3 + 9$
$= 16$

Exercises 6.12   Pages 111-112

1.
$$\begin{array}{r} x + 4 \\ x + 6 \\ \hline x^2 + 4x \\ 6x + 24 \\ \hline x^2 + 10x + 24 \end{array}$$

2.
$$\begin{array}{r} x + 1 \\ x - 2 \\ \hline x^2 + x \\ - 2x - 2 \\ \hline x^2 - x - 2 \end{array}$$

3.
$$\begin{array}{r} 2x + 3 \\ 4x - 1 \\ \hline 8x^2 + 12x \\ - 2x - 3 \\ \hline 8x^2 + 10x - 3 \end{array}$$

4.
$$\begin{array}{r} x^2 - x + 1 \\ x + 1 \\ \hline x^3 - x^2 + x \\ x^2 - x + 1 \\ \hline x^3 + 1 \end{array}$$

5.
$$\begin{array}{l} 2a + b - c \\ 3a + b \\ \hline 6a^2 + 3ab - 3ac \\ 2ab + b^2 - bc \\ \hline 6a^2 + 5ab - 3ac + b^2 - bc \end{array}$$

6.
$$\begin{array}{r} x + y \\ x + y \\ \hline x^2 + xy \\ xy + y^2 \\ \hline x^2 + 2xy + y^2 \end{array}$$

7.
$$\begin{array}{r} x - 4 \\ x + 9 \\ \hline x^2 - 4x \\ 9x - 36 \\ \hline x^2 + 5x - 36 \end{array}$$

8.
$$\begin{array}{r} 2x + 1 \\ 3x - 5 \\ \hline 6x^2 + 3x \\ -10x - 5 \\ \hline 6x^2 - 7x - 5 \end{array}$$

9.
$$\begin{array}{r} 5y - 3z \\ 4y + z \\ \hline 20y^2 - 12yz \\ 5yz - 3z^2 \\ \hline 20y^2 - 7yz - 3z^2 \end{array}$$

10.
$$\begin{array}{r} 2x + 3 \\ x + 2 \\ \hline 2x^2 + 3x \\ 4x + 6 \\ \hline 2x^2 + 7x + 6 \end{array}$$

11.
$$\begin{array}{r} 3\ell - 5t \\ 2\ell + 6t \\ \hline 6\ell^2 - 10\ell t \\ 18\ell t - 30t^2 \\ \hline 6\ell^2 + 8\ell t - 30t^2 \end{array}$$

12.
$$\begin{array}{r} 4x + 1 \\ 3x - 4 \\ \hline 12x^2 + 3x \qquad \\ - 16x - 4 \\ \hline 12x^2 - 13x - 4 \end{array}$$

13.
$$\begin{array}{r} 4y - 6b \\ 2y + b \\ \hline 8y^2 - 12by \qquad \\ 4by - 6b^2 \\ \hline 8y^2 - 8by - 6b^2 \end{array}$$

14.
$$\begin{array}{r} 5n + 1 \\ 4n - 5 \\ \hline 20n^2 + 4n \qquad \\ - 25n - 5 \\ \hline 20n^2 - 21n - 5 \end{array}$$

15.
$$\begin{array}{r} 2b + 5c \\ 5b - 2c \\ \hline 10b^2 + 25bc \qquad \\ - 4bc - 10c^2 \\ \hline 10b^2 + 21bc - 10c^2 \end{array}$$

16.
$$\begin{array}{r} h - 2k \\ 3h + k \\ \hline 3h^2 - 6hk \qquad \\ hk - 2k^2 \\ \hline 3h^2 - 5hk - 2k^2 \end{array}$$

17.
$$\begin{array}{r} ax + by \\ ax - by \\ \hline a^2x^2 + abxy \qquad \\ - abxy - b^2y^2 \\ \hline a^2x^2 \qquad - b^2y^2 \end{array}$$

18.
$$\begin{array}{r} c^2 + d^2 \\ c^2 - d^2 \\ \hline c^4 + c^2d^2 \qquad \\ - c^2d^2 - d^4 \\ \hline c^4 \qquad - d^4 \end{array}$$

19.
$$\begin{array}{r} 2b + 5c \\ 3b + 8c \\ \hline 6b^2 + 15bc \qquad \\ 16bc + 40c^2 \\ \hline 6b^2 + 31bc + 40c^2 \end{array}$$

20.
$$\begin{array}{r} 3a + b \\ 3a + b \\ \hline 9a^2 + 3ab \qquad \\ 3ab + b^2 \\ \hline 9a^2 + 6ab + b^2 \end{array}$$

21.
$$\begin{array}{r} \frac{1}{2}a + \frac{1}{3}b \\ \frac{1}{2}a + \frac{1}{3}b \\ \hline \frac{1}{4}a^2 + \frac{1}{6}ab \qquad \\ \frac{1}{6}ab + \frac{1}{9}b^2 \\ \hline \frac{1}{4}a^2 + \frac{2}{6}ab + \frac{1}{9}b^2 \\ = \frac{1}{4}a^2 + \frac{1}{3}ab + \frac{1}{9}b^2 \end{array}$$

22.
$$\begin{array}{r} 2n^2 - \ell \\ n^2 + 2\ell \\ \hline 2n^4 - n^2\ell \qquad \\ 4n^2\ell - 2\ell^2 \\ \hline 2n^4 + 3n^2\ell - 2\ell^2 \end{array}$$

23.
$$\begin{array}{r} \frac{2}{3}x - \frac{1}{4}y \\ \frac{3}{4}x + \frac{1}{2}y \\ \hline \frac{1}{2}x^2 - \frac{3}{16}xy \qquad \\ \frac{1}{3}xy - \frac{1}{8}y^2 \\ \hline \frac{1}{2}x^2 + \frac{7}{48}xy - \frac{1}{8}y^2 \end{array}$$

24.
$$\begin{array}{r} 2xy - 3y \\ 4xy + 7y \\ \hline 8x^2y^2 - 12xy^2 \qquad \\ 14xy^2 - 21y^2 \\ \hline 8x^2y^2 + 2xy^2 - 21y^2 \end{array}$$

25.
$$\begin{array}{r} 4ax + 3by \\ 4ax + 3by \\ \hline 16a^2x^2 + 12abxy \qquad \\ 12abxy + 9b^2y^2 \\ \hline 16a^2x^2 + 24abxy + 9b^2y^2 \end{array}$$

26.
$$\begin{array}{r} x^3 + x^2 + x + 1 \\ x - 1 \\ \hline x^4 + x^3 + x^2 + x \qquad \\ - x^3 - x^2 - x - 1 \\ \hline x^4 \qquad - 1 \end{array}$$

27.
$$\begin{array}{r} x^3 - 4x^2 - 7x + 10 \\ x - 2 \\ \hline x^4 - 4x^3 - 7x^2 + 10x \qquad \\ - 2x^3 + 8x^2 + 14x - 20 \\ \hline x^4 - 6x^3 + x^2 + 24x - 20 \end{array}$$

28.
$$\begin{array}{r} x^3 - 6x^2 - 9x + 14 \\ x + 1 \\ \hline x^4 - 6x^3 - 9x^2 + 14x \qquad \\ x^3 - 6x^2 - 9x + 14 \\ \hline x^4 - 5x^3 - 15x^2 + 5x + 14 \end{array}$$

29.
$$\begin{array}{r} a^3 - 4a^2 - 11a - 30 \\ a - 1 \\ \hline a^4 - 4a^3 - 11a^2 - 30a \qquad \\ - a^3 + 4a^2 + 11a + 30 \\ \hline a^4 - 5a^3 - 7a^2 - 19a + 30 \end{array}$$

30.
$$\begin{array}{r} a^4 - 2a^3 + 4a^2 - 8a - 3 \\ a + 2 \\ \hline a^5 - 2a^4 + 4a^3 - 8a^2 - 3a \qquad \\ 2a^4 - 4a^3 + 8a^2 - 16a - 6 \\ \hline a^5 \qquad - 19a - 6 \end{array}$$

31.
$$\begin{array}{l} x^2 + 2xy + y^2 \\ \underline{x^2 - 2xy + y^2} \\ x^4 + 2x^3y + x^2y^2 \\ \quad -2x^3y - 4x^2y^2 - 2xy^3 \\ \quad\quad\quad\quad\quad \underline{x^2y^2 + 2xy^3 + y^4} \\ x^4 \quad\quad - 2x^2y^2 \quad\quad\quad + y^4 \end{array}$$

32.
$$\begin{array}{l} b^2 + 5b - 4 \\ \underline{2b^2 - 3b - 4} \\ 2b^4 + 10b^3 - 8b^2 \\ \quad - 3b^3 - 15b^2 + 12b \\ \quad\quad\quad \underline{- 4b^2 - 20b + 16} \\ 2b^4 + 7b^3 - 27b^2 - 8b + 16 \end{array}$$

*33.
$$\begin{array}{l} x^{3a} - 3x^{2a} + 3x^a - 1 \\ \underline{x^{2a} - 2x^a + 1} \\ x^{5a} - 3x^{4a} + 3x^{3a} - x^{2a} \\ \quad - 2x^{4a} + 6x^{3a} - 6x^{2a} + 2x^a \\ \quad\quad\quad \underline{x^{3a} - 3x^{2a} + 3x^a - 1} \\ x^{5a} - 5x^{4a} + 10x^{3a} - 10x^{2a} + 5x^a - 1 \end{array}$$

*34.
$$\begin{array}{l} ax^{2n} + ay^{2n} \\ \underline{ax^{2n} - ay^{2n}} \\ a^2x^{4n} + a^2x^{2n}y^{2n} \\ \quad\quad \underline{- a^2x^{2n}y^{2n} - a^2y^{4n}} \\ a^2x^{4n} \quad\quad\quad\quad - a^2y^{4n} \end{array}$$

Exercises 6.13 Pages 113-114

1. $(a + n)x$

2. $(c - d)y$

3. $(-m-n)p$
$= -(m + n)p$

4. $(3a + b + c)x$

5. $(m-n)x$

6. $(d - e)y + (a + b)z$

7. $(a - 2)x + (c - b)y$

8. $(a^2 - b^2)x$

9. $(m - n)x + (m - n)y$

10. $(r - 3s)y$

11. $ax - by - bx - cy + dx - ey$
$= ax - bx + dx - by - cy - ey$
$= (a - b + d)x - (b + c + e)y$

12. $5ax + 3ay - 2dx + ny - 5x - y$
$= 5ax - 2dx - 5x + 3ay + ny - y$
$= (5a - 2d - 5)x + (3a + n - 1)y$

13. $cx - 2bx + 7ay + 3ax - lx - ty$
$= cx - 2bx + 3ax - lx + 7ay - ty$
$= (c - 2b + 3a - l)x + (7a - t)y$
$= (3a - 2b + c - l)x + (7a - t)y$

14. $bx + cy - 2ax + by - cx - dy$
$= -2ax + bx - cx + by + cy - dy$
$= (-2a + b - c)x + (b + c - d)y$

15. $x + ax - y + ay$
$= ax + x + ay - y$
$= (a + 1)x + (a - 1)y$

16. $bx - cy - 2ay + by$
$= bx - 2ay + by - cy$
$= bx - (2a - b + c)y$

17. $x - ay - ax - y$
$= -ax + x - ay - y$
$= (-a + 1)x - (a + 1)y$

18. $rx - ay - sx + 2cy$
$= rx - sx - ay + 2cy$
$= (r - s)x - (a - 2c)y$

19. $ax^3 + bx^2 - cx + ex^3 - dx^2 - fx$
$= ax^3 + ex^3 + bx^2 - dx^2 - cx - fx$
$= (a + e)x^3 + (b - d)x^2 - (c + f)x$

20. $x^3 + 3x^2 + 3x - ax^2 - 3ax^3 + bx$
$= x^3 - 3ax^3 + 3x^2 - ax^2 + 3x + bx$
$= (1 - 3a)x^3 + (3 - a)x^2 + (3 + b)x$

21. $x^2 - abx - x^3 - bx^2 - cx - mnx^3 + dx$
$= -x^3 - mnx^3 - bx^2 + x^2 - abx - cx + dx$
$= (-1 - mn)x^3 - (b - 1)x^2 - (ab + c - d)x$
$= -(1 + mn)x^3 - (b - 1)x^2 - (ab + c - d)x$
$= -(mn + 1)x^3 - (b - 1)x^2 - (ab + c - d)x$

22. $ax^4 - x^4 - ax^2 + x^2 + ax - x - abx^3 + x^3$
$= ax^4 - x^4 - abx^3 + x^3 - ax^2 + x^2 + ax - x$
$= (a - 1)x^4 - (ab - 1)x^3 - (a - 1)x^2 + (a - 1)x$

Algebraic Representation Exercises   Page 114

1. $5x$; x^5
2. xy; $x(y)$; $x \cdot y$
3. $(x + y - d)xy$
4. $$\begin{array}{l} a + b \\ \underline{a - b} \\ a^2 + ab \\ \underline{\quad - ab - b^2} \\ a^2 \qquad - b^2 \end{array}$$
5. $(a - b)12$ dollars
6. $m(x + y)(x + z)$
7. $x = d(y - c)$
8. $3600c + 60d$ seconds
9. $12xyz$ cents
10. ab miles; $(a - c)b$ miles
11. $(2b)^2 = 4b^2$ sq. ft.
$(x - y)^2$ sq. ft.
or $x^2 - 2xy + y^2$ sq. ft.
12. $(a + b)(a - b)$ sq. ft.
or $a^2 - b^2$ sq. ft.
13. square field: b^2 sq. ft.;
rectangular field:
$(a - b)b$ or $ab-b^2$ sq. ft.
14. $(a - b)(10t + u)$

Exercises 6.14   Pages 115-116

1. $5a^2$
2. $2x$
3. $3a^2b$
4. $-7a^3bc$
5. $5a^2b^3$
6. $5c^2d$
7. $3^0 = 1$
8. $-6x^2y^3$
9. $-4x^2z^2$
10. $-4y^2z$
11. $\frac{1}{2}a^2x$
12. 4^5mn^2 or $1024mn^2$
13. $3ac^2$
14. $3y^{2b}z^a$
15. $a^{2x}b^yc^{-2z}$ or $\dfrac{a^{2x}b^y}{c^{2z}}$

Exercises 6.15   Pages 116-117

1. $\dfrac{4c^2d - 20cd^2}{4cd} = \dfrac{4c^2d}{4cd} + \dfrac{-20cd}{4cd} = c - 5d$

2. $\dfrac{xz^2 + 3xz - x^2z^2}{xz} = \dfrac{xz^2}{xz} + \dfrac{3xz}{xz} + \dfrac{-x^2z^2}{xz} = z + 3 - xz$

3. $\dfrac{5x^2y - 10x^2y^2 + 15xy^2}{-5xy} = \dfrac{5x^2y}{-5xy} + \dfrac{-10x^2y^2}{-5xy} + \dfrac{15xy^2}{-5xy} = -x + 2xy - 3y$

4. $\dfrac{4a^2b^3 - 12a^3b^2 + 16a^4b}{4a^2b} = \dfrac{4a^2b^3}{4a^2b} + \dfrac{-12a^3b^2}{4a^2b} + \dfrac{16a^4b}{4a^2b} = b^2 - 3ab + 4a^2$

5. $\dfrac{24a^6b^2 + 32a^5b^3 + 40a^4b^4}{-8a^4b^2} = \dfrac{24a^6b^2}{-8a^4b^2} + \dfrac{32a^5b^3}{-8a^4b^2} + \dfrac{40a^4b^4}{-8a^4b^2} = -3a^2 - 4ab - 5b^2$

6. $\dfrac{14a^4b^3 + 49a^2b}{7ab} = \dfrac{14a^4b^3}{7ab} + \dfrac{49a^2b}{7ab} = 2a^3b^2 + 7a$

7. $\dfrac{35x^2y^3z^4 + 45x^4y^3z^2}{-5x^2y^2z} = \dfrac{35x^2y^3z^4}{-5x^2y^2z} + \dfrac{45x^4y^3z^2}{-5x^2y^2z} = -7yz^3 - 9x^2yz$

8. $\dfrac{36a^3b^4c^6 + 60a^2b^5c^7}{-12a^2b^4c^6} = \dfrac{36a^3b^4c^6}{-12a^2b^4c^6} + \dfrac{60a^2b^5c^7}{-12a^2b^4c^6} = -3a - 5bc$

9. $\dfrac{24r^3s^2 + 30r^2s^2 - 42r^2s^3}{6r^2s^2} = \dfrac{24r^3s^2}{6r^2s^2} + \dfrac{30r^2s^2}{6r^2s^2} + \dfrac{-42r^2s^3}{6r^2s^2} = 4r + 5 - 7s$

10. $\dfrac{9x^2yz + 36xy^2z^3 - 45xyz^5}{-9xyz} = \dfrac{9x^2yz}{-9xyz} + \dfrac{36xy^2z^3}{-9xyz} + \dfrac{-45xyz^5}{-9xyz} = -x - 4yz^2 + 5z^4$

11. $(8a^7b^3 + 28a^6b^4 - 16a^5b^5 - 4a^4b^6) \div 4a^4b^3$

$= \dfrac{8a^7b^3}{4a^4b^3} + \dfrac{28a^6b^4}{4a^4b^3} + \dfrac{-16a^5b^5}{4a^4b^3} + \dfrac{-4a^4b^6}{4a^4b^3} = 2a^3 + 7a^2b - 4ab^2 - b^3$

12. $(3x^3yz^2 + 15x^5y^2z^3 + 6x^4yz^3 - 18x^6y^3z) \div 3x^3yz$

$= \dfrac{3x^3yz^2}{3x^3yz} + \dfrac{15x^5y^2z^3}{3x^3yz} + \dfrac{6x^4yz^3}{3x^3yz} + \dfrac{-18x^6y^3z}{3x^3yz}$

$= z + 5x^2yz^2 + 2xz^2 - 6x^3y^2$

13. $\dfrac{a^2y - 2ay^2}{ay} = \dfrac{a^2y}{ay} + \dfrac{-2ay^2}{ay} = a - 2y$

$\dfrac{a^2y - 2ay^2}{-ay} = \dfrac{a^2y}{-ay} + \dfrac{-2ay^2}{-ay} = -a + 2y$

14. $\dfrac{9x^2y^2 + 15xy^2}{3xy^2} = \dfrac{9x^2y^2}{3xy^2} + \dfrac{15xy^2}{3xy^2} = 3x + 5$

$\dfrac{9x^2y^2 + 15xy^2}{-3xy^2} = \dfrac{9x^2y^2}{-3xy^2} + \dfrac{15xy^2}{-3xy^2} = -3x - 5$

15. $\dfrac{-xz^3 - 3xz + x^2z^2}{-xz} = \dfrac{-xz^3}{-xz} + \dfrac{-3xz}{-xz} + \dfrac{x^2z^2}{-xz} = z^2 + 3 - xz$

$\dfrac{-xz^3 - 3xz + x^2z^2}{xz} = \dfrac{-xz^3}{xz} + \dfrac{-3xz}{xz} + \dfrac{x^2z^2}{xz} = -z^2 - 3 + xz$

16. $\dfrac{3x^3 - 6x^5 + 9x^7 - 12x^9}{3x^2} = \dfrac{3x^3}{3x^2} + \dfrac{-6x^5}{3x^2} + \dfrac{9x^7}{3x^2} + \dfrac{-12x^9}{3x^2} = x - 2x^3 + 3x^5 - 4x^7$

$\dfrac{3x^3 - 6x^5 + 9x^7 - 12x^9}{-3x^2} = \dfrac{3x^3}{-3x^2} + \dfrac{-6x^5}{-3x^2} + \dfrac{9x^7}{-3x^2} + \dfrac{-12x^9}{-3x^2} = -x + 2x^3 - 3x^5 + 4x^7$

17. $\dfrac{30r^3s^3 + 15r^2s^2 - 45rs^4 + 75r}{15r} = \dfrac{30r^3s^3}{15r} + \dfrac{15r^2s^2}{15r} + \dfrac{-45rs^4}{15r} + \dfrac{75r}{15r}$

$\qquad\qquad = 2r^2s^3 + rs^2 - 3s^4 + 5$

$\dfrac{30r^3s^3 + 15r^2s^2 - 45rs^4 + 75r}{-15r} = \dfrac{30r^3s^3}{-15r} + \dfrac{15r^2s^2}{-15r} + \dfrac{-45rs^4}{-15r} + \dfrac{75r}{-15r}$

$\qquad\qquad = -2r^2s^3 - rs^2 + 3s^4 - 5$

18. $\dfrac{-t^5u - t^4uv + tu^4v - t^3u^3v^2 + tu^2v^3}{tu} =$

$\dfrac{-t^5u}{tu} + \dfrac{-t^4uv}{tu} + \dfrac{tu^4v}{tu} + \dfrac{-t^3u^3v^2}{tu} + \dfrac{tu^2v^3}{tu} = -t^4 - t^3v + u^3v - t^2u^2v^2 + uv^3$

$\dfrac{-t^5u - t^4uv + tu^4v - t^3u^3v^2 + tu^2v^3}{-tu} =$

$\dfrac{-t^5u}{-tu} + \dfrac{-t^4uv}{-tu} + \dfrac{tu^4v}{-tu} + \dfrac{-t^3u^3v^2}{-tu} + \dfrac{tu^2v^3}{-tu} = t^4 + t^3v - u^3v + t^2u^2v^2 - uv^3$

Exercises 6.16   Pages 119-120

1.
$$\begin{array}{r} x + 2 \\ x+2\ \overline{\smash{\big)}\ x^2 + 4x + 4} \\ \underline{x^2 + 2x} \\ 2x + 4 \\ \underline{2x + 4} \end{array}$$

2.
$$\begin{array}{r} x - 2 \\ x-2\ \overline{\smash{\big)}\ x^2 - 4x + 4} \\ \underline{x^2 - 2x} \\ -2x + 4 \\ \underline{-2x + 4} \end{array}$$

3.
$$\begin{array}{r} x - 3 + \frac{-8}{x + 4} \\ x+4\ \overline{\smash{\big)}\ x^2 + x - 20} \\ \underline{x^2 + 4x} \\ -\ 3x - 20 \\ \underline{-\ 3x - 12} \\ -8 \end{array}$$

4.
$$\begin{array}{r} x + 4 \\ x+3\ \overline{\smash{\big)}\ x^2 + 7x + 12} \\ \underline{x^2 + 3x} \\ 4x + 12 \\ \underline{4x + 12} \end{array}$$

5.
$$\begin{array}{r} x + 3 \\ x-6\ \overline{\smash{\big)}\ x^2 - 3x - 18} \\ \underline{x^2 - 6x} \\ 3x - 18 \\ \underline{3x - 18} \end{array}$$

6.
$$\begin{array}{r} \ell^2 - 8 \\ \ell^2+2\ \overline{\smash{\big)}\ \ell^4 - 6\ell^2 - 16} \\ \underline{\ell^4 + 2\ell^2} \\ -8\ell^2 - 16 \\ \underline{-8\ell^2 - 16} \end{array}$$

7.
$$\begin{array}{r} x + 3 \\ x+3\ \overline{\smash{\big)}\ x^2 + 6x + 9} \\ \underline{x^2 + 3x} \\ 3x + 9 \\ \underline{3x + 9} \end{array}$$

8.
$$\begin{array}{r} x + 5 \\ x+3\ \overline{\smash{\big)}\ x^2 + 8x + 15} \\ \underline{x^2 + 3x} \\ 5x + 15 \\ \underline{5x + 15} \end{array}$$

9.
$$\begin{array}{r} m + 3 \\ m-6\ \overline{\smash{\big)}\ m^2 - 3m - 18} \\ \underline{m^2 - 6m} \\ 3m - 18 \\ \underline{3m - 18} \end{array}$$

10.
$$\begin{array}{r} x + y \\ x+y\ \overline{\smash{\big)}\ x^2 + 2xy + y^2} \\ \underline{x^2 + xy} \\ xy + y^2 \\ \underline{xy + y^2} \end{array}$$

11.
$$\begin{array}{r} 3a^2 - 2a + 3 \\ a+4\ \overline{\smash{\big)}\ 3a^3 + 10a^2 - 5a + 12} \\ \underline{3a^3 + 12a^2} \\ -2a^2 - 5a \\ \underline{-2a^2 - 8a} \\ 3a + 12 \\ \underline{3a + 12} \end{array}$$

12.
$$\begin{array}{r} 5x^2 + x + 2 \\ x^2 - 1 \overline{\big)\, 5x^4 + x^3 - 3x^2 - x - 2} \\ \underline{5x^4 \qquad - 5x^2 \qquad\qquad} \\ x^3 + 2x^2 - x \quad \\ \underline{x^3 \qquad\quad - x \quad} \\ 2x^2 \qquad - 2 \\ \underline{2x^2 \qquad - 2} \end{array}$$

13.
$$\begin{array}{r} 5x^3 + 4x^2 + 3x + 2 \\ 5x^2 - 4x \overline{\big)\, 25x^5 + 0x^4 - x^3 - 2x^2 - 8x} \\ \underline{25x^5 - 20x^4 \qquad\qquad\qquad\qquad} \\ 20x^4 - x^3 \qquad\qquad\qquad \\ \underline{20x^4 - 16x^3 \qquad\qquad\qquad} \\ 15x^3 - 2x^2 \qquad\quad \\ \underline{15x^3 - 12x^2 \qquad\quad} \\ 10x^2 - 8x \\ \underline{10x^2 - 8x} \end{array}$$

14.
$$\begin{array}{r} a^7 - a^6 + 2a^5 - 2a^4 + 3a^3 - 3a^2 + 3a + \frac{-1}{a + 1} \\ a + 1 \overline{\big)\, a^8 + 0a^7 + a^6 + 0a^5 + a^4 + 0a^3 + 0a^2 + 3a - 1} \\ \underline{a^8 + a^7} \qquad\qquad\qquad\qquad\qquad\qquad\qquad\qquad\qquad \\ -a^7 + a^6 \qquad\qquad\qquad\qquad\qquad\qquad\qquad\qquad \\ \underline{-a^7 - a^6} \qquad\qquad\qquad\qquad\qquad\qquad\qquad\qquad \\ 2a^6 + 0a^5 \qquad\qquad\qquad\qquad\qquad\qquad\quad \\ \underline{2a^6 + 2a^5} \qquad\qquad\qquad\qquad\qquad\qquad\quad \\ -2a^5 + a^4 \qquad\qquad\qquad\qquad\qquad \\ \underline{-2a^5 - 2a^4} \qquad\qquad\qquad\qquad\qquad \\ 3a^4 + 0a^3 \qquad\qquad\qquad\quad \\ \underline{3a^4 + 3a^3} \qquad\qquad\qquad\quad \\ -3a^3 + 0a^2 \qquad\qquad\quad \\ \underline{-3a^3 - 3a^2} \qquad\qquad\quad \\ 3a^2 + 3a \qquad \\ \underline{3a^2 + 3a \qquad} \\ -1 \end{array}$$

Remainder may be shown as $\cdots 3a - \frac{1}{a + 1}$

15.
$$\begin{array}{r} b^6 + 2b^3 + b + 1 + \frac{4}{b^3 + 4} \\ b^3 + 4 \overline{\big)\, b^9 + 6b^6 + b^4 + 9b^3 + 4b + 8} \\ \underline{b^9 + 4b^6} \qquad\qquad\qquad\qquad\qquad \\ 2b^6 + b^4 + 9b^3 \qquad\qquad\quad \\ \underline{2b^6 \qquad\quad + 8b^3} \qquad\qquad\quad \\ b^4 + b^3 + 4b + 8 \\ \underline{b^4 \qquad\quad + 4b \qquad} \\ b^3 \qquad\quad + 8 \\ \underline{b^3 \qquad\quad + 4} \\ 4 \end{array}$$

16.
$$\begin{array}{r} z^4 + z^2 + 2 \\ 4z^2 + 2 \overline{\big)\, 4z^6 + 6z^4 + 10z^2 + 4} \\ \underline{4z^6 + 2z^4} \qquad\qquad\qquad \\ 4z^4 \quad 10z^2 \qquad \\ \underline{4z^4 + 2z^2} \qquad \\ 8z^2 + 4 \\ \underline{8z^2 + 4} \end{array}$$

17.
$$\begin{array}{r} x^2 - xy + y^2 \\ x^2 + y^2 \overline{\big)\, x^4 - x^3y + 2x^2y^2 - xy^3 + y^4} \\ \underline{x^4 \qquad\quad + x^2y^2} \qquad\qquad\quad \\ -x^3y + x^2y^2 - xy^3 \qquad\quad \\ \underline{-x^3y \qquad\qquad - xy^3} \qquad\quad \\ x^2y^2 \qquad\qquad + y^4 \\ \underline{x^2y^2 \qquad\qquad + y^4} \end{array}$$

18.
$$\begin{array}{r} 4m^2 + 2mn + n^2 \\ 2m + n \overline{\big)\, 8m^3 + 8m^2n + 4mn^2 + n^3} \\ \underline{8m^3 + 4m^2n} \qquad\qquad\qquad \\ 4m^2n + 4mn^2 \qquad\quad \\ \underline{4m^2n + 2mn^2} \qquad\quad \\ 2mn^2 + n^3 \\ \underline{2mn^2 + n^3} \end{array}$$

19. Divisor: $a^2 + 2a + 4$

Quotient: $a^2 - 2a + 4$

$a^2 + 2a + 4 \,\overline{)\, a^4 + 0a^3 + 4a^2 + 0a + 16}$

$\underline{a^4 + 2a^3 + 4a^2}$

$-2a^3 + 0a^2 + 0a$

$\underline{-2a^3 - 4a^2 - 8a}$

$4a^2 + 8a + 16$

$\underline{4a^2 + 8a + 16}$

20. Divisor: $x^2 - 2x - 3$

Quotient: $x^3 + 2x^2 + 7x + 20$

$x^2 - 2x - 3 \,\overline{)\, x^5 + 0x^4 + 0x^3 + 0x^2 - 61x - 60}$

$\underline{x^5 - 2x^4 - 3x^3}$

$2x^4 + 3x^3 + 0x^2$

$\underline{2x^4 - 4x^3 - 6x^2}$

$7x^3 + 6x^2 - 61x$

$\underline{7x^3 - 14x^2 - 21x}$

$20x^2 - 40x - 60$

$\underline{20x^2 - 40x - 60}$

21. Divisor: $a^2 + 4a + 5$

Quotient: $a^3 - 4a^2 + 11a - 24$

$a^2 + 4a + 5 \,\overline{)\, a^5 + 0a^4 + 0a^3 + 0a^2 - 41a - 120}$

$\underline{a^5 + 4a^4 + 5a^3}$

$-4a^4 - 5a^3 + 0a^2$

$\underline{-4a^4 - 16a^3 - 20a^2}$

$11a^3 + 20a^2 - 41a$

$\underline{11a^3 + 44a^2 + 55a}$

$- 24a^2 - 96a - 120$

$\underline{- 24a^2 - 96a - 120}$

22. Divisor: $5x^2 - 4x$

Quotient: $5x^3 + 4x^2 + 3x + 2$

$5x^2 - 4x \,\overline{)\, 25x^5 + 0x^4 - x^3 - 2x^2 - 8x}$

$\underline{25x^5 - 20x^4}$

$20x^4 - x^3$

$\underline{20x^4 - 16x^3}$

$15x^3 - 2x^2$

$\underline{15x^3 - 12x^2}$

$10x^2 - 8x$

$\underline{10x^2 - 8x}$

23.

$$\begin{array}{r|l} & a^7 - a^6 + 2a^5 - 2a^4 + 3a^3 - 3a^2 + 4a - 1 \\ \hline a + 1 & a^8 + 0a^7 + a^6 + 0a^5 + a^4 + 0a^3 + a^2 + 3a - 1 \\ & \underline{a^8 + a^7} \\ & \quad - a^7 + a^6 \\ & \quad \underline{- a^7 - a^6} \\ & \qquad 2a^6 + 0a^5 \\ & \qquad \underline{2a^6 + 2a^5} \\ & \qquad\quad - 2a^5 + a^4 \\ & \qquad\quad \underline{- 2a^5 - 2a^4} \\ & \qquad\qquad 3a^4 + 0a^3 \\ & \qquad\qquad \underline{3a^4 + 3a^3} \\ & \qquad\qquad\quad -3a^3 + a^2 \\ & \qquad\qquad\quad \underline{-3a^3 - 3a^2} \\ & \qquad\qquad\qquad 4a^2 + 3a \\ & \qquad\qquad\qquad \underline{4a^2 + 4a} \\ & \qquad\qquad\qquad\quad - a - 1 \\ & \qquad\qquad\qquad\quad \underline{- a - 1} \end{array}$$

24.

$$\begin{array}{r|l} & 2y^2 - 3y + 1 \\ \hline 2y^2 + 3y - 1 & 4y^4 + 0y^3 - 9y^2 + 6y - 1 \\ & \underline{4y^4 + 6y^3 - 2y^2} \\ & \quad - 6y^3 - 7y^2 + 6y \\ & \quad \underline{- 6y^3 - 9y^2 + 3y} \\ & \qquad 2y^2 + 3y - 1 \\ & \qquad \underline{2y^2 + 3y - 1} \end{array}$$

25.

$$\begin{array}{r|l} & x^2 - ax - b \\ \hline ax - b & ax^3 - a^2x^2 - bx^2 + 0x + b^2 \\ & \underline{ax^3 \qquad\quad - bx^2} \\ & \quad - a^2x^2 \qquad + 0x \\ & \quad \underline{- a^2x^2 \qquad + abx} \\ & \qquad\qquad - abx + b^2 \\ & \qquad\qquad \underline{- abx + b^2} \end{array}$$

26.

$$\begin{array}{r|l} & 5x^2 + 2xy - 3y^2 \\ \hline -5x + 6y & -25x^3 + 20x^2y + 27xy^2 - 18y^3 \\ & \underline{-25x^3 + 30x^2y} \\ & \quad -10x^2y + 27xy^2 \\ & \quad \underline{-10x^2y + 12xy^2} \\ & \qquad 15xy^2 - 18y^3 \\ & \qquad \underline{15xy^2 - 18y^3} \end{array}$$

27.

$$\begin{array}{r|l} & a^2 - 2ax + x^2 \\ \hline a^2 - 2ax + x^2 & a^4 - 4a^3x + 6a^2x^2 - 4ax^3 + x^4 \\ & \underline{a^4 - 2a^3x + a^2x^2} \\ & \quad -2a^3x + 5a^2x^2 - 4ax^3 \\ & \quad \underline{-2a^3x + 4a^2x^2 - 2ax^3} \\ & \qquad a^2x^2 - 2ax^3 + x^4 \\ & \qquad \underline{a^2x^2 - 2ax^3 + x^4} \end{array}$$

28.

$$
\begin{array}{l}
 x^4 - 2x^3 + 4x^2 - 8x + 16 \\
x + 2 \,\overline{)\, x^5 + 0x^4 + 0x^3 + 0x^2 + 0x + 32} \\
 \underline{x^5 + 2x^4} \\
 \; -2x^4 + 0x^3 \\
 \; \underline{-2x^4 - 4x^3} \\
 \; 4x^3 + 0x^2 \\
 \; \underline{4x^3 + 8x^2} \\
 \; -8x^2 + 0x \\
 \; \underline{-8x^2 - 16x} \\
 \; 16x + 32 \\
 \; \underline{16x + 32}
\end{array}
$$

*29.

$$
\begin{array}{l}
 x^4 - x^2y^2 + y^4 + \dfrac{-2y^6}{x^2 + y^2} \\
x^2 + y^2 \,\overline{)\, x^6 \qquad\qquad\qquad\qquad - y^6} \\
 \underline{x^6 + x^4y^2} \\
 \; -x^4y^2 + 0x^2y^4 \\
 \; \underline{-x^4y^2 - x^2y^4} \\
 \; x^2y^4 - y^6 \\
 \; \underline{x^2y^4 + y^6} \\
 \; -2y^6
\end{array}
$$

*30.

$$
\begin{array}{l}
 m^4 - m^3n + m^2n^2 - mn^3 + n^4 + \dfrac{-2n^5}{m + n} \\
m + n \,\overline{)\, m^5 \qquad\qquad\qquad\qquad\qquad\qquad - n^5} \\
 \underline{m^5 + m^4n} \\
 \; -m^4n + 0m^3n^2 \\
 \; \underline{-m^4n - m^3n^2} \\
 \; m^3n^2 + 0m^2n^3 \\
 \; \underline{m^3n^2 + m^2n^3} \\
 \; -m^2n^3 + 0mn^4 \\
 \; \underline{-m^2n^3 - mn^4} \\
 \; mn^4 - n^5 \\
 \; \underline{mn^4 + n^5} \\
 \; -2n^5
\end{array}
$$

*31.

$$
\begin{array}{l}
 m^4 - m^3n + m^2n^2 - mn^3 + n^4 \\
m + n \,\overline{)\, m^5 + \qquad\qquad\qquad\qquad\qquad\qquad + n^5} \\
 \underline{m^5 + m^4n} \\
 \; -m^4n + 0m^3n^2 \\
 \; \underline{-m^4n - m^3n^2} \\
 \; m^3n^2 + 0m^2n^3 \\
 \; \underline{m^3n^2 + m^2n^3} \\
 \; -m^2n^3 + 0mn^4 \\
 \; \underline{-m^2n^3 - mn^4} \\
 \; mn^4 + n^5 \\
 \; \underline{mn^4 + n^5}
\end{array}
$$

32.

$$
\begin{array}{r|l}
 & x^6 + x^5 - x^4 - x^3 + x^2 + x - 1 \\
\hline
x + 1 & x^7 + 2x^6 + 0x^5 - 2x^4 + 0x^3 + 2x^2 + 0x - 1 \\
 & \underline{x^7 + x^6} \\
 & x^6 + 0x^5 \\
 & \underline{x^6 + x^5} \\
 & -x^5 - 2x^4 \\
 & \underline{-x^5 - x^4} \\
 & -x^4 + 0x^3 \\
 & \underline{-x^4 - x^3} \\
 & x^3 + 2x^2 \\
 & \underline{x^3 + x^2} \\
 & x^2 + 0x \\
 & \underline{x^2 + x} \\
 & -x - 1 \\
 & \underline{-x - 1}
\end{array}
$$

33.

$$
\begin{array}{r|l}
 & 2x^2 - 3x - 4 \\
\hline
x^2 + 5x - 4 & 2x^4 + 7x^3 - 27x^2 - 8x + 16 \\
 & \underline{2x^4 + 10x^3 - 8x^2} \\
 & -3x^3 - 19x^2 - 8x \\
 & \underline{-3x^3 - 15x^2 + 12x} \\
 & -4x^2 - 20x + 16 \\
 & \underline{-4x^2 - 20x + 16}
\end{array}
$$

Algebraic Representation Exercises   Page 121

1. 500 cents; 5 dollars; 100 m cents; $\frac{m}{100}$ dollars

2. $6x = 48$
   $\frac{6x}{6} = \frac{48}{6}$
   $x = 8$

3. $25n = 300$
   $\frac{25n}{25} = \frac{300}{25}$
   $n = 12$

$\frac{x}{10}$ since $10(\frac{x}{10}) = x$

$\frac{s}{r}$ since $r(\frac{s}{r}) = s$

4. $\frac{a^3 - x^5}{m + n^2}$

5. n

6. $\frac{5}{100}x$; $\frac{y}{100}z$

7. ac days; $\frac{ac}{2}$ days; $\frac{ac}{x}$ days

8. $\frac{D}{d} = q + \frac{r}{d}$
   $d \cdot \frac{D}{d} = d(q + \frac{r}{d})$
   $D = dq + r$
   $D-r = dq + r-r$
   $D-r = dq$

9. $\frac{s}{r}$ mph; $\frac{m}{h}$ mph; $\frac{s + m}{r + h}$ mph

Exercises 6.17   Page 123

1. 1. Let t = tonnage used for wrapping paper 150
   2. t + 50 = tonnage used for newspapers 200
   3. total tons = total tons
      $(t) + (t + 50) = 350$
   4. $2t + 50 = 350$
      $2t + 50 - 50 = 350 - 50$
      $2t = 300$
      $\frac{2t}{2} = \frac{300}{2}$
      $t = 150$
   5. 150
      +200
      350 ✓

2\. 1. let f = combined width of sidewalks 20 ft.

2. 2f - 8 = width of the roadway 32 ft.

3. total width = total width

$(f) + (2f - 8) = 52$

4. $3f - 8 = 52$

$3f - 8 + 8 = 52 + 8$

$3f = 60$

$\frac{3f}{3} = \frac{60}{3}$

$f = 20$

5. $20 + 32 = 52$ ✓

3\. 1. let w = amount of other woods 1,800,000 board ft.

2. 3w - 1,200,000 = amount of white pine 4,200,000 board ft.

3. total board feet = total board feet

$(w) + (3w - 1{,}200{,}000) = 6{,}000{,}000$

4. $4w - 1{,}200{,}000 = 6{,}000{,}000$

$4w - 1{,}200{,}000 + 1{,}200{,}000 = 6{,}000{,}000 + 1{,}200{,}000$

$4w = 7{,}200{,}000$

$\frac{4w}{4} = \frac{7{,}200{,}000}{4}$

$w = 1{,}800{,}000$

5. $1{,}800{,}000 + 4{,}200{,}000 = 6{,}000{,}000$ ✓

4\. 1. let f = number of fish Michael caught 6

2. 2f - 4 = number Scott caught 8

3. total caught = total caught

$(f) + (2f - 4) = 14$

4. $3f - 4 = 14$

$3f - 4 + 4 = 14 + 4$

$3f = 18$

$\frac{3f}{3} = \frac{18}{3}$

$f = 6$

5. $6 + 8 = 14$ ✓

5\. 1. let x = number of miles traveled 6.125 or $6\frac{1}{8}$ miles

2. 8x = number of $\frac{1}{8}$ miles traveled 49

8x - 1 = number of $\frac{1}{8}$ miles traveled after the first $\frac{1}{8}$ mile 48

3. $1.75 + .25(8x-1) = 13.75$

4. $1.75 + 2x - .25 = 13.75$

$2x + 1.5 = 13.75$

$2x = 12.25$

$x = 6.125$ or $6\frac{1}{8}$

5. $1.75 + .25(8 \cdot 6\frac{1}{8} - 1) = 13.75$

$1.75 + .25(49-1) = 13.75$

$1.75 + 12 = 13.75$ ✓

6\. 1. let x = number of miles traveled 8.875 or $8\frac{7}{8}$ miles

2. 8x = number of $\frac{1}{8}$ miles traveled 71

8x-1 = number of $\frac{1}{8}$ miles traveled after the first $\frac{1}{8}$ mile 70

3. $1.75 + .25(8x-1) = 19.25$

4. $1.75 + 2x - .25 = 19.25$

$2x + 1.5 = 19.25$

$2x = 17.75$

$x = 8.875$ or $8\frac{7}{8}$

5. $1.75 + .25(8 \cdot 8\frac{7}{8} - 1) = 19.25$

$1.75 + .25(71-1) = 19.25$

$1.75 + 17.5 = 19.25$ ✓

7. 1. let x = number of filled donuts   <u>59</u>
    2.   2x = number of glazed donuts   <u>118</u>
    3.   total sold = total sold
         x + 2x + 74 = 251
    4.   3x + 74 = 251   5.   59
               3x = 177   118
                x = 59   + 74
                                 251 ✓

8. 1. let n = number of times late during rest of year   <u>54</u>
    2. 91 - n = number of times late during winter
    3. times late in winter = times late in winter
            .5n + 10 = 91 - n
    4.   .5n + 10 + n = 91 - n + n   5. .5(54) + 10 = 91-54
              1.5n + 10 = 91   37 = 37 ✓
        1.5n + 10 - 10 = 91 - 10
                1.5n = 81
               $\frac{1.5n}{1.5} = \frac{81}{1.5}$
                 n = 54

Alternate Solution

1. let n = number of times late during rest of year   <u>54</u>
2. .5n + 10 = number of times late during winter
3. total times late = total times late
    (n) + (.5n + 10) = 91
4.   1.5n + 10 = 91   5. $54 + \frac{1}{2}(54) + 10 = 91$ ✓
      1.5n + 10 - 10 = 91 - 10
            1.5n = 81
           $\frac{1.5n}{1.5} = \frac{81}{1.5}$
             n = 54

Review Exercises   Pages 123 -124

1. positive: 3, 7, 10, 4;   2. zero   3. positive; negative
    negative: -9, -4, -3, -2, -12;
    ax - 12bx + 5by or (a - 12b)x + 5aby

4. If the two factors have like signs, the product is positive; and if they have unlike signs, the product is negative. If the terms in division have like signs, the quotient is positive; if they have unlike signs, the quotient is negative.

5. They have opposite signs. If a = 5 and b = 3, a - b = 2 and b - a = -2.

6. Change the sign of every term in the parenthesis to its opposite sign when the parenthesis is removed.

7. $3a + 5b - 11c + b - 2a + c + 2c + 3a - b + 7c - b + 6a + 5b - 4a - 2c + b - a + c + b - a$
$= 3a - 2a + 3a + 6a - 4a - a - a + 5b + b - b - b + 5b + b + b - 11c + c + 2c + 7c - 2c + c$
$= 4a + 11b - 2c$

8.
$$\begin{array}{rrrrr} & -5w + & x - & 2y + & 3z \\ (+) & w + & 7x & & - 2z \\ \hline & -4w + & 8x - & 2y + & z \end{array}$$

$$\begin{array}{rrrrr} & -8w + & 10x - & y + & z \\ (-) & -4w + & 8x - & 2y + & z \\ \hline & -4w + & 2x + & y & \end{array}$$

9.
$$\begin{array}{rcl} x & = & r^2 + rs - s^2 \\ y & = & 2r^2 + 4rs + 2s^2 \\ \hline x + y & = & 3r^2 + 5rs + s^2 \\ z & = & r^2 - 3rs - s^2 \\ \hline x + y - z & = & 2r^2 + 8rs + 2s^2 \end{array}$$

10. $17x - [3y + 4z - (z + 5a + x - 3a - 2y)]$
$= 17x - [3y + 4z - z - 5a - x + 3a + 2y]$
$= 17x - [5y + 3z - 2a - x]$
$= 17x - 5y - 3z + 2a + x$
$= 2a + 18x - 5y - 3z$

11. $a + 2b - [4c - 2(a + 2b) - b]$
$= a + 2b - [4c - 2a - 4b - b]$
$= a + 2b - [-2a - 5b + 4c]$
$= a + 2b + 2a + 5b - 4c$
$= 3a + 7b - 4c$

12. $xz - (x + y + z)$
$= 2(5) - [2 + (-3) + 5]$
$= 10 - 4$
$= 6$

13. $3(x - y) + 2(y - x) - zy$
$= 3[2 - (-3)] + 2(-3 - 2) - 5(-3)$
$= 3(5) + 2(-5) - 5(-3)$
$= 15 - 10 + 15$
$= 20$

14. $x^2 - 3x(y + z) + y^2 - z$
$= 2^2 - 3(2)(-3 + 5) + (-3)^2 - 5$
$= 4 - 3(2)(2) + 9 - 5$
$= 4 - 12 + 9 - 5$
$= -4$

15. $(x - y)(y + z) - z^2(y - z)$
$= [2 - (-3)](-3 + 5) - 5^2(-3 - 5)$
$= 5(2) - 25(-8)$
$= 10 + 200$
$= 210$

16. $ax^2 - cy + ax - 2ax^2 + 2cy^2 - ax - cy^2 + ax^2 + cy$
$= (ax^2 - 2ax^2 + ax^2) + (ax - ax) + (-cy + cy) + (2cy^2 - cy^2)$
$= cy^2$

The check is left for the teacher.

17.
$$\begin{aligned} 3b + 5 &= -2 \\ 3b + 5 - 5 &= -2 - 5 \\ 3b &= -7 \\ \frac{3b}{3} &= \frac{-7}{3} \\ b &= \frac{-7}{3} \text{ or } -2\tfrac{1}{3} \end{aligned}$$

18.
$$\begin{aligned} 6 - 3x &= 14 - 5x \\ 6 - 3x + 5x &= 14 - 5x + 5x \\ 6 + 2x &= 14 \\ 6 - 6 + 2x &= 14 - 6 \\ 2x &= 8 \\ \frac{2x}{2} &= \frac{8}{2} \\ x &= 4 \end{aligned}$$

19.
$$\begin{aligned} 8a - 5 + 2a &= 4a - 14 + 3 \\ 10a - 5 &= 4a - 11 \\ 10a - 4a - 5 &= 4a - 4a - 11 \\ 6a - 5 &= -11 \\ 6a - 5 + 5 &= -11 + 5 \\ 6a &= -6 \\ \frac{6a}{6} &= \frac{-6}{6} \\ a &= -1 \end{aligned}$$

20.
$$\begin{aligned} 3x + 7(x - 2) - 13 &= 12 - 3x \\ 3x + 7x - 14 - 13 &= 12 - 3x \\ 10x - 27 &= 12 - 3x \\ 10x + 3x - 27 &= 12 - 3x + 3x \\ 13x - 27 &= 12 \\ 13x - 27 + 27 &= 12 + 27 \\ 13x &= 39 \\ \frac{13x}{13} &= \frac{39}{13} \\ x &= 3 \end{aligned}$$

21.
$$\begin{aligned} x^3 - 1 &= x(x^2 - x) + x + 3 + x^2 \\ x^3 - 1 &= x^3 - x^2 + x + 3 + x^2 \\ -1 &= x + 3 \\ -1 - 3 &= x + 3 - 3 \\ -4 &= x \end{aligned}$$

22.
$$\begin{aligned} (x-2)(x+3) - (x+5)(x-7) &= 1 \\ x^2 + x - 6 - (x^2 - 2x - 35) &= 1 \\ x^2 + x - 6 - x^2 + 2x + 35 &= 1 \\ 3x + 29 &= 1 \\ 3x + 29 - 29 &= 1 - 29 \\ 3x &= -28 \\ \frac{3x}{3} &= \frac{-28}{3} \\ x &= \frac{-28}{3} \\ &\text{or } -9\tfrac{1}{3} \end{aligned}$$

Word Problems Pages 125-129

1. a) 1. let s = length of shorter piece 4 in.
2. 8s = length of longer piece 32 in.
3. sum of pieces = sum of pieces
$(s) + (8s) = 36$
4.
$$\begin{aligned} 9s &= 36 \\ \frac{9s}{9} &= \frac{36}{9} \\ s &= 4 \end{aligned}$$
5.
$$\begin{array}{r} 4 \\ +32 \\ \hline 36 \checkmark \end{array}$$

b) 1. let s = length of shorter piece 14 in.
2. s + 8 = length of longer piece 22 in.
3. sum of pieces = sum of pieces
$(s) + (s + 8) = 36$
4.
$$\begin{aligned} 2s + 8 &= 36 \\ 2s + 8 - 8 &= 36 - 8 \\ 2s &= 28 \\ \frac{2s}{2} &= \frac{28}{2} \\ s &= 14 \end{aligned}$$
5.
$$\begin{array}{r} 14 \\ +22 \\ \hline 36 \checkmark \end{array}$$

c) 1. let s = length of one piece 15 in.
2. 2s - 9 = length of other piece 21 in.
3. sum of pieces = sum of pieces
$(s) + (2s - 9) = 36$
4.
$$\begin{aligned} 3s - 9 &= 36 \\ 3s - 9 + 9 &= 36 + 9 \\ 3s &= 45 \\ \frac{3s}{3} &= \frac{45}{3} \\ s &= 15 \end{aligned}$$
5.
$$\begin{array}{r} 15 \\ +21 \\ \hline 36 \checkmark \end{array}$$

2. 1. let w = width of yard 15 ft.
   2. w + 10 = length of yard 25 ft.
   3. perimeter = perimeter
   $(2w) + [2(w + 10)] = 80$
   4. $2w + 2w + 20 = 80$
   $4w + 20 = 80$
   $4w + 20 - 20 = 80 - 20$
   $4w = 60$
   $\frac{4w}{4} = \frac{60}{4}$
   $w = 15$

   5. $2(15) + 2(25) = 80$ ✓

3. 1. let x = first number 32
   2. x + 1 = second number 33
   x + 2 = third number 34
   3. sum = sum
   $(x) + (x + 1) + (x + 2) = 99$
   4. $3x + 3 = 99$
   $3x + 3 - 3 = 99 - 3$
   $3x = 96$
   $\frac{3x}{3} = \frac{96}{3}$
   $x = 32$

   5. 32 + 33 + 34 = 99 ✓

4. 1. let x = first odd number 19
   2. x + 2 = second odd number 21
   x + 4 = third odd number 23
   x + 6 = fourth odd number 25
   3. sum = sum
   $(x) + (x + 2) + (x + 4) + (x + 6) = 88$
   4. $4x + 12 = 88$
   $4x + 12 - 12 = 88 - 12$
   $4x = 76$
   $\frac{4x}{4} = \frac{76}{4}$
   $x = 19$

   5. 19 + 21 + 23 + 25 = 88 ✓

5. 1. let x = first even number 20
   2. x + 2 = second even number 22
   x + 4 = third even number 24
   3. sum = sum
   $(x) + (x + 2) + (x + 4) = 66$
   4. $3x + 6 = 66$
   $3x + 6 - 6 = 66 - 6$
   $3x = 60$
   $\frac{3x}{3} = \frac{60}{3}$
   $x = 20$

   5. 20 + 22 + 24 = 66 ✓

6. 1. let s = length of one of the equal sides <u>12 in.</u>
   2. 2s - 6 = length of base <u>18 in.</u>
   3.   perimeter = perimeter
      $(s) + (s) + (2s - 6) = 42$
   4. $4s - 6 = 42$
          $4s - 6 + 6 = 42 + 6$
                 $4s = 48$
             $\dfrac{4s}{4} = \dfrac{48}{4}$
                  $s = 12$

5. $\begin{array}{r} 12 \\ 12 \\ +18 \\ \hline 42 \checkmark \end{array}$

7. 1. let x = Hope's amount <u>$5.80</u>
   2. 2x = Alison's amount <u>$11.60</u>
      2x - 3.25 = Elizabeth's amount <u>$8.35</u>
   3.   sum together = sum together
      $(x) + (2x) + (2x - 3.25) = 25.75$
   4. $5x - 3.25 = 25.75$
          $5x - 3.25 + 3.25 = 25.75 + 3.25$
                     $5x = 29$
                 $\dfrac{5x}{5} = \dfrac{29}{5}$
                      $x = 5.80$

5. $\begin{array}{r} \$\ 5.80 \\ 11.60 \\ +\ 8.35 \\ \hline \$25.75 \checkmark \end{array}$

8. 1. let x = John's mark for fourth week <u>92</u>
   2.
   3.   average = average
      $\dfrac{78 + 66 + 84 + x}{4} = 80$
   4. $\dfrac{228 + x}{4} = 80$

          $4\left(\dfrac{228 + x}{4}\right) = 4(80)$

                $228 + x = 320$
          $228 - 228 + x = 320 - 228$
                      $x = 92$

5. $\begin{array}{r} 78 \\ 66 \\ 84 \\ +92 \\ \hline 4\ \overline{)320} \\ 80 \checkmark \end{array}$

9. 1. let n = smallest of the four numbers <u>4</u>
   2. $\left.\begin{array}{l} n + 1 \\ n + 2 \\ n + 3 \end{array}\right\}$ = other three numbers $\begin{array}{l} \underline{5} \\ \underline{6} \\ \underline{7} \end{array}$
   3.   difference = difference
      $(n + 2)(n + 3) - n(n + 1) = 22$
   4. $n^2 + 5n + 6 - n^2 - n = 22$
                     $4n + 6 = 22$
                 $4n + 6 - 6 = 22 - 6$
                        $4n = 16$
                    $\dfrac{4n}{4} = \dfrac{16}{4}$
                         $n = 4$

5. $\begin{array}{r} 4 \\ 5 \\ 6 \\ +7 \\ \hline 22 \checkmark \end{array}$

10. 1. let n = the smaller number $\underline{40}$
2. n + 12 = the larger number $\underline{52}$
3. result = result

$$2(n + 12) + 20 = 3n + 4$$

4.
$$\begin{aligned} 2n + 24 + 20 &= 3n + 4 \\ 2n + 44 &= 3n + 4 \\ 2n - 2n + 44 &= 3n - 2n + 4 \\ 44 &= n + 4 \\ 44 - 4 &= n + 4 - 4 \\ 40 &= n \end{aligned}$$

5.
$$\begin{array}{rr} 104 & 120 \\ +20 & +\ 4 \\ \hline 124 & 124 \end{array} \checkmark$$

11. 1. let x = amount paid $\underline{\$87,500}$
2.
3. selling price = selling price

$$x + .12x = 98,000$$

4.
$$\begin{aligned} 1.12x &= 98,000 \\ \frac{1.12x}{1.12} &= \frac{98,000}{1.12} \\ x &= 87,500 \end{aligned}$$

5.
$$\begin{array}{rr} \$\ 87,500 & \$87,500 \\ \times\ \ .12 & +10,500 \\ \hline 175000 & \$98,000\ \checkmark \\ 87500 & \\ \hline \$10,500.00 & \end{array}$$

12. 1. let x = cost of the car $\underline{\$12,500}$
2.
3. selling price = selling price

$$x - .60x = 5000$$

4.
$$\begin{aligned} .40x &= 5000 \\ \frac{.40x}{.40} &= \frac{5000}{.40} \\ x &= 12,500 \end{aligned}$$

5.
$$\begin{array}{rr} \$12,500 & \$12,500 \\ \times\ .60 & -7,500 \\ \hline \$7,500.00 & \$\ 5,000\ \checkmark \end{array}$$

13. 1. let b = amount of bonus per tenth subscription $\underline{\$3}$
2.
3. total earnings = total earnings

$$87(1.50) + 8b = 154.50$$

4.
$$\begin{aligned} 130.50 + 8b &= 154.50 \\ 130.50 - 130.50 + 8b &= 154.50 - 130.50 \\ 8b &= 24 \\ \frac{8b}{8} &= \frac{24}{8} \\ b &= 3 \end{aligned}$$

5. 130.50 + 8(3) = \$154.50

14. 1. let x = third number $\underline{15}$
2. 2x + 3 = first number $\underline{33}$
2x + 11 = second number $\underline{41}$
3. sum = sum

$$(x) + (2x + 3) + (2x + 11) = 89$$

4.
$$\begin{aligned} 5x + 14 &= 89 \\ 5x + 14 - 14 &= 89 - 14 \\ 5x &= 75 \\ \frac{5x}{5} &= \frac{75}{5} \\ x &= 15 \end{aligned}$$

5.
$$\begin{array}{r} 15 \\ 33 \\ +41 \\ \hline 89\ \checkmark \end{array}$$

15. 1. let s = age of son now <u>10</u>
    2. 4s = age of father now <u>40</u>
       s + 20 = age of son in 20 years 30
       4s + 20 = age of father in 20 years 60
    3. age in 20 years = age in 20 years

$$2(s + 20) = 4s + 20$$

    4.

$$\begin{aligned} 2s + 40 &= 4s + 20 \\ 2s + 40 - 2s &= 4s - 2s + 20 \\ 40 &= 2s + 20 \\ 40 - 20 &= 2s + 20 - 20 \\ 20 &= 2s \\ \frac{20}{2} &= \frac{2s}{2} \\ 10 &= s \end{aligned}$$

    5. 30 x 2 = 60
       40 + 20 = 60 ✓

16. 1. let d = age of daughter now <u>3</u>
    2. d + 28 = age of mother now <u>31</u>
       d + 11 = age of daughter in 11 years 14
       d + 39 = age of mother in 11 years 42
    3. age in 11 years = age in 11 years

$$d + 39 = 3(d + 11)$$

    4.

$$\begin{aligned} d + 39 &= 3d + 33 \\ d - d + 39 &= 3d - d + 33 \\ 39 &= 2d + 33 \\ 39 - 33 &= 2d + 33 - 33 \\ 6 &= 2d \\ \frac{6}{2} &= \frac{2d}{2} \\ 3 &= d \end{aligned}$$

    5. 42 is 3 x 14 ✓

17. 1. let x = first number <u>3</u>
       x + 1 = second number <u>4</u>
       x + 2 = third number <u>5</u>
       x + 3 = fourth number <u>6</u>
    3. product = product

$$x(x + 2) + 9 = (x + 1)(x + 3)$$

    4.

$$\begin{aligned} x^2 + 2x + 9 &= x^2 + 4x + 3 \\ 2x + 9 &= 4x + 3 \\ 2x - 2x + 9 &= 4x - 2x + 3 \\ 9 &= 2x + 3 \\ 9 - 3 &= 2x + 3 - 3 \\ 6 &= 2x \\ \frac{6}{2} &= \frac{2x}{2} \\ 3 &= x \end{aligned}$$

    5. 3 x 5 = 15   24
       4 x 6 = 24   -15
                       9 ✓

18. 1. let x = first integer
    2. x + 1 = second integer
       x + 2 = third integer
       x + 3 = fourth integer
    3.

$$\begin{aligned} (x + 1)(x + 2) - 2 &= x(x + 3) \\ x^2 + 3x + 2 - 2 &= x^2 + 3x \\ x^2 + 3x &= x^2 + 3x \end{aligned}$$

Since this is a statement of equality, any value of x will be a solution.

19. 1. let t = time Karen worked $6.40
2. 2t = time Mindy worked $12.80
6t = time Laura worked $38.40
3. earn together = earn together
$(t) + (2t) + (6t) = 57.60$
4. $9t = 57.60$
$\frac{9t}{9} = \frac{57.60}{9}$
$t = 6.40$

5. $ 6.40
12.80
+38.40
$57.60 ✓

20. 1. let u = cost of a used ball $1.15
2. u + .65 = cost of a new ball $1.80
3. total cost = total cost
$(10u) + [6(u + .65)] = 22.30$
4. $10u + 6u + 3.90 = 22.30$
$16u + 3.90 = 22.30$
$16u + 3.90 - 3.90 = 22.30 - 3.90$
$16u = 18.40$
$\frac{16u}{16} = \frac{18.40}{.16}$
$u = 1.15$

5. 6(1.80) + 10(1.15) = $22.30 ✓

21. $15x = 12(x + 6)$
$15x = 12x + 72$
$15x - 12x = 12x - 12x + 72$
$3x = 72$
$\frac{3x}{3} = \frac{72}{3}$
x = 24 oranges first day
x + 6 = 30 oranges second day

24(.15) = $3.60
30(.12) = $3.60 ✓

22. 1. let x = number of 20¢ cards 28
2. 52 - x = number of 30¢ cards 24
3. total cost = total cost
$.20x + .30(52-x) = 12.80$
4. $.20x + 15.60-.30x = 12.80$
$-.10x + 15.60-15.60 = 12.80 - 15.60$
$-.10x = -2.80$
$\frac{-.10x}{-.10} = \frac{-2.80}{-.10}$
$x = 28$

5. 28(.20)+24(.30) = $12.80 ✓

23. 1. let a = number of other tickets sold 150
2. 350 - a = number of pupils' tickets sold 200
3. receipts = receipts
$(3a) + [2(350 - a)] = 850$
4. $3a + 700 - 2a = 850$
$a + 700 = 850$
$a + 700 - 700 = 850 - 700$
$a = 150$

5. 150(3) + 200(2) = $850 ✓

24\. 1. let d = number of dimes <u>8</u>
2\. d + 3 = number of quarters <u>11</u>
3\. total value = total value
$(.10d) + [.25(d + 3)] = 3.55$
4\. $.10d + .25d + .75 = 3.55$
$.35d + .75 = 3.55$
$.35d + .75 - .75 = 3.55 - .75$
$.35d = 2.80$
$\frac{.35d}{.35} = \frac{2.80}{.35}$
$d = 8$

5\. $ .80
+2.75
$3.55 ✓

25\. 1. let x = the number of five dollar bills <u>2</u>
2\.
3\.
$5x + 1x + .25x + .10x = 12.70$
4\. $6.35x = 12.70$
$\frac{6.35x}{6.35} = \frac{12.70}{6.35}$
$x = 2$

5\. 5(2) + 1(2) + .25(2) + .10(2) = $12.70 ✓

26\. 1. let h = number of half dollars <u>5</u>
2\. 4h = number of quarters <u>20</u>
3h + 10 = number of dimes <u>25</u>
3\.
$(.50h) + [.25(4h)] + [.10(3h + 10)] = 10$
4\. $.50h + h + .30h + 1 = 10$
$1.80h + 1 = 10$
$1.80h + 1 - 1 = 10 - 1$
$1.80h = 9$
$\frac{1.80h}{1.80} = \frac{9.00}{1.80}$
$h = 5$
5\. 5(.50) + 20(.25) + 25(.10) = $10 ✓

27\. 1. let t = time in hours <u>4</u>
2\.

	rate	time	distance
first car	50	t	50t
second car	40	t	40t

3\. distance apart = distance apart
$50t + 40t = 360$
4\. $90t = 360$
$\frac{90t}{90} = \frac{360}{90}$
$t = 4$

5\. 4(50) + 4(40) = 360 ✓

28. 1. let r = rate of slower car 52 mph / 66 mph

2.

	rate	time	distance
slower car	r	3	3r
faster car	r + 7	3	3(r + 14)

3. distance apart = distance apart

$$3r + 3(r + 14) = 354$$

4.

$$3r + 3r + 42 = 354$$
$$6r + 42 = 354$$
$$6r + 42 - 42 = 354 - 42$$
$$6r = 312$$
$$\frac{6r}{6} = \frac{312}{6}$$
$$r = 52$$

5. $3(52) + 3(66) = 354$ ✓

29. 1. let m = number of original members 40

2. \$120 (redecorating cost)

3. cost before resignation = cost after resignation

$$30m = 40(m - 10)$$

4.

$$30m = 40m - 400$$
$$30m - 40m = 40m - 40m - 400$$
$$-10m = -400$$
$$\frac{-10m}{-10} = \frac{-400}{-10}$$
$$m = 40$$

5. $40(30) = \$1200$
$30(40) = \$1200$ ✓

30. 1. let t = time first train traveled 10.5 hr.

2.

	rate	time	distance
first train	40	t	40t
second train	56	t - 3	56(t - 3)

3. distance to overtake = distance to overtake

$$40t = 56(t - 3)$$

4.

$$40t = 56t - 168$$
$$40t - 56t = 56t - 56t - 168$$
$$-16t = -168$$
$$\frac{-16t}{-16} = \frac{-168}{-16}$$
$$t = 10.5$$

5. $40(10.5) = 420$
$56(7.5) = 420$ ✓

31. 1. let t = time driven at 24 mph 1/2 hr.
3 - t = time driven at 54 mph 2 1/2 hr.

2.

	rate	time	distance
towns	24	t	24t
country	54	3 - t	54(3 - t)

3. total distance = total distance

$$(24t) + [54(3 - t)] = 147$$

4.

$$24t + 162 - 54t = 147$$
$$-30t + 162 = 147$$
$$-30t + 162 - 162 = 147 - 162$$
$$-30t = -15$$
$$\frac{-30t}{-30} = \frac{-15}{-30}$$
$$t = 1/2$$

5. $\frac{1}{2}(24) + 2\frac{1}{2}(54) = 147$ ✓

32. 1. let s = amount in 14% stock <u>$5000</u>
2s = amount in 9% bonds <u>$10,000</u>
3. total income = total income
$(.14s) + [.09(2s)] = 1600$
4. $.14s + .18s = 1600$
$.32s = 1600$
$\frac{.32s}{.32} = \frac{1600}{.32}$
$s = 5000$

5. $.14(5000) + .09(10,000)$
$= 700 + 900$
$= \$1600$ ✓

33. 1. let x = amount invested at 12% <u>$3000</u>
2. 6600 - x = amount invested at 10% <u>$3600</u>
3. income = income
$.12x = .10(6600 - x)$
4. $.12x = 660 - .10x$
$.12x + .10x = 660 - .10x + .10x$
$.22x = 660$
$\frac{.22x}{.22} = \frac{660}{.22}$
$x = 3000$

5. $.12(3000) = \$360$
$.10(3600) = \$360$ ✓

34. 1. let p = amount invested at 8% <u>$4000</u>
2. 7000 - p = amount invested at 8 1/2% <u>$3000</u>
3. income = income
$.085(7000 - p) + 65 = .08p$
4. $595 - .085p + 65 = .08p$
$-.085p + .085p + 660 = .08p + .085p$
$660 = .165p$
$\frac{660}{.165} = \frac{.165p}{.165}$
$4000 = p$

5. $.08(4000) = \$320$
$.085(3000) + 65 = \$320$ ✓

35. 1. let s = length of a side of the square <u>12 ft.</u>
2. s + 4 = length of rectangle 16 ft.
s - 3 = width of rectangle 9 ft.
3. area = area
$s^2 = (s + 4)(s - 3)$
4. $s^2 = s^2 + s - 12$
$0 = s - 12$
$0 + 12 = s - 12 + 12$
$12 = s$

5. (12 ft.)(12 ft.) = 144 sq. ft.
(16 ft.)(9 ft.) = 144 sq. ft. ✓

36. 1. let x = number of days he had a fishing party $\underline{44}$
2. 56 - x = number of days without a fishing party 12
3. amount received = amount received

$24x - 8(56 - x) = 960$

4. $24x - 448 + 8x = 960$

$32x - 448 = 960$

$32x - 448 + 448 = 960 + 448$

$32x = 1408$

$\frac{32x}{32} = \frac{1408}{32}$

$x = 44$

5. $24(44) = \$1056$

$4(12) = -\ \ 96$

$\$\ 960$ ✓

37. 1. let t = time for second plane $\underline{2.2 \text{ hr.}}$
2. t + 1/2 = time for first plane $\underline{2.7 \text{ hr.}}$

	rate	time	distance
first plane	220	$t+\frac{1}{2}$	$220(t+\frac{1}{2})$
second plane	270	t	270t

3. distance = distance

$270t = 220(t + \frac{1}{2})$

4. $270t = 220t + 110$

$270t - 220t = 220t - 220t + 110$

$50t + 110$

$\frac{50t}{50} = \frac{110}{50}$

$t = 2.2$

5. $270(2.2) = 594$

$220(2.7) = 594$ ✓

38. 1. let b = amount earned by each boy $\underline{\$108}$
2. 4b = amount earned by each man $\$432$
3. earnings = earnings

$6b + 15(4b) = 7128$

4. $6b + 60b = 7128$

$66b = 7128$

$\frac{66b}{66} = \frac{7128}{66}$

$b = 108$

5. $6(108) + 15(432) = 648 + 6480 + \$7128$ ✓

39\. 1. let c = cost of cheaper chair $11.40
2. 30 - c = cost of better chair $18.60
3.
$$\text{cost} = \text{cost}$$
$$3c + 3 = 2(30 - c)$$
4.
$$3c + 3 = 60 - 2c$$
$$3c + 2c + 3 = 60 - 2c + 2c$$
$$5c + 3 = 60$$
$$5c + 3 - 3 = 60 - 3$$
$$5c = 57$$
$$\frac{5c}{5} = \frac{57}{5}$$
$$c = 11.40$$

5. 3(11.40) = $34.20 $37.20
2(18.60) = $37.20   -34.20
$ 3.00 ✓

40\. 1. let s = original amount in the office safe $675
2. 5s = original amount in the bank $3375
3.
$$\text{amount} = \text{amount}$$
$$8(s - 225) = 5s + 225$$
4.
$$8s - 1800 = 5s + 225$$
$$8s - 5s - 1800 = 5s - 5s + 225$$
$$3s - 1800 = 225$$
$$3s - 1800 + 1800 = 225 + 1800$$
$$3s = 2025$$
$$\frac{3s}{3} = \frac{2025}{3}$$
$$s = 675$$

5.

$675	$3375	$ 450
-225	+225	x 8
$450	$3600	$3600

$3600 = $3600 ✓

41\. 1. let c = dealer's cost of each radio $78
2.
3.
$$c + 22 = 2(c - 28)$$
4.
$$c + 22 = 2c - 56$$
$$c - 2c + 22 = 2c - 2c - 56$$
$$-c + 22 = -56$$
$$-c + 22 - 22 = -56 - 22$$
$$-c = -78$$
$$\frac{-c}{-1} = \frac{-78}{-1}$$
$$c = 78$$

5.

$ 78	$78
+ 22	-28
$100	$50

$100 is twice $50 ✓

42\. 1. t = time for faster runner
2.
3. $12t = 10(t + \frac{1}{60})$
4. $12t = 10t + \frac{1}{6}$
$$2t = \frac{1}{6}$$
$$t = \frac{1}{12} \text{ hr.}$$

$$d = rt$$
$$d = 12(\frac{1}{12})$$
$$d = 1$$

distance = 1 mile

5.

$12(\frac{1}{12})$	$10(\frac{1}{12} + \frac{1}{60})$
1	$10(\frac{6}{60})$
1	$\frac{6}{6}$

1 = 1 ✓

43. 1. let y = number of yards <u>4 yd.</u>
2. <u>$130</u> (money she had)
3. $29.50y + 12 = 2y(19.75) - 28$
4. $29.50y + 12 = 39.50y - 28$

$$29.50y - 39.50y + 12 = 39.50y - 39.50y - 28$$
$$-10y + 12 = -28$$
$$-10y + 12 - 12 = -28 - 12$$
$$-10y = -40$$
$$\frac{-10y}{-10} = \frac{-40}{-10}$$
$$y = 4$$

5. \$ 29.50 × 4 = 118.00; +12.00 = \$130.00 \$ 19.75 × 8 = 158.00; -28.00 = \$130.00 ✓

44. 1. let w = daily wage of father <u>168</u>
2. w - 100 = daily wage of Phillip <u>68</u>
3. $6(w-100) + 96 = 3w$
4. $6w - 600 + 96 = 3w$

$$6w - 504 = 3w$$
$$6w = 3w + 504$$
$$3w = 504$$
$$w = 168$$

5. (\$68 x 6) + \$96 = \$504
\$168 x 3 = \$504 ✓

45. 1. d = distance <u>240 mi.</u>
x = time 5 hr.
2.

	rate	time	distance
passenger train	80	x - 2	80(x - 2)
freight train	48	x	48x

3. $80(x - 2) = 48x$
4. $80x - 160 = 48x$

$$32x = 160$$
$$x = 5$$
$$48 \cdot 5 = 240$$

5. $\frac{240}{5} = 3$ hr.
5 - 2 = 3 hr. ✓

46. 1. let s = speed of first train 48 mph <u>288 mi.</u> (distance from New York)
2. s + 24 = speed of second train 72 mph

	speed	time	distance
first train	s	6	6s
second train	s+24	4	4(s+24)

3. distance = distance
$6s = 4(s + 24)$
4. $6s = 4s + 96$

$$6s - 4s = 4s - 4s + 96$$
$$2s = 96$$
$$\frac{2s}{2} = \frac{96}{2}$$
$$s = 48$$

5. 48 × 6 = 288 mi. 48 + 24 = 72 ✓ 72 × 4 = 288 mi.

47\. 1. let p = amount invested at 11 1/2% <u>$4500</u>
2. 10,000 - p = amount invested at 9% <u>$5500</u>
3. investment yield = investment yield

$$.115p - 22.50 = .09(10,000 - p)$$

4.

$$.115p - 22.50 = 900 - .09p$$
$$.115p + .09p - 22.50 = 900 - .09p + .09$$
$$.205p - 22.50 = 900$$
$$.205p - 22.50 + 22.50 = 900 + 22.50$$
$$.205p = 922.50$$
$$\frac{.205p}{.205} = \frac{922.50}{.205}$$
$$p = 4500$$

5.

$$\begin{array}{r} \$\ 4500 \\ \underline{\times\ .115} \\ 517.50 \\ \underline{-22.50} \\ \$495.00 \end{array} \qquad \begin{array}{r} \$\ 5500 \\ \underline{\times\ .09} \\ \$495.00 \end{array} \checkmark$$

48\. 1. let a = number of apples <u>105</u>
2.
3.

$$\frac{a}{3}(.25) + 3.75 = \frac{(a - 5)}{2}(.25)$$

4.

$$\frac{.25a}{3} + 3.75 = \frac{.25a}{2} - \frac{1.25}{2}$$
$$\frac{.25a}{3} - \frac{.25a}{2} + 3.75 = \frac{.25a}{2} - \frac{.25a}{2} - \frac{1.25}{2}$$
$$\frac{.25a}{3} - \frac{.25a}{2} + 3.75 = -\frac{1.25}{2}$$
$$\frac{.25a}{3} - \frac{.25a}{2} + 3.75 - 3.75 = -.625 - 3.75$$
$$\frac{.25a}{3} - \frac{.25a}{2} = -.625 - 3.75$$
$$\frac{.50a}{6} - \frac{.75a}{6} = -4.375$$
$$6\left(\frac{-.25a}{6}\right) = 6(-4.375)$$
$$-.25a = -26.250$$
$$\frac{-.25a}{-.25} = \frac{-26.250}{-.25}$$
$$a = 105$$

5.

$$\left(\frac{105}{3}\right)(.25) + 3.75 = \$12.50$$
$$\left(\frac{105 - 5}{2}\right)(.25) = \$12.50 \checkmark$$

49. 1. let x = Mr. Drake's age now 72
2. x - 24 = Mr. Drake's age 24 years ago 48
x + 8 = Mr. Drake's age 8 years from now 80
3. 24 years ago = 8 years from now

$$x - 24 = \frac{3}{5}(x + 8)$$

4.

$$x - 24 = \frac{3}{5}x + \frac{24}{5}$$
$$x - \frac{3}{5}x - 24 = \frac{3}{5}x - \frac{3}{5}x + \frac{24}{5}$$
$$\frac{2}{5}x - 24 = \frac{24}{5}$$
$$\frac{2}{5}x - 24 + 24 = \frac{24}{5} + 24$$
$$\frac{2}{5}x = \frac{24}{5} + 24$$
$$\frac{2}{5}x = \frac{24}{5} + \frac{120}{5}$$
$$\frac{2}{5}x = \frac{144}{5}$$
$$5(\frac{2}{5}x) = 5(\frac{144}{5})$$
$$2x = 144$$
$$\frac{2x}{2} = \frac{144}{2}$$
$$x = 72$$

5.

$$\begin{array}{r} 72 \\ -24 \\ \hline 48 \text{ yr.} \end{array} \qquad \begin{array}{r} 80 \\ \times .6 \\ \hline 48 \text{ yr.} \end{array} \checkmark$$

Test A Pages 129-130

I

1. $11a^2 - 5ab + 3b^2 + 6ab - 7a^2 + b^2 + 3b^2 - 2a^2 - 7ab + 4a^2 - ab + 4ab - 9b^2$
$= 11a^2 - 7a^2 - 2a^2 + 4a^2 - 5ab + 6ab - 7ab - ab + 4ab + 3b^2 + b^2 + 3b^2 - 9b^2$
$= 6a^2 - 3ab - 2b^2$

2.

$$\begin{array}{rrrrr} & 4x^3 + & x^2y - & 3xy^2 + & 5y^3 \\ (-) & 3x^3 - & 7x^2y + & 9xy^2 + & 8y^3 \\ \hline & x^3 + & 8x^2y - & 12xy^2 - & 3y^3 \end{array}$$

3.

$$\begin{array}{rrrrr} 4r^2 - & 3rt & - t^2 & & \\ 5r^2 + & 2rt & - 3t^2 & & \\ \hline 20r^4 - & 15r^3t - & 5r^2t^2 & & \\ & 8r^3t - & 6r^2t^2 - & 2rt^3 & \\ & & - 12r^2t^2 + & 9rt^3 + & 3t^4 \\ \hline 20r^4 - & 7r^3t - & 23r^2t^2 + & 7rt^3 + & 3t^4 \end{array}$$

4.

$$\begin{array}{r|l} & 2x^2 + 5x - 7 \\ \hline 2x - 3 & 4x^3 + 4x^2 - 29x + 21 \\ & 4x^3 - 6x^2 \\ \hline & \quad 10x^2 - 29x \\ & \quad 10x^2 - 15x \\ \hline & \qquad -14x + 21 \\ & \qquad -14x + 21 \\ \hline \end{array}$$

5. $6x - [5 - (2x + 7) - (8 - 3x)]$
$= 6x - (5 - 2x - 7 - 8 + 3x)$
$= 6x - (-10 + x)$
$= 6x + 10 - x$
$= 5x + 10$

6. $$\begin{aligned} &5ax + 3mn - 4ms - 6ab \\ &= (3mn - 4ms) + (5ax - 6ab) \\ &= (3mn - 4ms) - (6ab - 5ax) \end{aligned}$$

II The check is left for the teacher.

1. $$\begin{aligned} 8m - 3 &= 6m - 15 \\ 8m - 6m - 3 &= 6m - 6m - 15 \\ 2m - 3 &= -15 \\ 2m - 3 + 3 &= -15 + 3 \\ 2m &= -12 \\ \frac{2m}{2} &= \frac{-12}{2} \\ m &= -6 \end{aligned}$$

2. $$\begin{aligned} 5x - 9 - 4 - x &= 8 - 3x + 7 \\ 4x - 13 &= 15 - 3x \\ 4x + 3x - 13 &= 15 - 3x + 3x \\ 7x - 13 &= 15 \\ 7x - 13 + 13 &= 15 + 13 \\ 7x &= 28 \\ \frac{7x}{7} &= \frac{28}{7} \\ x &= 4 \end{aligned}$$

3. $$\begin{aligned} 4a - 2(3a - 5) &= 3(a - 2) - 4 \\ 4a - 6a + 10 &= 3a - 6 - 4 \\ -2a + 10 &= 3a - 10 \\ -2a + 2a + 10 &= 3a + 2a - 10 \\ 10 &= 5a - 10 \\ 10 + 10 &= 5a - 10 + 10 \\ 20 &= 5a \\ \frac{20}{5} &= \frac{5a}{5} \\ 4 &= a \end{aligned}$$

4. $$\begin{aligned} (2x - 3)(x + 7) &= 3 + x(2x + 7) \\ 2x^2 + 11x - 21 &= 3 + 2x^2 + 7x \\ 11x - 21 &= 3 + 7x \\ 11x - 7x - 21 &= 3 + 7x - 7x \\ 4x - 21 &= 3 \\ 4x - 21 + 21 &= 3 + 21 \\ 4x &= 24 \\ \frac{4x}{4} &= \frac{24}{4} \\ x &= 6 \end{aligned}$$

Test B Page 130

I

1. $$\begin{aligned} &4x^2 - 7xy - 12y^2 + 5y^2 + 9x^2 - 7xy + 11xy - 15x^2 + 5y^2 + 2x^2 + 3y^2 + 12xy - 4y^2 \\ &= 4x^2 + 9x^2 - 15x^2 + 2x^2 - 7xy - 7xy + 11xy + 12xy - 12y^2 + 5y^2 + 5y^2 + 3y^2 - 4y^2 \\ &= 9xy - 3y^2 \end{aligned}$$

2. $$\begin{array}{rrrrr} & 6x^3 & - 8x^2y & + 3xy^2 & - 7y^3 \\ (-) & 3x^3 & + 3x^2y & + 8xy^2 & - 7y^3 \\ \hline & 3x^3 & - 10x^2y & - 5xy^2 & \end{array}$$

3. $$\begin{array}{rrrrrr} & 5a^2 & - 2ab & + 3b^2 & & \\ (\times) & 2a^2 & - 3ab & - 6b^2 & & \\ \hline & 10a^4 & - 4a^3b & + 6a^2b^2 & & \\ & & - 15a^3b & + 6a^2b^2 & - 9ab^3 & \\ & & & - 30a^2b^2 & + 12ab^3 & - 18b^4 \\ \hline & 10a^4 & - 19a^3b & - 18a^2b^2 & + 3ab^3 & - 18b^4 \end{array}$$

4. $$\begin{array}{r|rrrr} & 3a^2 & - 4a & - 5 & \\ \hline 2a - 3 & 6a^3 & - 17a^2 & + 2a & + 15 \\ & 6a^3 & - 9a^2 & & \\ \hline & & - 8a^2 & + 2a & \\ & & - 8a^2 & + 12a & \\ \hline & & & - 10a & + 15 \\ & & & - 10a & + 15 \end{array}$$

5. $$\begin{aligned} &5 - [3 + (x - 4) - (5x + 3)] \\ &= 5 - (3 + x - 4 - 5x - 3) \\ &= 5 - (-4 - 4x) \\ &= 5 + 4 + 4x \\ &= 4x + 9 \end{aligned}$$

6. $$\begin{aligned} &ay^2 - 3z - 6ax + 4yz \\ &= (ay^2 - 6ax) + (-3z + 4yz) \\ &= (ay^2 - 6ax) - (3z - 4yz) \end{aligned}$$

II The check is left for the teacher.

1.
$$5a + 3 = 2a - 9$$
$$5a - 2a + 3 = 2a - 2a - 9$$
$$3a + 3 = -9$$
$$3a + 3 - 3 = -9 - 3$$
$$3a = -12$$
$$\frac{3a}{3} = \frac{-12}{3}$$
$$a = -4$$

2.
$$6x - 7 + 2x + 8 = 4x + 21 - 6x$$
$$8x + 1 = -2x + 21$$
$$8x + 2x + 1 = -2x + 2x + 21$$
$$10x + 1 = 21$$
$$10x + 1 - 1 = 21 - 1$$
$$10x = 20$$
$$\frac{10x}{10} = \frac{20}{10}$$
$$x = 2$$

3.
$$2x + 5 - 3(x + 7) = 4 - 6x$$
$$2x + 5 - 3x - 21 = 4 - 6x$$
$$-x - 16 = 4 - 6x$$
$$-x + 6x - 16 = 4 - 6x + 6x$$
$$5x - 16 = 4$$
$$5x - 16 + 16 = 4 + 16$$
$$5x = 20$$
$$\frac{5x}{5} = \frac{20}{5}$$
$$x = 4$$

4.
$$(x + 2)(3x - 5) = 3x(x - 8) + 15$$
$$3x^2 + x - 10 = 3x^2 - 24x + 15$$
$$x - 10 = -24x + 15$$
$$x + 24x - 10 = -24x + 24x + 15$$
$$25x - 10 = 15$$
$$25x - 10 + 10 = 15 + 10$$
$$25x = 25$$
$$\frac{25x}{25} = \frac{25}{25}$$
$$x = 1$$

Test C Pages 130-131

I

1. a^5 2. a^{m+n} 3. $\frac{a^m}{a^n} = a^{m-n}$ 4. $a^{3-5} = a^{-2}$

II The check is left for the teacher.

$$(x - 2)(x^2 + 2x + 4) - (x^2 - x + 1)(x + 1) = 5x + 1$$
$$x^3 + 2x^2 + 4x - 2x^2 - 4x - 8 - (x^3 - x^2 + x + x^2 - x + 1) = 5x + 1$$
$$x^3 - 8 - (x^3 + 1) = 5x + 1$$
$$x^3 - 8 - x^3 - 1 = 5x + 1$$
$$-9 = 5x + 1$$
$$-9 - 1 = 5x + 1 - 1$$
$$-10 = 5x$$
$$\frac{-10}{5} = \frac{5x}{5}$$
$$-2 = x$$

III

1. a) n nickels and n - 4 dimes   <u>40</u> nickels, <u>36</u> dimes

b) $5n$ and $10(n - 4)$

c) $5n + 10(n - 4) = 5n + 10n - 40 = 15n - 40$

d) $15n - 40 = 560$

e)
$$15n - 40 + 40 = 560 + 40$$
$$15n = 600$$
$$\frac{15n}{15} = \frac{600}{15}$$
$$n = 40$$

2\. 1. let x = number of pounds of tea <u>3 lb.</u>
2\. x + 2 = number of pounds of coffee <u>5 lb.</u>
3\. total cost = total cost

$$3x + 2.10(x + 2) = 19.50$$

4\.
$$3x + 2.10x + 4.20 = 19.50$$
$$5.10x + 4.20 = 19.50$$
$$5.10x + 4.20 - 4.20 = 19.50 - 4.20$$
$$5.10x = 15.30$$
$$\frac{5.10x}{5.10} = \frac{15.30}{5.10}$$
$$x = 3$$

5\. \$3.00 × 3 = \$9.00; \$2.10 × 5 = \$10.50; \$9.00 + 10.50 = \$19.50 ✓

3\. a) 6r
b) $4(r + 4) = 4r + 16$
c) $6r + 4r + 16 = 526$
d)
$$10r + 16 = 526$$
$$10r + 16 - 16 = 526 - 16$$
$$10r = 510$$
$$\frac{10r}{10} = \frac{510}{10}$$
$$r = 51$$

First man's rate was 51 mph; second man's rate was 55 mph.
First man traveled 6(51) = 306 miles; second man traveled 4(55) = 220 miles.

4\. 1. let s = speed before bad weather <u>54 mph</u>
s - 9 = speed after bad weather <u>45 mph</u>
2\.

	speed	time	distance
before trouble	s	2	2s
after trouble	s - 9	4	4(s - 9)

3\. distance = distance

$$2s + 4(s - 9) = 288$$

4\.
$$2s + 4s - 36 = 288$$
$$6s - 36 = 288$$
$$6s - 36 + 36 = 288 + 36$$
$$6s = 324$$
$$\frac{6s}{6} = \frac{324}{6}$$
$$s = 54$$

5\. 54 × 2 = 108; 45 × 4 = 180; 108 + 180 = 288 mi. ✓

5\. 1. w = Amanda's hourly wage <u>\$7.60</u>
2\. w + .30 = Ellen's hourly wage <u>\$7.90</u>
3\. total earned = total earned

$$36w + 40(w + .30) = 589.60$$

4\.
$$36w + 40w + 12.00 = 589.60$$
$$76w + 12.00 = 589.60$$
$$76w + 12.00 - 12.00 = 589.60 - 12.00$$
$$76w = 577.60$$
$$\frac{76w}{76} = \frac{577.60}{76}$$
$$w = \$7.60$$

5\. \$7.60 × 36 = \$273.60; \$7.90 × 40 = \$316.00; \$273.60 + 316.00 = \$589.60 ✓

UNIT 7 — Special Products and Factoring

Exercises 7.1 Pages 133-136

Answers are given in the text.

Exercises 7.2 Pages 135-136

The FOIL METHOD of multiplying two binomials is an excellent method for students to use in mastering this basic process of multiplication. The method is a mental process done using the letters of the word FOIL.

First Last; Inner; Outer

$$(2x + y)(3x - 4y) = \underset{\text{First}}{(2x)(3x)} + \underset{\text{Outer}}{(2x)(-4y)} + \underset{\text{Inner}}{(3x)(y)} + \underset{\text{Last}}{(y)(-4y)}$$

$$= 6x^2 - 8xy + 3xy - 4y^2$$

$$= 6x^2 - 5xy - 4y^2$$

1. 12	2. 6	3. 6	4. $12y^2$	5. 15	6. $30a^2$	7. 35
8. 24	9. $6y^2$	10 $6b^2$	11. $15x^2$	12. $-21a^2$	13. $-6y^2$	14. $18b^2$
15. $-4x^2$	16. $-10x^2$	17. 22x	18. (-14xy)	19. (-22x)	20. 49xy	21. 18a

22. $(4x + 3)(3x + 2)$
$= 12x^2 + 17x + 6$

23. $(x - 7y)(2x - 3y)$
$= 2x^2 - 17xy + 21y^2$

24. $(2x - 8)(3x + 5)$
$= 6x^2 - 14x - 40$

25. $(4x + 3)(3x - 4)$
$= 12x^2 - 7x - 12$

26. $(x + 9b)(x + 6b)$
$= x^2 + 15bx + 54b^2$

27. $(2x + 5c)(3x - 2c)$
$= 6x^2 + 11cx - 10c^2$

28. $(2x + 4y)(3x - 5y)$
$= 6x^2 + 2xy - 20y^2$

29. $(3a + 2b)(5a - 6b)$
$= 15a^2 - 8ab - 12b^2$

30. $(2a + 5b)(5a + 2b)$
$= 10a^2 + 29ab + 10b^2$

31. $(7n^2 - 2p)(2n^2 - 7p)$
$= 14n^4 - 53n^2p + 14p^2$

32. $(2m - 3n)(4m - 6n)$
$= 8m^2 - 24mn + 18n^2$

33. $(5x^2 - y)(3x^2 + y)$
$= 15x^4 + 2x^2y - y^2$

34. $(7y^2 - 2y)(3y^2 + y)$
$= 21y^4 + y^3 - 2y^2$

35. $(2x + 5)(3x + 4)$
$= 6x^2 + 23x + 20$

36. $(3x - 2)(2x - 3)$
$= 6x^2 - 13x + 6$

37. $(3a - 4)(4a + 3)$
$= 12a^2 - 7a - 12$

38. $(3x - y)(x - 3y)$
$= 3x^2 - 10xy + 3y^2$

39. $(7z - a)(3z + 2a)$
$= 21z^2 + 11az - 2a^2$

40. $(a - 7b)(a + 3b)$
$= a^2 - 4ab - 21b^2$

41. $(x^2 - 5)(x^2 - 6)$
$= x^4 - 11x^2 + 30$

42. $(mn + 11)(mn + 2)$
$= m^2n^2 + 13mn + 22$

43. $(5x - 3)(5x - 3)$
$= 25x^2 - 30x + 9$

44. $(4a^2 + 7b)(4a^2 + 7b)$
$= 16a^4 + 56a^2b + 49b^2$

45. $(x - 6)(x + 6)$
$= x^2 - 36$

46. $(5x + 3)(5x - 3)$
$= 25x^2 - 9$

47. $(3ab + 10c^2)(3ab - 10c^2)$
$= 9a^2b^2 - 100c^4$

Exercises 7.4 Pages 137-138

1. $(x + 5)(x + 6)$
$= x^2 + 11x + 30$

2. $(x + 7)(x + 8)$
$= x^2 + 15x + 56$

3. $(x - 7)(x + 8)$
$= x^2 + x - 56$

4. $(x + 7)(x - 8)$
$= x^2 - x - 56$

5. $(x - 5)(x - 4)$
$= x^2 - 9x + 20$

6. $(x - 3)(x - 2)$
$= x^2 - 5x + 6$

7. $(x - 5)(x - 1)$
$= x^2 - 6x + 5$

8. $(x + 5)(x + 8)$
$= x^2 + 13x + 40$

9. $(p - 4)(p + 1)$
$= p^2 - 3p - 4$

10. $(r - 3)(r - 1)$
$= r^2 - 4r + 3$

11. $(n - 6)(n + 15)$
$= n^2 + 9n - 90$

12. $(x^2 + 5)(x^2 - 3)$
$= x^4 + 2x^2 - 15$

13. $(x^3 - 7)(x^3 + 6)$
$= x^6 - x^3 - 42$

14. Answer is given in text.

15. $(x^n - a)(x^n - 2a)$
$= x^{2n} - 3ax^n + 2a^2$

16. $(y - 2b)(y + 3b)$
$= y^2 + by - 6b^2$

17. $(z - 4a)(z + 3a)$
$= z^2 - az - 12a^2$

18. $(2x - .7)(2x + .5)$
$= 4x^2 - .4x - .35$

19. $(4x^2 + 1)(4x^2 - 7)$
$= 16x^4 - 24x^2 - 7$

20. $(ab - 6)(ab + 4)$
$= a^2b^2 - 2ab - 24$

21. $(x^2y^2 - a)(x^2y^2 + 2a)$
$= x^4y^4 + ax^2y^2 - 2a^2$

22. $(3xy + y^2)(y^2 - xy)$
$= 3xy^3 - 3x^2y^2 + y^4 - xy^3$
$= y^4 + 2xy^3 - 3x^2y^2$

23. $(b^2c^2 + ef)(b^2c^2 + ef)$
$= b^4c^4 + 2b^2c^2ef + e^2f^2$

24. $(.3x^2 + 2y^2)(.3x^2 - 2y^2)$
$= .09x^4 - 4y^4$

25. $(.5ab + 2c^2)(.5ab + 2c^2)$
$= .25a^2b^2 + 2abc^2 + 4c^4$

Exercises 7.5 Pages 139-140

1. $(y + 3)^2$
$= y^2 + 6y + 9$

2. $(k + 10)^2$
$= k^2 + 20k + 100$

3. $(2y - 5)^2$
$= 4y^2 - 20y + 25$

4. $(a - 2b)^2$
$= a^2 - 4ab + 4b^2$

5. $(k - 10)^2$
$= k^2 - 20k + 100$

6. $(3a + 2bc)^2$
$= 9a^2 + 12abc + 4b^2c^2$

7. $(a - 4t)^2$
$= a^2 - 8at + 16t^2$

8. $(a + b)^2$
$= a^2 + 2ab + b^2$

9. $(8x - 5ay)^2$
$= 64x^2 - 80axy + 25a^2y^2$

10. $(x + m)^2$
$= x^2 + 2mx + m^2$

11. $(2a - 6x)^2$
$= 4a^2 - 24ax + 36x^2$

12. $(2a + 3b)^2$
$= 4a^2 + 12ab + 9b^2$

13. $(m - n)^2$
$= m^2 - 2mn + n^2$

14. $(3m - 8n)^2$
$= 9m^2 - 48mn + 64n^2$

15. $(2x - 7y)^2$
$= 4x^2 - 28xy + 49y^2$

16. $(x - 6)^2$
$= x^2 - 12x + 36$

17. $(p + 3q)^2$
$= p^2 + 6pq + 9q^2$

18. $(8x - 5y)^2$
$= 64x^2 - 80xy + 25y^2$

19. $(p - 8)^2$
$= p^2 - 16p + 64$

20. $(4a - 3)^2$
$= 16a^2 - 24a + 9$

21. $(5m - 3n)^2$
$= 25m^2 - 30mn + 9n^2$

22. $(r + 7)^2$
$= r^2 + 14r + 49$

23. $(5x + 4)^2$
$= 25x^2 + 40x + 16$

24. $(3p - 5q)^2$
$= 9p^2 - 30pq + 25q^2$

25. $(y^2 - 6)^2$
$= y^4 - 12y^2 + 36$

26. $(ab - 3)^2$
$= a^2b^2 - 6ab + 9$

27. $(4xy - 7)^2$
$= 16x^2y^2 - 56xy + 49$

28. $(x + \frac{1}{2})^2$
$= x^2 + x + \frac{1}{4}$

29. $(r + \frac{4}{9})^2$
$= r^2 + \frac{8}{9}r + \frac{16}{81}$

30. $(2x - \frac{1}{2})^2$
$= 4x^2 - 2x + \frac{1}{4}$

31. $(y - \frac{1}{3})^2$
$= y^2 - \frac{2}{3}y + \frac{1}{9}$

32. $(s - \frac{3}{5})^2$
$= s^2 - \frac{6}{5}s + \frac{9}{25}$

33. $(3x + \frac{1}{3})^2$
$= 9x^2 + 2x + \frac{1}{9}$

34. $(a + \frac{4}{3})^2$
$= a^2 + \frac{8}{3}a + \frac{16}{9}$

35. $(x - \frac{4}{11})^2$
$= x^2 - \frac{8}{11}x + \frac{16}{121}$

36. $(2x - \frac{1}{5})^2$
$= 4x^2 - \frac{4}{5}x + \frac{1}{25}$

37. $(5\frac{1}{2})^2 = (5 + .5)^2$
$= 5^2 + 1(5) + (.5)^2$
$= 5(5 + 1) + .25$
$= 5(6) + .25$
$= 30.25$

38. $41^2 = (40 + 1)^2$
$= 40^2 + 2(40) + 1^2$
$= 40(40 + 2) + 1$
$= 40(42) + 1$
$= 1681$

39. $53^2 = (50 + 3)^2$
$= 50^2 + 6(50) + 3^2$
$= 50(50 + 6) + 9$
$= 50(56) + 9$
$= 2809$

40. $29^2 = (30 - 1)^2$
$= 30^2 - 2(30) + 1^2$
$= 30(30 - 2) + 1$
$= 30(28) + 1$
$= 841$

41. $(7.5)^2 = (7 + .5)^2$
$= 7^2 + 1(7) + (.5)^2$
$= 7(7 + 1) + .25$
$= 7(8) + .25$
$= 56.25$

42. $(8\frac{1}{2})^2 = (8 + .5)^2$
$= 8^2 + 1(8) + (.5)^2$
$= 8(8 + 1) + .25$
$= 8(9) + .25$
$= 72.25$

43. $42^2 = (40 + 2)^2$
$= 40^2 + 4(40) + 2^2$
$= 40(40 + 4) + 4$
$= 40(44) + 4$
$= 1764$

44. $12\frac{1}{2} = (12 + .5)^2$
$= 12^2 + 1(12) + (.5)^2$
$= 12(12 + 1) + .25$
$= 12(13) + .25$
$= 156.25$

45. $48^2 = (50 - 2)^2$
$= 50^2 - 4(50) + 2^2$
$= 50(50 - 4) + 4$
$= 50(46) + 4$
$= 2304$

46. $(9.5)^2 = (10 - .5)^2$
$= 10^2 - 1(10) + (.5)^2$
$= 10(10 - 1) + .25$
$= 10(9) + .25$
$= 90.25$

Exercises 7.6 Page 141

1. $(x + y)(x - y)$
$= x^2 - y^2$

2. $(a + c)(a - c)$
$= a^2 - c^2$

3. $(p + q)(p - q)$
$= p^2 - q^2$

4. $(p + 5)(p - 5)$
$= p^2 - 25$

5. $(x + 1)(x - 1)$
$= x^2 - 1$

6. $(x^2 + 1)(x^2 - 1)$
$= x^4 - 1$

7. $(ab - c^2)(ab + c^2)$
$= a^2b^2 - c^4$

8. $(4y + z^2)(4y - z^2)$
$= 16y^2 - z^4$

9. $(rs - 5m)(rs + 5m)$
$= r^2s^2 - 25m^2$

10. $(3m - 4n)(3m + 4n)$
$= 9m^2 - 16n^2$

11. $(12 + xy)(12 - xy)$
$= 144 - x^2y^2$

12. $(3m^2 - b)(3m^2 + b)$
$= 9m^4 - b^2$

13. $(2x^3 + 5y^2)(2x^3 - 5y^2)$
$= 4x^6 - 25y^4$

14. $(2a^2 + 3b^2)(2a^2 - 3b^2)$
$= 4a^4 - 9b^4$

15. $(-5n - b)(-5n + b)$
$= 25n^2 - b^2$

16. $(\frac{1}{2}x + 3)(\frac{1}{2}x - 3)$
$= \frac{1}{4}x^2 - 9$

17. $(\frac{2}{3}a - 4b)(\frac{2}{3}a + 4b)$
$= \frac{4}{9}a^2 - 16b^2$

18. $(20 + 1)(20 - 1)$
$= 20^2 - 1^2$
$= 400 - 1$
$= 399$

19. 29×31
$= (30 - 1)(30 + 1)$
$= 30^2 - 1^2$
$= 900 - 1$
$= 899$

20. 58×62
$= (60 - 2)(60 + 2)$
$= 60^2 - 2^2$
$= 3600 - 4$
$= 3596$

21. $(10.5)^2 - (6.3)^2$
$= (10.5 + 6.3)(10.5 - 6.3)$

Review Exercises Page 141

1. $(2x + 1)(x + 2)$
$= 2x^2 + 5x + 2$

2. $(y - 4)(y - 4)$
$= y^2 - 8y + 16$

3. $(2x + 3)(x + 1)$
$= 2x^2 + 5x + 3$

4. $(5a - 2b)(3a - 4b)$
$= 15a^2 - 26ab + 8b^2$

5. $(5x - 1)(x - 7)$
$= 5x^2 - 36x + 7$

6. $(11xy + 6)(11xy - 6)$
$= 121x^2y^2 - 36$

7. $(3ab - 5c)^2$
$= 9a^2b^2 - 30abc + 25c^2$

8. $(z - 2r)(z - 10r)$
$= z^2 - 12rz + 20r^2$

9. $(5y - 1)(5y + 2)$
$= 25y^2 + 5y - 2$

10. $(2a + 3y)^2$
$= 4a^2 + 12ay + 9y^2$

11. $(x - 6)(x - 4)$
$= x^2 - 10x + 24$

12. $(9m - 1)(9m + 1)$
$= 81m^2 - 1$

13. $(7x^2 + 4)(7x^2 - 4)$
$= 49x^4 - 16$

14. $(2x + 7)(x - 4)$
$= 2x^2 - x - 28$

15. $(x - 5a)(x + a)$
$= x^2 - 4ax - 5a^2$

16. $(x - 8)(x + 11)$
$= x^2 + 3x - 88$

17. $(4xy + 3yz)^2$
$= 16x^2y^2 + 24xy^2z + 9y^2z^2$

18. $(8a^2 + 5b^3)^2$
$= 64a^4 + 80a^2b^3 + 25b^6$

19. $(z - 2)(z - 19)$
$= z^2 - 21z + 38$

20. $(2m^2n - 8y)(2m^2n + 8y)$
$= 4m^4n^2 - 64y^2$

Exercises 7.7 Pages 142-143

1. See pages 133 and 134 in text.

2. $3ab^2 - 9a^2b$
$= 3ab(b - 3a)$

3. $5x^3 - 5x^2$
$= 5x^2(x - 1)$

4. $8x^2 + 2x^4$
$= 2x^2(4 + x^2)$

5. $3x^3 - 6x^2y$
$= 3x^2(x - 2y)$

6. $4a^2 - 6ab$
$= 2a(2a - 3b)$

7. $5m^2 - 3mn$
$= m(5m - 3n)$

8. $3x^3y^2 - 3x^2y^3$
$= 3x^2y^2(x - y)$

9. $4a^3b - 6a^2b^2$
$= 2a^2b(2a - 3b)$

10. $5m^4n - 10m^3n^2$
$= 5m^3n(m - 2n)$

11. $3x^4 - 9x^3 - 6x^2$
$= 3x^2(x^2 - 3x - 2)$

12. $x^{12} + x^{11} + x^{10} - x^9$
$= x^9(x^3 + x^2 + x - 1)$

13. $ac - bc - cy - abc$
$= c(a - b - y - ab)$

14. $3x^3y^3 - 3x^2y^2 + 12xy$
$= 3xy(x^2y^2 - xy + 4)$

15. $3m^5 - 12m^3n^2 + 6mn^4$
$= 3m(m^4 - 4m^2n^2 + 2n^4)$

16. $a(x - y) + 5(x - y)$
$= (x - y)(a + 5)$

17. $4(a + b) - x(a + b)$
$= (a + b)(4 - x)$

18. $c^2(y + z)^2 - d(y + z)^2$
$= (y + z)^2(c^2 - d)$

19. $5(x - y) - 2a(y - x) = 5(x - y) + 2a(x - y)$
$= (x - y)(5 + 2a)$

20. $6x(2a - b) - 3y(b - 2a)$
$= 6x(2a - b) + 3y(2a - b)$
$= (2a - b)(6x + 3y)$
$= 3(2a - b)(2x + y)$

21. $a(x - y) - b(x - y) - c(y - x)$
$= a(x - y) - b(x - y) + c(x - y)$
$= (x - y)(a - b + c)$

Exercises 7.8 Pages 144-145

1. $x^2 + 7x + 12$
$= (x + 3)(x + 4)$

2. $y^2 - 7y + 12$
$= (y - 4)(y - 3)$

3. $p^2 - 8p + 12$
$= (p - 6)(p - 2)$

4. $r^2 + 8r + 12$
$= (r + 6)(r + 2)$

5. $15 + 2a - a^2$
$= (5 - a)(3 + a)$

6. $b^2 + b - 12$
$= (b + 4)(b - 3)$

7. $30 - r^2 + r$
$= 30 + r - r^2$
$= (6 - r)(5 + r)$

8. $c^2 - c - 72$
$= (c - 9)(c + 8)$

9. $c^2 - 5c - 14$
$= (c - 7)(c + 2)$

10. $x^2 - x - 110$
$= (x - 11)(x + 10)$

11. $x^2 - 3x + 2$
$= (x - 2)(x - 1)$

12. $a^2 + 9a + 14$
$= (a + 7)(a + 2)$

13. $y^2 - 5y + 6$
$= (y - 3)(y - 2)$

14. $b^2 + 2b - 15$
$= (b + 5)(b - 3)$

15. $x^2 + bx - 20b^2$
$= (x + 5b)(x - 4b)$

16. $2x^2 - 2xy - 12y^2$
$= 2(x^2 - xy - 6y^2)$
$= 2(x - 3y)(x + 2y)$

*17. $-12r^2 - dr + d^2$
$= d^2 - dr - 12r^2$
$= (d - 4r)(d + 3r)$

*18. $4xy - x^2 + 21y^2$
$= -x^2 + 4xy + 21y^2$
$= -(x^2 - 4xy - 21y^2)$
$= -(x - 7y)(x + 3y)$

19. $x^2 + 5ax + 6a^2$
$= (x + 3a)(x + 2a)$

20. $x^2 - 6ax + 5a^2$
$= (x - 5a)(x - a)$

21. $y^2 - 4by - 12b^2$
$= (y - 6b)(y + 2b)$

22. $y^2 - 3ny - 28n^2$
$= (y - 7n)(y + 4n)$

23. $z^2 - anz - 2a^2n^2$
$= (z - 2an)(z + an)$

*24. $-x^2 + 25x - 100$
$= -(x^2 - 25x + 100)$
$= -(x - 20)(x - 5)$
$= (20 - x)(x - 5)$
or $(x - 20)(5-x)$

25. $x^4 + 19cx^2 + 90c^2$
$= (x^2 + 9c)(x^2 + 10c)$

26. $x^6 + 12ax^3 + 20a^2$
$= (x^3 + 10a)(x^3 + 2a)$

27. $x^8 - 11b^2x^4 + 24b^4$
$= (x^4 - 8b^2)(x^4 - 3b^2)$

28. $n^2x^2 - 11nxy + 30y^2$
$= (nx - 6y)(nx - 5y)$

29. $2y^2 + 3y + 1$
$= (2y + 1)(y + 1)$

30. $5x^2 + 9x - 2$
$= (5x - 1)(x + 2)$

31. $3x^2 - 7x - 6$
$= (3x + 2)(x - 3)$

32. $4r^2 + 8r + 3$
$= (2r + 3)(2r + 1)$

33. $6x^2 - 7x + 2$
$= (3x - 2)(2x - 1)$

34. $2x^2 - 5x - 12$
$= (2x + 3)(x - 4)$

35. $10t^2 + t - 3$
$= (5t + 3)(2t - 1)$

36. $6n^2 - 13n + 6$
$= (3n - 2)(2n - 3)$

37. $2x^2 + 5x + 2$
$= (2x + 1)(x + 2)$

38. $2x^2 + 5x + 3$
$= (2x + 3)(x + 1)$

39. $5x^2 - 36x + 7$
$= (5x - 1)(x - 7)$

40. $6a^2 + 13a + 6$
$= (3a + 2)(2a + 3)$

41. $2x^2 + x - 15$
$= (2x - 5)(x + 3)$

42. $5x^2 + 13x + 6$
$= (5x + 3)(x + 2)$

43. $3x^2 - 17x + 10$
$= (3x - 2)(x - 5)$

44. $6x^2 - 11x - 35$
$= (3x + 5)(2x - 7)$

45. $15x^2 + 17x - 4$
$= (5x - 1)(3x + 4)$

46. $15x^2 - 14x - 8$
$= (5x + 2)(3x - 4)$

47. $2x^2 + 3xy - 2y^2$
$= (2x - y)(x + 2y)$

48. $3x^2 - 10xy + 3y^2$
$= (3x - y)(x - 3y)$

49. $5y^2 - 6y + 1$
$= (5y - 1)(y - 1)$

50. $3a^2 + 4a + 1$
$= (3a + 1)(a + 1)$

51. $2x^2 - x - 28$
$= (2x + 7)(x - 4)$

52. $5a^2 + 16a + 3$
$= (5a + 1)(a + 3)$

53. $x^2 + 4x + 4$
$= (x + 2)(x + 2)$

54. $m^2 - 7m - 30$
$= (m - 10)(m + 3)$

55. $x^2 - 15x - 700$
$= (x - 35)(x + 20)$

56. $9x^2 - 42x + 49$
$= (3x - 7)(3x - 7)$

Exercises 7.9 Pages 146-147

1. $x^2 + 2xy + y^2$

2. $a^2 - 2ab + b^2$

3. $y^2 + 2yz + z^2$

4. $c^2 - 2cd + d^2$

5. $x^2 + 4xy + 4y^2$

6. $r^2 - 8rs + 16s^2$

7. $4a^2 + 4ab + b^2$

8. $p^2 - 2pq + q^2$

9. $9x^2 + 6xy + y^2$

10. $x^2 + 2xy + y^2$
$= (x + y)^2$

11. $p^2 - 2pq + q^2$
$= (p - q)^2$

12. $c^2 + 2cd + d^2$
$= (c + d)^2$

13. $x^2 - 2x + 1$
$= (x - 1)^2$

14. $x^2 + 6x + 9$
$= (x + 3)^2$

15. $4 - 4a + a^2$
$= (2 - a)^2$

16. $4a - 4a^2 + a^3$
$= a(4 - 4a + a^2)$
$= a(2 - a)^2$

17. $m^2 - 8m + 16$
$= (m - 4)^2$

18. $a^2 - 16a + 64$
$= (a - 8)^2$

19. $1 + 8b + 16b^2$
$= (1 + 4b)^2$

20. $3x^2 + 6xy + 3y^2$
$= 3(x^2 + 2xy + y^2)$
$= 3(x + y)^2$

21. $2m^2 - 8mn + 8n^2$
$= 2(m^2 - 4mn + 4n^2)$
$= 2(m - 2n)^2$

22. $1 - 6a^3 + 9a^6$
$= (1 - 3a^3)^2$

23. $5x^2 + 30x + 45$
$= 5(x^2 + 6x + 9)$
$= 5(x + 3)^2$

24. $16p^2 - 24p + 9$
$= (4p - 3)^2$

25. $9 + 42b^3 + 49b^6$
$= (3 + 7b^3)^2$

26. $36n^8 - 12n^4 + 1$
$= (6n^4 - 1)^2$

27. Answer is given in text.

28. $4x^2y^2 - 20xy + 25$
$= (2xy - 5)^2$

29. $8a^2b + 40ab^2 + 50b^3$
$= 2b(4a^2 + 20ab + 25b^2)$
$= 2b(2a + 5b)^2$

30. $4x^{2a} + 8x^ay^b + 4y^{2b}$
$= 4(x^{2a} + 2x^ay^b + y^{2b})$
$= 4(x^a + y^b)^2$

31. $x^{2n} - 2x^ny^nz^n + y^{2n}z^{2n}$
$= (x^n - y^nz^n)^2$

32. $2x + 20a^2x + 50a^4x$
$= 50a^4x + 20a^2x + 2x$
$= 2x(25a^4 + 10a^2 + 1)$
$= 2x(5a^2 + 1)^2$

*33. $x^2 + 2x(x - y) + (x - y)^2$
$= [x + (x - y)] [x + (x - y)]$
$= (2x - y)^2$

*34. $(r + s)^2 - 4(r + s) + 4$
$= [(r + s) - 2] [(r + s) - 2]$
$= (r + s - 2)^2$

Factoring Speed Tests   Pages 147-148

I

1. $x^2 + 6x + 8 = (x + 4)(x + 2)$

2. $a^2 + 8a + 15 = (a + 5)(a + 3)$

3. $b^2 - 12b + 32 = (b - 8)(b - 4)$

4. $r^2 - 14r + 48 = (r - 8)(r - 6)$

5. $r^2 - 19r + 90 = (r - 9)(r - 10)$

6. $x^2 - 8x - 20 = (x - 10)(x + 2)$

7. $y^2 + 8y - 33 = (y + 11)(y - 3)$

8. $k^2 + 5k - 36 = (k + 9)(k - 4)$

9. $a^2 + 7a - 8 = (a + 8)(a - 1)$

10. $x^2 - 6xy - 16y^2 = (x - 8y)(x + 2y)$

11. $r^2s^2 - 11rst + 24t^2 = (rs - 8t)(rs - 3t)$

12. $a^2 + 16ab + 39b^2 = (a + 3b)(a + 13b)$

13. $c^2 - 16cd + 48d^2 = (c - 4d)(c - 12d)$

14. $x^2 - 22ax - 135a^2 = (x - 27a)(x + 5a)$

15. $c^2 - 34cx - 440x^2 = (c - 44x)(c + 10x)$

16. $m^2 - 5.2m + 1.0 = (m - .2)(m - 5)$

17. $z^2 + 1.5z + .5 = (z + 1)(z + .5)$

18. $x^2 + \frac{3}{4}x + \frac{1}{8} = (x + \frac{1}{2})(x + \frac{1}{4})$

19. $x^2 + 3x + \frac{9}{4} = (x + \frac{3}{2})^2$

20. $y^2 - .10y - .02 = (y + .1)(y - .2)$

II

1. $x^2 + 6x + 9 = (x + 3)^2$

2. $m^2 + 4mn + 4n^2 = (m + 2n)^2$

3. $r^2s^2 - 8rs + 16 = (rs - 4)^2$

4. $16p^2 - 24p + 9 = (4p - 3)^2$

5. $4x^4 + 4x^2y^2 + y^4 = (2x^2 + y^2)^2$

6. $9 + 42b^3 + 49b^6 = (3 + 7b^3)^2$

7. $9a^2 - 60ab + 100b^2 = (3a - 10b)^2$

8. $1 - 6m^4 + 9m^8 = (1 - 3m^4)^2$

9. $4x^2y^2 - 20xy + 25 = (2xy - 5)^2$

10. $49x^2 + 70x + 25 = (7x + 5)^2$

11. $x^2 - 20xy + 100y^2 = (x - 10y)^2$

12. $49a^4 + 112a^2 + 64 = (7a^2 + 8)^2$

13. $16b^2 - 16bc + 4c^2 = 4(4b^2 - 4bc + c^2) = 4(2b - c)^2$

14. $25x^2 + 70xy + 49y^2 = (5x + 7y)^2$

15. $x^2 - \frac{2}{3}x + \frac{1}{9} = (x - \frac{1}{3})^2$

16. $a^2 - \frac{2}{5}a + \frac{1}{25} = (a - \frac{1}{5})^2$

17. $9b^2 - \frac{6}{5}b + \frac{1}{25} = (3b - \frac{1}{5})^2$

18. $16m^2 - \frac{8}{3}mn + \frac{1}{9}n^2 = (4m - \frac{1}{3}n)^2$

Exercises 7.10 Pages 148-149

1. $x^2 - 4$
$= (x + 2)(x - 2)$

2. $a^2 - 9$
$= (a + 3)(a - 3)$

3. $x^2 - y^2$
$= (x + y)(x - y)$

4. $z^2 - 4$
$= (z + 2)(z - 2)$

5. $c^2 - d^2$
$= (c + d)(c - d)$

6. $a^2 - 16$
$= (a + 4)(a - 4)$

7. $x^2 - m^2$
$= (x + m)(x - m)$

8. $25 - c^2$
$= (5 + c)(5 - c)$

9. $x^4 - 49$
$= (x^2 + 7)(x^2 - 7)$

10. $a^4 - 81$
$= (a^2 + 9)(a^2 - 9)$
$= (a^2 + 9)(a + 3)(a - 3)$

11. $25x^2 - 1$
$= (5x + 1)(5x - 1)$

12. $b^2c^2 - 16$
$= (bc + 4)(bc - 4)$

13. $a^2x^2 - 4c^2$
$= (ax + 2c)(ax - 2c)$

14. $25 - 9x^2$
$= (5 + 3x)(5 - 3x)$

15. $9b^2 - c^2d^2$
$= (3b + cd)(3b - cd)$

16. $a^{16} - b^8 = (a^8 + b^4)(a^8 - b^4) = (a^8 + b^4)(a^4 + b^2)(a^4 - b^2)$
$= (a^8 + b^4)(a^4 + b^2)(a^2 + b)(a^2 - b)$

17. $4x^2 - 25y^2$
$= (2x + 5y)(2x - 5y)$

18. $9a^2 - 49b^2$
$= (3a + 7b)(3a - 7b)$

19. $m^4 - 16n^4$
$= (m^2 + 4n^2)(m^2 - 4n^2)$
$= (m^2 + 4n^2)(m + 2n)(m - 2n)$

20. $16a^4 - 81b^4$
$= (4a^2 + 9b^2)(4a^2 - 9b^2)$
$= (4a^2 + 9b^2)(2a + 3b)(2a - 3b)$

21. $x^3 - xy^2$
$= x(x^2 - y^2)$
$= x(x + y)(x - y)$

22. $8s^2 - 2t^2$
$= 2(4s^2 - t^2)$
$= 2(2s + t)(2s - t)$

23. $169 - a^2b^2$
$= (13 + ab)(13 - ab)$

24. $2x^4 - 2y^4$
$= 2(x^4 - y^4)$
$= 2(x^2 + y^2)(x^2 - y^2)$
$= 2(x^2 + y^2)(x + y)(x - y)$

25. $121b^2 - a^2c^2$
$= (11b + ac)(11b - ac)$

26. $400x^2 - 36y^2$
$= 4(100x^2 - 9y^2)$
$= 4(10x + 3y)(10x - 3y)$

27. $144m^2 - 16n^2$
$= 16(9m^2 - n^2)$
$= 16(3m + n)(3m - n)$

28. $18c^2 - 50$
$= 2(9c^2 - 25)$
$= 2(3c + 5)(3c - 5)$

29. $3x^4 - 3y^6$
$= 3(x^4 - y^6)$
$= 3(x^2 + y^3)(x^2 - y^3)$

30. $36a^4 - 225$
$= 9(4a^4 - 25)$
$= 9(2a^2 + 5)(2a^2 - 5)$

31. $x^4y^4 - 256$
$= (x^2y^2 + 16)(x^2y^2 - 16)$
$= (x^2y^2 + 16)(xy + 4)(xy - 4)$

32. $3m^5 - 3m$
$= 3m(m^4 - 1)$
$= 3m(m^2 + 1)(m^2 - 1)$
$= 3m(m^2 + 1)(m + 1)(m - 1)$

33. $4a^4 - 4b^4$
$= 4(a^4 - b^4)$
$= 4(a^2 + b^2)(a^2 - b^2)$
$= 4(a^2 + b^2)(a + b)(a - b)$

34. $5x^8 - 5$
$= 5(x^8 - 1)$
$= 5(x^4 + 1)(x^4 - 1)$
$= 5(x^4 + 1)(x^2 + 1)(x^2 - 1)$
$= 5(x^4 + 1)(x^2 + 1)(x + 1)(x - 1)$

35. $2x^8 - 2y^8$
$= 2(x^8 - y^8)$
$= 2(x^4 + y^4)(x^4 - y^4)$
$= 2(x^4 + y^4)(x^2 + y^2)(x^2 - y^2)$
$= 2(x^4 + y^4)(x^2 + y^2)(x + y)(x - y)$

36. $a2 - \frac{1}{9}$
$= (a + \frac{1}{3})(a - \frac{1}{3})$

37. $x^2 - .01$
$= (x + .1)(x - .1)$

38. $x^4 - \frac{1}{16}$
$= (x^2 + \frac{1}{4})(x^2 - \frac{1}{4})$
$= (x^2 + \frac{1}{4})(x + \frac{1}{2})(x - \frac{1}{2})$

39. Answer is given in text.

40. $x^{4a} - y^{4b}$
$= (x^{2a} + y^{2b})(x^{2a} - y^{2b})$
$= (x^{2a} + y^{2b})(x^a + y^b)(x^a - y^b)$

41. $4a^2 - .25$
$= (2a + .5)(2a - .5)$

<u>Exercises 7.11</u> Pages 149-150

1. $a^2 - (b + c)^2$
$= [a + (b + c)][a - (b + c)]$
$= (a + b + c)(a - b - c)$

2. $a^2 - (a + b)^2$
$= [a - (a + b)][a + (a + b)]$
$= (a - a - b)(a + a + b)$
$= -b(2a + b)$

3. $b^2 - (2a + b)^2$
$= [b - (2a + b)][b + (2a + b)]$
$= (b - 2a - b)(b + 2a + b)$
$= -2a(2a + 2b)$
$= -4a(a + b)$

4. $4c^2 - (b + c)^2$
$= [2c + (b + c)][2c - (b + c)]$
$= (2c + b + c)(2c - b - c)$
$= (3c + b)(c - b)$

5. $9b^2 - (a - x)^2$
$= [3b + (a - x)][3b - (a - x)]$
$= (3b + a - x)(3b - a + x)$

6. $9a^2 - (2a - 5)^2$
$= [3a + (2a - 5)][3a - (2a - 5)]$
$= (3a + 2a - 5)(3a - 2a + 5)$
$= (5a - 5)(a + 5)$
$= 5(a - 1)(a + 5)$

7. $x^4 - (3x^2 - 2y)^2$
$= [x^2 + (3x^2 - 2y)][x^2 - (3x^2 - 2y)]$
$= (x^2 + 3x^2 - 2y)(x^2 - 3x^2 + 2y)$
$= (4x^2 - 2y)(-2x^2 + 2y)$
$= (2)(2x^2 - y)(-2)(x^2 - y)$
$= -4(2x^2 - y)(x^2 - y)$

8. $49a^2 - (5a - 4b)^2$
$= [7a + (5a - 4b)][7a - (5a - 4b)]$
$= (7a + 5a - 4b)(7a - 5a + 4b)$
$= (12a - 4b)(2a + 4b)$
$= (4)(3a - b)(2)(a + 2b)$
$= 8(3a - b)(a + 2b)$

9. $(2a + 3b)^2 - (a + b)^2$
$= [(2a + 3b) + (a + b)][(2a + 3b) - (a + b)]$
$= (2a + 3b + a + b)(2a + 3b - a - b)$
$= (3a + 4b)(a + 2b)$

10. $(2x + 5)^2 - (5 - 3x)^2$
$= [(2x + 5) - (5 - 3x)][(2x + 5) + (5 - 3x)]$
$= (2x + 5 - 5 + 3x)(2x + 5 + 5 - 3x)$
$= 5x(10 - x)$

11. $a^2 - x^2 - 9y^2 + 6xy$
$= a^2 - (x^2 - 6xy + 9y^2)$
$= a^2 - (x - 3y)^2$
$= [a + (x - 3y)][a - (x - 3y)]$
$= (a + x - 3y)(a - x + 3y)$

12. $9a^2 + 4bc - 4c^2 - b^2$
$= 9a^2 - (b^2 - 4bc + 4c^2)$
$= 9a^2 - (b - 2c)^2$
$= [3a + (b - 2c)][3a - (b - 2c)]$
$= (3a + b - 2c)(3a - b + 2c)$

13. $4x^2 + y^2 - 4xy - a^2$
$= (4x^2 - 4xy + y^2) - a^2$
$= (2x - y)^2 - a^2$
$= (2x - y + a)(2x - y - a)$

14. $r^2 - s^2 - 25 + 10s$
$= r^2 - (s^2 - 10s + 25)$
$= r^2 - (s - 5)^2$
$= [r + (s - 5)][r - (s - 5)]$
$= (r + s - 5)(r - s + 5)$

15. $x^2 + 6x - 16y^2 + 9$
$= x^2 + 6x + 9 - 16y^2$
$= (x + 3)^2 - (4y)^2$
$= (x + 3 + 4y)(x + 3 - 4y)$

16. $x^2 + 4x - y^2 + 4$
$= x^2 + 4x + 4 - y^2$
$= (x + 2)^2 - y^2$
$= (x + 2 + y)(x + 2 - y)$

<u>Exercises 7.12</u> Page 151

1. $8x^2 + 56x + 96$
$= 8(x^2 + 7x + 12)$
$= 8(x + 3)(x + 4)$

2. $15y^2 - 135$
$= 15(y^2 - 9)$
$= 15(y + 3)(y - 3)$

3. $ab^2 - ab - 12a$
$= a(b^2 - b - 12)$
$= a(b - 4)(b + 3)$

4. $3x^2 + 21x + 36$
$= 3(x^2 + 7x + 12)$
$= 3(x + 3)(x + 4)$

5. $12x^2 - 12y^2$
$= 12(x^2 - y^2)$
$= 12(x + y)(x - y)$

6. $45 + 6a - 3a^2$
$= 3(15 + 2a - a^2)$
$= 3(5 - a)(3 + a)$

7. $5a^2 + 10ab + 5b^2$
$= 5(a^2 + 2ab + b^2)$
$= 5(a + b)^2$

8. $2x^4 - 2y^4$
$= 2(x^4 - y^4)$
$= 2(x^2 + y^2)(x^2 - y^2)$
$= 2(x^2 + y^2)(x + y)(x - y)$

9. $2a^8 - 2b^8$
$= 2(a^8 - b^8)$
$= 2(a^4 + b^4)(a^4 - b^4)$
$= 2(a^4 + b^4)(a^2 + b^2)(a^2 - b^2)$
$= 2(a^4 + b^4)(a^2 + b^2)(a + b)(a - b)$

10. $m^4 - 1$
$= (m^2 + 1)(m^2 - 1)$
$= (m^2 + 1)(m + 1)(m - 1)$

11. $2m^2n + 4mn^2 + n^3$
$= n(2m^2 + 4mn + n^2)$

12. $25x^2 + 70x + 49$
$= (5x + 7)^2$

13. $3x^2 - 12$
$= 3(x^2 - 4)$
$= 3(x + 2)(x - 2)$

14. $m^2 - 4$
$= (m + 2)(m - 2)$

15. $50 - 2x^2$
$= 2(25 - x^2)$
$= 2(5 + x)(5 - x)$

16. $11a^4 - 11b^4$
$= 11(a^4 - b^4)$
$= 11(a^2 + b^2)(a^2 - b^2)$
$= 11(a^2 + b^2)(a + b)(a - b)$

17. $n^2x^2 - 11nxy + 30y^2$
$= (nx - 6y)(nx - 5y)$

18. $3x^{10} - 33b^2x^5 + 72b^4$
$= 3(x^{10} - 11b^2x^5 + 24b^4)$
$= 3(x^5 - 8b^2)(x^5 - 3b^2)$

19. $5x^2 - 45x - 110$
$= 5(x^2 - 9x - 22)$
$= 5(x - 11)(x + 2)$

20. $y^4 - 2y^2 + 1$
$= (y^2 - 1)(y^2 - 1)$
$= (y + 1)^2(y - 1)^2$

21. $120x^4 - 120y^4$
$= 120(x^4 - y^4)$
$= 120(x^2 + y^2)(x^2 - y^2)$
$= 120(x^2 + y^2)(x + y)(x - y)$

22. $13a^4 - 13b^4$
$= 13(a^4 - b^4)$
$= 13(a^2 + b^2)(a^2 - b^2)$
$= 13(a^2 + b^2)(a + b)(a - b)$

23. $8x^2 - 48ax + 40a^2$
$= 8(x^2 - 6ax + 5a^2)$
$= 8(x - 5a)(x - a)$

24. $9x^2 + 45ax + 54a^2$
$= 9(x^2 + 5ax + 6a^2)$
$= 9(x + 3a)(x + 2a)$

25. $3m^4 - 12$
$= 3(m^4 - 4)$
$= 3(m^2 + 2)(m^2 - 2)$

26. $2m^4 - 128$
$= 2(m^4 - 64)$
$= 2(m^2 + 8)(m^2 - 8)$

27. $2a^4 - 4a^2 + 2$
$= 2(a^4 - 2a^2 + 1)$
$= 2(a^2 - 1)(a^2 - 1)$
$= 2(a + 1)^2 (a - 1)^2$

28. $7y^2 - 28by - 84b^2$
$= 7(y^2 - 4by - 12b^2)$
$= 7(y - 6b)(y + 2b)$

29. $10b^2 + 10b - 120$
$= 10(b^2 + b - 12)$
$= 10(b + 4)(b - 3)$

30. $5a^4b^4 - 5c^4d^4$
$= 5(a^4b^4 - c^4d^4)$
$= 5(a^2b^2 + c^2d^2)(a^2b^2 - c^2d^2)$
$= 5(a^2b^2 + c^2d^2)(ab + cd)(ab - cd)$

<u>Review Exercises</u> Pages 152-154

1. $8x^3 - 2x^2$
$= 2x^2(4x - 1)$

2. $c^2 - 4$
$= (c + 2)(c - 2)$

3. $4a^2 - 4c^2$
$= 4(a^2 - c^2)$
$= 4(a + c)(a - c)$

4. $3x^5 - 3x$
$= 3x(x^4 - 1)$
$= 3x(x^2 + 1)(x^2 - 1)$
$= 3x(x^2 + 1)(x + 1)(x - 1)$

5. $x^2 - 9$
$= (x + 3)(x - 3)$

6. $x^3 - x$
$= x(x^2 - 1)$
$= x(x + 1)(x - 1)$

7. $y^{2a} - 1$
$= (y^a + 1)(y^a - 1)$

8. $a^2x - x$
$= x(a^2 - 1)$
$= x(a + 1)(a - 1)$

9. Answer is given in text.

10. $y^{2n+1} - y$
$= y(y^{2n} - 1)$
$= y(y^n + 1)(y^n - 1)$

11. $x^4 - y^4$
$= (x^2 + y^2)(x^2 - y^2)$
$= (x^2 + y^2)(x + y)(x - y)$

12. $a^2 - .04b^2$
$= (a + .2b)(a - .2b)$

13. $d^3 - 9d$
$= d(d^2 - 9)$
$= d(d + 3)(d - 3)$

14. $a^3 - a^2y$
$= a^2(a - y)$

15. $4x^3 - 4x$
$= 4x(x^2 - 1)$
$= 4x(x + 1)(x - 1)$

16. $x^2 - 2x + 1$
$= (x - 1)^2$

17. $a^2x - 2a^2x^2$
$= a^2x(1 - 2x)$

18. $x^2 + 3x + 2$
$= (x + 2)(x + 1)$

19. $a^2 - (b + c)^2$
$= [a + (b + c)][a - (b + c)]$
$= (a + b + c)(a - b - c)$

20. $x^2 - x - 6$
$= (x + 2)(x - 3)$

21. $x^2 + x - 6$
$= (x + 3)(x - 2)$

22. $x^2 + x - 2$
$= (x + 2)(x - 1)$

23. $x^2 - 2.9x - .3$
$= (x - 3)(x + .1)$

24. $5a^2b^2 + 5a^4b^4$
$= 5a^2b^2(1 + a^2b^2)$

25. $x^2 + .5x + .06$
$= (x + .3)(x + .2)$

26. $(x - y)^2 - z^2$
$= [(x - y) + z][(x - y) - z]$
$= (x - y + z)(x - y - z)$

27. $4a^2 - 9b^2$
$= (2a + 3b)(2a - 3b)$

28. $x^{2a} - y^{2a}$
$= (x^a + y^a)(x^a - y^a)$

29. $a^{4n} - b^2$
$= (a^{2n} + b)(a^{2n} - b)$

30. $x^{2n+2} - 1$
$= x^{2(n+1)} - 1$
$= (x^{n+1})^2 - 1$
$= (x^{n+1} + 1)(x^{n+1} - 1)$

31. $8x^4y^4 + 10x^3y^3$
$= 2x^3y^3(4xy + 5)$

32. $x^2 + 2xy + y^2$
$= (x + y)2$

33. $x + 3xy + 2y^2$
$= (x + y)(x + 2y)$

34. $3 + 4x + x^2$
$= (3 + x)(1 + x)$

35. $b^2 - 1.96$
$(b + 1.4)(b - 1.4)$

36. $a^4 - 256$
$= (a^2 + 16)(a^2 - 16)$
$= (a^2 + 16)(a + 4)(a - 4)$

37. $450 - 2a^2$
$= 2(225 - a^2)$
$= 2(15 + a)(15 - a)$

38. $2x^2 + x - 1$
$= (2x - 1)(x + 1)$

39. $x^2 + 9x - 90$
$= (x + 15)(x - 6)$

40. $3x^2 - 2x - 8$
$= (3x + 4)(x - 2)$

41. $15 + 6x - 9x^2$
$= 3(5 + 2x - 3x^2)$
$= 3(5 - 3x)(1 + x)$

42. $17 - 16a - a^2$
$= (17 + a)(1 - a)$

43. $a^2b^2 + ab - 56$
$= (ab + 8)(ab - 7)$

44. $6x + 5x^2 - x^3$
$= x(6 + 5x - x^2)$
$= x(6 - x)(1 + x)$

45. $a^2x^2 - 4ax + 3$
$= (ax - 3)(ax - 1)$

46. $x^2 - ax - 72a^2$
$= (x - 9a)(x + 8a)$

47. $n^2 - an - 90a^2$
$= (n - 10a)(n + 9a)$

48. $x^2 - xy - 132y^2$
$= (x - 12y)(x + 11y)$

49. $3x^2 + 30x + 27$
$= 3(x^2 + 10x + 9)$
$= 3(x + 9)(x + 1)$

50. $6x^2 - 19x + 15$
$= (3x - 5)(2x - 3)$

51. $4a - 3ax - ax^2$
$= -ax^2 - 3ax + 4a$
$= -a(x^2 + 3x - 4)$
$= -a(x + 4)(x - 1)$

52. $x^{2n} + 2x^ny^p + y^{2p}$
$= (x^n + y^p)^2$

53. $b^4c - 13b^2c + 42c$
$= c(b^4 - 13b^2 + 42)$
$= c(b^2 - 7)(b^2 - 6)$

54. $2x^3 + 28x^2 + 66x$
$= 2x(x^2 + 14x + 33)$
$= 2x(x + 11)(x + 3)$

55. $y^2 + 16ay - 36a^2$
$= (y + 18a)(y - 2a)$

56. $ax^2 + 10ax - 39a$
$= a(x^2 + 10x - 39)$
$= a(x + 13)(x - 3)$

57. $7x^2 - 77xy - 84y^2$
$= 7(x^2 - 11xy - 12y^2)$
$= 7(x - 12y)(x + y)$

58. $y^2 - 25xy + 136x^2$
$= (y - 17x)(y - 8x)$

59. $a^2z^4 + 2a^2z^2 + a^2$
$= a^2(z^4 + 2z^2 + 1)$
$= a^2(z^2 + 1)^2$

60. $8x^4 - 6x^2 - 35$
$= (4x^2 + 7)(2x^2 - 5)$

61. $77 - 30x^2 - 37x$
$= 77 - 37x - 30x^2$
$= (7 + 3x)(11 - 10x)$

62. $5x^8 + 10x^4 - 15$
$= 5(x^8 + 2x^4 - 3)$
$= 5(x^4 + 3)(x^4 - 1)$
$= 5(x^4 + 3)(x^2 + 1)(x^2 - 1)$
$= 5(x^4 + 3)(x^2 + 1)(x + 1)(x - 1)$

63. $5x^2 - 26xy + 5y^2$
$= (5x - y)(x - 5y)$

64. $8a^2 - 21ab - 9b^2$
$= (8a + 3b)(a - 3b)$

65. $a^2 + b^2 - c^2 - 2ab$
$= a^2 - 2ab + b^2 - c^2$
$= (a - b)^2 - c^2$
$= [(a - b) + c][(a - b) - c]$
$= (a - b + c)(a - b - c)$

66. $60a^2 + 8ax - 3x^2$
$= (10a + 3x)(6a - x)$

67. $10a^2c + 33ac - 7c$
$= c(10a^2 + 33a - 7)$
$= c(2a + 7)(5a - 1)$

68. $25x^2 + 60xy + 36y^2$
$= (5x + 6y)^2$

69. $6ax^2 + 5axy - 6ay^2$
$= a(6x^2 + 5xy - 6y^2)$
$= a(3x - 2y)(2x + 3y)$

70. $25x^2 - 9y^2 - 24yz - 16z^2$
$= 25x^2 - (9y^2 + 24yz + 16z^2)$
$= (5x)^2 - (3y + 4z)^2$
$= [5x + (3y + 4z)][5x - (3y + 4z)]$
$= (5x + 3y + 4z)(5x - 3y - 4z)$

71. $16 - y^2$
$= (4 + y)(4 - y)$

72. $a^2 - 16d^2$
$= (a + 4d)(a - 4d)$

73. $x^2 + 5xy$
$= x(x + 5y)$

74. $9r^2 - 25s^2$
$= (3r + 5s)(3r - 5s)$

75. $x^2 - 6x + 5$
$= (x - 5)(x - 1)$

76. $r^2 + 6r + 9$
$= (r + 3)^2$

77. $4a^{2n} - 16b^2$
$= 4(a^{2n} - 4b^2)$
$= 4(a^n + 2b)(a^n - 2b)$

78. $x^4 + 2x^2 + 1$
$= (x^2 + 1)^2$

79. $x^2y^2 - 64a^2$
$= (xy + 8a)(xy - 8a)$

80. $m^2 + 8m + 7$
$= (m + 7)(m + 1)$

81. $(y^2 + 4)^2 - 16y^2$
$= (y^2 + 4)^2 - (4y)^2$
$= [(y^2 + 4) + 4y][(y^2 + 4) - 4y]$
$= (y^2 + 4y + 4)(y^2 - 4y + 4)$
$= (y + 2)^2(y - 2)^2$

82. $(a - b)^2 - (c - d)^2$
$= [(a - b) + (c - d)][(a - b) - (c - d)]$
$= (a - b + c - d)(a - b - c + d)$

83. $x^2 + 20xy + 100y^2$
$= (x + 10y)^2$

84. $b^8 - 81$
$= (b^4 + 9)(b^4 - 9)$
$= (b^4 + 9)(b^2 + 3)(b^2 - 3)$

85. $x^4y^8 - z^8$
$= (x^2y^4 + z^4)(x^2y^4 - z^4)$
$= (x^2y^4 + z^4)(xy^2 + z^2)(xy^2 - z^2)$

86. $3x^3 - 12x$
$= 3x(x^2 - 4)$
$= 3x(x + 2)(x - 2)$

87. $x^4y - y^5$
$= y(x^4 - y^4)$
$= y(x^2 + y^2)(x^2 - y^2)$
$= y(x^2 + y^2)(x + y)(x - y)$

88. $x^2 + x - 6$
$= (x + 3)(x - 2)$

89. $z^2 - 8z - 9$
$= (z - 9)(z + 1)$

90. $9 + 12d + 4d^2$
$= (3 + 2d)^2$

91. $z^2 + bz - 12b^2$
$= (z + 4b)(z - 3b)$

92. $(x^2 + y^2)^2 - (y^2 - z^2)^2$
$= [(x^2 + y^2) + (y^2 - z^2)][(x^2 + y^2) - (y^2 - z^2)]$
$= (x^2 + 2y^2 - z^2)(x^2 + z^2)$

93. $c^2 - 17c + 72$
$= (c - 9)(c - 8)$

94. $4a^2 + 32a + 39$
$= (2a + 3)(2a + 13)$

95. $a^2 - 6ad - 72d^2$
$= (a - 12d)(a + 6d)$

96. $16a^2 + 8ab - 15b^2$
$= (4a - 3b)(4a + 5b)$

97. $9x^4 + 12x^2y^2 + 4y^4$
$= (3x^2 + 2y^2)^2$

98. $3a^4 - 30a^2b^2 + 75b^4$
$= 3(a^4 - 10a^2b^2 + 25b^4)$
$= 3(a^2 - 5b^2)^2$

99. $28x - 15 - 12x^2$
$= -12x^2 + 28x - 15$
$= -(12x^2 - 28x + 15)$
$= -(6x - 5)(2x - 3)$

100. $(m - 2a)^2 - 4(a + b)^2$
$= (m - 2a)^2 - [2(a + b)]^2$
$= [(m - 2a) + 2(a + b)][(m - 2a) - 2(a + b)]$
$= (m - 2a + 2a + 2b)(m - 2a - 2a - 2b)$
$= (m + 2b)(m - 4a - 2b)$

101. $12a^2 - 11ad - 15d^2$
$= (3a - 5d)(4a + 3d)$

102. $a^2 + 2ac - b^2 + c^2$
$= a^2 + 2ac + c^2 - b^2$
$= (a + c)^2 - b^2$
$= (a + c + b)(a + c - b)$
$= (a + b + c)(a - b + c)$

103. $5 \cdot 110^2 - 5 \cdot 10^2$
$= 5(110^2 - 10^2)$
$= 5(110 + 10)(110 - 10)$

104. $3x^2 - 3x + \frac{9}{16}$
$= (3x - \frac{3}{4})(x - \frac{3}{4})$ or $3(x - \frac{1}{4})(x - \frac{3}{4})$

105. $(2a + 3b)^2 - 4c(2a + 3b) + 4c^2$
$= [(2a + 3b) - 2c][(2a + 3b) - 2c]$
$= (2a + 3b - 2c)^2$

106. $a^2(2a - 3b) + b^2(3b - 2a)$
$= a^2(2a - 3b) - b^2(2a - 3b)$
$= (2a - 3b)(a^2 - b^2)$
$= (2a - 3b)(a + b)(a - b)$

107. $23 \cdot 15.5 + 23 \cdot 11.5 - 23 \cdot 2$
$= 23(15.5 + 11.5 - 2)$

Exercises 7.14 Page 155

The check is left for the teacher.

1. $x^2 + 8x = 20$
$x^2 + 8x - 20 = 0$
$(x + 10)(x - 2) = 0$

$x + 10 = 0$ $x = -10$ $x - 2 = 0$ $x = 2$

2. $3z^2 = 16 - 2z$
$3z^2 + 2z - 16 = 0$
$(3z + 8)(z - 2) = 0$

$3z + 8 = 0$ $3z = -8$ $z = -\frac{8}{3}$ $z - 2 = 0$ $z = 2$

3. $y^2 - 7y - 18 = 0$
$(y - 9)(y + 2) = 0$

$y - 9 = 0$ $y = 9$ $y + 2 = 0$ $y = -2$

4. $4x^2 + 12x + 5 = 0$
$(2x + 5)(2x + 1) = 0$

$2x + 5 = 0$ $2x = -5$ $x = -\frac{5}{2}$ $2x + 1 = 0$ $2x = -1$ $x = -\frac{1}{2}$

5. $x^4 - 25x^2 + 144 = 0$
$(x^2 - 16)(x^2 - 9) = 0$
$(x + 4)(x - 4)(x + 3)(x - 3) = 0$

$x + 4 = 0$ $x = -4$ $x - 4 = 0$ $x = 4$ $x + 3 = 0$ $x = -3$ $x - 3 = 0$ $x = 3$

6. $y^2 - 25 = 0$
$(y + 5)(y - 5) = 0$

$y + 5 = 0$ $y = -5$ $y - 5 = 0$ $y = 5$

7. $x^2 + 7x = 0$
$x(x + 7) = 0$

$x = 0$ $x + 7 = 0$ $x = -7$

8. $x^4 = 13x^2 - 36$
$x^4 - 13x^2 + 36 = 0$
$(x^2 - 9)(x^2 - 4) = 0$
$(x + 3)(x - 3)(x + 2)(x - 2) = 0$

$x + 3 = 0$ $x = -3$ $x - 3 = 0$ $x = 3$ $x + 2 = 0$ $x = -2$ $x - 2 = 0$ $x = 2$

9.
$$x^3 - 5x^2 = 14x$$
$$x^3 - 5x^2 - 14x = 0$$
$$x(x^2 - 5x - 14) = 0$$
$$x(x - 7)(x + 2) = 0$$

$x = 0$ $\quad x - 7 = 0$, $x = 7$ $\quad x + 2 = 0$, $x = -2$

10.
$$(x - 2)(x + 3) + (x - 3)(x + 2) = 4(x + 1)$$
$$x^2 + x - 6 + x^2 - x - 6 = 4x + 4$$
$$2x^2 - 12 = 4x + 4$$
$$2x^2 - 4x - 16 = 0$$
$$2(x^2 - 2x - 8) = 0$$
$$2(x - 4)(x + 2) = 0$$

$2 \neq 0$ $\quad x - 4 = 0$, $x = 4$ $\quad x + 2 = 0$, $x = -2$

Word Problems Page 155

1. 1. let x = one number $\quad$ 9 or -6
   2. x - 3 = other number $\quad$ 6 or -9
   3. sum of squares = sum of squares
   $$x^2 + (x - 3)^2 = 117$$
   4.
   $$x^2 + x^2 - 6x + 9 = 117$$
   $$2x^2 - 6x - 108 = 0$$
   $$2(x^2 - 3x - 54) = 0$$
   $$2(x - 9)(x + 6) = 0$$

   $x - 9 = 0$, $x = 9$ $\quad x + 6 = 0$, $x = -6$

   $x = 9, -6$

   5. $(9)^2 + (6)^2 = 117$ ✓
   $(-6)^2 + (-9)^2 = 117$ ✓

2. 1. let w = width $\quad$ 5 ft.
   2. 3w + 1 = length $\quad$ 16 ft.
   3. area = area
   $$w(3w + 1) = 80$$
   4.
   $$3w^2 + w = 80$$
   $$3w^2 + w - 80 = 0$$
   $$(3w + 16)(w - 5) = 0$$

   $3w + 16 = 0$, $3w = -16$, ~~$w = -5\frac{1}{3}$~~ $\quad w - 5 = 0$, $w = 5$

   Reject since width cannot be negative.

   5. 16
   x5
   80 ✓

3. 1. let x = first consecutive number $\quad$ 8 or -5
   2. x + 1 = second consecutive number $\quad$ 9 or -4
   x + 2 = third consecutive number $\quad$ 10 or -3
   3.
   $$2x^2 - 38 = (x + 1)(x + 2)$$
   4.
   $$2x^2 - 38 = x^2 + 3x + 2$$
   $$x^2 - 3x - 40 = 0$$
   $$(x - 8)(x + 5) = 0$$

   $x - 8 = 0$, $x = 8$ $\quad x + 5 = 0$, $x = -5$

   $x = 8, -5$

   5. $2(8)^2 = 128$
   $(9)(10) = \underline{-90}$
   38 ✓
   $2(-5)^2 = 50$
   $(-4)(-3) = \underline{-12}$
   38 ✓

4\. 1. let x = first odd positive number <u>11</u>
2\. $x + 2$ = next consecutive odd number <u>13</u>

3\. $x^2 - 7(x + 2) = 30$
4\. $x^2 - 7x - 14 = 30$
$x^2 - 7x - 44 = 0$
$(x - 11)(x + 4) = 0$

$x - 11 = 0$ $x + 4 = 0$ Reject since -4
$x = 11$ ~~$x = -4$~~ is not positive.

5\. $(11)^2 - 7(13) = 30$
$121 - 91 = 30$
$30 = 30$ ✓

5\. 1. let x = the number <u>-9</u> or <u>8</u>
2\.

3\. $x^2 + x = 72$
4\. $x^2 + x - 72 = 0$
$(x + 9)(x - 8) = 0$

$x + 9 = 0$ $x - 8 = 0$
$x = -9$ $x = 8$
$x = -9, 8$

5\. 81 64
(+) -9 +8
72 ✓ 72 ✓

6\. 1. let x = the number <u>-3</u> or <u>3</u>
2\. $2x$ = the number twice as large

3\. $x^2 + (2x)^2 = 45$
4\. $x^2 + 4x^2 = 45$
$5x^2 = 45$
$5x^2 - 45 = 0$
$5(x^2 - 9) = 0$
$5(x + 3)(x - 3) = 0$

$x + 3 = 0$ $x - 3 = 0$
$x = -3$ $x = 3$
$x = \pm 3$

5\. $(-3)^2 + (-6)^2 = 45$
$(3)^2 + (6)^2 = 45$
$45 = 45$

7\. 1. let t = time driven <u>4 hr.</u>
2\. $t + 48$ = rate driven <u>52 mph</u>
3\. distance = distance
$t(t + 48) = 208$
4\. $t^2 + 48t = 208$
$t^2 + 48t - 208 = 0$
$(t + 52)(t - 4) = 0$

$t + 52 = 0$ $t - 4 = 0$
~~$t = -52$~~ $t = 4$

Reject since the
time is negative.

5\. 52
x 4
208 ✓

8. 1. let c = cost of goods <u>$30</u> or <u>$70</u>
2.
3. $c - 21 = \frac{c}{100}(c)$
4. $c - 21 = \frac{c^2}{100}$

$\frac{c^2}{100} - c + 21 = 0$

$c^2 - 100c + 2100 = 0$

$(c - 70)(c - 30) = 0$

$c - 70 = 0 \qquad c - 30 = 0$

$c = 70 \qquad c = 30$

5. $\begin{array}{r} 30 \\ -21 \\ \hline 9 \end{array}$ $\frac{9}{30} = \frac{3}{10} =$ 30% which is the same number as $30 ✓

$\begin{array}{r} 70 \\ -21 \\ \hline 49 \end{array}$ $\frac{49}{70} = \frac{7}{10} =$ 70% which is the same number as $70 ✓

9. 1. let x = first consecutive integer $\frac{-7}{-6}$ or $\frac{6}{7}$
2. x + 1 = second consecutive integer
3. $[x + (x + 1)]^2 - [x^2 + (x + 1)^2] = 84$
4. $(2x + 1)^2 - [x^2 + x^2 + 2x + 1] = 84$

$4x^2 + 4x + 1 - [2x^2 + 2x + 1] = 84$

$4x^2 + 4x + 1 - 2x^2 - 2x - 1 - 84 = 0$

$2x^2 + 2x - 84 = 0 \qquad x + 7 = 0 \qquad x - 6 = 0$

$2(x^2 + x - 42) = 0 \qquad x = -7 \qquad x = 6$

$2(x + 7)(x - 6) = 0 \qquad x = -7, 6$

5. $\begin{array}{r} -7 \\ -6 \\ \hline -13 \end{array}$ $\begin{array}{r} (-7)^2 = 49 \\ (-6)^2 = 36 \\ \hline 85 \end{array}$ $\begin{array}{r} (-13)^2 - 85 = 84 \\ 169 - 85 = 84 \\ 84 = 84 ✓ \end{array}$ $\begin{array}{r} 6 \\ 7 \\ \hline 13 \end{array}$ $\begin{array}{r} (6)^2 = 36 \\ (7)^2 = 49 \\ \hline 85 \end{array}$ $\begin{array}{r} (13)^2 - 85 = 84 \\ 169 - 85 = 84 \\ 84 = 84 ✓ \end{array}$

10. 1. let x = the short leg <u>3</u>
2. x + 1 = the longer leg <u>4</u>
x + 2 = the hypotenuse <u>5</u>
3. $x^2 + (x + 1)^2 = (x + 2)^2$
4. $x^2 + x^2 + 2x + 1 = x^2 + 4x + 4$

$2x^2 + 2x + 1 = x^2 + 4x + 4$

$x^2 - 2x - 3 = 0$

$(x - 3)(x + 1) = 0$

$x - 3 = 0 \qquad x + 1 = 0$

$x = 3 \qquad$ ~~x = -1~~ Reject since the length of the leg of a triangle cannot be negative.

5. $(3)^2 + (4)^2 = (5)^2$

$9 + 16 = 25$

$25 = 25$ ✓

11. 1. let s = length of a side <u>4 ft.</u>
2.
3. area = perimeter

$s^2 = 4s$

4. $s^2 - 4s = 0$

$s(s - 4) = 0$

~~s = 0~~ $\qquad s - 4 = 0$

$s = 4$

Reject since the length of a side would not be zero.

5. $(4)^2 = 4(4)$

$16 = 16$ ✓

Test A — Special Products Page 156

1. $(x + 2)(x + 3)$
$= x^2 + 5x + 6$

2. $(y - 6)(y - 4)$
$= y^2 - 10y + 24$

3. $(p + 7)^2$
$= p^2 + 14p + 49$

4. $(a + 8)(a - 2)$
$= a^2 + 6a - 16$

5. $(m - 6)(m + 3)$
$= m^2 - 3m - 18$

6. $(b - 5)^2$
$= b^2 - 10b + 25$

7. $(2c + 3)(3c + 4)$
$= 6c^2 + 17c + 12$

8. $(3x + 5)(4x - 2)$
$= 12x^2 + 14x - 10$

9. $(y - 8)(3y + 10)$
$= 3y^2 - 14y - 80$

10. $(2z + 9)^2$
$= 4z^2 + 36z + 81$

11. $(5b + 8)(5b - 8)$
$= 25b^2 - 64$

12. $(5a - 3b)^2$
$= 25a^2 - 30ab + 9b^2$

13. $(3x - 2b)(3x + 2b)$
$= 9x^2 - 4b^2$

14. $(6x^2y - 11z)(6x^2y + z)$
$= 36x^2y - 60x^2yz - 11z^2$

15. $(8x^3 + 7yz^2)(8x^3 - 7yz^2)$
$= 64x^6 - 49y^2z^4$

16. $(7ab - 2ac)^2$
$= 49a^2b^2 - 28a^2bc + 4a^2c^2$

17. $(2ay - 15)(ay + 7)$
$= 2a^2y^2 - ay - 105$

18. $(4rs + t^2)(4rs - 2t^2)$
$= 16r^2s^2 - 4rst^2 - 2t^4$

19. $(x - 11)(x - 10)$
$= x^2 - 21x + 110$

20. $(ab + 4)(2ab - 3)$
$= 2a^2b^2 + 5ab - 12$

Test B — Special Products Page 156

1. $(x + 3)(x + 12)$
$= x^2 + 15x + 36$

2. $(b - 9)(b - 5)$
$= b^2 - 14b + 45$

3. $(a + 8)^2$
$= a^2 + 16a + 64$

4. $(c + 8)(c - 5)$
$= c^2 + 3c - 40$

5. $(b - 7)(b + 3)$
$= b^2 - 4b - 21$

6. $(x - 9)^2$
$= x^2 - 18x + 81$

7. $(3y + 5)(2y + 3)$
$= 6y^2 + 19y + 15$

8. $(5a - 4)(3a + 7)$
$= 15a^2 + 23a - 28$

9. $(3a - 4z)(2a + 5z)$
$= 6a^2 + 7az - 20z^2$

10. $(3m + 5)^2$
$= 9m^2 + 30m + 25$

11. $(6a + 7)(6a - 7)$
$= 36a^2 - 49$

12. $(4a - 5)^2$
$= 16a^2 - 40a + 25$

13. $(5x^2y - 3t)(5x^2y + 3t)$
$= 25x^4y^2 - 9t^2$

14. $(4ab - 11c)(2ab + 4c)$
$= 8a^2b^2 - 6abc - 44c^2$

15. $(8a^4 - 5z)(8a^4 + 5z)$
$= 64a^8 - 25z^2$

16. $(3x^3y - 8y^2)^2$
$= 9x^6y^2 - 48x^3y^2z + 64y^2z^2$

17. $(4ax - 5m)(ax + m)$
$= 4a^2x^2 - amx - 5m^2$

18. $(3cd + 7)(cd - 6)$
$= 3c^2d^2 - 11cd - 42$

19. $(6a^2 - 10a^3b)^2$
$= 36a^4 - 120a^5b + 100a^6b^2$

20. $(m^4 - 14n)(m^4 + 5n)$
$= m^8 - 9m^4n - 70n^2$

Test C — Special Products   Page 157

1. $(\frac{2}{3}mn - \frac{1}{2})^2$
$= \frac{4}{9}m^2n^2 - \frac{2}{3}mn + \frac{1}{4}$

2. $(\frac{4x}{5} - \frac{2y}{3})(\frac{4x}{5} + \frac{2y}{3})$
$= \frac{16x^2}{25} - \frac{4y^2}{9}$

3. $(\frac{a}{3} - 7)(\frac{a}{3} + 8)$
$= \frac{a^2}{9} + \frac{a}{3} - 56$

4. $(\frac{a^2}{3} + \frac{12}{a^2})^2$
$= \frac{a^4}{9} + 8 + \frac{144}{a^4}$

5. $(\frac{2}{3}x - 5)(\frac{3}{2}x + 2)$
$= x^2 + \frac{4}{3}x - \frac{15}{2}x - 10$
$= x^2 + \frac{8}{6}x - \frac{45}{6}x - 10$
$= x^2 - \frac{37}{6}x - 10$

6. $(\frac{3}{5}ab + \frac{1}{3})^2$
$= \frac{9}{25}a^2b^2 + \frac{2}{5}ab + \frac{1}{9}$

7. $(\frac{3m}{4} + \frac{6n}{5})(\frac{3m}{4} - \frac{6n}{5})$
$= \frac{9m^2}{16} - \frac{36n^2}{25}$

8. $(\frac{c}{4} - 6)(\frac{c}{4} + 8)$
$= \frac{c^2}{16} + \frac{c}{2} - 48$

9. $(\frac{2x}{y^2} + \frac{3y}{4x})^2$
$= \frac{4x^2}{y^4} + \frac{3}{y} + \frac{9y^2}{16x^2}$

10. $(3a + \frac{2}{3})(2a - \frac{4}{3})$
$= 6a^2 - 4a + \frac{4}{3}a - \frac{8}{9}$
$= 6a^2 - \frac{12a}{3} + \frac{4}{3}a - \frac{8}{9}$
$= 6a^2 - \frac{8a}{3} - \frac{8}{9}$

11. $(3a - 0.5)^2$
$= 9a^2 - 3a + .25$

12. $(4x - 0.2y)(3x + 0.5y)$
$= 12x^2 + 1.4xy - .1y^2$

13. $(0.6m - n)(0.6m + n)$
$= .36m^2 - n^2$

14. $(5x + 0.2y)^2$
$= 25x^2 + 2xy + .04y^2$

15. $(0.5a - b)^2$
$= .25a^2 - ab + b^2$

16. $(\frac{a}{b} + \frac{b}{a})^2$
$= \frac{a^2}{b^2} + 2 + \frac{b^2}{a^2}$

17. $[(a + b) - 5][(a + b) + 5]$
$= (a + b)^2 - 25$
$= a^2 + 2ab + b^2 - 25$

18. $23 \cdot 17$
$= (20 + 3)(20 - 3)$
$= 400 - 9$
$= 391$

19. $(7ax - 3ay)(3ax + 7ay)$
$= 21a^2x^2 + 40a^2xy - 21a^2y^2$

20. $(\frac{x}{3} - \frac{3y}{2})^2$
$= \frac{x^2}{9} - xy + \frac{9y^2}{4}$

Test A — Factoring   Page 157

1. $3m^3n - 15m^2n^2 + 9mn^3$
$= 3mn(m^2 - 5mn + 3n^2)$

2. $4a^2 + 20ab + 25b^2$
$= (2a + 5b)^2$

3. $x^2 - x - 6$
$= (x - 3)(x + 2)$

4. $a^2 + 7a - 18$
$= (a + 9)(a - 2)$

5. $a^2 - 11ab + 30b^2$
$= (a - 6b)(a - 5b)$

6. $9a^4 - 6a^2 + 1$
$= (3a^2 - 1)^2$

7. $3b^2 + 5ab + 2a^2$
$= (3b + 2a)(b + a)$

8. $6a^2 - a - 2$
$= (3a - 2)(2a + 1)$

9. $8a^2 + 2a - 3$
$= (4a + 3)(2a - 1)$

10. $5a^2 - 12ab + 4b^2$
$= (5a - 2b)(a - 2b)$

11. $7 - 28c^4$
$= 7(1 - 4c^4)$
$= 7(1 + 2c^2)(1 - 2c^2)$

12. $5 + 10a^2 + 5a^4$
$= 5(1 + 2a^2 + a^4)$
$= 5(1 + a^2)^2$

13. $36x^2y^4 - 100x^4y^2$
$= 4x^2y^2(9y^2 - 25x^2)$
$= 4x^2y^2(3y + 5x)(3y - 5x)$

14. $3a^4c - 12a^2b^2c + 12b^4c$
$= 3c(a^4 - 4a^2b^2 + 4b^4)$
$= 3c(a^2 - 2b^2)^2$

15. $6x^2 - 9x - 15$
$= 3(2x^2 - 3x - 5)$
$= 3(2x - 5)(x + 1)$

16. $256x^4 - 81y^4$
$= (16x^2 + 9y^2)(16x^2 - 9y^2)$
$= (16x^2 + 9y^2)(4x + 3y)(4x - 3y)$

Test B — Factoring Page 158

1. $5x^4y^2 - 35x^3y^3 + 15x^2y^4$
$= 5x^2y^2(x^2 - 7xy + 3y^2)$

2. $9x^2 - 24xy + 16y^2$
$= (3x - 4y)^2$

3. $a^2 - a - 12$
$= (a - 4)(a + 3)$

4. $x^2 + 6x - 27$
$= (x + 9)(x - 3)$

5. $y^2 - 9yz + 18z^2$
$= (y - 6z)(y - 3z)$

6. $a^2 + 11a + 10$
$= (a + 10)(a + 1)$

7. $25x^4 - 10x^2 + 1$
$= (5x^2 - 1)^2$

8. $8x^2 - x - 7$
$= (8x + 7)(x - 1)$

9. $12a^2 + 5a - 3$
$= (4a + 3)(3a - 1)$

10. $7d^2 - 17de + 6e^2$
$= (7d - 3e)(d - 2e)$

11. $49x^2 - 144y^2z^2$
$= (7x + 12yz)(7x - 12yz)$

12. $3 - 48y^4$
$= 3(1 - 16y^4)$
$= 3(1 + 4y^2)(1 - 4y^2)$
$= 3(1 + 4y^2)(1 + 2y)(1 - 2y)$

13. $5a^2b^2 - 25abc - 70c^2$
$= 5(a^2b^2 - 5abc - 14c^2)$
$= 5(ab + 2c)(ab - 7c)$

14. $16a^4b^2 - 36a^2b^4$
$= 4a^2b^2(4a^2 - 9b^2)$
$= 4a^2b^2(2a + 3b)(2a - 3b)$

15. $12x^2 - 12xy - 9y^2$
$= 3(4x^2 - 4xy - 3y^2)$
$= 3(2x + y)(2x - 3y)$

16. $81a^4 - 16b^4$
$= (9a^2 + 4b^2)(9a^2 - 4b^2)$
$= (9a^2 + 4b^2)(3a + 2b)(3a - 2b)$

Test C — Factoring Page 158

1. $3a(2x + y) - 2(2x + y)$
$= (2x + y)(3a - 2)$

2. $(x - e)^2 - 4y^2$
$= (x - e)^2 - (2y)^2$
$= [(x - 3) + 2y][(x - e) - 2y]$
$= (x - e + 2y)(x - e - 2y)$

3. $(a + 2b)^2 - (c - d)^2$
$= [(a + 2b) + (c - d)][(a + 2b) - (c - d)]$
$= (a + 2b + c - d)(a + 2b - c + d)$

4. $5x(a - 5b) - 3y(5b - a)$
$= 5x(a - 5b) + 3y(a - 5b)$
$= (a - 5b)(5x + 3y)$

5. $xy - y + 2x - 2$
$= y(x - 1) + 2(x - 1)$
$= (x - 1)(y + 2)$

6. $x^2 + 6x + 9 - 4y^2$
$= (x^2 + 6x + 9) - 4y^2$
$= (x + 3)^2 - (2y)^2$
$= [(x + 3) + 2y][(x + 3) - 2y]$
$= (x + 3 + 2y)(x + 3 - 2y)$

7. $5x(3a - b) - 4y(3a - b)$
$= (3a - b)(5x - 4y)$

8. $(c - t)^2 - (d + 3e)^2$
$= [(c - t) + (d + 3e)][(c - t) - (d + 3e)]$
$= (c - t + d + 3e)(c - t - d - 3e)$

9. $2m(p - q) - 3n(q - p)$
$= 2m(p - q) + 3n(p - q)$
$= (p - q)(2m + 3n)$

10. $ac - 2bc + ad - 2bd$
$= c(a - 2b) + d(a - 2b)$
$= (a - 2b)(c + d)$

11. $a^2 + 4ab + 4b^2 - 25c^2$
$= (a^2 + 4ab + 4b^2) - 25c^2$
$= (a + 2b)^2 - (5c)^2$
$= (a + 2b + 5c)(a + 2b - 5c)$

12. $25c^2 - a^2 + 4ab - 4b^2$
$= 25c^2 - (a^2 - 4ab + 4b^2)$
$= (5c)^2 - (a - 2b)^2$
$= [5c + (a - 2b)][5c - (a - 2b)]$
$= (5c + a - 2b)(5c - a + 2b)$

13. $25 - (a + b)^2$
$= 5^2 - (a + b)^2$
$= [5 + (a + b)][5 - (a + b)]$
$= (5 + a + b)(5 - a - b)$

14. $7a^4 - 112b^4$
$= 7(a^4 - 16b^4)$
$= 7(a^2 + 4b^2)(a^2 - 4b^2)$
$= 7(a^2 + 4b^2)(a + 2b)(a - 2b)$

15. $3x(m - n) + y(m - n)$
$= (m - n)(3x + y)$

16. $5a(x - 2y) + 3b(2y - x)$
$= 5a(x - 2y) - 3b(x - 2y)$
$= (x - 2y)(5a - 3b)$

UNIT 8 — Fractions

Inventory Test on Fractions Page 161

1.(a) $\frac{4}{5}$ (b) $\frac{3}{4}$ 2.(a) $3\frac{2}{3}$ (b) $21\frac{1}{3}$ 3.(a) $\frac{7}{5}$ b) $\frac{101}{12}$

4.(a) $\dfrac{\frac{1}{3}+\frac{1}{2}}{\frac{2}{3}+\frac{3}{4}} = \dfrac{\frac{2}{6}+\frac{3}{6}}{\frac{8}{12}+\frac{9}{12}} = \dfrac{\frac{5}{6}}{\frac{17}{12}} = \frac{5}{\cancel{6}}\cdot\frac{\overset{2}{\cancel{12}}}{17} = \frac{10}{17}$

(b) $\dfrac{3-\frac{4}{5}}{6\frac{1}{2}} = \dfrac{2\frac{1}{5}}{6\frac{1}{2}} = \dfrac{\frac{11}{5}}{\frac{13}{2}} = \frac{11}{5}\cdot\frac{2}{13} = \frac{22}{65}$

5.(a) $\frac{1}{2}+\frac{1}{3} = \frac{3}{6}+\frac{2}{6} = \frac{5}{6}$

(b) $\frac{3}{5}-\frac{2}{10} = \frac{6}{10}-\frac{2}{10} = \frac{4}{10} = \frac{2}{5}$

(c) $\frac{3}{8}+\frac{5}{6}-\frac{2}{3} = \frac{9}{24}+\frac{20}{24}-\frac{16}{24} = \frac{13}{24}$

(d) $7-\frac{4}{5} = 6\frac{1}{5}$

(e) $6\frac{2}{3}+5\frac{3}{4}-1\frac{1}{6} = 6\frac{8}{12}+5\frac{9}{12}-1\frac{2}{12} = 11\frac{17}{12}-1\frac{2}{12} = 10\frac{15}{12} = 11\frac{3}{12} = 11\frac{1}{4}$

(f) $3 \times \frac{5}{6} = \frac{15}{6} = 2\frac{3}{6} = 2\frac{1}{2}$

(g) $\frac{3}{5}\times\frac{7}{8} = \frac{21}{40}$

(h) $\frac{\cancel{2}}{\cancel{3}} \times \frac{\cancel{9}}{\underset{\cancel{2}}{\cancel{10}}} \times \frac{\cancel{5}}{\underset{4}{\cancel{12}}} = \frac{1}{4}$

(i) $2\frac{2}{5}\times 4\frac{1}{2} = \frac{\overset{6}{\cancel{12}}}{5}\cdot\frac{9}{\cancel{2}} = \frac{54}{5} = 10\frac{4}{5}$

(j) $6 \div \frac{1}{3} = 6\cdot\frac{3}{1} = 18$

(k) $8 \div \frac{4}{5} = 8\cdot\frac{5}{4} = \frac{40}{4} = 10$

(l) $\frac{8}{15}\div\frac{10}{21} = \frac{\overset{4}{\cancel{8}}}{\underset{5}{\cancel{15}}} \div \frac{\overset{7}{\cancel{21}}}{\underset{5}{\cancel{10}}} = \frac{28}{25} = 1\frac{3}{25}$

(m) $12 \div 2\frac{2}{3} = 12 \div \frac{8}{3} = \overset{3}{\cancel{12}}\cdot\frac{3}{\underset{2}{\cancel{8}}} = \frac{9}{2} = 4\frac{1}{2}$

(n) $8\frac{4}{5}\div 2\frac{1}{3} = \frac{44}{5}\div\frac{7}{3} = \frac{44}{5}\cdot\frac{3}{7} = \frac{132}{35} = 3\frac{27}{35}$

(o) $\frac{2}{3}\times\frac{5}{8}\div\frac{15}{16} = \frac{\cancel{2}}{3}\cdot\frac{\cancel{5}}{\underset{\cancel{4}}{\cancel{8}}}\cdot\frac{\overset{4}{\cancel{16}}}{\underset{3}{\cancel{15}}} = \frac{4}{9}$

Key to Unit 8, pages 170-175

Exercises 8.3a   Pages 170-171

1. $\frac{-3}{-4} = \frac{3}{4}$ 2. $\frac{2}{-5} = -\frac{2}{5}$ 3. $\frac{-a - x}{2x} = \frac{-(a + x)}{2x} = -\frac{a + x}{2x}$

4. $\frac{-4c}{-b - y} = \frac{-4c}{-(b + y)} = \frac{4c}{b + y}$ 5. $-\frac{-a - b}{c + d} = -\frac{-(a + b)}{c + d} = \frac{a + b}{c + d}$

6. $-\frac{-2}{-a - y} = -\frac{-2}{-(a + y)} = -\frac{2}{a + y}$ 7. $-\frac{-2 - m}{2 + n} = -\frac{-(2 + m)}{2 + n} = \frac{2 + m}{2 + n}$

8. $\frac{-3(x + y)}{4(-a - b)} = \frac{-3(x + y)}{-4(a + b)} = \frac{3(x + y)}{4(a + b)}$ 9. $\frac{-4(a + b)}{5(-x - y)} = \frac{-4(a + b)}{-5(x + y)} = \frac{4(a + b)}{5(x + y)}$

Exercises 8.3b   Pages 171-172

1. $\frac{-b}{b - a} = \frac{-b}{-(-b + a)} = \frac{-b}{-(a - b)} = \frac{b}{a - b}$

2. $\frac{-a}{b - a + c} = \frac{-a}{-(-b + a - c)} = \frac{-a}{-(a - b - c)} = \frac{a}{a - b - c}$

3. $\frac{3}{1 - x} = \frac{3}{-(-1 + x)} = \frac{3}{-(x - 1)} = -\frac{3}{x - 1}$

$-\frac{2}{4 - x^2} = -\frac{2}{-(-4 + x^2)} = -\frac{2}{-(x^2 - 4)} = \frac{2}{x^2 - 4}$

4. $\frac{1}{(b - a)(c - b)} = \frac{1}{-(-b + a)[-(-c + b)]} = \frac{1}{-(a - b)[-(b - c)]} = \frac{1}{(a - b)(b - c)}$

5. $\frac{(m - n)(m + n)}{(a - c)(b - a)} = \frac{m^2 - n^2}{(a - c)[-(-b + a)]} = \frac{-(-m^2 + n^2)}{-(a - c)(a - b)} = \frac{-m^2 + n^2}{(a - c)(a - b)}$

6. $\frac{(a - b)(b - a + c)}{(y - x)(z - y)(z - x)} = \frac{(a - b)(-a + b + c)}{[-(-y + x)][-(-z + y)][-(-z + x)]} =$

$\frac{-(a - b)(a - b - c)}{-(x - y)(y - z)(x - z)} = \frac{(a - b)(a - b - c)}{(x - y)(y - z)(x - z)}$

7. $\frac{-2a}{9 - a^2} = \frac{-2a}{-(-9 + a^2)} = \frac{-2a}{-(a^2 - 9)} = \frac{2a}{a^2 - 9} = \frac{2a}{(a + 3)(a - 3)}$

Exercises 8.4   Pages 174-175

1. $\frac{a^2xy^2}{a^3xy} = \frac{y}{a}$ 2. $\frac{m^3n^3}{am^2n^4} = \frac{m}{an}$ 3. $\frac{a^2b^2x^2}{b^3xy^2} = \frac{a^2x}{by^2}$

4. $\frac{16m^2nx^2z^2}{40am^3yz^3} = \frac{2nx^2}{5amyz}$ 5. $\frac{210bc^2d}{750ab^2c} = \frac{7cd}{25ab}$ 6. $\frac{-25x^2y^5z^2}{-100x^4y^3} = \frac{y^2z^2}{4x^2}$

7. $\frac{-7a^2bcd^3}{42ab^2cd^4} = -\frac{a}{6bd}$

8. $\frac{tr^2 + ts^2}{3t} = \frac{t(r^2 + s^2)}{3t} = \frac{r^2 + s^2}{3}$

9. $\frac{2x}{4x^2 - 6ax} = \frac{2x}{2x(2x - 3a)} = \frac{1}{2x - 3a}$

10. $\frac{xz}{xz + yz} = \frac{xz}{z(x + y)} = \frac{x}{x + y}$

11. $\frac{a}{a^2 + ab} = \frac{a}{a(a + b)} = \frac{1}{a + b}$

12. $\frac{3b^3}{3b + 3} = \frac{3b^3}{3(b + 1)} = \frac{b^3}{b + 1}$

13. $\frac{bc + bd}{bx + by} = \frac{b(c + d)}{b(x + y)} = \frac{c + d}{x + y}$

14. $\frac{mn - rs}{amn - ars} = \frac{mn - rs}{a(mn - rs)} = \frac{1}{a}$

15. $\frac{5a + 10b}{5c + 15d} = \frac{5(a + 2b)}{5(c + 3d)} = \frac{a + 2b}{c + 3d}$

16. $\frac{7a - 21b}{14a - 28b} = \frac{7(a - 3b)}{14(a - 2b)} = \frac{a - 3b}{2(a - 2b)}$

17. $\frac{5c + 10d}{7c + 14d} = \frac{5(c + 2d)}{7(c + 2d)} = \frac{5}{7}$

18. $\frac{x - y}{(x - y)^2} = \frac{x - y}{(x - y)(x - y)} = \frac{1}{x - y}$

19. $\frac{d + e}{d^2 - e^2} = \frac{d + e}{(d + e)(d - e)} = \frac{1}{d - e}$

20. $\frac{a + b}{(a + b)^2} = \frac{a + b}{(a + b)(a + b)} = \frac{1}{a + b}$

21. $\frac{b - c}{b^2 - c^2} = \frac{b - c}{(b + c)(b - c)} = \frac{1}{b + c}$

22. $\frac{(x - y)^2}{x^2 - y^2} = \frac{(x - y)(x - y)}{(x + y)(x - y)} = \frac{x - y}{x + y}$

23. $\frac{3y + 1}{9y^2 - 1} = \frac{3y + 1}{(3y + 1)(3y - 1)} = \frac{1}{3y - 1}$

24. $\frac{5a - 6b}{25a^2 - 36b^2} = \frac{5a - 6b}{(5a + 6b)(5a - 6b)} = \frac{1}{5a + 6b}$

25. $\frac{4a + 7}{16a^2 - 49} = \frac{4a + 7}{(4a + 7)(4a - 7)} = \frac{1}{4a - 7}$

26. $\frac{a - b}{a^2 - 2ab + b^2} = \frac{a - b}{(a - b)(a - b)} = \frac{1}{a - b}$

27. $\frac{x + y}{x^2 + 2xy + y^2} = \frac{x + y}{(x + y)(x + y)} = \frac{1}{x + y}$

28. $\frac{c + 2}{c^2 + 4c + 4} = \frac{c + 2}{(c + 2)(c + 2)} = \frac{1}{c + 2}$

29. $\frac{s - 3}{s^2 - 6s + 9} = \frac{s - 3}{(s - 3)(s - 3)} = \frac{1}{s - 3}$

30. $\frac{b^3 - 3b^2}{b^2 - 6b + 9} = \frac{b^2(b - 3)}{(b - 3)(b - 3)} = \frac{b^2}{b - 3}$

31. $\dfrac{x^2 + 2xy + y^2}{x^2 - y^2} = \dfrac{(x + y)(x + y)}{(x + y)(x - y)} = \dfrac{x + y}{x - y}$

32. $\dfrac{b^2 - 3b + 2}{b^2 - 1} = \dfrac{(b - 2)(b - 1)}{(b + 1)(b - 1)} = \dfrac{b - 2}{b + 1}$

33. $\dfrac{a^2 - 3a - 10}{a^2 - 6a + 5} = \dfrac{(a - 5)(a + 2)}{(a - 5)(a - 1)} = \dfrac{a + 2}{a - 1}$

34. $\dfrac{1 + 5m + 6m^2}{1 + 6m + 8m^2} = \dfrac{(1 + 3m)(1 + 2m)}{(1 + 2m)(1 + 4m)} = \dfrac{1 + 3m}{1 + 4m}$

35. $\dfrac{a^2 - 7a + 12}{a^2 - 8a + 16} = \dfrac{(a - 3)(a - 4)}{(a - 4)(a - 4)} = \dfrac{a - 3}{a - 4}$

36. $\dfrac{y^2 - 81}{y^2 + 7y - 18} = \dfrac{(y + 9)(y - 9)}{(y + 9)(y - 2)} = \dfrac{y - 9}{y - 2}$

37. $\dfrac{a^2 - 11a + 24}{a^2 - a - 6} = \dfrac{(a - 8)(a - 3)}{(a - 3)(a + 2)} = \dfrac{a - 8}{a + 2}$

38. $\dfrac{x^2 - 6x - 7}{x^2 - 11x + 28} = \dfrac{(x - 7)(x + 1)}{(x - 7)(x - 4)} = \dfrac{x + 1}{x - 4}$

39 $\dfrac{2x^2 - 2x - 12}{6x^2 - 10x - 44} = \dfrac{2(x^2 - x - 6)}{2(3x^2 - 5x - 22)} = \dfrac{2(x - 3)(x + 2)}{2(3x - 11)(x + 2)} = \dfrac{x - 3}{3x - 11}$

40. $\dfrac{x^3 - 6x^2 + 5x}{x^3 + 2x^2 - 35x} = \dfrac{x(x^2 - 6x + 5)}{x(x^2 + 2x - 35)} = \dfrac{x(x - 5)(x - 1)}{x(x + 7)(x - 5)} = \dfrac{x - 1}{x + 7}$

41. $\dfrac{7x - 2x^2 - 3}{2x^2 + 11x - 6} = \dfrac{-(2x^2 - 7x + 3)}{2x^2 + 11x - 6} = \dfrac{-(2x - 1)(x - 3)}{(2x - 1)(x + 6)} = \dfrac{-(x - 3)}{x + 6} = \dfrac{3 - x}{6 + x}$

42. $\dfrac{10nx + 10ny}{25nx^2 - 25ny^2} = \dfrac{10n(x + y)}{25n(x^2 - y^2)} = \dfrac{10n(x + y)}{25n(x + y)(x - y)} = \dfrac{2}{5(x - y)}$

43. $\dfrac{x^{n+2} - x^n}{x^{n+1} - x^n} = \dfrac{x^n(x^2 - 1)}{x^n(x - 1)} = \dfrac{x^n(x + 1)(x - 1)}{x^n(x - 1)} = x + 1$

44. $\dfrac{b^2 + b - 12}{3b^2 + 9b - 54} = \dfrac{(b + 4)(b - 3)}{3(b^2 + 3b - 18)} = \dfrac{(b + 4)(b - 3)}{3(b + 6)(b - 3)} = \dfrac{b + 4}{3(b + 6)}$

45. $\dfrac{x^2 - 2x^4 + x^6}{x^6 - x^2} = \dfrac{x^2(1 - 2x^2 + x^4)}{x^2(x^4 - 1)} = \dfrac{x^2(1 - x^2)(1 - x^2)}{x^2(x^2 - 1)(x^2 + 1)} = \dfrac{x^2(x^2 - 1)(x^2 - 1)}{x^2(x^2 - 1)(x^2 + 1)} = \dfrac{x^2 - 1}{x^2 + 1}$

46. $\dfrac{a^2b(a + 2b)^4}{ab(a^2 - 4b^2)^2} = \dfrac{a^2b(a + 2b)^4}{ab(a^2 - 4b^2)(a^2 - 4b^2)} = \dfrac{a^2b(a + 2b)(a + 2b)(a + 2b)(a + 2b)}{ab(a + 2b)(a - 2b)(a + 2b)(a - 2b)}$

$= \dfrac{a(a + 2b)^2}{(a - 2b)^2}$

47. $\frac{x^3 + 5x^2 - 6x}{2x^2 - 2} = \frac{x(x^2 + 5x - 6)}{2(x^2 - 1)} = \frac{x(x + 6)(x - 1)}{2(x + 1)(x - 1)} = \frac{x(x + 6)}{2(x + 1)}$

48. $\frac{a^3 + 2a^2b + ab^2}{a^5 - 2a^3b^2 + ab^4} = \frac{a(a^2 + 2ab + b^2)}{a(a^4 - 2a^2b^2 + b^4)} = \frac{a(a + b)(a + b)}{a(a^2 - b^2)(a^2 - b^2)}$

$= \frac{a(a + b)(a + b)}{a(a + b)(a - b)(a + b)(a - b)} = \frac{1}{(a - b)^2}$

Exercises 8.5 Page 176

1. $\frac{5a}{6} = \frac{5a}{6} \cdot \frac{(7)}{(7)} = \frac{35a}{42}$

2. $\frac{3x}{11b} \cdot \frac{(5)}{(5)} = \frac{15x}{55b}$

3. $\frac{3a}{14x} \cdot \frac{(6y)}{(6y)} = \frac{18ay}{84xy}$

4. $\frac{4a^2}{5y} \cdot \frac{(4y^2)}{(4y^2)} = \frac{16a^2y^2}{20y^3}$

5. $\frac{x - 3}{x - 1} \cdot \frac{(x - 1)}{(x - 1)} = \frac{(x - 3)(x - 1)}{(x - 1)^2} = \frac{x^2 - 4x + 3}{(x - 1)^2}$

6. $\frac{2x - 5}{2x + 5} \cdot \frac{(2x + 5)}{(2x + 5)} = \frac{(2x - 5)(2x + 5)}{(2x + 5)^2} = \frac{4x^2 - 25}{(2x + 5)^2}$

7. $\frac{-1}{x - 2} \cdot \frac{(x + 2)}{(x + 2)} = \frac{-(x + 2)}{x^2 - 4} = \frac{-(x + 2)}{-(4 - x^2)} = \frac{x + 2}{4 - x^2} = \frac{2 + x}{4 - x^2}$

8. $\frac{ab}{3 - b} \cdot \frac{(3 + b)}{(3 + b)} = \frac{3ab + ab^2}{9 - b^2} = \frac{-(-3ab - ab^2)}{-(-9 + b^2)} = \frac{-3ab - ab^2}{b^2 - 9} = -\frac{3ab + ab^2}{b^2 - 9}$

9. $\frac{x - 5}{1} \cdot \frac{(x + 5)}{(x + 5)} = \frac{x^2 - 25}{x + 5}$

Exercises 8.6 Pages 176-177

1. $\frac{27a}{9} = 3a$

2. $\frac{26b}{13b} = 2$

3. $\frac{45x^2y^3z}{15xy} = 3xy^2z$

4. $\frac{36ac + 9c}{9c} = \frac{36ac}{9c} + \frac{9c}{9c} = 4a + 1$

5. $\frac{a^2 + c^2}{a} = \frac{a^2}{a} + \frac{c^2}{a} = a + \frac{c^2}{a}$

6. $\frac{12x^2 - 6x}{6x} = \frac{12x^2}{6x} - \frac{6x}{6x} = 2x - 1$

7. $\frac{4x^3 - 8x^2 + 2x - 1}{2x} = \frac{4x^3}{2x} - \frac{8x^2}{2x} + \frac{2x}{2x} - \frac{1}{2x} = 2x^2 - 4x + 1 - \frac{1}{2x}$

8. $\frac{ab - bc - cd + d^2}{b} = \frac{ab}{b} - \frac{bc}{b} - \frac{cd}{b} + \frac{d^2}{b} = a - c - \frac{cd - d^2}{b}$ or $a - c + \frac{d^2 - cd}{b}$

9. $\frac{a^2x^3 - ax^2 - x - 1}{ax} = \frac{a^2x^3}{ax} - \frac{ax^2}{ax} - \frac{x}{ax} - \frac{1}{ax} = ax^2 - x - \frac{x + 1}{ax}$

10. $\frac{x^2 - x - 12}{x - 4} = \frac{(x - 4)(x + 3)}{x - 4} = x + 3$

Exercises 8.7 Page 178

1. $\frac{2m}{1}\cdot\frac{(m-n)}{(m-n)} = \frac{2m(m-n)}{m-n}$; $\frac{m+n}{m-n}$ 2. $\frac{x}{2}\cdot\frac{(5)}{(5)} = \frac{5x}{10}$; $\frac{3y}{5}\cdot\frac{(2)}{(2)} = \frac{6y}{10}$

3. $\frac{2a}{5b}$; $\frac{3x}{1}\cdot\frac{(5b)}{(5b)} = \frac{15bx}{5b}$ 4. $\frac{a^2b}{c^2d}\cdot\frac{(d)}{(d)} = \frac{a^2bd}{c^2d^2}$; $\frac{ab^2}{cd^2}\cdot\frac{(c)}{(c)} = \frac{ab^2c}{c^2d^2}$

5. $\frac{x^2}{2xy} = \frac{x}{2y}\cdot\frac{(2a)}{(2a)} = \frac{2ax}{4ay}$; $\frac{3}{4ay}$ 6. $\frac{3\cancel{x}y}{c\cancel{x}} = \frac{3y}{c}\cdot\frac{(3b)}{(3b)} = \frac{9by}{3bc}$; $\frac{2a\cancel{y}}{3b\cancel{y}} = \frac{2a}{3b}\cdot\frac{(c)}{(c)} = \frac{2ac}{3bc}$

7. $\frac{3}{x^2y^4}\cdot\frac{(x^2)}{(x^2)} = \frac{3x^2}{x^4y^4}$; $\frac{-6}{x^3y^3}\cdot\frac{(xy)}{(xy)} = \frac{-6xy}{x^4y^4}$; $\frac{3}{x^4y^2}\cdot\frac{(y^2)}{(y^2)} = \frac{3y^2}{x^4y^4}$

8. $\frac{3ab}{8a^2c} = \frac{3b}{8ac}\cdot\frac{(b^2c)}{(b^2c)} = \frac{3b^3c}{8ab^2c^2}$; $\frac{7a^2}{4b^2c}\cdot\frac{(2ac)}{(2ac)} = \frac{14a^3c}{8ab^2c^2}$;

$$\frac{5a^3}{a^3bc^2} = \frac{5}{bc^2}\cdot\frac{(8ab)}{(8ab)} = \frac{40ab}{8ab^2c^2}$$

9. $\frac{(m-n)}{a}\cdot\frac{(m+n)}{(m+n)} = \frac{m^2-n^2}{a(m+n)}$; $\frac{2}{1}\cdot\frac{[a(m+n)]}{[a(m+n)]} = \frac{2a(m+n)}{a(m+n)}$; $\frac{a}{(m+n)}\cdot\frac{(a)}{(a)} = \frac{a^2}{a(m+n)}$

10. $\frac{(x+y)}{2}\cdot\frac{(6)}{(6)} = \frac{6(x+y)}{12}$; $\frac{x-y}{4}\cdot\frac{(3)}{(3)} = \frac{3(x-y)}{12}$; $\frac{x^2-y^2}{6}\cdot\frac{(2)}{(2)} = \frac{2(x^2-y^2)}{12}$

11. $\frac{x^2}{x^2-1}$; $\frac{x}{(x+1)}\cdot\frac{(x-1)}{(x-1)} = \frac{x(x-1)}{x^2-1}$; $\frac{x}{(x-1)}\cdot\frac{(x+1)}{(x+1)} = \frac{x(x+1)}{x^2-1}$

12. $\frac{a^3}{a^4-16}$; $\frac{a}{(a^2+4)}\cdot\frac{(a^2-4)}{(a^2-4)} = \frac{a(a^2-4)}{a^4-16}$; $\frac{2a}{4-a^2} = \frac{-2a}{a^2-4}\cdot\frac{(a^2+4)}{(a^2+4)} = \frac{-2a(a^2+4)}{a^4-16}$

13. $\frac{4a}{b-a}$ $\frac{-4a}{a-b}\cdot\frac{(a+b)}{(a+b)} = \frac{-4a(a+b)}{a^2-b^2}$; $\frac{3b}{(a+b)}\cdot\frac{(a-b)}{(a-b)} = \frac{3b(a-b)}{a^2-b^2}$; $\frac{1}{a^2-b^2}$

14. $\frac{a}{(1-ax)}\cdot\frac{(1+ax)}{(1+ax)} = \frac{a(1+ax)}{1-a^2x^2}$; $\frac{x}{(1+ax)}\cdot\frac{(1-ax)}{(1-ax)}$ $\frac{x(1-ax)}{1-a^2x^2}$;

$$\frac{-ax}{ax-1} = \frac{ax}{(1-ax)}\cdot\frac{(1+ax)}{(1+ax)} = \frac{ax(1+ax)}{1-a^2x^2}$$

15. $$\frac{1}{x^2+7x+10} = \frac{1}{(x+5)(x+2)}\cdot\frac{(x-1)}{(x-1)} = \frac{x-1}{(x+5)(x+2)(x-1)}$$

$$\frac{1}{x^2+x-2} = \frac{1}{(x+2)(x-1)}\cdot\frac{(x+5)}{(x+5)} = \frac{x+5}{(x+5)(x+2)(x-1)}$$

$$\frac{1}{x^2+4x-5} = \frac{1}{(x+5)(x-1)}\cdot\frac{(x+2)}{(x+2)} = \frac{x+2}{(x+5)(x+2)(x-1)}$$

16. $\frac{3x}{x^2 - 3x + 2} = \frac{3x}{(x-2)(x-1)} \cdot \frac{(x-3)}{(x-3)} = \frac{3x(x-3)}{(x-3)(x-2)(x-1)}$

$\frac{x-1}{x^2 - 5x + 6} = \frac{x-1}{(x-3)(x-2)} \cdot \frac{(x-1)}{(x-1)} = \frac{(x-1)^2}{(x-3)(x-2)(x-1)}$

$\frac{x+3}{x^2 - 4x + 3} = \frac{x+3}{(x-3)(x-1)} \cdot \frac{(x-2)}{(x-2)} = \frac{(x+3)(x-2)}{(x-3)(x-2)(x-1)}$

Exercises 8.8 Pages 180

1. $\frac{2x}{5} + \frac{3x}{2} = \frac{2x}{5} \cdot \frac{2}{2} + \frac{3x}{2} \cdot \frac{5}{5} = \frac{4x}{10} + \frac{15x}{10} = \frac{19x}{10}$
   LCD = 10

2. $\frac{4a}{3} + \frac{6b}{5} = \frac{4a}{3} \cdot \frac{5}{5} + \frac{6b}{5} \cdot \frac{3}{3} = \frac{20a}{15} + \frac{18b}{15} = \frac{20a + 18b}{15}$
   LCD = 15

3. $\frac{2a}{3b} + \frac{3a}{2b} = \frac{2a}{3b} \cdot \frac{2}{2} + \frac{3a}{2b} \cdot \frac{3}{3} = \frac{4a}{6b} + \frac{9a}{6b} = \frac{13a}{6b}$
   LCD = 6b

4. $\frac{-5}{7x} + \frac{-2}{3x} = \frac{-5}{7x} \cdot \frac{3}{3} + \frac{-2}{3x} \cdot \frac{7}{7} = \frac{-15}{21x} + \frac{-14}{21x} = -\frac{29}{21x}$
   LCD = 21x

5. $\frac{4m}{3} - \frac{5m}{6} = \frac{4m}{3} \cdot \frac{2}{2} - \frac{5m}{6} = \frac{8m}{6} - \frac{5m}{6} = \frac{3m}{6} = \frac{m}{2}$
   LCD = 6

6. $\frac{-x}{2} - \frac{4x}{9} = \frac{-x}{2} \cdot \frac{9}{9} - \frac{4x}{9} \cdot \frac{2}{2} = \frac{-9x}{18} - \frac{8x}{18} = \frac{-17x}{18}$
   LCD = 18

7. $\frac{3}{y} - (-\frac{y}{3}) = \frac{3}{y} + \frac{y}{3} = \frac{3}{y} \cdot \frac{3}{3} + \frac{y}{3} \cdot \frac{y}{y} = \frac{9}{3y} + \frac{y^2}{3y} = \frac{9 + y^2}{3y}$
   LCD = 3y

8. $\frac{a-b}{2} - \frac{a+b}{3} = \frac{a-b}{2} \cdot \frac{3}{3} - \frac{a+b}{3} \cdot \frac{2}{2} = \frac{3(a-b)}{6} - \frac{2(a+b)}{6} = \frac{3a - 3b}{6} - \frac{2a + 2b}{6}$

$$= \frac{3a - 3b - (2a + 2b)}{6}$$

$$= \frac{3a - 3b - 2a - 2b}{6}$$

$$= \frac{a - 5b}{6}$$

   LCD = 6

9. $$\frac{2x+1}{3} + \frac{x-2}{4} - \frac{x-3}{6} + \frac{5-x}{2} = \frac{2x+1}{3}\cdot\frac{4}{4} + \frac{x-2}{4}\cdot\frac{3}{3} - \frac{x-3}{6}\cdot\frac{2}{2} + \frac{5-x}{2}\cdot\frac{6}{6}$$
$$= \frac{4(2x+1)}{12} + \frac{3(x-2)}{12} - \frac{2(x-3)}{12} + \frac{6(5-x)}{12}$$
$$= \frac{8x+4}{12} + \frac{3x-6}{12} - \frac{2x-6}{12} + \frac{30-6x}{12}$$
$$= \frac{8x + 4 + 3x - 6 - 2x + 6 + 30 - 6x}{12}$$
$$= \frac{3x+34}{12}$$

LCD = 12

10. $$\frac{x-2}{6} - \frac{x-4}{9} + \frac{2-3x}{4} - \frac{2x+1}{12} = \frac{x-2}{6}\cdot\frac{6}{6} - \frac{x-4}{9}\cdot\frac{4}{4} + \frac{2-3x}{4}\cdot\frac{9}{9} - \frac{2x+1}{12}\cdot\frac{3}{3}$$
$$= \frac{6(x-2)}{36} - \frac{4(x-4)}{36} + \frac{9(2-3x)}{36} - \frac{3(2x+1)}{36}$$
$$= \frac{6x-12}{36} - \frac{4x-16}{36} + \frac{18-27x}{36} - \frac{6x+3}{36}$$
$$= \frac{6x - 12 - 4x + 16 + 18 - 27x - 6x - 3}{36}$$
$$= \frac{-31x+19}{36}$$

LCD = 36

11. $$\frac{x-1}{3} - \frac{x-2}{18} - \frac{4x-3}{27} + \frac{1-x}{6} = \frac{x-1}{3}\cdot\frac{18}{18} - \frac{x-2}{18}\cdot\frac{3}{3} - \frac{4x-3}{27}\cdot\frac{2}{2} + \frac{1-x}{6}\cdot\frac{9}{9}$$
$$= \frac{18(x-1)}{54} - \frac{3(x-2)}{54} - \frac{2(4x-3)}{54} + \frac{9(1-x)}{54}$$
$$= \frac{18x-18}{54} - \frac{3x-6}{54} - \frac{8x-6}{54} + \frac{9-9x}{54}$$
$$= \frac{18x - 18 - 3x + 6 - 8x + 6 + 9 - 9x}{54}$$
$$= \frac{-2x+3}{54}$$

LCD = 54

12. $$\frac{2-6x}{5} + \frac{4x-1}{2} - \frac{5x-3}{6} - \frac{1-x}{3} = \frac{2-6x}{5}\cdot\frac{6}{6} + \frac{4x-1}{2}\cdot\frac{15}{15} - \frac{5x-3}{6}\cdot\frac{5}{5} - \frac{1-x}{3}\cdot\frac{10}{10}$$
$$= \frac{6(2-6x)}{30} + \frac{15(4x-1)}{30} - \frac{5(5x-3)}{30} - \frac{10(1-x)}{30}$$
$$= \frac{12-36x}{30} + \frac{60x-15}{30} - \frac{25x-15}{30} - \frac{10-10x}{30}$$
$$= \frac{12 - 36x + 60x - 15 - 25x + 15 - 10 + 10x}{30}$$
$$= \frac{9x+2}{30}$$

LCD = 30

13. $$\begin{aligned}\frac{x+3}{4}-\frac{x-2}{5}+\frac{x-4}{10}-\frac{x+3}{6} &= \frac{x+3}{4}\cdot\frac{15}{15}-\frac{x-2}{5}\cdot\frac{12}{12}+\frac{x-4}{10}\cdot\frac{6}{6}-\frac{x+3}{6}\cdot\frac{10}{10}\\ &= \frac{15(x+3)}{60}-\frac{12(x-2)}{60}+\frac{6(x-4)}{60}-\frac{10(x+3)}{60}\\ &= \frac{15x+45}{60}-\frac{12x-24}{60}+\frac{6x-24}{60}-\frac{10x-30}{60}\\ &= \frac{15x+45-12x+24+6x-24-10x-30}{60}\\ &= \frac{-x+15}{60}\end{aligned}$$

LCD = 60

14. $$\begin{aligned}\frac{1-2a}{5}+\frac{2a-1}{4}-\frac{2a-a^2+1}{8} &= \frac{1-2a}{5}\cdot\frac{8}{8}+\frac{2a-1}{4}\cdot\frac{10}{10}-\frac{2a-a^2+1}{8}\cdot\frac{5}{5}\\ &= \frac{8(1-2a)}{40}+\frac{10(2a-1)}{40}-\frac{5(2a-a^2+1)}{40}\\ &= \frac{8-16a}{40}+\frac{20a-10}{40}-\frac{10a-5a^2-5}{40}\\ &= \frac{8-16a+20a-10-10a+5a^2-5}{40}\\ &= \frac{5a^2-6a-7}{40}\end{aligned}$$

LCD = 40

15. $$\begin{aligned}\frac{3+x-x^2}{4}-\frac{1-x+x^2}{6}-\frac{1-2x-2x^2}{3} &= \frac{3+x-x^2}{4}\cdot\frac{3}{3}-\frac{1-x+x^2}{6}\cdot\frac{2}{2}-\frac{1-2x-2x^2}{3}\cdot\frac{4}{4}\\ &= \frac{3(3+x-x^2)}{12}\quad\frac{2(1-x+x^2)}{12}\quad\frac{4(1-2x-2x^2)}{12}\\ &= \frac{9+3x-3x^2}{12}-\frac{2-2x+2x^2}{12}-\frac{4-8x-8x^2}{12}\\ &= \frac{9+3x-3x^2-2+2x-2x^2-4+8x+8x^2}{12}\\ &= \frac{3x^2+13x+3}{12}\end{aligned}$$

LCD = 12

16. $$\begin{aligned}a+\frac{b}{2} &= \frac{a}{1}\cdot\frac{2}{2}+\frac{b}{2}\\ &= \frac{2a}{2}+\frac{b}{2}\\ &= \frac{2a+b}{2}\end{aligned}$$

LCD = 2

17. $$\begin{aligned}x-\frac{y}{2} &= \frac{x}{1}\cdot\frac{2}{2}-\frac{y}{2}\\ &= \frac{2x}{2}-\frac{y}{2}\\ &= \frac{2x-y}{2}\end{aligned}$$

LCD = 2

18. $$\begin{aligned}\frac{a^2-c^2}{c}+5c &= \frac{a^2-c^2}{c}+\frac{5c}{1}\cdot\frac{c}{c}\\ &= \frac{a^2-c^2}{c}+\frac{5c^2}{c}\\ &= \frac{a^2+4c^2}{c}\end{aligned}$$

LCD = c

19. $$\begin{aligned}\frac{1-x}{3}-4x &= \frac{1-x}{3}-\frac{4x}{1}\cdot\frac{3}{3}\\ &= \frac{1-x}{3}-\frac{12x}{3}\\ &= \frac{1-13x}{3}\end{aligned}$$

LCD = 3

20. $$\begin{aligned}a+x-\frac{x^2}{a-x} &= \frac{a}{1}\cdot\frac{a-x}{a-x}+\frac{x}{1}\cdot\frac{a-x}{a-x}-\frac{x^2}{a-x}\\ &= \frac{a(a-x)}{a-x}+\frac{x(a-x)}{a-x}-\frac{x^2}{a-x}\\ &= \frac{a^2-ax+ax-x^2-x^2}{a-x}\\ &= \frac{a^2-2x^2}{a-x}\end{aligned}$$

LCD = a - x

21. $$a - b - \frac{b^2}{a+b} = \frac{a}{1}\cdot\frac{a+b}{a+b} - \frac{b}{1}\cdot\frac{a+b}{a+b} - \frac{b^2}{a+b}$$
$$= \frac{a(a+b)}{a+b} - \frac{b(a+b)}{a+b} - \frac{b^2}{a+b}$$
$$= \frac{a^2 + ab - ab - b^2 - b^2}{a+b}$$
$$= \frac{a^2 - 2b^2}{a+b}$$

LCD = $a + b$

22. $$\frac{a-b}{ab} + \frac{b-c}{bc} = \frac{a-b}{ab}\cdot\frac{c}{c} + \frac{b-c}{bc}\cdot\frac{a}{a}$$
$$= \frac{c(a-b)}{abc} + \frac{a(b-c)}{abc}$$
$$= \frac{ac - bc}{abc} + \frac{ab - ac}{abc}$$
$$= \frac{ac - bc + ab - ac}{abc}$$
$$= \frac{ab - bc}{abc}$$
$$= \frac{b(a-c)}{abc}$$
$$= \frac{a-c}{ac}$$

LCD = abc

23. $$\frac{a+b}{a-b} - \frac{a-b}{a+b} = \frac{a+b}{a-b}\cdot\frac{a+b}{a+b} - \frac{a-b}{a+b}\cdot\frac{a-b}{a-b}$$
$$= \frac{(a+b)^2}{a^2-b^2} - \frac{(a-b)^2}{a^2-b^2}$$
$$= \frac{a^2 + 2ab + b^2}{a^2 - b^2} - \frac{a^2 - 2ab + b^2}{a^2 - b^2}$$
$$= \frac{a^2 + 2ab + b^2 - a^2 + 2ab - b^2}{a^2 - b^2}$$
$$= \frac{4ab}{a^2 - b^2}$$

LCD = $(a - b)(a + b)$

24. $$x + y - \frac{x^2 + y^2}{x - y} = \frac{x+y}{1}\cdot\frac{x-y}{x-y} - \frac{x^2+y^2}{x-y}$$
$$= \frac{(x+y)(x-y)}{x-y} - \frac{x^2+y^2}{x-y}$$
$$= \frac{x^2 - y^2}{x-y} - \frac{x^2 + y^2}{x-y}$$
$$= \frac{x^2 - y^2 - x^2 - y^2}{x-y}$$
$$= \frac{-2y^2}{x-y}$$
$$= \frac{2y^2}{y-x}$$

LCD = $x - y$

25. $\frac{x}{x - 2} - \frac{x - 2}{x + 2} = \frac{x}{x - 2} \cdot \frac{x + 2}{x + 2} - \frac{x - 2}{x + 2} \cdot \frac{x - 2}{x - 2}$

$= \frac{x(x + 2)}{(x - 2)(x + 2)} - \frac{(x - 2)^2}{(x - 2)(x + 2)}$

$= \frac{x^2 + 2x}{(x - 2)(x + 2)} - \frac{x^2 - 4x + 4}{(x - 2)(x + 2)}$

$= \frac{x^2 + 2x - x^2 + 4x - 4}{(x - 2)(x + 2)}$

$= \frac{6x - 4}{(x - 2)(x + 2)}$

$= \frac{6x - 4}{x^2 - 4}$

LCD = $(x - 2)(x + 2)$

26. $x + 1 + \frac{x^2 - 3}{x - 1} = \frac{x + 1}{1} \cdot \frac{x - 1}{x - 1} + \frac{x^2 - 3}{x - 1}$

$= \frac{(x + 1)(x - 1)}{x - 1} + \frac{x^2 - 3}{x - 1}$

$= \frac{x^2 - 1}{x - 1} + \frac{x^2 - 3}{x - 1}$

$= \frac{2x^2 - 4}{x - 1}$

LCD = $x - 1$

27. $\frac{a}{a^2 - ab} - \frac{b - a}{a^2 - 2ab + b^2} = \frac{a}{a(a - b)} - \frac{b - a}{(a - b)^2}$

$= \frac{a}{a(a - b)} \cdot \frac{a - b}{a - b} - \frac{b - a}{(a - b)^2} \cdot \frac{a}{a}$

$= \frac{a(a - b)}{a(a - b)^2} - \frac{a(b - a)}{a(a - b)^2}$

$= \frac{a^2 - ab}{a(a - b)^2} - \frac{ab - a^2}{a(a - b)^2}$

$= \frac{a^2 - ab - ab + a^2}{a(a - b)^2}$

$= \frac{2a^2 - 2ab}{a(a - b)^2}$

$= \frac{2a(a - b)}{a(a - b)^2}$

$= \frac{2}{a - b}$

LCD = $a(a - b)(a - b)$

28. $$\frac{a+1}{a^2+a+1}+\frac{a-1}{a^2-a+1} = \frac{a+1}{a^2+a+1}\cdot\frac{a^2-a+1}{a^2-a+1}+\frac{a-1}{a^2-a+1}\cdot\frac{a^2+a+1}{a^2+a+1}$$

$$= \frac{(a+1)(a^2-a+1)}{(a^2+a+1)(a^2-a+1)}+\frac{(a-1)(a^2+a+1)}{(a^2+a+1)(a^2-a+1)}$$

$$= \frac{a^3+1}{(a^2+a+1)(a^2-a+1)}+\frac{a^3-1}{(a^2+a+1)(a^2-a+1)}$$

$$= \frac{2a^3}{(a^2+a+1)(a^2-a+1)}$$

LCD = $(a^2 + a + 1)(a^2 - a + 1)$

29. $$\frac{a}{a^2+ab}+\frac{b}{a^2-ab} = \frac{a}{a(a+b)}+\frac{b}{a(a-b)}$$

$$= \frac{a}{a(a+b)}\cdot\frac{a-b}{a-b}+\frac{b}{a(a-b)}\cdot\frac{a+b}{a+b}$$

$$= \frac{a(a-b)}{a(a+b)(a-b)}+\frac{b(a+b)}{a(a+b)(a-b)}$$

$$= \frac{a^2-ab+ab+b^2}{a(a+b)(a-b)}$$

$$= \frac{a^2+b^2}{a(a+b)(a-b)}$$

LCD = $a(a + b)(a - b)$

30. $$\frac{ax^2}{a^2-x^2}-\frac{2ax}{a^2+ax} = \frac{ax^2}{(a+x)(a-x)}-\frac{2ax}{a(a+x)}$$

$$= \frac{ax^2}{(a+x)(a-x)}\cdot\frac{a}{a}-\frac{2ax}{a(a+x)}\cdot\frac{a-x}{a-x}$$

$$= \frac{a^2x^2}{a(a+x)(a-x)}-\frac{2ax(a-x)}{a(a+x)(a-x)}$$

$$= \frac{a^2x^2}{a(a+x)(a-x)}-\frac{2a^2x-2ax^2}{a(a+x)(a-x)}$$

$$= \frac{a^2x^2-2a^2x+2ax^2}{a(a+x)(a-x)}$$

$$= \frac{ax(ax-2a+2x)}{a(a+x)(a-x)}$$

$$= \frac{x(ax-2a+2x)}{(a+x)(a-x)}$$

$$= \frac{ax^2-2ax+2x^2}{a^2-x^2}$$

LCD = $a(a + x)(a - x)$

31. $\dfrac{12x}{x^2 - 3x} - \dfrac{12}{x^2 - 5x + 6} = \dfrac{12x}{x(x - 3)} - \dfrac{12}{(x - 3)(x - 2)}$

$= \dfrac{12}{x - 3} - \dfrac{12}{(x - 3)(x - 2)}$

$= \dfrac{12}{x - 3} \cdot \dfrac{x - 2}{x - 2} - \dfrac{12}{(x - 3)(x - 2)}$

$= \dfrac{12(x - 2)}{(x - 3)(x - 2)} - \dfrac{12}{(x - 3)(x - 2)}$

$= \dfrac{12x - 24 - 12}{(x - 3)(x - 2)}$

$= \dfrac{12x - 36}{(x - 3)(x - 2)}$

$= \dfrac{12(x - 3)}{(x - 3)(x - 2)}$

$= \dfrac{12}{x - 2}$

LCD = $(x - 3)(x - 2)$

32. $\dfrac{4a + 1}{a^2 - 1} - \dfrac{2a}{a + a^2} = \dfrac{4a + 1}{(a + 1)(a - 1)} - \dfrac{2a}{a(1 + a)}$

$= \dfrac{4a + 1}{(a + 1)(a - 1)} - \dfrac{2}{a + 1}$

$= \dfrac{4a + 1}{(a + 1)(a - 1)} - \dfrac{2}{a + 1} \cdot \dfrac{a - 1}{a - 1}$

$= \dfrac{4a + 1}{(a + 1)(a - 1)} - \dfrac{2(a - 1)}{(a + 1)(a - 1)}$

$= \dfrac{4a + 1 - 2a + 2}{(a + 1)(a - 1)}$

$= \dfrac{2a + 3}{(a + 1)(a - 1)}$

$= \dfrac{2a + 3}{a^2 - 1}$

LCD = $(a + 1)(a - 1)$

33. $m - \frac{m^2 + n^2}{m - n} + n = \frac{m}{1} \cdot \frac{m - n}{m - n} - \frac{m^2 + n^2}{m - n} + \frac{n}{1} \cdot \frac{m - n}{m - n}$

$= \frac{m(m - n)}{m - n} - \frac{m^2 + n^2}{m - n} + \frac{n(m - n)}{m - n}$

$= \frac{m^2 - mn - m^2 - n^2 + mn - n^2}{m - n}$

$= \frac{-2n^2}{m - n}$ or $\frac{2n^2}{n - m}$

LCD = $m - n$

34. $\frac{1}{x} + 1 + \frac{2x}{1 + x} - 2 = \frac{1}{x} \cdot \frac{x + 1}{x + 1} + \frac{1}{1} \cdot \frac{x(x + 1)}{x(x + 1)} + \frac{2x}{1 + x} \cdot \frac{x}{x} - \frac{2}{1} \cdot \frac{x(x + 1)}{x(x + 1)}$

$= \frac{x + 1}{x(x + 1)} + \frac{x(x + 1)}{x(x + 1)} + \frac{2x^2}{x(x + 1)} - \frac{2x(x + 1)}{x(x + 1)}$

$= \frac{x + 1 + x^2 + x + 2x^2 - 2x^2 - 2x}{x(x + 1)}$

$= \frac{x^2 + 1}{x(x + 1)}$ or $\frac{x^2 + 1}{x^2 + x}$

LCD = $x(x + 1)$

35. $3a - 2x - \frac{8a^2 - 4x^2}{3a + 2x} = \frac{3a}{1} \cdot \frac{3a + 2x}{3a + 2x} - \frac{2x}{1} \cdot \frac{3a + 2x}{3a + 2x} - \frac{8a^2 - 4x^2}{3a + 2x}$

$= \frac{3a(3a + 2x)}{3a + 2x} - \frac{2x(3a + 2x)}{3a + 2x} - \frac{8a^2 - 4x^2}{3a + 2x}$

$= \frac{9a^2 + 6ax - 6ax - 4x^2 - 8a^2 + 4x^2}{3a + 2x}$

$= \frac{a^2}{3a + 2x}$

LCD = $3a + 2x$

36. $\frac{1}{a + b} - \frac{1}{a - b} + \frac{2a}{a^2 - b^2} = \frac{1}{a + b} \cdot \frac{a - b}{a - b} - \frac{1}{a - b} \cdot \frac{a + b}{a + b} + \frac{2a}{(a + b)(a - b)}$

$= \frac{a - b}{(a + b)(a - b)} - \frac{a + b}{(a + b)(a - b)} + \frac{2a}{(a + b)(a - b)}$

$= \frac{a - b - a - b + 2a}{(a + b)(a - b)}$

$= \frac{2a - 2b}{(a + b)(a - b)}$

$= \frac{2(a - b)}{(a + b)(a - b)}$

$= \frac{2}{a + b}$

LCD = $(a + b)(a - b)$

37. $\frac{a+x}{a-x} + \frac{a-x}{a+x} + \frac{4ax}{a^2-x^2} = \frac{a+x}{a-x} \cdot \frac{a+x}{a+x} + \frac{a-x}{a+x} \cdot \frac{a-x}{a-x} + \frac{4ax}{a^2-x^2}$

$= \frac{(a+x)^2}{(a+x)(a-x)} + \frac{(a-x)^2}{(a+x)(a-x)} + \frac{4ax}{(a+x)(a-x)}$

$= \frac{a^2 + 2ax + x^2 + a^2 - 2ax + x^2 + 4ax}{(a+x)(a-x)}$

$= \frac{2a^2 + 4ax + 2x^2}{(a+x)(a-x)}$

$= \frac{2(a^2 + 2ax + x^2)}{(a+x)(a-x)}$

$= \frac{2(a+x)(a+x)}{(a+x)(a-x)}$

$= \frac{2(a+x)}{a-x}$

LCD = $(a - x)(a + x)$

38. $\frac{a}{a-2} - \frac{a-2}{a+2} + \frac{3}{4-a^2} = \frac{a}{a-2} - \frac{a-2}{a+2} + \frac{-3}{a^2-4}$

$= \frac{a}{a-2} \cdot \frac{a+2}{a+2} - \frac{a-2}{a+2} \cdot \frac{a-2}{a-2} + \frac{-3}{a^2-4}$

$= \frac{a(a+2)}{(a-2)(a+2)} - \frac{(a-2)^2}{(a-2)(a+2)} + \frac{-3}{(a-2)(a+2)}$

$= \frac{a^2 + 2a - (a^2 - 4a + 4) + (-3)}{(a-2)(a+2)}$

$= \frac{a^2 + 2a - a^2 + 4a - 4 - 3}{(a-2)(a+2)}$

$= \frac{6a - 7}{(a-2)(a+2)}$

LCD = $(a + 2)(a - 2)$

39. $\frac{a+1}{a-1} + \frac{2}{a+1} + \frac{4a}{1-a^2} = \frac{a+1}{a-1} + \frac{2}{a+1} - \frac{4a}{a^2-1}$

$= \frac{a+1}{a-1} \cdot \frac{a+1}{a+1} + \frac{2}{a+1} \cdot \frac{a-1}{a-1} - \frac{4a}{a^2-1}$

$= \frac{(a+1)^2}{(a-1)(a+1)} + \frac{2(a-1)}{(a-1)(a+1)} - \frac{4a}{(a-1)(a+1)}$

$= \frac{a^2 + 2a + 1 + 2a - 2 - 4a}{(a-1)(a+1)}$

$= \frac{a^2 - 1}{(a-1)(a+1)}$

$= \frac{(a+1)(a-1)}{(a+1)(a-1)}$

$= 1$

LCD = $(a + 1)(a - 1)$

40. $$\frac{5x+2}{x^2-4} + \frac{2}{x-2} - \frac{3}{2-x} = \frac{5x+2}{x^2-4} + \frac{2}{x-2} + \frac{3}{x-2}$$

$$= \frac{5x+2}{x^2-4} + \frac{5}{x-2}$$

$$= \frac{5x+2}{x^2-4} + \frac{5}{x-2} \cdot \frac{x+2}{x+2}$$

$$= \frac{5x+2}{(x+2)(x-2)} + \frac{5(x+2)}{(x+2)(x-2)}$$

$$= \frac{5x+2+5x+10}{(x+2)(x-2)}$$

$$= \frac{10x+12}{(x+2)(x-2)}$$

$$= \frac{2(5x+6)}{(x+2)(x-2)}$$

LCD = $(x + 2)(x - 2)$

41. $$\frac{x(a+x)}{a-x} - \frac{3ax-x^2}{x-a} + 4a = \frac{x(a+x)}{a-x} + \frac{3ax-x^2}{a-x} + \frac{4a(a-x)}{a-x}$$

$$= \frac{ax+x^2+3ax-x^2+4a^2-4ax}{a-x}$$

$$= \frac{4a^2}{a-x}$$

LCD = $a - x$

42. $$\frac{x^2}{(x+y)^2} + \frac{x}{x+y} + 2 = \frac{x^2}{(x+y)^2} + \frac{x}{x+y} \cdot \frac{x+y}{x+y} + 2 \cdot \frac{(x+y)^2}{(x+y)^2}$$

$$= \frac{x^2}{(x+y)^2} + \frac{x(x+y)}{(x+y)^2} + \frac{2(x+y)^2}{(x+y)^2}$$

$$= \frac{x^2+x^2+xy+2(x^2+2xy+y^2)}{(x+y)^2}$$

$$= \frac{2x^2+xy+2x^2+4xy+2y^2}{(x+y)^2}$$

$$= \frac{4x^2+5xy+2y^2}{(x+y)^2}$$

LCD = $(x + y)^2$

43. $$\frac{1}{b} + \frac{b + 2}{3b - 6} - \frac{b}{2b - 4} = \frac{1}{b} + \frac{b + 2}{3(b - 2)} - \frac{b}{2(b - 2)}$$
$$= \frac{1}{b} \cdot \frac{6(b - 2)}{6(b - 2)} + \frac{b + 2}{3(b - 2)} \cdot \frac{2b}{2b} - \frac{b}{2(b - 2)} \cdot \frac{3b}{3b}$$
$$= \frac{6(b - 2)}{6b(b - 2)} + \frac{2b(b + 2)}{6b(b - 2)} - \frac{3b(b)}{6b(b - 2)}$$
$$= \frac{6b - 12 + 2b^2 + 4b - 3b^2}{6b(b - 2)}$$
$$= \frac{-b^2 + 10b - 12}{6b(b - 2)} \quad \text{or} \quad -\frac{b^2 - 10b + 12}{6b(b - 2)}$$

LCD = $6b(b - 2)$

44. $$\frac{x}{x^2 + xy} + \frac{x + y}{xy - y^2} - \frac{y}{x^2 - y^2} = \frac{x}{x(x + y)} + \frac{x + y}{y(x - y)} - \frac{y}{(x - y)(x + y)}$$
$$= \frac{1}{x + y} + \frac{x + y}{y(x - y)} - \frac{y}{(x - y)(x + y)}$$
$$= \frac{1}{x + y} \cdot \frac{y(x - y)}{y(x - y)} + \frac{x + y}{y(x - y)} \cdot \frac{x + y}{x + y} - \frac{y}{(x + y)(x - y)} \cdot \frac{y}{y}$$
$$= \frac{y(x - y)}{y(x - y)(x + y)} + \frac{(x + y)^2}{y(x - y)(x + y)} - \frac{y^2}{y(x - y)(x + y)}$$
$$= \frac{xy - y^2 + x^2 + 2xy + y^2 - y^2}{y(x - y)(x + y)}$$
$$= \frac{x^2 + 3xy - y^2}{y(x + y)(x - y)}$$

LCD = $y(x + y)(x - y)$

<u>Exercises 8.9</u> Pages 182-183

1. $\frac{\cancel{2}}{3} \cdot \frac{5}{\underset{3}{\cancel{6}}} = \frac{5}{9}$

2. $\frac{\cancel{3}}{\cancel{4}} \cdot \frac{\cancel{4}}{\underset{5}{\cancel{15}}} = \frac{1}{5}$

3. $\frac{\overset{b}{\cancel{3ab}}}{\underset{2x}{\cancel{4xy}}} \cdot \frac{\cancel{2y}}{\underset{a}{\cancel{3a^2}}} = \frac{b}{2ax}$

4. $\frac{\overset{x}{\cancel{5xy}}}{\underset{2c}{\cancel{2ac}}} \cdot \frac{\overset{3x}{\cancel{3ax}}}{\underset{2y}{\cancel{10y^2}}} = \frac{3x^2}{4cy}$

5. $\frac{\overset{2b}{\cancel{\overset{4b}{\cancel{4ab}}}}}{\underset{5c}{\cancel{\underset{10c}{\cancel{10c^2}}}}} \cdot \frac{\overset{3b}{\cancel{3bc}}}{\underset{a^2}{\cancel{a^3}}} = \frac{6b^2}{5a^2c}$

6. $\frac{\overset{n}{\cancel{4mn}}}{\underset{y}{\cancel{3xy}}} \cdot \frac{\overset{-5b}{\cancel{-15bx}}}{\underset{4m}{\cancel{16m^2}}} = \frac{-5bn}{4my}$

7. $\frac{\overset{a}{\cancel{\overset{2a}{\cancel{2ax}}}}}{\underset{3y}{\cancel{\underset{6y}{\cancel{12by}}}}} \cdot \frac{\overset{-5b}{\cancel{-10b^2}}}{\underset{x}{\cancel{x^2}}} = \frac{-5ab}{3xy} = -\frac{5ab}{3xy}$

8. $\frac{a}{a + b} \cdot \frac{b}{a - b} = \frac{ab}{a^2 - b^2}$

9. $\frac{\overset{y}{\cancel{xy^2}}}{\underset{4\cancel{(5 - 2x)}}{20 - 8x}} \cdot \frac{\overset{5\cancel{(5 - 2x)}}{25 - 10x}}{\underset{x}{\cancel{x^2y}}} = \frac{5y}{4x}$

10. $$\frac{1 - 6x + 5x^2}{x^2 - 3x + 2} \cdot \frac{2 - x}{1 - x} = \frac{(1 - 5x)(1 - x)}{(x - 2)(x - 1)} \cdot \frac{x - 2}{x - 1}$$
$$= \frac{(5x - 1)\cancel{(x - 1)}}{\underset{1}{\cancel{(x - 2)}\cancel{(x - 1)}}} \cdot \frac{\cancel{x - 2}}{x - 1}$$
$$= \frac{5x - 1}{x - 1}$$

11. $$\frac{a + c}{2} \cdot \frac{6}{a^2 - c^2} = \frac{\cancel{a + c}}{\cancel{2}} \cdot \frac{\overset{3}{\cancel{6}}}{\cancel{(a + c)}(a - c)} = \frac{3}{a - c}$$

12. $$\frac{a^2 - b^2}{4} \cdot \frac{4}{a - b} = \frac{(a + b)\cancel{(a - b)}}{\cancel{4}} \cdot \frac{\cancel{4}}{\cancel{a - b}} = a + b$$

13. $$\frac{x^2 - y^2}{11} \cdot \frac{22}{x - y} = \frac{(x + y)\cancel{(x - y)}}{\cancel{11}} \cdot \frac{\overset{2}{\cancel{22}}}{\cancel{x - y}} = 2(x + y) = 2x + 2y$$

14. $$\frac{b + c}{b^2 - 1} \cdot \frac{b + 1}{b + c} = \frac{\cancel{b + c}}{\cancel{(b + 1)}(b - 1)} \cdot \frac{\cancel{b + 1}}{\underset{1}{\cancel{b + c}}} = \frac{1}{b - 1}$$

15. $$\frac{a^2 + 2ab + b^2}{5} \cdot \frac{10}{a + b} = \frac{(a + b)\cancel{(a + b)}}{\cancel{5}} \cdot \frac{\overset{2}{\cancel{10}}}{\underset{1}{\cancel{a + b}}} = 2(a + b) = 2a + 2b$$

16. $$\frac{x^2 - 7x + 10}{mn} \cdot \frac{5mn}{x - 5} = \frac{\cancel{(x - 5)}(x - 2)}{\cancel{mn}} \cdot \frac{\overset{5}{\cancel{5mn}}}{\cancel{x - 5}} = 5(x - 2) = 5x - 10$$

17. $$\frac{(x + y)^2}{x^2 + 8x + 15} \cdot \frac{x + 5}{x + y} = \frac{(x + y)\cancel{(x + y)}}{\cancel{(x + 5)}(x + 3)} \cdot \frac{\cancel{x + 5}}{\cancel{x + y}} = \frac{x + y}{x + 3}$$

18. $$\frac{a^2 - b^2}{a^2 + ab} \cdot \frac{4a}{a - b} = \frac{\cancel{(a + b)}\cancel{(a - b)}}{\cancel{a}\cancel{(a + b)}} \cdot \frac{\overset{4}{\cancel{4a}}}{\cancel{a - b}} = 4$$

19. $$\frac{3a^2}{5a - 10} \cdot \frac{3a - 6}{4a^3} = \frac{\overset{3}{\cancel{3a^2}}}{5\cancel{(a - 2)}} \cdot \frac{3\cancel{(a - 2)}}{\underset{4a}{\cancel{4a^3}}} = \frac{9}{20a}$$

Key to Unit 8, pages 182-183

20. $\frac{x^2 + 2x + 1}{y} \cdot \frac{4y^2}{x^2 - 1} = \frac{(x + 1)\cancel{(x + 1)}}{\cancel{y}} \cdot \frac{\overset{4y}{\cancel{4y^2}}}{\cancel{(x + 1)}(x - 1)} = \frac{4y(x + 1)}{x - 1}$

21. $\frac{c + d}{5x} \cdot \frac{10x^2}{c^2 - cd - 2d^2} \cdot \frac{ac - 2ad}{2x} = \frac{\cancel{c + d}}{\cancel{5x}} \cdot \frac{\overset{2x}{\cancel{10x^2}}}{\cancel{(c - 2d)}\cancel{(c + d)}} \cdot \frac{a\cancel{(c - 2d)}}{\cancel{2x}} = a$

22. $\frac{a - b}{(a + b)^2} \cdot \frac{a^2 - b^2}{3} \cdot \frac{4}{a^2 - 2ab + b^2}$

$= \frac{\cancel{a - b}}{(a + b)\cancel{(a + b)}} \cdot \frac{\cancel{(a + b)}\cancel{(a - b)}}{3} \cdot \frac{4}{\cancel{(a - b)}\cancel{(a - b)}}$

$= \frac{4}{3(a + b)}$

$= \frac{4}{3a + 3b}$

23. $\frac{x^2 + x - 2}{4x - 12} \cdot \frac{3}{x^2 - x - 6} \cdot \frac{x - 3}{x - 1}$

$= \frac{\cancel{(x + 2)}\cancel{(x - 1)}}{4(x - 3)} \cdot \frac{3}{\cancel{(x - 3)}\cancel{(x + 2)}} \cdot \frac{\cancel{x - 3}}{\cancel{x - 1}}$

$= \frac{3}{4(x - 3)}$

$= \frac{3}{4x - 12}$

24. $\frac{a - 3}{a + 7} \cdot \frac{a^2 + 4a - 21}{a^2 - 9} = \frac{a - 3}{\cancel{a + 7}} \cdot \frac{\cancel{(a + 7)}(a - 3)}{(a + 3)\cancel{(a - 3)}} = \frac{a - 3}{a + 3}$

25. $\frac{x}{} \cdot \frac{x^2 - y^2}{x - y} \cdot \frac{y^2}{x^2} = \frac{\cancel{x}}{\cancel{y}} \cdot \frac{(x + y)(x - y)}{\cancel{x - y}} \cdot \frac{\cancel{y^2}}{\cancel{x^2}} = \frac{y(x + y)}{x}$

26. $\frac{x^2 + 3x + 2}{x^2 - 3x - 10} \cdot \frac{x^2 - 6x + 5}{x^2 + 8x + 7} = \frac{\cancel{(x + 2)}\cancel{(x + 1)}}{\cancel{(x - 5)}\cancel{(x + 2)}} \cdot \frac{\cancel{(x - 5)}(x - 1)}{(x + 7)\cancel{(x + 1)}} = \frac{x - 1}{x + 7}$

27. $\frac{p+2}{x-3}\cdot\frac{3x^2-27}{p^2-24}\cdot\frac{p-2}{3x+9} = \frac{\cancel{p+2}}{\cancel{x-3}}\cdot\frac{\cancel{3(x+3)(x-3)}}{\cancel{(p+2)(p-2)}}\cdot\frac{\cancel{p-2}}{\cancel{3(x+3)}} = 1$

28. $\frac{(a-b)^2}{a+b}\cdot\frac{b}{a^2-ab}\cdot\frac{(a+b)^2}{a^2-b^2} = \frac{\cancel{(a-b)(a-b)}}{\cancel{a+b}}\cdot\frac{b}{a\cancel{(a-b)}}\cdot\frac{\cancel{(a+b)(a+b)}}{\underset{1}{\cancel{(a+b)(a-b)}}} = \frac{b}{a}$

29. $\left(\frac{2}{3x}-1\right)\cdot\frac{9x^2y}{4-9x^2}\cdot\frac{2+3x}{4y^3} = \frac{\cancel{2-3x}}{\cancel{3x}}\cdot\frac{\overset{3x}{\cancel{\overset{3xy}{\cancel{9x^2y}}}}}{\cancel{(2+3x)}\cancel{(2-3x)}}\cdot\frac{\cancel{2+3x}}{\underset{4y^2}{\cancel{4y^3}}} = \frac{3x}{4y^2}$

30. $\frac{4a-b}{2x+y}\cdot\frac{2a}{4a^2-ab}\cdot\frac{4x^2-y^2}{4} = \frac{\cancel{4a-b}}{\cancel{2x+y}}\cdot\frac{\overset{2}{\cancel{2a}}}{\cancel{a(4a-b)}}\cdot\frac{\cancel{(2x+y)}(2x-y)}{\underset{2}{\cancel{4}}} = \frac{2x-y}{2}$

31. $\frac{p^4-q^4}{(p-q)^2}\cdot\frac{p-q}{p^2+pq}\cdot\frac{p^2}{p^2+q^2} = \frac{\cancel{(p^2+q^2)(p+q)(p-q)}}{\cancel{(p-q)(p-q)}}\cdot\frac{\cancel{p-q}}{\cancel{p(p+q)}}\cdot\frac{\overset{p}{\cancel{p^2}}}{\cancel{p^2+q^2}} = p$

Exercises 8.10 Page 184

1. $\frac{b}{a}$ 2. $\frac{p}{3m}$ 3. $\frac{1}{rs}$ 4. $\frac{bc}{2a^2}$ 5. $\frac{1}{3tu}$ 6. $3m$ 7. $\frac{ab}{4}$ 8. $\frac{b-y}{a-x}$

Exercises 8.11 Pages 184-185

1. $\frac{5mn}{6bx}\div\frac{10m^2n}{3ax^2} = \frac{\cancel{5mn}}{\underset{2b}{\cancel{6bx}}}\cdot\frac{\overset{ax}{\cancel{3ax^2}}}{\underset{2m}{\cancel{10m^2n}}} = \frac{ax}{4bm}$

2. $\frac{3abm}{7}\div abx = \frac{\overset{3m}{\cancel{3abm}}}{7}\cdot\frac{1}{\underset{x}{\cancel{abx}}} = \frac{3m}{7x}$

3. $\frac{my-y^2}{(m+y)^2}\div\frac{y^2}{m^2-y^2} = \frac{my-y^2}{(m+y)^2}\cdot\frac{m^2-y^2}{y^2} = \frac{\cancel{y}(m-y)}{(m+y)\cancel{(m+y)}}\cdot\frac{\cancel{(m+y)}(m-y)}{\underset{y}{\cancel{y^2}}} = \frac{(m-y)^2}{y(m+y)}$

4. $\frac{(a-b)^2}{a+b}\div\frac{a^2-ab}{b} = \frac{(a-b)^2}{a+b}\cdot\frac{b}{a^2-ab} = \frac{(a-b)\cancel{(a-b)}}{a+b}\cdot\frac{b}{a\cancel{(a-b)}} = \frac{b(a-b)}{a(a+b)}$

5. $(4a+2)\div\frac{2a+1}{5a} = 4a+2\cdot\frac{5a}{2a+1} = \frac{2\cancel{(2a+1)}}{1}\cdot\frac{5a}{\cancel{2a+1}} = 10a$

6. $$\frac{a^4 - b^4}{a^2 - 2ab + b^2} \div \frac{a^2 + b^2}{a^2 - ab} = \frac{a^4 - b^4}{a^2 - 2ab + b^2} \cdot \frac{a^2 - ab}{a^2 + b^2}$$

$$= \frac{\cancel{(a^2 + b^2)}(a + b)\cancel{(a - b)}}{\cancel{(a - b)}\cancel{(a - b)}} \cdot \frac{a\cancel{(a - b)}}{\cancel{a^2 + b^2}}$$

$$= a(a + b)$$

$$= a^2 + ab$$

7. $$(x \div \frac{1}{y}) \div (y^2 \div \frac{1}{x^2}) = (x \cdot \frac{y}{1}) \div (y^2 \cdot \frac{x^2}{1})$$

$$= xy \div x^2y^2$$

$$= \frac{\cancel{xy}}{1} \cdot \frac{1}{\cancel{x^2y^2}_{\,xy}}$$

$$= \frac{1}{xy}$$

8. $$(a + c) \div \left(\frac{a^2 - c^2}{1 + x} \div \frac{a - c}{1 - x^2}\right) = (a + c) \div \left(\frac{a^2 - c^2}{1 + x} \cdot \frac{1 - x^2}{a - c}\right)$$

$$= (a + c) \div \left[\frac{(a + c)\cancel{(a - c)}}{\cancel{1 + x}} \cdot \frac{\cancel{(1 + x)}(1 - x)}{\cancel{a - c}}\right]$$

$$= (a + c) \div \left[(a + c)(1 - x)\right]$$

$$= \frac{\cancel{(a + c)}}{1} \cdot \frac{1}{\cancel{(a + c)}(1 - x)}$$

$$= \frac{1}{1 - x}$$

<u>Exercises 8.12</u> Pages 185 -186

1. $$\frac{\frac{a}{b}}{\frac{c}{d}} = \frac{a}{b} \div \frac{c}{d} = \frac{a}{b} \cdot \frac{d}{c} = \frac{ad}{bc}$$

2. $$\frac{\frac{4}{7}}{\frac{7}{m}} = \frac{4}{7} \div \frac{7}{m} = \frac{4}{7} \cdot \frac{m}{7} = \frac{4m}{49}$$

3. $$\frac{\frac{3}{p}}{\frac{p}{6}} = \frac{3}{p} \div \frac{p}{6} = \frac{3}{p} \cdot \frac{6}{p} = \frac{18}{p^2}$$

4. $$\frac{\frac{x^2}{y^2}}{\frac{x}{y}} = \frac{x^2}{y^2} \div \frac{x}{y} = \frac{\overset{x}{\cancel{x^2}}}{\underset{y}{\cancel{y^2}}} \cdot \frac{\cancel{y}}{\cancel{x}} = \frac{x}{y}$$

5. $$\frac{\frac{2a}{3b}}{\frac{4a^2}{9b^2}} = \frac{\cancel{2a}}{\cancel{3b}} \cdot \frac{\overset{3b}{\cancel{9b^2}}}{\underset{2a}{\cancel{4a^2}}} = \frac{3b}{2a}$$

6. $$\frac{\frac{x^2}{y}}{\frac{2x^2}{y^2}} = \frac{\cancel{x^2}}{\cancel{y}} \cdot \frac{\overset{y}{\cancel{y^2}}}{\underset{2}{\cancel{2x^2}}} = \frac{y}{2}$$

7. $$\frac{\frac{2p}{q}}{\frac{p}{t}} = \frac{2p}{q} \cdot \frac{t}{p} = \frac{2t}{q}$$

8. $$\frac{\frac{2b}{3c}}{\frac{4b^2}{9c^2}} = \frac{2b}{3c} \cdot \frac{9c^2}{4b^2} = \frac{3c}{2b}$$

9. $$\frac{a + \frac{1}{4}}{b - \frac{1}{2}} = \frac{\frac{4a}{4} + \frac{1}{4}}{\frac{2b}{2} - \frac{1}{2}}$$
$$= \frac{\frac{4a + 1}{4}}{\frac{2b - 1}{2}}$$
$$= \frac{4a + 1}{4} \cdot \frac{2}{2b - 1}$$
$$= \frac{4a + 1}{2(2b - 1)}$$
$$= \frac{4a + 1}{4b - 2}$$

10. $$\frac{p + \frac{a}{b}}{q - \frac{c}{d}} = \frac{\frac{bp}{b} + \frac{a}{b}}{\frac{dq}{d} - \frac{c}{d}}$$
$$= \frac{\frac{bp + a}{b}}{\frac{dq - c}{d}}$$
$$= \frac{bp + a}{b} \cdot \frac{d}{dq - c}$$
$$= \frac{d(bp + a)}{b(dq - c)}$$
$$= \frac{bdp + ad}{bdq - bc}$$

11. $$\frac{\frac{x + 2y}{w - 4z}}{\frac{x - 2y}{w + 4z}} = \frac{x + 2y}{w - 4z} \cdot \frac{w + 4z}{x - 2y}$$
$$= \frac{(x + 2y)(w + 4z)}{(x - 2y)(w - 4z)}$$

12. $$\frac{\frac{w}{x} + \frac{y}{z}}{\frac{a}{b} - \frac{c}{d}} = \frac{\frac{wz}{xz} + \frac{xy}{xz}}{\frac{ad}{bd} - \frac{bc}{bd}}$$
$$= \frac{\frac{wz + xy}{xz}}{\frac{ad - bc}{bd}}$$
$$= \frac{wz + xy}{xz} \cdot \frac{bd}{ad - bc}$$
$$= \frac{bd(wz + xy)}{xz(ad - bc)}$$

Exercises 8.13 Pages 187-188

The check is left for the teacher.

1. $$2x + \frac{x}{3} = \frac{35}{3}$$
$$3(2x + \frac{x}{3}) = 3(\frac{35}{3})$$
$$6x + x = 35$$
$$7x = 35$$
$$x = 5$$

2. $$\frac{x}{4} + 10 = 13$$
$$4(\frac{x}{4} + 10) = 4(13)$$
$$x + 40 = 52$$
$$x = 12$$

3. $$\frac{x}{2} + \frac{x}{6} = \frac{10}{3}$$
$$6(\frac{x}{2} + \frac{x}{6}) = 6(\frac{10}{3})$$
$$3x + x = 20$$
$$4x = 20$$
$$x = 5$$

4.
$$7\frac{1}{2} - \frac{3x}{14} = \frac{x}{7}$$
$$\frac{15}{2} - \frac{3x}{14} = \frac{x}{7}$$
$$14\left(\frac{15}{2} - \frac{3x}{14}\right) = 14\left(\frac{x}{7}\right)$$
$$105 - 3x = 2x$$
$$-5x = -105$$
$$x = 21$$

5.
$$\frac{x}{2} + \frac{x}{3} - \frac{x}{4} + \frac{3x}{10} - \frac{5x}{12} = 7$$
$$60\left(\frac{x}{2} + \frac{x}{3} - \frac{x}{4} + \frac{3x}{10} - \frac{5x}{12}\right) = 60(7)$$
$$30x + 20x - 15x + 18x - 25x = 420$$
$$28x = 420$$
$$x = 15$$

6.
$$\frac{25x}{18} - \frac{5x}{9} + \frac{2x}{3} - \frac{5x}{6} = 2$$
$$18\left(\frac{25x}{18} - \frac{5x}{9} + \frac{2x}{3} - \frac{5x}{6}\right) = 18(2)$$
$$25x - 10x + 12x - 15x = 36$$
$$12x = 36$$
$$x = 3$$

7.
$$\frac{2x}{3} - \frac{7x}{8} + \frac{5x}{18} + \frac{x}{24} = \frac{4}{9}$$
$$72\left(\frac{2x}{3} - \frac{7x}{8} + \frac{5x}{18} + \frac{x}{24}\right) = 72\left(\frac{4}{9}\right)$$
$$48x - 63x + 20x + 3x = 32$$
$$8x = 32$$
$$x = 4$$

8.
$$\frac{3x}{4} + \frac{7x}{16} - \frac{x}{2} - \frac{9x}{16} = \frac{1}{8}$$
$$16\left(\frac{3x}{4} + \frac{7x}{16} - \frac{x}{2} - \frac{9x}{16}\right) = 16\left(\frac{1}{8}\right)$$
$$12x + 7x - 8x - 9x = 2$$
$$2x = 2$$
$$x = 1$$

9.
$$1.07x + .52 = .15x + 10.12 + .68x$$
$$100(1.07x + .52) = 100(.15x + 10.12 + .68x)$$
$$107x + 52 = 15x + 1012 + 68x$$
$$107x + 52 = 83x + 1012$$
$$24x + 52 = 1012$$
$$24x = 960$$
$$x = 40$$

10.
$$\frac{.2x}{7} - \frac{.1x}{4} - \frac{.1x}{2} + \frac{.4x}{7} = \frac{.3}{14}$$
$$10\left(\frac{.2x}{7} - \frac{.1x}{4} - \frac{.1x}{2} + \frac{.4x}{7}\right) = 10\left(\frac{.3}{14}\right)$$
$$\frac{2x}{7} - \frac{x}{4} - \frac{x}{2} + \frac{4x}{7} = \frac{3}{14}$$
$$28\left(\frac{2x}{7} - \frac{x}{4} - \frac{x}{2} + \frac{4x}{7}\right) = 28\left(\frac{3}{14}\right)$$
$$8x - 7x - 14x + 16x = 6$$
$$3x = 6$$
$$x = 2$$

11.
$$\frac{3x}{4} - \frac{7x}{12} = \frac{11x}{36} - \frac{8x}{9} + \frac{3}{2}$$
$$36\left(\frac{3x}{4} - \frac{7x}{12}\right) = 36\left(\frac{11x}{36} - \frac{8x}{9} + \frac{3}{2}\right)$$
$$27x - 21x = 11x - 32x + 54$$
$$6x = -21x + 54$$
$$27x = 54$$
$$x = 2$$

12.
$$\frac{n + 4}{.3} + \frac{2 - 2n}{.6} = \frac{n + 1}{.2} - \frac{10}{.3}$$
$$\frac{1}{10}\left(\frac{n + 4}{.3} + \frac{2 - 2n}{.6}\right) = \frac{1}{10}\left(\frac{n + 1}{.2} - \frac{10}{.3}\right)$$
$$\frac{n + 4}{3} + \frac{2 - 2n}{6} = \frac{n + 1}{2} - \frac{10}{3}$$
$$6\left(\frac{n + 4}{3} + \frac{2 - 2n}{6}\right) = 6\left(\frac{n + 1}{2} - \frac{10}{3}\right)$$
$$2(n + 4) + 2 - 2n = 3(n + 1) - 20$$
$$2n + 8 + 2 - 2n = 3n + 3 - 20$$
$$10 = 3n - 17$$
$$-3n = -27$$
$$n = 9$$

13.
$$2.5x - 3.35 = 2.9 - 3.05x$$
$$100(2.5x - 3.35) = 100(2.9 - 3.05x)$$
$$250x - 335 = 290 - 305x$$
$$555x - 335 = 290$$
$$555x = 625$$
$$x \approx 1.13$$

14.
$$\begin{aligned} 3.72x + 1.83 &= 1.85x + 4.9 \\ 100(3.72x + 1.83) &= 100(1.85x + 4.9) \\ 372x + 183 &= 185x + 490 \\ 187x + 183 &= 490 \\ 187x &= 307 \\ x &\approx 1.64 \end{aligned}$$

15.
$$\begin{aligned} \frac{3x - 5}{x + 6} &= \frac{1}{8} \\ 8\cancel{(x + 6)}\left(\frac{3x - 5}{\cancel{x + 6}}\right) &= \cancel{8}(x + 6)\left(\frac{1}{\cancel{8}}\right) \\ 8(3x - 5) &= x + 6 \\ 24x - 40 &= x + 6 \\ 23x - 40 &= 6 \\ 23x &= 46 \\ x &= 2 \end{aligned}$$

16.
$$\begin{aligned} \frac{m - 2}{m + 3} &= \frac{3}{4} \\ 4\cancel{(m + 3)}\left(\frac{m - 2}{\cancel{m + 3}}\right) &= \cancel{4}(m + 3)\left(\frac{3}{\cancel{4}}\right) \\ 4(m - 2) &= 3(m + 3) \\ 4m - 8 &= 3m + 9 \\ m - 8 &= 9 \\ m &= 17 \end{aligned}$$

17.
$$\begin{aligned} \frac{9x + 5}{14} + \frac{8x - 7}{6x + 2} &= \frac{36x + 15}{56} + \frac{10\frac{1}{4}}{14} \\ \frac{8x - 7}{6x + 2} &= \frac{36x + 15}{56} + \frac{41}{56} - \frac{4(9x + 5)}{56} \\ \frac{8x - 7}{6x + 2} &= \frac{36x + 15 + 41 - 36x - 20}{56} \\ \frac{8x - 7}{6x + 2} &= \frac{36}{56} \\ \frac{8x - 7}{6x + 2} &= \frac{9}{14} \\ 14\cancel{(6x + 2)}\left(\frac{8x - 7}{\cancel{6x + 2}}\right) &= \cancel{14}(6x + 2)\left(\frac{9}{\cancel{14}}\right) \\ 112x - 98 &= 54x + 18 \\ 58x &= 116 \\ x &= 2 \end{aligned}$$

18.
$$\begin{aligned} \frac{3x - 2}{2x - 5} + \frac{3x - 21}{5} &= \frac{6x - 22}{10} \\ \frac{3x - 2}{2x - 5} &= \frac{6x - 22}{10} - \frac{3x - 21}{5} \\ \frac{3x - 2}{2x - 5} &= \frac{\cancel{6x} - 22 - \cancel{6x} + 42}{10} \\ \frac{3x - 2}{2x - 5} &= \frac{20}{10} \\ \frac{3x - 2}{2x - 5} &= 2 \\ 3x - 2 &= 4x - 10 \\ 8 &= x \end{aligned}$$

19.
$$\begin{aligned} \frac{4x + 3}{9} &= \frac{8x + 19}{18} - \frac{7x - 29}{5x - 12} \\ \frac{4x + 3}{9} - \frac{8x + 19}{18} &= -\frac{7x - 29}{5x - 12} \\ \frac{\cancel{8x} + 6 - \cancel{8x} - 19}{18} &= -\frac{7x - 29}{5x - 12} \\ \frac{-13}{18} &= -\frac{7x - 29}{5x - 12} \\ \cancel{18}(5x - 12)\left(-\frac{13}{\cancel{18}}\right) &= 18\cancel{(5x - 12)}\left(\frac{7x - 29}{\cancel{5x - 12}}\right) \\ -65x + 156 &= -126x + 522 \\ 61x &= 366 \\ x &= 6 \end{aligned}$$

20.
$$\begin{aligned} \frac{6p^2 + p}{15p} - \frac{2p - 4}{7p - 13} &= \frac{2p - 1}{5} \\ \frac{\cancel{p}(6p + 1)}{15\cancel{p}} + \frac{1 - 2p}{5} &= \frac{2p - 4}{7p - 13} \\ \frac{\cancel{6p} + 1 + 3 - \cancel{6p}}{15} &= \frac{2p - 4}{7p - 13} \\ \frac{4}{15} &= \frac{2p - 4}{7p - 13} \\ 28p - 52 &= 30p - 60 \\ 8 &= 2p \\ 4 &= p \end{aligned}$$

21.
$$\begin{aligned} \frac{4x}{2x - 3} &= \frac{3x}{2x - 3} - \frac{1}{10} \\ \frac{x}{2x - 3} &= -\frac{1}{10} \\ 10\cancel{(2x - 3)}\left(\frac{x}{\cancel{2x - 3}}\right) &= \cancel{10}(2x - 3)\left(\frac{-1}{\cancel{10}}\right) \\ 10x &= -2x + 3 \\ 12x &= 3 \\ x &= \frac{3}{12} \\ x &= \frac{1}{4} \end{aligned}$$

22.

$$\frac{9n}{n-2} = \frac{8n}{n-1} + 1$$

$$\cancel{(n-2)}(n-1)\left(\frac{9n}{\cancel{n-2}}\right) = (n-2)(n-1)\left(\frac{8n}{n-1} + 1\right)$$

$$9n(n-1) = 8n(n-2) + (n-2)(n-1)$$

$$9n^2 - 9n = 8n^2 - 16n + n^2 - 3n + 2$$

$$9n^2 - 9n = 9n^2 - 19n + 2$$

$$10n = 2$$

$$n = \frac{2}{10}$$

$$n = \frac{1}{5}$$

23.

$$\frac{x}{x+2} = \frac{x+2}{2x} + \frac{1}{2}$$

$$\frac{x}{x+2} = \frac{x+2}{2x} + \frac{x}{2x}$$

$$\frac{x}{x+2} = \frac{2x+2}{2x}$$

$$\frac{x}{x+2} = \frac{2(x+1)}{2x}$$

$$\frac{x}{x+2} = \frac{x+1}{x}$$

$$x\cancel{(x+2)}\left(\frac{x}{\cancel{x+2}}\right) = \cancel{x}(x+2)\left(\frac{x+1}{\cancel{x}}\right)$$

$$\cancel{x^2} = \cancel{x^2} + 3x + 2$$

$$-3x = 2$$

$$x = -\frac{2}{3}$$

24.

$$\frac{2n}{n-2} + \frac{n}{n+2} = \frac{3n^2+8}{n^2-4}$$

$$(n-2)\ (n+2)\ \frac{2n}{n-2} + \frac{n}{n+2} = (n-2)\ (n+2)\left[\frac{3n^2+8}{(n-2)\ (n+2)}\right]$$

$$2n(n+2) + n(n-2) = 3n^2 + 8$$

$$2n^2 + 4n + n^2 - 2n = 3n^2 + 8$$

$$2n = 8$$

$$n = 4$$

25.

$$\frac{n}{n+2} - \frac{n+20}{n^2-4} = \frac{n}{n-2}$$

$$(n+2)(n-2)\left[\frac{n}{n+2} - \frac{n+20}{(n+2)(n-2)}\right] = (n+2)\cancel{(n-2)}\left(\frac{n}{\cancel{n-2}}\right)$$

$$n(n-2) - (n+20) = n(n+2)$$

$$\cancel{n^2} - 2n - n - 20 = \cancel{n^2} + 2n$$

$$-3n - 20 = 2n$$

$$-5n = 20$$

$$n = -4$$

26.

$$\frac{2}{n+1} = \frac{6}{2n+1} - \frac{1}{n-3}$$

$$\cancel{(n+1)}(2n+1)(n-3)\left(\frac{2}{\cancel{n+1}}\right) = (n+1)(2n+1)(n-3)\left[\frac{6}{2n+1} - \frac{1}{n-3}\right]$$

$$\begin{aligned} 2(2n+1)(n-3) &= 6(n+1)(n-3) - (n+1)(2n+1) \\ (4n+2)(n-3) &= (6n+6)(n-3) - (2n^2+3n+1) \\ 4n^2 - 10n - 6 &= 6n^2 - 12n - 18 - 2n^2 - 3n - 1 \\ \cancel{4n^2} - 10n - 6 &= \cancel{4n^2} - 15n - 19 \\ 5n &= -13 \\ n &= \frac{-13}{5} \end{aligned}$$

27.

$$\frac{x-3}{2x+6} - \frac{x^2+6}{6x^2-54} = \frac{x+3}{3x-9}$$

$$\frac{x-3}{2(x+3)} - \frac{x^2+6}{6(x+3)(x-3)} = \frac{x+3}{3(x-3)}$$

$$6(x+3)(x-3)\left[\frac{x-3}{2(x+3)} - \frac{x^2+6}{6(x+3)(x-3)}\right] = 6(x+3)(x-3)\left[\frac{x+3}{3(x-3)}\right]$$

$$\begin{aligned} 3(x-3)^2 - (x^2+6) &= 2(x+3)^2 \\ 3(x^2-6x+9) - (x^2+6) &= 2(x^2+6x+9) \\ 3x^2 - 18x + 27 - x^2 - 6 &= 2x^2 + 12x + 18 \\ -18x + 21 &= 12x + 18 \\ -30x &= -3 \\ x &= \frac{1}{10} \end{aligned}$$

28.

$$\begin{aligned} \frac{x}{2} - 2\left(\frac{4x}{5} - 3\right) &= 4 - \frac{3}{2}\left(\frac{x}{2} + 1\right) \\ \frac{x}{2} - \frac{8x}{5} + 6 &= 4 - \frac{3x}{4} - \frac{3}{2} \\ 20\left[\frac{x}{2} - \frac{8x}{5} + 6\right] &= 20\left[4 - \frac{3x}{4} - \frac{3}{2}\right] \\ 10x - 32x + 120 &= 80 - 15x - 30 \\ -22x + 120 &= -15x + 50 \\ -7x &= -70 \\ x &= 10 \end{aligned}$$

29.

$$\begin{aligned} \frac{2-x}{x-3} + \frac{7}{5} &= \frac{3}{3-x} \\ \frac{2-x}{x-3} + \frac{7}{5} &= \frac{-3}{x-3} \\ 5(x-3)\ \frac{2-x}{x-3} + \frac{7}{5} &= 5\cancel{(x-3)}\left(\frac{-3}{\cancel{x-3}}\right) \\ 5(2-x) + 7(x-3) &= -15 \\ 10 - 5x + 7x - 21 &= -15 \\ 2x - 11 &= -15 \\ 2x &= -4 \\ x &= -2 \end{aligned}$$

30.

$$\frac{2}{x+3} + \frac{1}{3-x} = \frac{6x}{x^2-9}$$

$$\frac{2}{x+3} - \frac{1}{x-3} = \frac{6x}{(x+3)(x-3)}$$

$$(x+3)(x-3)\left[\frac{2}{x+3} - \frac{1}{x-3}\right] = (x+3)(x-3)\left[\frac{6x}{(x+3)(x-3)}\right]$$

$$\begin{aligned} 2(x-3) - (x+3) &= 6x \\ 2x - 6 - x - 3 &= 6x \\ x - 9 &= 6x \\ -5x &= 9 \\ x &= -\frac{9}{5} \end{aligned}$$

31.

$$\frac{2x+1}{2x-1} = \frac{2x-1}{2x+1} - \frac{8}{1-4x^2}$$

$$\frac{2x+1}{2x-1} = \frac{2x-1}{2x+1} + \frac{8}{4x^2-1}$$

$$\frac{2x+1}{2x-1} = \frac{2x-1}{2x+1} + \frac{8}{(2x+1)(2x-1)}$$

$$(2x+1)(2x-1)\left(\frac{2x+1}{2x-1}\right) = (2x+1)(2x-1)\left[\frac{2x-1}{2x+1} + \frac{8}{(2x+1)(2x-1)}\right]$$

$$(2x+1)^2 = (2x-1)^2 + 8$$

$$\cancel{4x^2} + 4x + \cancel{1} = \cancel{4x^2} - 4x + \cancel{1} + 8$$

$$8x = 8$$

$$x = 1$$

32.

$$\frac{x+2}{x-2} = \frac{2x^2-8x}{x^2-4} - \frac{x-2}{2+x}$$

$$(x+2)\cancel{(x-2)}\left(\frac{x+2}{\cancel{x-2}}\right) = (x+2)(x-2)\left[\frac{2x(x-4)}{(x+2)(x-2)} - \frac{x-2}{x+2}\right]$$

$$(x+2)^2 = 2x^2 - 8x - (x-2)^2$$

$$x^2 + 4x + 4 = 2x^2 - 8x - (x^2 - 4x + 4)$$

$$x^2 + 4x + 4 = 2x^2 - 8x - x^2 + 4x - 4$$

$$\cancel{x^2} + 4x + 4 = \cancel{x^2} - 4x - 4$$

$$8x = -8$$

$$x = -1$$

33.

$$\frac{x-1}{x} + \frac{x}{x-1} = \frac{5}{2}$$

$$2x(x-1)\left[\frac{x-1}{x} + \frac{x}{x-1}\right] = \cancel{2}x(x-1)\left(\frac{5}{\cancel{2}}\right)$$

$$2(x-1)^2 + 2x^2 = 5x(x-1)$$

$$2(x^2 - 2x + 1) + 2x^2 = 5x^2 - 5x$$

$$2x^2 - 4x + 2 + 2x^2 = 5x^2 - 5x$$

$$4x^2 - 4x + 2 = 5x^2 - 5x$$

$$-x^2 + x + 2 = 0$$

$$x^2 - x - 2 = 0$$

$$(x-2)(x+1) = 0$$

$x - 2 = 0$ $\quad$ $x + 1 = 0$

$x = 2$ $\quad$ $x = -1$

2 and -1 are solutions

Note: Since $x \neq 0$ and $x - 1 \neq 0$, when $x = 2$ or when $x = -1$, the fractions, $\frac{x-1}{x}$ and $\frac{x}{x-1}$, are real numbers. Therefore, both values are solutions.

34.

$$\frac{7}{x-3} - \frac{4}{x+2} = \frac{41}{x^2 - x - 6}$$

$$\frac{7}{x-3} - \frac{4}{x+2} = \frac{41}{(x-3)(x+2)}$$

$$(x-3)(x+2)\left[\frac{7}{x-3} - \frac{4}{x+2}\right] = \cancel{(x-3)}\cancel{(x+2)}\left[\frac{41}{\cancel{(x-3)}\cancel{(x+2)}}\right]$$

$$7(x+2) - 4(x-3) = 41$$

$$7x + 14 - 4x + 12 = 41$$

$$3x + 26 = 41$$

$$3x = 15$$

$$x = 5$$

35.

$$\frac{3x}{x-2} - \frac{2}{x+3} + \frac{2}{2-x} = 0$$

$$\frac{3x}{x-2} - \frac{2}{x+3} - \frac{2}{x-2} = 0$$

$$\frac{3x-2}{x-2} - \frac{2}{x+3} = 0$$

$$(x-2)(x+3)\left[\frac{3x-2}{x-2} - \frac{2}{x+3}\right] = (x-2)(x+3)(0)$$

$$(x+3)(3x-2) - 2(x-2) = 0$$

$$3x^2 + 7x - 6 - 2x + 4 = 0$$

$$3x^2 + 5x - 2 = 0$$

$$(3x-1)(x+2) = 0$$

$$3x - 1 = 0 \qquad x + 2 = 0$$

$$3x = 1 \qquad x = -2$$

$$x = \frac{1}{3}$$

$\frac{1}{3}$ and -2 are solutions

Note: $x - 2 \neq 0$, $x + 3 \neq 0$, and $2 - x \neq 0$ when $x = \frac{1}{3}$ or when $x = -2$. Therefore, the fractions, $\frac{3x}{x-2}$, $\frac{2}{x+3}$, and $\frac{2}{2-x}$, are real numbers and both values are solutions.

Algebraic Representation Exercises   Page 189

1. $\frac{p}{m-n}$

2. $n\left(\frac{1+m}{2}\right)$

3. $\frac{s(r-1)}{(t+v)^2}$

4. $m - \frac{1}{a}(m) = m - \frac{m}{a}$ mints

5. $\frac{z}{x}$

6. $\frac{a+b-c}{(a+b)^2}$

7. $\frac{d}{r}$ hours

8. $\frac{v+w}{x}$ dollars

9. $\left(\frac{s}{x-y} - \frac{s}{x}\right)$ hours

10. $\frac{a+b}{c-b}$

11. $\frac{1}{x} + \frac{1}{y} + \frac{1}{z}$

12. $x - \left[\frac{1}{m}(x) + \frac{1}{n}(x) + \frac{1}{s}(x) + \frac{1}{r}(x)\right] = x - \left(\frac{x}{m} + \frac{x}{n} + \frac{x}{s} + \frac{x}{r}\right)$ dollars

Word Problems Involving Fractions Pages 189-194

1\. 1. let d = denominator

$\frac{d - 5}{d}$ = original fraction $\frac{3}{8}$

2\. d - 5 = numerator

3\.

$$\frac{d - 5 + 1}{d} = \frac{1}{2}$$

$$\frac{d - 4}{d} = \frac{1}{2}$$

4\. $2d\left(\frac{d - 4}{d}\right) = 2d\left(\frac{1}{2}\right)$

$2d - 8 = d$

$d = 8$

5\. $\frac{3 + 1}{8} = \frac{4}{8} = \frac{1}{2}$ ✓

2\. 1. let n = numerator

2\. n + 3 = denominator

$\frac{n}{n + 3}$ = the fraction $\frac{5}{8}$

3\.

$$\frac{n - 3}{n + 3} = \frac{1}{4}$$

4\. $4(n + 3)\left(\frac{n - 3}{n + 3}\right) = 4(n + 3)\left(\frac{1}{4}\right)$

$4n - 12 = n + 3$

$3n = 15$

$n = 5$

5\. $\frac{5 - 3}{8} = \frac{2}{8} = \frac{1}{4}$ ✓

3\. 1. let d = denominator

2\. d + 1 = numerator

$\frac{d + 1}{d}$ = the fraction $\frac{4}{3}$

3\.

$$\frac{d + 1 - 1}{d + 1} = \frac{3}{4}$$

4\.

$$\frac{d}{d + 1} = \frac{3}{4}$$

$4(d + 1)\left(\frac{d}{d + 1}\right) = 4(d + 1)\left(\frac{3}{4}\right)$

$4d = 3d + 3$

$d = 3$

5\. $\frac{4 - 1}{3 + 1} = \frac{3}{4}$ ✓

4\. 1. let t = time of the second plane 3 hr.

2\. let $\frac{2}{3}t$ = time of the first plane 2 hr.

3\. $\frac{2}{3}t + 1 = t$

4\. $1 = \frac{1}{3}t$ (subtract $\frac{2}{3}t$ from both sides)

$3 = t$

5\. $\frac{2}{3}(3) = 2$ ✓

5. 1. let x = number of columns <u>12</u>

2. $\frac{1}{3}x$ = advertisements 4

$\frac{1}{4}x$ = miscellaneous news 3

3. $x - (\frac{1}{3}x + \frac{1}{4}x) = 5$

4. $12(x - \frac{1}{3}x - \frac{1}{4}x) = 12(5)$

$$12x - 4x - 3x = 60$$
$$5x = 60$$
$$x = 12$$

5. 12 - (4 + 3) = 5 ✓

6. 1. let x = total floor area <u>1500 sq. ft.</u>

2. $\frac{1}{3}x$ = area of bedrooms <u>500 sq. ft.</u>

$\frac{1}{5}x$ = area of living room <u>300 sq. ft.</u>

3. $x - (\frac{1}{3}x + \frac{1}{5}x) = 700$

4. $15(x - \frac{1}{3}x - \frac{1}{5}x) = 15(700)$

$$15x - 5x - 3x = 10{,}500$$
$$7x = 10{,}500$$
$$x = 1{,}500$$

5. 1,500 - (500 + 300) = 700 ✓

7. 1. let w = weight <u>20 oz.</u>

2. $(w - 8)(\frac{150}{w}) = 90$

3. $\not{w}(w - 8)(\frac{150}{\not{w}}) = 90w$

4. $150w - 1200 = 90w$

$$60w = 1200$$
$$w = 20$$

5. $20 - 8 = 12$ $\quad \frac{150}{20} = 7.50$ $\quad \$7.50 \times 12 = \$90.00$ ✓

8. 1. let x = greater part <u>32</u>

2. 56 - x = other part <u>24</u>

3. $\frac{3}{8}x - \frac{1}{4}(56 - x) = 6$

4. $\frac{3}{8}x - 14 + \frac{x}{4} = 6$

$$8(\frac{3}{8}x - 14 + \frac{x}{4}) = 8(6)$$
$$3x - 112 + 2x = 48$$
$$5x = 160$$
$$x = 32$$

5. $\frac{3}{8}(32) = 12$

$\frac{1}{4}(24) = 6$

$12 - 6 = 6$ ✓

9. 1. let x = the fraction $\underline{\frac{3}{5} ; \frac{5}{3}}$

2. $\frac{1}{x}$ = the reciprocal

3.
$$\text{sum} = \text{sum}$$
$$x + \frac{1}{x} = \frac{34}{15}$$

4.
$$15x(x + \frac{1}{x}) = 15x(\frac{34}{15})$$
$$15x^2 + 15 = 34x$$
$$15x^2 - 34x + 15 = 0$$
$$(5x - 3)(3x - 5) = 0$$
$$5x - 3 = 0 \qquad 3x - 5 = -0$$
$$5x = 3 \qquad 3x = 5$$
$$x = \frac{3}{5} \qquad x = \frac{5}{3}$$

5.
$$\frac{3}{5} + \frac{5}{3} = \frac{9}{15} + \frac{25}{15} = \frac{34}{15} \checkmark$$
$$\frac{5}{3} + \frac{3}{5} = \frac{25}{15} + \frac{9}{15} = \frac{34}{15} \checkmark$$

10. 1. let t = world's tonnage of nickel <u>1,080,000 tons</u>

2.

3. $t - (\frac{1}{3}t + \frac{1}{6}t + \frac{1}{9}t) = 420,000$

4. $t - (\frac{6}{18}t + \frac{3}{18}t + \frac{2}{18}t) = 420,000$
$$t - \frac{11}{18}t = 420,000$$
$$\frac{7}{18}t = 420,000$$
$$t = 1,080,000$$

5.
$$\frac{1}{2}(12,000) = 6000$$
$$\frac{11}{60}(12,000) = +2200$$
$$8200$$
$$12,000 - 8,200 = 3,800 \checkmark$$

11.(a)
$$d = rt \qquad d = rt$$
$$\frac{d}{t} = \frac{r\cancel{t}}{\cancel{t}} \qquad \frac{d}{r} = \frac{\cancel{r}t}{\cancel{r}}$$
$$r = \frac{d}{t} \qquad t = \frac{d}{r}$$

(b)
$$c = qp \qquad c = qp$$
$$\frac{c}{q} = \frac{\cancel{q}p}{\cancel{q}} \qquad \frac{c}{p} = \frac{q\cancel{p}}{\cancel{p}}$$
$$p = \frac{c}{q} \qquad q = \frac{c}{p}$$

(c) Distance equals rate times time; cost equals quantity times price per item.

12. 1. let x = number of children at the party <u>8</u>

$\frac{40}{x}$ = price per child $5

2.

	Number	Total Amount	Amount per Child
Was	x	40	$\frac{40}{x}$
Might Be	x + 4	51	$\frac{51}{x + 4}$

3.
$$\frac{40}{x} - .75 = \frac{51}{x + 4}$$

4.
$$x(x + 4)(\frac{40}{x} - .75) = x(x + 4)(\frac{51}{x + 4})$$
$$40(x + 4) - x(x + 4)(.75) = 51x$$
$$40x + 160 - .75x^2 - 3x = 51x$$
$$37x - .75x^2 + 160 = 51x$$
$$100(-.75x^2 - 14x + 160) = 100(0)$$
$$-75x^2 - 1400x + 16,000 = 0$$
$$-25(3x^2 + 56x - 640) = 0$$
$$(3x + 80)(x - 8) = 0$$

$$3x + 80 = 0 \qquad x - 8 = 0$$
$$3x = -80 \qquad x = 8$$
~~$x = \frac{-80}{3}$~~

Reject since negative.

5. $12(4.25) = 51 \checkmark$

13. 1. let x = number of pounds <u>8</u>

$\frac{8.64}{x}$ = price per pound <u>$1.08</u>

2.

	Number	Total Cost	Price per Pound
Now	x	8.64	$\frac{8.64}{x}$
Next Week	x + 1	8.64	$\frac{8.64}{x + 1}$

3. $$\frac{8.64}{x} - .12 = \frac{8.64}{x + 1}$$

4. $$x(x + 1)\left(\frac{8.64}{x} - .12\right) = x(x + 1)\left(\frac{8.64}{x + 1}\right)$$

$$8.64(x + 1) - .12x(x + 1) = 8.64x$$
$$8.64x + 8.64 - .12x^2 - .12x = 8.64x$$
$$-.12x^2 - .12x + 8.64 = 0$$
$$-.12(x^2 + x - 72) = 0$$
$$(x + 9)(x - 8) = 0$$

~~x + 9 = 0~~ ~~x = -9~~ Reject since negative.

x - 8 = 0
x = 8

5. $1.08 − .12 = $ .96

$8.64 ÷ $.96 = 9, which is 1 more than 8 ✓

14. 1. let x = number in the group <u>5</u>

$\frac{40}{x}$ = cost per person <u>$8</u>

2.

	Number	Total Cost	Cost Per Person
Now	x	40	$\frac{40}{x}$
If	x + 3	40	$\frac{40}{x + 3}$

3. $$\frac{40}{x} - 3 = \frac{40}{x + 3}$$

4. $$x(x + 3)\left(\frac{40}{x} - 3\right) = x(x + 3)\left(\frac{40}{x + 3}\right)$$

$$(x + 3)(40) - 3x(x + 3) = 40x$$
$$40x + 120 - 3x^2 - 9x = 40x$$
$$-3x^2 - 9x + 120 = 0$$
$$-3(x^2 + 3x - 40) = 0$$
$$(x + 8)(x - 5) = 0$$

x + 8 = 0, ~~x = -8~~ Reject since negative.

x - 5 = 0
x = 5

5. $40 ÷ 8 = $5. $5 is $3 less than $8 ✓

15. 1. let d = distance to sail   9 mi.

2.

	Rate	Time	Distance
Downwind	12	$\frac{d}{12}$	d
Upwind	4	$\frac{d}{4}$	d

3. $$\frac{d}{12} + \frac{d}{4} = 3$$

4. $$12\left(\frac{d}{12} + \frac{d}{4}\right) = 12(3)$$
$$d + 3d = 36$$
$$4d = 36$$
$$d = 9$$

5. $\frac{9}{12} + \frac{9}{4} = \frac{3}{4} + \frac{9}{4} = \frac{12}{4} = 3$ ✓

16. 1. let r = rate of faster aircraft   600 mph

r - 12 = rate of slower aircraft   480 mph

2.

	Rate	Time	Distance
Fast	r	$\frac{4800}{r}$	4800
Slow	r -120	$\frac{4800}{r-120}$	4800

3. $$\frac{4800}{r} + 2 = \frac{4800}{r-120}$$

4. $$r(r-120)\left(\frac{4800}{r} + 2\right) = r\cancel{(r-120)}\left(\frac{4800}{\cancel{r-120}}\right)$$
$$4800(r-120) + 2r(r-120) = 4800r$$
$$\cancel{4800r} - 576{,}000 + 2r^2 - 240r = \cancel{4800r}$$
$$2r^2 - 240r - 576{,}000 = 0$$
$$r^2 - 120r - 288{,}000 = 0$$
$$(r-600)(r+480) = 0$$
$$r - 600 = 0 \qquad \cancel{r + 480 = 0}$$
$$r = 600 \qquad \cancel{r = -480}$$

Reject since negative.

5. $$600\overline{)4800}^{\,8}$$
$$480\overline{)4800}^{\,10}$$

2 hour difference ✓

17. 1. let s = speed of average cyclist   14 mph

s + 11 = speed of elite cyclist   25 mph

2.

	Rate	Time	Distance
Average	s	$\frac{70}{s}$	70
Elite	s+11	$\frac{125}{s+11}$	125

3. $$\frac{70}{s} = \frac{125}{s+11}$$

4 $$\cancel{s}(s+11)\left(\frac{70}{\cancel{s}}\right) = s\cancel{(s+11)}\left(\frac{125}{\cancel{s+11}}\right)$$
$$(s+11)(70) = 125s$$
$$70s + 770 = 125s$$
$$770 = 55s$$
$$s = 14$$

5. $\frac{70}{14} = 5$ hr.

$\frac{125}{25} = 5$ hr. ✓

18. 1. let x = greater number $\underline{20}$
2. 38 - x = other number $\underline{18}$
3. $\frac{1}{10}x = \frac{1}{9}(38 - x)$
4. $90(\frac{1}{10}x) = 90(\frac{1}{9})(38 - x)$
$9x = 10(38 - x)$
$9x = 380 - 10x$
$19x = 380$
$x = 20$

5. $\frac{1}{10}(20) = 2$
$\frac{1}{9}(18) = 2$ ✓

19. 1. let x = the smaller number $\underline{2}$
2. $\frac{1}{x}$ = reciprocal of the smaller number $\underline{\frac{1}{2}}$
x + 8 = the larger number $\underline{10}$
$\frac{1}{x + 8}$ = reciprocal of the larger number $\underline{\frac{1}{10}}$
3. $2(\frac{1}{x} + \frac{1}{x + 8}) = 3(\frac{1}{x} - \frac{1}{x + 8})$
4. $\frac{2}{x} + \frac{2}{x + 8} = \frac{3}{x} - \frac{3}{x + 8}$
$x(x + 8)(\frac{2}{x} + \frac{2}{x + 8}) = x(x + 8)(\frac{3}{x} - \frac{3}{x + 8})$
$2(x + 8) + 2x = 3(x + 8) - 3x$
$2x + 16 + 2x = \cancel{3x} + 24 - \cancel{3x}$
$4x = 8$
$x = 2$

5. 10
-2
8 ✓

$2(\frac{1}{2} + \frac{1}{10}) = 2(\frac{6}{10}) = \frac{6}{5}$
$3(\frac{1}{2} - \frac{1}{10}) = 3(\frac{4}{10}) = \frac{6}{5}$ ✓

20. 1. let d = distance at 54 mph $\underline{216\text{ mi.}}$
360 - d = distance at 48 mph $\underline{144\text{ mi.}}$
2.

	Rate	Time	Distance
Faster Part	54	$\frac{d}{54}$	d
Slower Part	48	$\frac{360 - d}{48}$	360 - d

3. $\frac{d}{54} + \frac{360 - d}{48} = 7$
4. $432(\frac{d}{54} + \frac{360 - d}{48}) = 432(7)$
$8d + 9(360 - d) = 3024$
$8d + 3240 - 9d = 3024$
$-d = -216$
$d = 216$

5. $\frac{216}{54} = 4$
$\frac{144}{48} = 3$
7 hr. ✓

21\. 1. let v = number of volumes $\underline{16}$

$\frac{192}{v}$ = price of a volume $12

2\.

	Number	Total Cost	Price Per Volume
Now	v	192	$\frac{192}{v}$
If	v + 8	192	$\frac{192}{v + 8}$

3\.

$$\frac{192}{v} - 4 = \frac{192}{v + 8}$$

4\.

$$v(v + 8)(\frac{192}{v} - 4) = v(v + 8)(\frac{192}{v + 8})$$
$$192(v + 8) - 4v(v + 8) = 192v$$
$$192v + 1536 - 4v^2 - 32v = 192v$$
$$-4v^2 - 32v + 1536 = 0$$
$$-4(v^2 + 8v - 384) = 0$$
$$(v + 24)(v - 16) = 0$$

~~v + 24 = 0~~   v - 16 = 0

~~v = -24~~   v = 16

Reject since negative.

5\. 16
+8
24

$8 which is $4 less than $12 ✓ ($24 \overline{)\$192}$)

22\. 1. let x = number hours together $\underline{1\frac{1}{5} \text{ hr.}}$

2\.

	Time Together	Part of Job 1 Hour	Part of Job x Hours
Scott	x	$\frac{1}{2}$	$\frac{x}{2}$
Peter	x	$\frac{1}{3}$	$\frac{x}{3}$

3\. $\frac{x}{2} + \frac{x}{3} = 1$

4\.
$$6(\frac{x}{2} + \frac{x}{3}) = 6$$
$$3x + 2x = 6$$
$$5x = 6$$
$$x = 1\frac{1}{5}$$

5\. $\frac{1\frac{1}{5}}{2} + \frac{1\frac{1}{5}}{3} = \frac{6}{10} + \frac{6}{15} = \frac{3}{5} + \frac{2}{5} = 1$ ✓

23. 1. t = time required using both pipes $13\frac{1}{3}$ min.

2.

	Time Together	Part of Job 1 Minute	t Minutes
First Pipe	t	$\frac{1}{24}$	$\frac{t}{24}$
Second Pipe	t	$\frac{1}{30}$	$\frac{t}{30}$

3. $\frac{1}{24}t + \frac{1}{30}t = 1$

4. $120(\frac{1}{24}t + \frac{1}{30}t) = 120$

$5t + 4t = 120$

$9t = 120$

$t = 13\frac{1}{3}$

5. $\frac{13\frac{1}{3}}{24} + \frac{13\frac{1}{3}}{30} = \frac{40}{72} + \frac{40}{90} = \frac{5}{9} + \frac{4}{9} = 1$ ✓

24. 1. let t = time to fill 40 min.

2.

	Time Together	Part of Job 1 Minute	t Minutes
First Pipe	t	$\frac{1}{24}$	$\frac{t}{24}$
Second Pipe	t	$\frac{1}{30}$	$\frac{t}{30}$
Third Pipe	t	$\frac{1}{20}$	$\frac{t}{20}$

3. $\frac{1}{24}t + \frac{1}{30}t - \frac{1}{20}t = 1$

4. $120(\frac{1}{24}t + \frac{1}{30}t - \frac{1}{20}t) = 120$

$5t + 4t - 6t = 120$

$3t = 120$

$t = 40$

5. $\frac{40}{24} + \frac{40}{30} - \frac{40}{20} = \frac{5}{3} + \frac{4}{3} - 2 = 3 - 2 = 1$ ✓

25. 1. let t = time together $4\frac{4}{5}$ hr.

2.

	Time Together	Part of Job 1 Hour	t Hours
First Man	t	$\frac{1}{8}$	$\frac{t}{8}$
Second Man	t	$\frac{1}{12}$	$\frac{t}{12}$

3. $\frac{1}{8}t + \frac{1}{12}t = 1$

4. $24(\frac{1}{8}t + \frac{1}{12}t) = 24$

$3t + 2t = 24$

$5t = 24$

$t = 4\frac{4}{5}$

5. $\frac{4\frac{4}{5}}{8} + \frac{4\frac{4}{5}}{12} = \frac{3}{5} + \frac{2}{5} = 1$ ✓

26. 1. let x = the number $\underline{12}$

2.

3. $\frac{3 + x}{8 + x} = \not{2}(\frac{3}{\not{8}_{4}})$

4. $\frac{3 + x}{8 + x} = \frac{3}{4}$

$4\cancel{(8 + x)}(\frac{3 + x}{\cancel{8 + x}}) = \not{4}(8 + x)(\frac{3}{\not{4}})$

$12 + 4x = 24 + 3x$

$x = 12$

5. $\frac{3 + 12}{8 + 12} = \frac{15}{20} = \frac{3}{4}$ $\frac{3}{4}$ is $2(\frac{3}{8})$ ✓

27. 1. let c = rate of current $\underline{4 \text{ mph}}$

6 + c = rate downstream

6 - c = rate upstream

2.

	Rate	Time	Distance
Downstream	6 + c	$\frac{8}{6 + c}$	8
Upstream	6 - c	$\frac{8}{6 - c}$	8

3. $\frac{8}{6 + c} + \frac{8}{6 - c} = \frac{24}{5}$

4. $5(6 + c)(6 - c)(\frac{8}{6 + c} + \frac{8}{6 - c}) = \not{5}(6 + c)(6 - c)(\frac{24}{\not{5}})$

$40(6 - c) + 40(6 + c) = 24(36 - c^2)$

$240 - \cancel{40c} + 240 + \cancel{40c} = 864 - 24c^2$

$24c^2 - 384 = 0$

$c^2 - 16 = 0$

$(c + 4)(c - 4) = 0$

$\cancel{c + 4 = 0}$ $\quad c - 4 = 0$

$\cancel{c = -4}$ $\quad c = 4$

Reject since negative.

5. $\begin{array}{r} 6 \\ +4 \\ \hline 10 \end{array}$ $\frac{8}{10} = \frac{4}{5}$ hr.

$\begin{array}{r} 6 \\ -4 \\ \hline 2 \end{array}$ $\frac{8}{2} = 4$ hr.

$4\frac{4}{5}$ hr. or 4 hr. 48 min. ✓

28. 1. let x = the number $\underline{3}$

2.

3. $\frac{5 + x}{9 + x} = \frac{2}{3}$

4. $3\cancel{(9 + x)}(\frac{5 + x}{\cancel{9 + x}}) = \not{3}(9 + x)(\frac{2}{\not{3}})$

$15 + 3x = 18 + 2x$

$x = 3$

5. $\frac{5 + 3}{9 + 3} = \frac{8}{12} = \frac{2}{3}$ ✓

29. 1. let x = number of oranges <u>24</u>

2.

3. $\frac{1}{2}x - 4 = \frac{1}{3}x$

4. $6(\frac{1}{2}x - 4) = 6(\frac{1}{3})x$

$3x - 24 = 2x$

$x = 24$

5. $\frac{1}{2}(24) = 12$ $\quad$ 12

$\frac{1}{3}(24) = 8$ $\quad$ -8

4 ✓

30. 1. let x = number of days Mr. Moradiajam works <u>9</u>

x + 5 = number of days Mr. Wiggins works <u>14</u>

2.

	Time Together	Part of Job: 1 Day	Part of Job: x Days
Mr. Moradiajam	x	$\frac{1}{30}$	$\frac{x}{30}$
Mr. Wiggins	x	$\frac{1}{20}$	$\frac{x}{20}$

3. $\frac{1}{20}x + \frac{1}{30}x + 5(\frac{1}{20}) = 1$

4. $60(\frac{1}{20}x + \frac{1}{30}x + \frac{1}{4}) = 60$

$3x + 2x + 15 = 60$

$5x = 45$

$x = 9$

5. $\frac{9}{20} + \frac{9}{30} + \frac{5}{20} = \frac{27}{60} + \frac{18}{60} + \frac{15}{60} = \frac{60}{60} = 1$ ✓

31. 1. let x = time for fast excavator <u>10 da.</u>

x + 5 = time for slow excavator <u>15 da.</u>

2.

	Time Together	Part of Job: 1 Day	Part of Job: 6 Days
Fast Excavator	6	$\frac{1}{x}$	$6(\frac{1}{x})$
Slow Excavator	6	$\frac{1}{x + 5}$	$6(\frac{1}{x + 5})$

3. $6(\frac{1}{x}) + 6(\frac{1}{x + 5}) = 1$

4. $\frac{6}{x} + \frac{6}{x + 5} = 1$

$x(x + 5)(\frac{6}{x} + \frac{6}{x + 5}) = x(x + 5)(1)$

$6(x + 5) + 6x = x^2 + 5x$

$6x + 30 + 6x = x^2 + 5x$

$-x^2 + 7x + 30 = 0$

$x^2 - 7x - 30 = 0$

$(x - 10)(x + 3) = 0$

$x - 10 = 0$ $\quad$ ~~$x + 3 = 0$~~

$x = 10$ $\quad$ ~~$x = -3$~~

Reject since negative.

5. $6(\frac{1}{10}) + 6(\frac{1}{15}) = \frac{3}{5} + \frac{2}{5} = 1$ ✓

32. First Question

1. let x = amount of water 1 qt.
2.

	Quarts	Percent Alcohol	Quarts of Alcohol
First	3	80	.80(3)
Second	3 + x	60	.60(3 + x)

3. .60(3 + x) = .80(3)
4. 1.8 + .6x = 2.4
   .6x = .6
   x = 1
5. 1 × .6 = .6 1.8 + .6 = 2.4 ✓

Second Question

1. let x = amount of alcohol 3 qt.
2.

	Quarts	Percent Alcohol	Quarts of Alcohol
First	3	80	.80(3)
Second	3 + x	90	.90(3 + x)

3. .9(3 + x) = 2.4 + x
4. 2.7 + .9x = 2.4 + x
   -.1x = -.3
   x = 3
5. 6 × .9 = 5.4 2.4 + 3.0 = 5.4 ✓

33. 1. Let x = number of liters to add 2 L
   4 + x = liters of mix
2.

	Liters	Percent Peroxide	Liters of Peroxide
First	4	3	.03(4)
Second	4 + x	2	.02(4 + x)

3. .03(4) = .02(4 + x)
4. .12 = .08 + .02x
   -.02x = -.04
   x = 2
5. 6 × .02 = .12 L 4 × .03 = .12 L ✓

34. 1. let x = number of gallons of water 10 gal.
2.

	Gallons	Percent Butter Fat	Gallons of Butter Fat
First	20	6	.06(20)
Second	20 + x	4	.04(20 + x)

3. .06(20) = .04(20 + x)
4. 1.2 = .8 + .04x
   -.04x = -.4
   4x = 40
   x = 10
5. 10 × .04 = .40 .4 + .8 = 1.2 ✓

35. 1. let x = pounds of potash <u>1 lb.</u>

2.

	Pounds	Percent Potash	Pounds of Potash
First	18	5	.05(18)
Second	18 + x	10	.10(18 + x)

3. $.05(18) + x = .10(18 + x)$

4. $.9 + x = 1.8 + .1x$

$.9x = .9$

$x = 1$

5. $\begin{array}{r} 18 \\ +\ 1 \\ \hline 19 \end{array}$ $\begin{array}{r} 19 \\ \times .10 \\ \hline 1.9 \end{array}$ $\begin{array}{r} .9 \\ +1.0 \\ \hline 1.9 \end{array}$ ✓

36. 1. let x = number of days together $1\frac{4}{5}$ da.

2.

	Time Together	Part of Job 1 Day	Part of Job x Days
One Man	x	$\frac{1}{4\frac{1}{2}}$	$\frac{x}{4\frac{1}{2}}$
Other Man	x	$\frac{1}{3}$	$\frac{x}{3}$

3. $\frac{1}{4\frac{1}{2}}x + \frac{1}{3}x = 1$

4. $\frac{2}{9}x + \frac{1}{3}x = 1$

$9(\frac{2}{9}x + \frac{1}{3}x) = 9$

$2x + 3x = 9$

$5x = 9$

$x = 1\frac{4}{5}$

5. $\frac{1\frac{4}{5}}{4\frac{1}{2}} + \frac{1\frac{4}{5}}{3} = \frac{\frac{9}{5}}{\frac{9}{2}} + \frac{\frac{9}{5}}{3} = \frac{2}{5} + \frac{3}{5} = 1$ ✓

37. 1. let x = number of ounces of other metal <u>24 oz.</u>

2.

	Ounces	Percent Silver	Ounces of Silver
First	56	100	1.00(56)
Second	56 + x	70	.70(56 + x)

3. $56 = .7(56 + x)$

4. $56 = 39.2 + .7x$

$-.7x = -16.8$

$x = 24$

5. $\begin{array}{r} 56 \\ +24 \\ \hline 80 \end{array}$ $\begin{array}{r} 80 \\ \times\ .7 \\ \hline 56.0 \end{array}$ ✓

38. 1. let x = pounds of fresh water <u>10 lb.</u>

2.

	Pounds	Percent of Salt	Pounds of Salt
First	30	16	.16(30)
Second	30 + x	12	.12(30 + x)

3. $.16(30) = .12(30 + x)$

4. $4.8 = 3.6 + .12x$

$-.12x = -1.2$

$12x = 120$

$x = 10$

5. $\begin{array}{r} .16 \\ \times\ 30 \\ \hline 4.8 \end{array}$ $\begin{array}{r} .12 \\ \times\ 10 \\ \hline 1.2 \end{array}$ $\begin{array}{r} 1.2 \\ +3.6 \\ \hline 4.8 \end{array}$ ✓

39. 1. let x = time for third pipe <u>15 min.</u>

2.

	Time Together	Part of Job 1 Minute	4 Minutes
First Pipe	4	$\frac{1}{12}$	$4(\frac{1}{12})$
Second Pipe	4	$\frac{1}{10}$	$4(\frac{1}{10})$
Third Pipe	4	$\frac{1}{x}$	$4(\frac{1}{x})$

3. $4(\frac{1}{12}) + 4(\frac{1}{10}) + 4(\frac{1}{x}) = 1$

4.
$$\frac{1}{3} + \frac{2}{5} + \frac{4}{x} = 1$$
$$15x(\frac{1}{3} + \frac{2}{5} + \frac{4}{x}) = 15x$$
$$5x + 6x + 60 = 15x$$
$$-4x = -60$$
$$x = 15$$

5.
$$4(\frac{1}{12}) + 4(\frac{1}{10}) + 4(\frac{1}{15})$$
$$= \frac{1}{3} + \frac{2}{5} + \frac{4}{15}$$
$$= \frac{5}{15} + \frac{6}{15} + \frac{4}{15} = \frac{15}{15} = 1 \checkmark$$

40. 1. let d = denominator

2. d - 5 = numerator

$\frac{d-5}{d}$ = the original fraction <u>$\frac{6}{11}$</u>

3.
$$\frac{d - 5 + 4}{d + 4} = \frac{2}{3}$$

4.
$$\frac{d - 1}{d + 4} = \frac{2}{3}$$
$$3(\cancel{d+4})(\frac{d-1}{\cancel{d+4}}) = \cancel{3}(d + 4)(\frac{2}{\cancel{3}})$$
$$3d - 3 = 2d + 8$$
$$d = 11$$

5. $\frac{6 + 4}{11 + 4} = \frac{10}{15} = \frac{2}{3} \checkmark$

41. 1. let x = ounces of 10% solution <u>24 oz.</u>

2.

	Ounces	Percent Developer	Ounces of Developer
First	x	10	.10(x)
Second	8	50	.50(8)
Third	x + 8	20	.20(x + 8)

3. .10(x) + .50(8) = .20(x + 8)

4.
$$.1x + 4 = .2x + 1.6$$
$$-.1x = -2.4$$
$$x = 24$$

5.
$$\begin{array}{r} 24 \\ \times\ .1 \\ \hline 2.4 \\ +4.0 \\ \hline 6.4 \end{array} \qquad \begin{array}{r} 24 \\ +\ 8 \\ \hline 32 \\ \times .2 \\ \hline 6.4 \checkmark \end{array}$$

42. 1. let x = first even number $\underline{8}$
2. x + 2 = second even number $\underline{10}$
x + 4 = third even number $\underline{12}$
3. $3x - 2(x + 2) = \frac{1}{3}(x + 4)$
4.
$$3x - 2x - 4 = \frac{1}{3}x + \frac{4}{3}$$
$$x - 4 = \frac{1}{3}x + \frac{4}{3}$$
$$3(x - 4) = 3(\frac{1}{3}x + \frac{4}{3})$$
$$3x - 12 = x + 4$$
$$2x = 16$$
$$x = 8$$

5. $\begin{array}{r} 8 \\ \times 3 \\ \hline 24 \end{array} \quad \begin{array}{r} 10 \\ \times 2 \\ \hline 20 \end{array} \quad \begin{array}{r} 24 \\ -20 \\ \hline 4 \end{array}$

$\frac{1}{3}(12) = 4$ ✓

Review of Fractions Pages 194-196

1. Signs of numerator, denominator, and the fraction itself; The sign of the fraction is the sign written before the division line.

2. When both are changed or one is changed and the sign of the fraction is changed.

3. Change the sign of the fraction to its opposite; no change in the sign of the fraction.

4. $\frac{(x-y)(x-y)}{(z-w)(u-z)} = \frac{x^2 - 2xy + y^2}{(z-w)(u-z)} = \frac{-1(x^2 - 2xy + y^2)}{-1(z-w)(u-z)} = \frac{-x^2 + 2xy - y^2}{(-z+w)(u-z)} = \frac{-x^2 + 2xy - y^2}{(w-z)(u-z)}$

5. When the numerator and denominator have no common factor, except 1; multiplying or dividing both terms of a fraction by the same number does not change the value of the fraction.

6. $\frac{x(4a^2 - 9b^2)}{4a^2x^2 + 12abx^2 + 9b^2x^2} = \frac{x(2a + 3b)(2a - 3b)}{x^2(4a^2 + 12ab + 9b^2)}$

$= \frac{\cancel{x}\cancel{(2a + 3b)}(2a - 3b)}{\cancel{x^2}\cancel{(2a + 3b)}(2a + 3b)} = \frac{2a - 3b}{x(2a + 3b)}$

x

7. Ask the question, "What do I multiply the given denominator by to get the required denominator?"

8. $\frac{3b}{(a - 2b)} \cdot \frac{(a - 2b)}{(a - 2b)} = \frac{3b(a - 2b)}{(a - 2b)(a - 2b)} = \frac{3b(a - 2b)}{a^2 - 4ab + 4b^2}$

9. (a) The reciprocal of a fraction is 1 divided by the fraction; the same using 1 as denominator for integers.
(b) $\frac{y}{x}$; $\frac{x - y}{a + b}$; $\frac{1}{x}$

10.(a) A fraction whose numerator or denominator or both contain a fraction; Answers will vary.

(b) Answers will vary.

11.
$$x - y - \frac{2y}{x + y}$$
$$= \frac{(x - y)}{1} \cdot \frac{(x + y)}{(x + y)} - \frac{2y}{x + y}$$
$$= \frac{x^2 - y^2}{x + y} - \frac{2y}{x + y}$$
$$= \frac{x^2 - 2y - y^2}{x + y}$$

12.
$$\frac{m^2 + n^2}{m + n} - n - m$$
$$= \frac{m^2 + n^2}{m + n} - (m + n)$$
$$= \frac{m^2 + n^2}{m + n} - \frac{(m + n)}{1} \cdot \frac{(m + n)}{(m + n)}$$
$$= \frac{m^2 + n^2}{m + n} - \frac{(m^2 + 2mn + n^2)}{m + n}$$
$$= \frac{m^2 + n^2 - m^2 - 2mn - n^2}{m + n}$$
$$= \frac{-2mn}{m + n}$$

13.
$$x - 2 - \frac{6 - 5x}{x - 3}$$
$$= \frac{(x - 2)}{1} \cdot \frac{(x - 3)}{(x - 3)} - \frac{6 - 5x}{x - 3}$$
$$= \frac{x^2 - 5x + 6}{x - 3} - \frac{6 - 5x}{x - 3}$$
$$= \frac{x^2}{x - 3}$$

14.
$$2x - 3 - \frac{4x^2}{2x + 3}$$
$$= \frac{(2x - 3)}{1} \cdot \frac{(2x + 3)}{(2x + 3)} - \frac{4x^2}{2x + 3}$$
$$= \frac{4x^2 - 9}{2x + 3} - \frac{\quad}{2x + 3}$$
$$= \frac{-9}{2x + 3}$$
$$= -\frac{9}{2x + 3}$$

15.
$$\frac{s + t}{2rl} + \frac{s - t}{4rl} - \frac{s^2 + t^2}{4r\ell(s + t)}$$
$$= \frac{(s + t)(2)(s + t)}{4r\ell(s + t)} + \frac{(s - t)(s + t)}{4r\ell(s + t)} - \frac{s^2 + t^2}{4r\ell(s + t)}$$
$$= \frac{2s^2 + 4st + 2t^2}{4r\ell(s + t)} + \frac{s^2 - t^2}{4r\ell(s + t)} - \frac{s^2 + t^2}{4r\ell(s + t)}$$
$$= \frac{2s \quad + 4st + 2t^2 + \cancel{s^2} - t^2 - \cancel{s^2} - t^2}{4r\ell(s + t)}$$
$$= \frac{2s^2 + 4st}{4r\ell(s + t)}$$
$$= \frac{2s(s + 2t)}{4r\ell(s + t)}$$
$$= \frac{s(s + 2t)}{2r\ell(s + t)}$$
$$= \frac{s^2 + 2st}{2r\ell(s + t)}$$

16.
$$\frac{a + x}{x + 2} + \frac{a - x}{2 - x} - \frac{2(x2 - 2a)}{x \quad - 4}$$
$$= \frac{a + x}{x + 2} - \frac{a - x}{x - 2} - \frac{2(x^2 - 2a)}{(x + 2)(x - 2)}$$
$$= \frac{(a + x)(x - 2)}{(x + 2)(x - 2)} - \frac{(a - x)(x + 2)}{(x + 2)(x - 2)} - \frac{2(x^2 - 2a)}{(x + 2)(x - 2)}$$
$$= \frac{ax - 2a + x^2 - 2x - (ax + 2a - x^2 - 2x) - 2x^2 + 4a}{(x + 2)(x - 2)}$$
$$= \frac{ax - 2a + x^2 - 2x - ax - 2a + x^2 + 2x - 2x^2 + 4a}{(x + 2)(x - 2)}$$
$$= \frac{0}{(x + 2)(x - 2)} = 0$$

17. $$\left(\frac{a^2 + 2ab + b^2}{a^2 - 2ab + b^2} - \frac{a + b}{a - b}\right)\left(\frac{3a - 3b}{2b} \div \frac{6a + 6b}{2a - 2b}\right)$$

$$= \left[\frac{a^2 + 2ab + b^2}{(a - b)(a - b)} - \frac{(a + b)(a - b)}{(a - b)(a - b)}\right]\left[\frac{3(a - b)}{2b} \cdot \frac{2(a - b)}{6(a + b)}\right]$$

$$= \frac{a^2 + 2ab + b^2 - a^2 + b^2}{(a - b)(a - b)} \cdot \frac{6(a - b)(a - b)}{12b(a + b)}$$

$$= \frac{2ab + 2b^2}{\cancel{(a - b)}\cancel{(a - b)}} \cdot \frac{\cancel{(a - b)}\cancel{(a - b)}}{2b(a + b)}$$

$$= \frac{2ab + 2b^2}{2b(a + b)}$$

$$= \frac{2b(a + b)}{2b(a + b)}$$

$$= 1$$

18. $$\left(4 - \frac{6}{a + 1}\right) \div \left(8 - \frac{4a - 8}{a^2 - 1}\right)$$

$$= \left(\frac{4(a + 1)}{a + 1} - \frac{6}{a + 1}\right) \div \left(\frac{8(a^2 - 1)}{a^2 - 1} - \frac{4a - 8}{a^2 - 1}\right)$$

$$= \left(\frac{4a + 4 - 6}{a + 1}\right) \div \left(\frac{8a^2 - 8 - 4a + 8}{a^2 - 1}\right)$$

$$= \frac{4a - 2}{a + 1} \cdot \frac{(a + 1)(a - 1)}{8a^2 - 4a}$$

$$= \frac{\cancel{2}\cancel{(2a - 1)}}{\cancel{a + 1}} \cdot \frac{\cancel{(a + 1)}(a - 1)}{\underset{2a}{\cancel{4a}}\cancel{(2a - 1)}}$$

$$= \frac{a - 1}{2a}$$

19. $$\left(\frac{4x}{x^2 - 4} + \frac{2}{2 - x}\right) \div \left(\frac{6x}{x^2 - 3x - 10}\right)$$

$$= \left[\frac{4x}{(x + 2)(x - 2)} - \frac{2(x + 2)}{(x - 2)(x + 2)}\right] \div \frac{6x}{(x - 5)(x + 2)}$$

$$= \frac{4x - 2x - 4}{(x + 2)(x - 2)} \cdot \frac{(x - 5)(x + 2)}{6x}$$

$$= \frac{2x - 4}{(x + 2)(x - 2)} \cdot \frac{(x - 5)(x + 2)}{6x}$$

$$= \frac{\cancel{2}\cancel{(x - 2)}}{\cancel{(x + 2)}\cancel{(x - 2)}} \cdot \frac{(x - 5)\cancel{(x + 2)}}{\underset{3x}{\cancel{6x}}}$$

$$= \frac{x - 5}{3x}$$

20. $\left(\frac{2x}{x-2} - \frac{x}{x-1}\right) \div \left(\frac{2x}{x-3} - \frac{2x}{x-2}\right)$

$= \frac{2x(x-1) - x(x-2)}{(x-2)(x-1)} \div \frac{2x(x-2) - 2x(x-3)}{(x-3)(x-2)}$

$= \frac{2x^2 - 2x - x^2 + 2x}{(x-2)(x-1)} \div \frac{2x^2 - 4x - 2x^2 + 6x}{(x-3)(x-2)}$

$= \frac{x^2}{(x-2)(x-1)} \div \frac{2x}{(x-3)(x-2)}$

$= \frac{\cancel{x^2}^{\,x}}{\cancel{(x-2)}(x-1)} \cdot \frac{(x-3)\cancel{(x-2)}}{\cancel{2x}_{\,2}}$

$= \frac{x(x-3)}{2(x-1)}$

$= \frac{x^2 - 3x}{2x - 2}$

21. The process of changing an equation containing fractions to an equation without fractions; multiplication axiom of equality.

22. Follow the six principles listed in the text, take care with the signs, and make sure result is in lowest terms.

The check is left for the teacher.

23.
$$\frac{5x}{2} - \frac{7x}{4} = 6$$
$$4\left(\frac{5x}{2} - \frac{7x}{4}\right) = 4(6)$$
$$10x - 7x = 24$$
$$3x = 24$$
$$x = 8$$

24.
$$\frac{10 - 7x}{6 - 7x} = \frac{5x - 4}{5x}$$
$$5x\cancel{(6 - 7x)}\left(\frac{10 - 7x}{\cancel{6 - 7x}}\right) = \cancel{5x}(6 - 7x)\left(\frac{5x - 4}{\cancel{5x}}\right)$$
$$50x - 35x^2 = 30x - 24 - 35x^2 + 28x$$
$$50x = 58x - 24$$
$$-8x = -24$$
$$x = 3$$

25.
$$\frac{4}{x+2} + \frac{7}{x+3} = \frac{37}{x^2 + 5x + 6}$$
$$(x+2)(x+3)\left(\frac{4}{x+2} + \frac{7}{x+3}\right) = \cancel{(x+2)}\cancel{(x+3)}\left[\frac{37}{\cancel{(x+2)}\cancel{(x+3)}}\right]$$
$$4(x+3) + 7(x+2) = 37$$
$$4x + 12 + 7x + 14 = 37$$
$$11x + 26 = 37$$
$$11x = 11$$
$$x = 1$$

26.
$$\frac{x+3}{x-3} - \frac{x}{4} = \frac{12}{24} - \frac{x-3}{4}$$
$$4(x-3)\left(\frac{x+3}{x-3} - \frac{x}{4}\right) = 4(x-3)\left(\frac{1}{2} - \frac{x-3}{4}\right)$$
$$4(x+3) - x(x-3) = 2(x-3) - (x-3)^2$$
$$4x + 12 - x^2 + 3x = 2x - 6 - (x^2 - 6x + 9)$$
$$-x^2 + 7x + 12 = -x^2 + 8x - 15$$
$$-x = -27$$
$$x = 27$$

27.
$$\frac{x+7}{x+2}+\frac{x+8}{3}=\frac{3x-15}{9}-3$$
$$9(x+2)\left(\frac{x+7}{x+2}+\frac{x+8}{3}\right)=9(x+2)\left(\frac{3x-15}{9}-3\right)$$
$$9(x+7)+3(x+2)(x+8)=(x+2)(3x-15)-27(x+2)$$
$$9x+63+3(x^2+10x+16)=3x^2-9x-30-27x-54$$
$$9x+63+3x^2+30x+48=3x^2-36x-84$$
$$39x+111=-36x-84$$
$$75x=-195$$
$$x=-\frac{195}{75}=-\frac{13}{5}$$

28.
$$2.04x-3.10-2.95x=8.12-5.00x+1.05$$
$$-.91x-3.10=-5.00x+9.17$$
$$4.09x=12.27$$
$$409x=1227$$
$$x=3$$

29.
$$\frac{4}{x-4}=\frac{5x-12}{x^2-16}\quad\frac{8}{16-x^2}$$
$$\frac{4}{x-4}=\frac{5x-12}{(x+4)(x-4)}+\frac{8}{x^2-16}$$
$$(x+4)(x-4)\left(\frac{4}{x-4}\right)=(x+4)(x-4)\left[\frac{5x-4}{(x+4)(x-4)}\right]$$
$$4(x+4)=5x-4$$
$$4x+16=5x-4$$
$$-x=-20$$
$$x=20$$

30.
$$\frac{3}{x+1}+\frac{24}{1-x^2}=\frac{3}{1-x}$$
$$(1+x)(1-x)\left[\frac{3}{(1+x)}+\frac{24}{(1+x)(1-x)}\right]=(1+x)\cancel{(1-x)}\left(\frac{3}{\cancel{1-x}}\right)$$
$$3(1-x)+24=3(1+x)$$
$$3-3x+24=3+3x$$
$$-3x+27=3+3x$$
$$-6x=-24$$
$$x=4$$

<u>Test IA</u> Page 196

1. $$\frac{a}{b}+\frac{c}{d}-\frac{e}{f}=\frac{a}{b}\cdot\frac{(df)}{(df)}+\frac{c}{d}\cdot\frac{(bf)}{(bf)}-\frac{e}{f}\cdot\frac{(bd)}{(bd)}=\frac{adf+bcf-bde}{bdf}$$

2. $$\frac{a}{b}\div\frac{c}{d}\cdot\frac{e}{f}=\left(\frac{a}{b}\cdot\frac{d}{c}\right)\cdot\frac{e}{f}=\left(\frac{ad}{bc}\right)\frac{e}{f}=\frac{ade}{bcf}$$

3. $$\frac{\frac{a}{b}+\frac{c}{d}}{\frac{e}{b}-\frac{b}{d}}=\frac{\frac{ad}{bd}+\frac{bc}{bd}}{\frac{de}{bd}-\frac{b^2}{bd}}=\frac{\frac{ad+bc}{bd}}{\frac{de-b^2}{bd}}=\frac{ad+bc}{\cancel{bd}}\cdot\frac{\cancel{bd}}{de-b^2}=\frac{ad+bc}{de-b^2}$$

4. $\dfrac{36x^2 - 9y^2}{6x^2 + xy - y^2} = \dfrac{9(4x^2 - y^2)}{(3x - y)(2x + y)}$

$= \dfrac{9\cancel{(2x + y)}(2x - y)}{(3x - y)\cancel{(2x + y)}}$

$= \dfrac{9(2x - y)}{3x - y}$

5. $x + 2 - \dfrac{3x - 5}{x - 2} = \dfrac{(x + 2)(x - 2)}{x - 2} - \dfrac{3x - 5}{x - 2}$

$= \dfrac{x^2 - 4 - 3x + 5}{x - 2}$

$= \dfrac{x^2 - 3x + 1}{x - 2}$

6. $\dfrac{a + b}{3} - \dfrac{a - b}{2} + \dfrac{2a - b}{4} = \dfrac{4(a + b)}{12} - \dfrac{6(a - b)}{12} + \dfrac{3(2a - b)}{12}$

$= \dfrac{4a + 4b - 6a + 6b + 6a - 3b}{12}$

$= \dfrac{4a + 7b}{12}$

7. $\dfrac{x + 1}{x^2 - 4} + \dfrac{x - 2}{x^2 - x - 6} - \dfrac{x + 2}{x^2 - 5x + 6} = \dfrac{x + 1}{(x + 2)(x - 2)} + \dfrac{x - 2}{(x - 3)(x + 2)} - \dfrac{x + 2}{(x - 3)(x - 2)}$

$= \dfrac{(x + 1)(x - 3)}{(x + 2)(x - 2)(x - 3)} + \dfrac{(x - 2)^2}{(x + 2)(x - 2)(x - 3)} - \dfrac{(x + 2)^2}{(x + 2)(x - 2)(x - 3)}$

$= \dfrac{x^2 - 2x - 3 + x^2 - 4x + 4 - (x^2 + 4x + 4)}{(x + 2)(x - 2)(x - 3)}$

$= \dfrac{2x^2 - 6x + 1 - x^2 - 4x - 4}{(x + 2)(x - 2)(x - 3)}$

$= \dfrac{x^2 - 10x - 3}{(x + 2)(x - 2)(x - 3)}$

8. $\dfrac{m + n}{m - n} - \dfrac{m}{m + n} - \dfrac{2m^2}{n^2 - m^2} = \dfrac{m + n}{m - n} - \dfrac{m}{m + n} + \dfrac{2m^2}{m^2 - n^2}$

$= \dfrac{(m + n)^2}{(m + n)(m - n)} - \dfrac{m(m - n)}{(m + n)(m - n)} + \dfrac{2m^2}{(m + n)(m - n)}$

$= \dfrac{m^2 + 2mn + n^2 - m^2 + mn + 2m^2}{(m + n)(m - n)}$

$= \dfrac{2m^2 + 3mn + n^2}{(m + n)(m - n)}$

$= \dfrac{(2m + n)\cancel{(m + n)}}{\cancel{(m + n)}(m - n)}$

$= \dfrac{2m + n}{m - n}$

9. $$\frac{4 - \frac{3a}{a+b}}{6 + \frac{5b^2}{a^2 - b^2}} = \frac{\frac{4(a+b)}{a+b} - \frac{3a}{a+b}}{\frac{6(a^2 - b^2)}{a^2 - b^2} + \frac{5b^2}{a^2 - b^2}}$$

$$= \frac{\frac{4a + 4b - 3a}{a+b}}{\frac{6a^2 - 6b^2 + 5b^2}{(a+b)(a-b)}}$$

$$= \frac{a + 4b}{\cancel{a+b}} \cdot \frac{\cancel{(a+b)}(a-b)}{6a^2 - b^2}$$

$$= \frac{(a+4b)(a-b)}{6a^2 - b^2}$$

10. $$\frac{y^2 + 2y}{y^2 - 4y + 4} \cdot \frac{y^2 - 5y + 6}{y^2 - 4y + 3} \div \frac{y^2 - 2y - 8}{y^2 - 6y + 8} = \frac{y(y+2)}{(y-2)(y-2)} \cdot \frac{(y-3)(y-2)}{(y-3)(y-1)} \div \frac{(y-4)(y+2)}{(y-4)(y-2)}$$

$$= \frac{y\cancel{(y+2)}}{\cancel{(y-2)}\cancel{(y-2)}} \cdot \frac{\cancel{(y-3)}\cancel{(y-2)}}{\cancel{(y-3)}(y-1)} \cdot \frac{\cancel{(y-4)}\cancel{(y-2)}}{\cancel{(y-4)}\cancel{(y+2)}}$$

$$= \frac{y}{y-1}$$

<u>Test IB</u> Page 197

1. $$\frac{x}{y} - \frac{m}{n} + \frac{p}{q} = \frac{x}{y} \cdot \frac{(nq)}{(nq)} - \frac{m}{n} \cdot \frac{(yq)}{(yq)} + \frac{p}{q} \cdot \frac{yn}{yn} = \frac{nqx - mqy + npy}{nqy}$$

2. $$\frac{m}{n} \cdot \frac{p}{q} \div \frac{x}{y} = \frac{m}{n} \cdot \frac{p}{q} \cdot \frac{y}{x} = \frac{mpy}{nqx}$$

3. $$\frac{\frac{x}{y} - \frac{m}{n}}{\frac{z}{y} + \frac{p}{n}} = \frac{\frac{xn}{ny} - \frac{my}{ny}}{\frac{zn}{ny} + \frac{py}{ny}} = \frac{nx - my}{\cancel{ny}} \cdot \frac{\cancel{ny}}{nz + py} = \frac{nx - my}{nz + py}$$

4. $$\frac{16x^2 - 4y^2}{8x^2 + 2xy - 3y^2} = \frac{4(4x^2 - y^2)}{(4x + 3y)(2x - y)}$$

$$= \frac{4(2x + y)\cancel{(2x - y)}}{(4x + 3y)\cancel{(2x - y)}}$$

$$= \frac{4(2x + y)}{4x + 3y}$$

5. $$2a - 5 - \frac{4a + 3}{2a + 5} = \frac{(2a - 5)(2a + 5)}{2a + 5} - \frac{4a + 3}{2a + 5}$$

$$= \frac{4a^2 - 25 - 4a - 3}{2a + 5}$$

$$= \frac{4a^2 - 4a - 28}{2a + 5}$$

$$= \frac{4(a^2 - a - 7)}{2a + 5}$$

6. $$\frac{m+n}{4} - \frac{m-n}{8} + \frac{2m-3n}{6} = \frac{6(m+n)}{24} - \frac{3(m-n)}{24} + \frac{4(2m-3n)}{24}$$
$$= \frac{6m + 6n - 3m + 3n + 8m - 12n}{24}$$
$$= \frac{11m - 3n}{24}$$

7. $$\frac{x+2}{x^2-9} - \frac{x-3}{x^2-x-12} + \frac{x-2}{x^2-7x+12} = \frac{x+2}{(x+3)(x-3)} - \frac{x-3}{(x-4)(x+3)} + \frac{x-2}{(x-4)(x-3)}$$
$$= \frac{(x+2)(x-4)}{(x+3)(x-3)(x-4)} - \frac{(x-3)^2}{(x+3)(x-3)(x-4)} + \frac{(x-2)(x+3)}{(x+3)(x-3)(x-4)}$$
$$= \frac{x^2 - 2x - 8 - (x^2 - 6x + 9) + x^2 + x - 6}{(x+3)(x-3)(x-4)}$$
$$= \frac{2x^2 - x - 14 - x^2 + 6x - 9}{(x+3)(x-3)(x-4)}$$
$$= \frac{x^2 + 5x - 23}{(x+3)(x-3)(x-4)}$$

8. $$\frac{a-5b}{a+5b} + \frac{2a}{a-5b} + \frac{3a^2+25b^2}{25b^2-a^2} = \frac{(a-5b)^2}{(a+5b)(a-5b)} + \frac{2a(a+5b)}{(a+5b)(a-5b)} - \frac{3a^2+25b^2}{a^2-25b^2}$$
$$= \frac{a^2 - 10ab + 25b^2 + 2a^2 + 10ab - 3a^2 - 25b^2}{(a+5b)(a-5b)}$$
$$= \frac{0}{(a+5b)(a-5b)} = 0$$

9. $$\frac{3 + \frac{3x}{x+2y}}{2 - \frac{x^2-7y^2}{x^2-4y^2}} = \frac{\frac{3(x+2y)}{x+2y} + \frac{3x}{x+2y}}{\frac{2(x^2-4y^2)}{x^2-4y^2} - \frac{x^2-7y^2}{x^2-4y^2}} = \frac{\frac{3x+6y+3x}{x+2y}}{\frac{2x^2-8y^2-x^2+7y^2}{x^2-4y^2}}$$
$$= \frac{\frac{6x+6y}{x+2y}}{\frac{x^2-y^2}{x^2-4y^2}} = \frac{\frac{6(x+y)}{x+2y}}{\frac{(x+y)(x-y)}{(x+2y)(x-2y)}}$$
$$= \frac{6\cancel{(x+y)}}{\cancel{x+2y}} \cdot \frac{\cancel{(x+2y)}(x-2y)}{\cancel{(x+y)}(x-y)}$$
$$= \frac{6(x-2y)}{x-y}$$

10. $$\frac{m^2+3mn}{m^2-4mn+4n^2} \cdot \frac{m^2+3mn-10n^2}{m^2-9n^2} \div \frac{mn+5n^2}{m^2-5mn+6n^2}$$
$$= \frac{m(m+3n)}{(m-2n)(m-2n)} \cdot \frac{(m+5n)(m-2n)}{(m+3n)(m-3n)} \div \frac{n(m+5n)}{(m-3n)(m-2n)}$$
$$= \frac{m\cancel{(m+3n)}}{\cancel{(m-2n)}\cancel{(m-2n)}} \cdot \frac{\cancel{(m+5n)}\cancel{(m-2n)}}{\cancel{(m+3n)}\cancel{(m-3n)}} \cdot \frac{\cancel{(m-3n)}\cancel{(m-2n)}}{n\cancel{(m+5n)}}$$
$$= \frac{m}{n}$$

Test IIA   Page 197

The check is left for the teacher.

I 1.

$$\frac{x}{2} - \frac{4x}{3} = 10$$
$$6\left(\frac{x}{2} - \frac{4x}{3}\right) = 6(10)$$
$$3x - 8x = 60$$
$$-5x = 60$$
$$x = -12$$

2.

$$\frac{x - 9}{x - 5} + \frac{x - 5}{x - 8} = 2$$
$$(x - 5)(x - 8)\left(\frac{x - 9}{x - 5} + \frac{x - 5}{x - 8}\right) = 2(x - 5)(x - 8)$$
$$(x - 8)(x - 9) + (x - 5)^2 = (2x - 10)(x - 8)$$
$$x^2 - 17x + 72 + x^2 - 10x + 25 = 2x^2 - 26x + 80$$
$$\cancel{2x^2} - 27x + 97 = \cancel{2x^2} - 26x + 80$$
$$-x = -17$$
$$x = 17$$

3.

$$\frac{2y - 3}{4} - \frac{5y + 2}{12} + \frac{y + 1}{6} = 0$$
$$12\left(\frac{2y - 3}{4}\right) - 12\left(\frac{5y + 2}{12}\right) + 12\left(\frac{y + 1}{6}\right) = 12(0)$$
$$3(2y - 3) - (5y + 2) + 2(y + 1) = 0$$
$$6y - 9 - 5y - 2 + 2y + 2 = 0$$
$$3y - 9 = 0$$
$$3y = 9$$
$$y = 3$$

4.

$$\frac{3}{x + 1} + \frac{x^2}{x^2 - 1} = \frac{x + 1}{x - 1}$$
$$(x + 1)(x - 1)\left[\frac{3}{x + 1} + \frac{x^2}{(x + 1)(x - 1)}\right] = (x + 1)\cancel{(x - 1)}\left(\frac{x + 1}{\cancel{x - 1}}\right)$$
$$3(x - 1) + x^2 = (x + 1)^2$$
$$3x - 3 + x^2 = x^2 + 2x + 1$$
$$x = 4$$

5.

$$C = \frac{en}{R + nr}$$
$$C(R + nr) = (R + nr)\frac{en}{R + nr}$$
$$CR + Cnr = en$$
$$Cnr = en - Cr$$
$$\frac{Cnr}{Cn} = \frac{en - Cr}{Cn}$$
$$r = \frac{en - Cr}{Cn}$$

$$C = \frac{en}{R + nr}$$
$$C(R + nr) = \cancel{(R + nr)}\frac{en}{\cancel{R + nr}}$$
$$CR + Cnr = en$$
$$Cnr - en = -CR$$
$$n(Cr - e) = -CR$$
$$\frac{n\cancel{(Cr - e)}}{\cancel{Cr - e}} = \frac{-CR}{Cr - e}$$
$$n = \frac{-CR}{Cr - e}$$
$$n = \frac{CR}{e - Cr}$$

II

1. let t = time working together

	Together	1 Minute	t Minutes
Shane	t	$\frac{1}{25}$	$\frac{1}{25}(t)$
Dennis	t	$\frac{1}{35}$	$\frac{1}{35}(t)$

$$\frac{1}{25}t + \frac{1}{35}t = 1$$

2. let d = denominator

$\frac{1}{2}d + 3$ = numerator

$$\frac{\frac{1}{2}d + 3}{d} = \text{fraction}$$

$$\frac{\frac{1}{2}d + 3}{d} = \frac{2}{3}$$

3. let x = needed grade

$$\frac{76 + 88 + 82 + 90 + x}{5} = 85$$

4. let x = larger part

75 - x = smaller part

$$\frac{1}{3}x - 1 = \frac{2}{3}(75 - x)$$

5. let d = distance at 70 mph

370 - d = distance at 50 mph

	Rate	Time	Distance
Part A	70	$\frac{d}{70}$	d
Part B	50	$\frac{370 - d}{50}$	370 - d

$$\frac{d}{70} + \frac{370 - d}{50} = 6$$

Test IIB   Page 198

The check is left for the teacher

I 1.

$$\frac{x}{3} - \frac{5x}{4} = 11$$
$$12\left(\frac{x}{3} - \frac{5x}{4}\right) = 12(11)$$
$$4x - 15x = 132$$
$$-11x = 132$$
$$x = -12$$

2.

$$\frac{3x - 5}{5} + \frac{x + 6}{10} - \frac{8x - 1}{15} = 0$$
$$30\left(\frac{3x - 5}{5} + \frac{x + 6}{10} - \frac{8x - 1}{15}\right) = 30(0)$$
$$6(3x - 5) + 3(x + 6) - 2(8x - 1) = 0$$
$$18x - 30 + 3x + 18 - 16x + 2 = 0$$
$$5x - 10 = 0$$
$$5x = 10$$
$$x = 2$$

3.

$$\frac{y^2}{y^2 - 9} - \frac{3}{y - 3} = \frac{y - 3}{y + 3}$$
$$(y + 3)(y - 3)\left[\frac{y^2}{(y + 3)(y - 3)} - \frac{3}{y - 3}\right] = (y + 3)(y - 3)\left(\frac{y - 3}{y + 3}\right)$$
$$y^2 - 3(y + 3) = (y - 3)^2$$
$$y^2 - 3y - 9 = y^2 - 6y + 9$$
$$3y = 18$$
$$y = 6$$

4.

$$\frac{x - 3}{x + 4} + \frac{x - 1}{x - 5} = 2$$

$$(x + 4)(x - 5)\left(\frac{x - 3}{x + 4} + \frac{x - 1}{x - 5}\right) = 2(x + 4)(x - 5)$$

$$(x - 5)(x - 3) + (x + 4)(x - 1) = (2x + 8)(x - 5)$$

$$x^2 - 8x + 15 + x^2 + 3x - 4 = 2x^2 - 2x - 40$$

$$2x^2 - 5x + 11 = 2x^2 - 2x - 40$$

$$-3x = -51$$

$$x = 17$$

5.

$$F = \frac{pr}{M - sr}$$

$$F(M - sr) = \cancel{(M - sr)}\frac{pr}{\cancel{M - sr}}$$

$$FM - Fsr = pr$$

$$-Fsr = pr - FM$$

$$\frac{-Fsr}{-Fr} = \frac{pr - FM}{-Fr}$$

$$s = \frac{FM - pr}{Fr}$$

$$F = \frac{pr}{M - sr}$$

$$F(M - sr) = \cancel{(M - sr)}\frac{pr}{\cancel{M - sr}}$$

$$FM - Fsr = pr$$

$$FM = pr + Fsr$$

$$FM = r(p + Fs)$$

$$\frac{FM}{p + Fs} = \frac{r(p + Fs)}{p + Fs}$$

$$r = \frac{FM}{p + Fs}$$

II

1. let x = time working together

Together	1 Hour	x Hours
x	$\frac{1}{1\frac{3}{4}}$	$\frac{1}{1\frac{3}{4}}(x)$
x	$\frac{1}{2\frac{1}{2}}$	$\frac{1}{2\frac{1}{2}}(x)$

$$\frac{1}{1\frac{3}{4}}x + \frac{1}{2\frac{1}{2}}x = 1$$

2. let n = numerator
   2n - 5 = denominator

$$\frac{n}{2n - 5} = \frac{3}{5}$$

3. let x = grade on Thursday

$$\frac{80 + 83 + 96 + x + (x - 4)}{5} = 87$$

4. let x = the larger
   46 - x = the smaller

$$\frac{1}{4}x - \frac{1}{6}(46 - x) = 4$$

5. let s = speed of train
   $\frac{360}{s}$ = time for trip

	Speed	Time	Distance
Now	s	$\frac{360}{s}$	360
If	s+60	$\frac{360}{s+60}$	360

$$\frac{360}{s + 60} + \frac{1}{2} = \frac{360}{s}$$

(The following additional steps are given for the teacher's reference:

s2 + 780s + 720s + 43,200

$s^2 + 60s - 43,200 = 0$

Equations of this nature will be studied in Unit 14.)

Test C   Pages 198 -199

I

1. $$\left(\frac{a^2}{b^2} - 4\right) \div \left(2 + \frac{a^2 + 4b^2}{2ab}\right) = \left(\frac{a^2}{b^2} - \frac{4b^2}{b^2}\right) \div \left(\frac{4ab}{2ab} + \frac{a^2 + 4b^2}{2ab}\right)$$

$$= \frac{a^2 - 4b^2}{b^2} \div \frac{a^2 + 4ab + 4b^2}{2ab}$$

$$= \frac{a^2 - 4b}{b^2} \cdot \frac{2ab}{a^2 + 4ab + 4b^2}$$

$$= \frac{\cancel{(a + 2b)}(a - 2b)}{\underset{b}{\cancel{b^2}}} \cdot \frac{\overset{2a}{\cancel{2ab}}}{\cancel{(a + 2b)}(a + 2b)}$$

$$= \frac{2a(a - 2b)}{b(a + 2b)}$$

2. $$\frac{2x + 1}{x^2 + x - 6} - \frac{x - 3}{2x^2 - 5x + 2} + \frac{x - 2}{2x^2 + 5x - 3} = \frac{2x + 1}{(x + 3)(x - 2)} - \frac{x - 3}{(2x - 1)(x - 2)} + \frac{x - 2}{(2x - 1)(x + 3)}$$

$$= \frac{(2x + 1)(2x - 1)}{(x + 3)(x - 2)(2x - 1)} - \frac{(x - 3)(x + 3)}{(x + 3)(x - 2)(2x - 1)} + \frac{(x - 2)^2}{(x + 3)(x - 2)(2x - 1)}$$

$$= \frac{4x^2 - 1 - (x^2 - 9) + x^2 - 4x + 4}{(x + 3)(x - 2)(2x - 1)}$$

$$= \frac{4x^2 - 1 - x^2 + 9 + x^2 - 4x + 4}{(x + 3)(x - 2)(2x - 1)}$$

$$= \frac{4x^2 - 4x + 12}{(x + 3)(x - 2)(2x - 1)}$$

$$= \frac{4(x^2 - x + 3)}{(x + 3)(x - 2)(2x - 1)}$$

3. $$\frac{\frac{6x}{y} - 7 - \frac{3y}{x}}{\frac{6}{y^2} + \frac{11}{xy} + \frac{3}{x^2}} = \frac{\frac{6x^2}{xy} - \frac{7xy}{xy} - \frac{3y^2}{xy}}{\frac{6x^2}{x^2y^2} + \frac{11xy}{x^2y^2} + \frac{3y^2}{x^2y^2}}$$

$$= \frac{\frac{6x^2 - 7xy - 3y^2}{xy}}{\frac{6x^2 + 11xy + 3y^2}{x^2y^2}}$$

$$= \frac{\cancel{(3x + y)}(2x - 3y)}{\cancel{xy}} \cdot \frac{\overset{xy}{\cancel{x^2y^2}}}{\cancel{(3x + y)}(2x + 3y)}$$

$$= \frac{xy(2x - 3y)}{2x + 3y}$$

II The check is left for the teacher.

1.

$$\frac{x+3}{5} - \frac{3x+4}{15} = \frac{x+7}{3x-4} + \frac{1}{3}$$

$$\frac{x+3}{5} - \frac{3x+4}{15} - \frac{1}{3} = \frac{x+7}{3x-4}$$

$$\frac{3x+9-3x-4-5}{15} = \frac{x+7}{3x-4}$$

$$0 = \frac{x+7}{3x-4}$$

$$0 = x+7$$

$$-7 = x$$

2.

$$\frac{y+1}{2y-3} - \frac{y-1}{4y-6} = \frac{2}{2y+3} - \frac{y^2+7}{9-4y^2}$$

$$\frac{y+1}{2y-3} - \frac{y-1}{2(2y-3)} = \frac{2}{2y+3} + \frac{y^2+7}{4y^2\ 9}$$

$$2(2y+3)(2y-3)\left[\frac{y+1}{2y-3} - \frac{y-1}{2(2y-3)}\right] = 2(2y+3)(2y-3)\left[\frac{2}{2y+3} + \frac{y^2+7}{(2y+3)(2y-3)}\right]$$

$$2(2y+3)(y+1) - (2y+3)(y-1) = 4(2y-3) + 2(y^2+7)$$

$$(4y+6)(y+1) - (2y^2+y-3) = 8y - 12 + 2y^2 + 14$$

$$4y^2 + 10y + 6 - 2y^2 - y + 3 = 2y^2 + 8y + 2$$

$$2y^2 + 9y + 9 = 2y^2 + 8y + 2$$

$$y = -7$$

3.

$$C = \frac{E}{R + \frac{r}{n}}$$

$$C\left(R + \frac{r}{n}\right) = \frac{E}{\cancel{R + \frac{r}{n}}} \cdot \cancel{\left(R + \frac{r}{n}\right)}$$

$$CR + \frac{Cr}{n} = E$$

$$\frac{Cr}{n} = E - CR$$

$$\cancel{n}\left(\frac{Cr}{\cancel{n}}\right) = n(E - CR)$$

$$Cr = n(E - CR)$$

$$\frac{Cr}{E - CR} = \frac{n\cancel{(E - CR)}}{\cancel{E - CR}}$$

$$n = \frac{Cr}{E - CR}$$

III

1. 1. let x = time working together

2.

	Together	1 Hour	x Hours
First Worker	x	$\frac{1}{f}$	$x(\frac{1}{f})$
Second Worker	x	$\frac{1}{s}$	$x(\frac{1}{s})$
Third Worker	x	$\frac{1}{t}$	$x(\frac{1}{t})$

3. $x(\frac{1}{f}) + x(\frac{1}{s}) + x(\frac{1}{t}) = 1$

4. $\frac{x}{f} + \frac{x}{s} + \frac{x}{t} = 1$

$$fst(\frac{x}{f} + \frac{x}{s} + \frac{x}{t}) = fst$$
$$stx + ftx + fsx = fst$$
$$x(st + ft + fs) = fst$$
$$x = \frac{fst}{st + ft + fs}$$

5. No check required.

2. let f = 9, s = 6, t = 8

$$x = \frac{fst}{st + ft + fs}$$
$$x = \frac{9(6)(8)}{6(8) + 9(8) + 9(6)}$$
$$x = \frac{432}{48 + 72 + 54}$$
$$x = \frac{432}{174}$$
$$x = 2\frac{84}{174} = 2\frac{14}{29} \text{ da. or } 2.5 \text{ da.}$$

3. 1. let x = time working together $\underline{2\frac{14}{29} \text{ da.}}$

2.

	Together	1 Hour	x Hours
First Worker	x	$\frac{1}{9}$	$\frac{1}{9}(x)$
Second Worker	x	$\frac{1}{6}$	$\frac{1}{6}(x)$
Third Worker	x	$\frac{1}{8}$	$\frac{1}{8}(x)$

3. $\frac{1}{9}x + \frac{1}{6}x + \frac{1}{8}x = 1$

4. $432(\frac{1}{9}x + \frac{1}{6}x + \frac{1}{8}x) = 432$

$$48x + 72x + 54x = 432$$
$$174x = 432$$
$$x = \frac{432}{174}$$
$$x = 2\frac{14}{29} \text{ da.}$$

5. $\frac{1}{9}(2\frac{14}{29}) + \frac{1}{6}(2\frac{14}{29}) + \frac{1}{8}(2\frac{14}{29})$

$$= \frac{72}{261} + \frac{72}{174} + \frac{72}{232}$$
$$= \frac{2,906,496 + 4,359,744 + 3,269,808}{10,536,048}$$
$$= 1 \checkmark$$

UNIT 9 — Ratio, Proportion, and Variation

Exercises 9.1   Page 201

1. $\frac{8m}{4m} = \frac{2}{1}$ $\frac{4m}{8m} = \frac{1}{2}$

2. $\frac{6}{9} = \frac{2}{3}$, $\frac{12x}{16y} = \frac{3x}{4y}$, $\frac{am}{bm} = \frac{a}{b}$;

$\frac{20ab}{10bc} = \frac{2a}{c}$; $\frac{m + n}{m^2 - n^2} = \frac{\cancel{m + n}}{(\cancel{m + n})(m - n)} = \frac{1}{m - n}$

3. $\frac{2}{3} = .\overline{6}$ $\frac{4}{9} = .\overline{4}$ $\frac{4}{9} = .\overline{4}$

$\frac{3}{4} = .75$ $\frac{2}{5} = .4$ $\frac{2}{3} = .\overline{6}$

$\frac{3}{4}$ is greater $\frac{4}{9}$ is greater $\frac{2}{3}$ is greater

4. $\frac{\frac{1}{2}}{\frac{1}{4}} = \frac{1}{\cancel{2}} \cdot \frac{\overset{2}{\cancel{4}}}{} = \frac{2}{1}$ $\frac{\frac{1}{2}}{\frac{1}{3}} = \frac{1}{2}(3) = \frac{3}{2}$ $\frac{\frac{2}{3}}{\frac{3}{4}} = \frac{2}{3} \cdot \frac{4}{3} = \frac{8}{9}$

5. $\frac{15}{30} = \frac{1}{2}$

$\frac{21}{7} = \frac{3}{1}$

$\frac{3}{5280} = \frac{1}{1760}$

6. $\frac{\frac{4x}{5}}{\frac{2x^2}{5}} = \frac{\overset{2}{\cancel{4x}}}{\cancel{5}} \cdot \frac{\cancel{5}}{\underset{x}{\cancel{2x^2}}} = \frac{2}{x}$ $\frac{\frac{3}{4}ab}{\frac{1}{2}ac} = \frac{3\cancel{a}b}{\underset{2}{\cancel{4}}} \cdot \frac{\cancel{2}}{\cancel{a}c} = \frac{3b}{2c}$

$\frac{2\frac{1}{2}}{7\frac{1}{2}} = \frac{\frac{5}{2}}{\frac{15}{2}} = \frac{\cancel{5}}{\cancel{2}} \cdot \frac{\cancel{2}}{\underset{3}{\cancel{15}}} = \frac{1}{3}$ $\frac{.7\cancel{m}}{.8\cancel{m}} = \frac{.7}{.8} = \frac{7}{8}$

$\frac{x^2 - y^2}{(x - y)^2} = \frac{(x + y)\cancel{(x - y)}}{(x - y)\cancel{(x - y)}} = \frac{x + y}{x - y}$

7. $\frac{80}{90} = \frac{8}{9}$ $\frac{90}{80} = \frac{9}{8}$

8. $\frac{120}{120} = \frac{1}{1}$

9. $\frac{1}{2} = \frac{75}{x}$ x = 150 mph

$2x(\frac{1}{2}) = 2x(\frac{75}{x})$

$x = 150$

10. $\frac{7}{4} = \frac{x}{120}$ x = 210 billion cu. ft.

$120(\frac{7}{4}) = 120(\frac{x}{120})$

$210 = x$

Exercises 9.2 Pages 203

1. $\frac{3}{5} = \frac{x}{55}$

$\overset{11}{\cancel{55}}(\frac{3}{\cancel{5}}) = \cancel{55}(\frac{x}{\cancel{55}})$

$33 = x$

2. $\frac{2}{3} = \frac{4}{x}$

$2x = 12$

$x = 6$

3. $\frac{5}{x} = \frac{4}{3}$

$4x = 15$

$x = \frac{15}{4} = 3\frac{3}{4}$

4. $\frac{1}{x} = \frac{x}{9}$

$x^2 = 9$

$x^2 - 9 = 0$

$(x + 3)(x - 3) = 0$

$x = -3, 3$

5. $\frac{x + 2}{x} = \frac{10}{6}$

$6(x + 2) = 10x$

$6x + 12 = 10x$

$-4x = -12$

$x = 3$

6. $\frac{x}{x - 1} = \frac{15}{12}$

$12x = 15x - 15$

$-3x = -15$

$x = 5$

7. $\frac{x + 2}{x - 2} = \frac{3}{1}$

$x + 2 = 3x - 6$

$-2x = -8$

$x = 4$

8. $\frac{2}{x} = \frac{x}{8}$

$x^2 = 16$

$x^2 - 16 = 0$

$(x + 4)(x - 4) = 0$

$x = -4, 4$

9. $\frac{16}{x} = \frac{x}{4}$

$x^2 = 64$

$x^2 - 64 = 0$

$(x + 8)(x - 8) = 0$

$x = -8, 8$

10. $\frac{5}{x} = \frac{x}{45}$

$x^2 = 225$

$x^2 - 225 = 0$

$(x + 15)(x - 15) = 0$

$x = -15, 15$

11. $5\frac{1}{2}(6\frac{1}{2}) \mid 3(4)$

$\frac{11}{2}(\frac{13}{2}) \mid 3(4)$

$\frac{143}{4} \neq 12$

No

12. $4(6\frac{1}{2}) \mid 2(13)$

$26 = 26$

Yes

13. $5(14x) \mid 7x(10)$

$70x = 70x$

Yes

14. $2.4a(2a) \mid .8a(6a)$

$4.8a^2 = 4.8a^2$

Yes

15. $\frac{a}{b} = \frac{c}{d}$

$ad = bc$

$\frac{a\cancel{d}}{c\cancel{d}} = \frac{b\cancel{c}}{\cancel{c}d}$

$\frac{a}{c} = \frac{b}{d}$

$\frac{a}{b} = \frac{c}{d}$

$ad = bc$

$\frac{\cancel{a}d}{\cancel{a}c} = \frac{b\cancel{c}}{a\cancel{c}}$

$\frac{d}{c} = \frac{b}{a}$

$\frac{b}{a} = \frac{d}{c}$

Word Problems   Pages 204 -205

1. 1. let x = Minnesota's output   40%
   2.
   3. $\frac{5}{8} = \frac{25}{x}$
   4. $5x = 200$
      $x = 40$
   5. $\frac{5}{8} = \frac{25}{40}$ ✓

2. 1. let x = number of pens   270 million
   2.
   3. $\frac{x}{285} = \frac{18}{19}$
   4. $19x = 5130$
      $x = 270$
   5. $\frac{270}{285} = \frac{18}{19}$ ✓

3. 1. let x = usual limit for recreational divers   130 ft.
   2.
   3. $\frac{260}{x} = \frac{10}{5}$
   4. $10x = 1300$
      $x = 130$
   5. $\frac{260}{130} = \frac{2}{1} = \frac{10}{5}$ ✓

4. 1. let x = pounds of green tea   1000
   2.
   3. $\frac{x}{4200} = \frac{5}{21}$
   4. $21x = 21{,}000$
      $x = 1000$
   5. $\frac{1000}{4200} = \frac{5}{21}$ ✓

5. 1. let x = amount produced by old machine   60 pins/min.
   2. 960 - x = amount produced by new machine   900 pins/min.
   3. $\frac{x}{960 - x} = \frac{1}{15}$
   4. $15x = 960 - x$
      $16x = 960$
      $x = 60$
   5. $\frac{60}{900} = \frac{1}{15}$ ✓

6. 1. let x = the number $\frac{1}{2}$
   2.
   3. $\frac{x + 1}{x + 2} = \frac{x + 4}{x + 7}$
   4. $(x + 1)(x + 7) = (x + 2)(x + 4)$
      $x^2 + 8x + 7 = x^2 + 6x + 8$
      $2x = 1$
      $x = \frac{1}{2}$

      $\frac{x + 1}{x + 2} = \frac{x + 7}{x + 4}$
      $(x + 1)(x + 4) = (x + 2)(x + 7)$
      $x^2 + 5x + 4 = x^2 + 9x + 14$
      $-4x = 10$
      $x = \frac{-10}{4} = \frac{-5}{2}$

   Neglect this solution since the number is to be positive.

   5. $\frac{1\frac{1}{2}}{2\frac{1}{2}} \;\Big|\; \frac{4\frac{1}{2}}{7\frac{1}{2}}$
      $\frac{\frac{3}{2}}{\frac{5}{2}} \;\Big|\; \frac{\frac{9}{2}}{\frac{15}{2}}$
      $\frac{3}{5} \;\Big|\; \frac{9}{15}$
      $\frac{3}{5} = \frac{3}{5}$ ✓

7. 1. let e = greatest length of Lake Erie <u>250 mi.</u>
   2. e + 50 = greatest length of Lake Michigan <u>300 mi.</u>
   3. $\frac{e}{e + 50} = \frac{5}{6}$
   4. $6e = 5e + 250$
      $e = 250$
   5. $\frac{250}{300} = \frac{5}{6}$ ✓

8. 1. let x = thousands lost at Lisbon <u>60</u> (60,000)
   2. x + 55 = thousands lost at Messina <u>115</u> (115,000)
   3. $\frac{x}{x + 55} = \frac{12}{23}$
   4. $23x = 12x + 660$
      $11x = 660$
      $x = 60$
   5. $\frac{60,000}{115,000} = \frac{60}{115} = \frac{12}{23}$ ✓

9. 1. let x = ounces of copper <u>48 oz.</u>
   2. 72 - x = ounces of zinc <u>24 oz.</u>
   3. $\frac{x}{72 - x} = \frac{2}{1}$
   4. $x = 144 - 2x$
      $3x = 144$
      $x = 48$
   5. $\frac{48}{24} = \frac{2}{1}$ ✓

10. 1. let x = foreign sales in thousands <u>345</u> (345,000 lb.)
    2. 555 - x = domestic sales in thousands 210
    3. $\frac{555 - x}{x} = \frac{14}{23}$
    4. $14x = 12,765 - 23x$
       $37x = 12,765$
       $x = 345$
    5. $\frac{210,000}{345,000} = \frac{210}{345} = \frac{14}{23}$ ✓

11. 1. let x = number rejected <u>170</u>
    2. total produced = 930 + x
    3. $\frac{10x}{930+x} = \frac{17}{11}$
    4. $110x = 15,810 + 17x$
       $93x = 15,810$
       $x = 170$
    5. $\frac{1700}{1100} = \frac{17}{11}$ ✓

12. 1. let x = pounds of copper <u>750 lb.</u>
    2. 1000 - x = pounds of tin <u>250 lb.</u>
    3. $\frac{x}{1000 - x} = \frac{3}{1}$
    4. $x = 3000 - 3x$
       $4x = 3000$
       $x = 750$
    5. $\frac{750}{250} = \frac{3}{1}$ ✓

<u>Exercises 9.4</u> Pages 206 -207

1. $d = 50t$
   $d = 50(6) = 300$ mi.

   $d = 50t$
   $d = 50(7)$
   $d = 350$ mi.

   $d = 50t$
   $d = 50(8)$
   $d = 400$ mi.

2. yes

3. $\frac{50}{1}$; same

4. 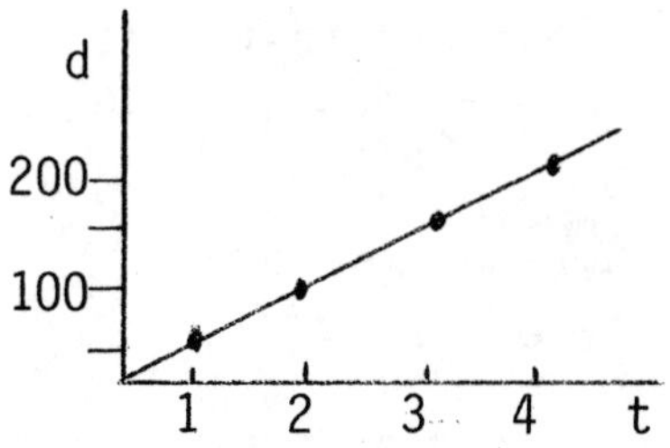

<u>Exercises 9.6</u> Pages 207-208

1.
$$\frac{h}{h'} = \frac{a}{a'}$$
$$\frac{4\frac{1}{2}}{6\frac{3}{4}} = \frac{a}{9}$$
$$\frac{\frac{9}{2}}{\frac{27}{4}} = \frac{a}{9}$$
$$\frac{\cancel{9}}{\cancel{2}}\left(\frac{\overset{2}{\cancel{4}}}{\underset{3}{\cancel{27}}}\right) = \frac{a}{9}$$
$$\frac{2}{3} = \frac{a}{9}$$
$$3a = 18$$
$$a = 6 \text{ in.}$$

2.
$$\frac{p}{p'} - \frac{a}{a'}$$
$$\frac{210}{p'} = \frac{2}{3}$$
$$2p' = 630$$
$$p' = 315 \text{ yd.}$$

3.
$$\frac{A}{A'} = \frac{b}{b'}$$
$$\frac{12}{36} = \frac{b}{7.5}$$
$$\frac{1}{3} = \frac{b}{7.5}$$
$$3b = 7.5$$
$$b = 2.5 \text{ in.}$$

4.
$$\frac{A}{A'} = \frac{h}{h'}$$
$$\frac{12}{A'} = \frac{2.3}{6.9}$$
$$\frac{12}{A'} = \frac{1}{3}$$
$$A' = 36 \text{ sq. ft.}$$

5.
$$\frac{A}{A'} = \frac{a^2}{a'^2}$$
$$\frac{A}{112\frac{1}{2}} = \frac{3^2}{9^2}$$
$$\frac{A}{\frac{225}{2}} = \frac{9}{81}$$
$$\frac{2A}{225} = \frac{1}{9}$$
$$18A = 225$$
$$A = 12\frac{1}{2} \text{ sq. in.}$$

6.
$$\frac{A}{A'} = \frac{a2}{a'2}$$
$$\frac{A}{A'} = \frac{(3\frac{1}{3})^2}{10^2}$$
$$\frac{A}{A'} = \frac{(\frac{10}{3})^2}{100}$$
$$\frac{A}{A'} = \frac{\cancel{100}}{9}\left(\frac{1}{\cancel{100}}\right)$$
$$\frac{A}{A'} = \frac{1}{9}$$

7.
$$\frac{c}{c'} = \frac{r}{r'}$$
$$\frac{62\frac{2}{7}}{c'} = \frac{10}{30}$$
$$\frac{62\frac{2}{7}}{c'} = \frac{1}{3}$$
$$c' = 3(62\tfrac{2}{7})$$
$$c' = 186\tfrac{6}{7} \text{ in.}$$

8. Let diameter be $d = 2x$ and $d' = x$
$$\frac{c}{c'} = \frac{d}{d'}$$
$$\frac{c}{c'} = \frac{2x}{x}$$
$$\frac{c}{c'} = \frac{2}{1}$$
The circumferences are in the ratio of 2 to 1 also.

9.
$$\frac{A}{A'} = \frac{r^2}{r'^2}$$
$$\frac{A}{616} = \frac{7^2}{14^2}$$
$$\frac{A}{616} = \left(\frac{7}{14}\right)^2$$
$$\frac{A}{616} = \left(\frac{1}{2}\right)^2$$
$$\frac{A}{616} = \frac{1}{4}$$
$$4A = 616$$
$$A = 154 \text{ sq. in.}$$

10. Let the diameters be $d = 2x$ and $d' = x$.

$\frac{A}{A'} = \frac{d^2}{d'^2}$

$\frac{A}{A'} = \frac{(2x)^2}{(x)^2}$

$\frac{A}{A'} = \frac{4x^2}{x^2}$

$\frac{A}{A'} = \frac{4}{1}$

11. $\frac{A}{A'} = \frac{d^2}{d'^2}$

$\frac{A}{A'} = \frac{10^2}{8^2}$

$\frac{A}{A'} = \frac{100}{64}$

$\frac{A}{A'} = \frac{25}{16}$

12. $\frac{A}{A'} = \frac{r^2}{r'^2}$

$\frac{A}{A'} = \frac{x^2}{y^2}$

Exercises 9.7 Pages 209-211

1. $\frac{A}{A'} = \frac{a^2}{a'^2}$

$\frac{A}{324} = \frac{21^2}{42^2}$

$\frac{A}{324} = (\frac{21}{42})^2$

$\frac{A}{324} = (\frac{1}{2})^2$

$\frac{A}{324} = \frac{1}{4}$

$4A = 324$

$A = 81$ sq. ft.

2. $\frac{V}{V'} = \frac{a^3}{a'^3}$

$\frac{V}{V'} = \frac{2^3}{3^3}$

$\frac{V}{V'} = \frac{8}{27}$

3. $\frac{V}{V'} = \frac{B}{B'}$

$\frac{640}{V'} = \frac{16}{25}$

$16V' = 16,000$

$V' = 1000$ cu. in.

4. $\frac{V}{V'} = \frac{h}{h'}$

$\frac{V}{966} = \frac{1}{6}$

$6V = 966$

$v = 161$ cu. in.

5. $\frac{V}{V'} = \frac{lwh}{l'w'h'}$

$\frac{V}{V'} = \frac{\cancel{18}(\cancel{12})(\cancel{6})}{\cancel{36}(\cancel{24})(\cancel{12})}$ (each cancels to $\frac{1}{2}$: $\frac{1 \cdot 1 \cdot 1}{2 \cdot 2 \cdot 2}$)

$\frac{V}{V'} = \frac{1}{8}$

6. $\frac{A}{A'} = (\frac{r}{r'})^2$

$\frac{A}{640\pi} = (\frac{8}{16})^2$

$\frac{A}{640\pi} = (\frac{1}{2})^2$

$\frac{A}{640\pi} = \frac{1}{4}$

$4A = 640\pi$

$A = 160\pi$ sq. in.

7. $\frac{A}{A'} = (\frac{d}{d'})^2$

$\frac{A}{A'} = (\frac{2}{3})^2$

$\frac{A}{A'} = \frac{4}{9}$

8. $\frac{A}{A'} = (\frac{h}{h'})^2$

$\frac{A}{A'} = (\frac{18}{36})^2$

$\frac{A}{A'} = (\frac{1}{2})^2$

$\frac{A}{A'} = \frac{1}{4}$

9. $\frac{A}{A'} = (\frac{h}{h'})^2$

$\frac{64\pi}{256\pi} = (\frac{h}{h'})^2$

$\frac{1}{4} = (\frac{h}{h'})^2$

$\sqrt{\frac{1}{4}} = \frac{h}{h'}$

$\frac{h}{h'} = \frac{1}{2}$

10. (a) The volumes of similar cylinders of revolution vary as the cubes of their altitudes.

(b) The volumes of similar cylinders of revolution vary as the cubes of their radii.

(c) The volumes of similar cylinders of revolution vary as the cubes of their diameters.

11. $\frac{V}{V'} = (\frac{d}{d'})^3$
$\frac{V}{V'} = (\frac{15}{25})^3$
$\frac{V}{V'} = (\frac{3}{5})^3$
$\frac{V}{V'} = \frac{27}{125}$

12. $\frac{V}{V'} = (\frac{h}{h'})^3$
$\frac{V}{V'} = (\frac{20}{14})^3$
$\frac{V}{V'} = (\frac{10}{7})^3$
$\frac{V}{V'} = \frac{1000}{343}$

13. (a) The lateral areas of similar cones of revolution vary as the squares of their altitudes.
(b) The lateral areas of similar cones of revolution vary as the squares of their radii.
(c) The lateral areas of similar cones of revolution vary as the squares of their diameters.
(d) The volumes of similar cones of revolution vary as the cubes of their altitudes.
(e) The volumes of similar cones of revolution vary as the cubes of their radii.
(f) The volumes of similar cones of revolution vary as the cubes of their diameters.

14. $\frac{A}{A'} = \frac{d^2}{d'^2} = (\frac{d}{d'})^2$ and
$\frac{V}{V'} = \frac{d^3}{d'^3} = (\frac{d}{d'})^3$

15. $\frac{V}{V'} = (\frac{d}{d'})^3$
$\frac{V}{V'} = (\frac{1}{3})^3 = \frac{1}{27}$

16. $\frac{A}{A'} = (\frac{h}{h'})^2$ $\qquad \frac{V}{V'} = (\frac{h}{h'})^3$
$\frac{A}{A'} = (\frac{8.4}{5.6})^2$ $\qquad \frac{V}{V'} = (\frac{8.4}{5.6})^3$
$\frac{A}{A'} = (\frac{84}{56})^2$ $\qquad \frac{V}{V'} = (\frac{3}{2})^3$
$\frac{A}{A'} = (\frac{3}{2})^2$ $\qquad \frac{V}{V'} = \frac{27}{8}$
$\frac{A}{A'} = \frac{9}{4}$

17. $\frac{v}{v'} = (\frac{r}{r'})^3$
$\frac{111.65}{v'} = (\frac{3.5}{7})^3$
$\frac{111.65}{v'} = (\frac{1}{2})^3$
$\frac{111.65}{v'} = \frac{1}{8}$
$v' = 893.2$ cu. in.

18. $\frac{A}{A'} = (\frac{r}{r'})^2$
$\frac{100}{A'} = (\frac{r}{2r})^2$
$\frac{100}{A'} = (\frac{1}{2})^2$
$\frac{100}{A'} = \frac{1}{4}$
$A' = 400$ sq. in.

Test A Page 212

I 1. $\frac{3}{x} = \frac{5}{12}$
$5x = 36$
$x = 7\frac{1}{5}$

2. $\frac{x}{7} = \frac{2}{3}$
$3x = 14$
$x = 4\frac{2}{3}$

3. $\frac{3}{8} = \frac{6}{x - 1}$
$3x - 3 = 48$
$3x = 51$
$x = 17$

4. $\frac{x + 3}{27} = \frac{2}{9}$
$9x + 27 = 54$
$9x = 27$
$x = 3$

II 1. 1. let B = number of Baldwins   <u>55 barrels</u>
2. 143 - B = number of Mackintosh Reds   <u>88 barrels</u>
3. $\frac{5}{8} = \frac{B}{143 - B}$
4. $8B = 715 - 5B$
$13B = 715$
$B = 55$
5. $\begin{array}{r} 55 \\ +88 \\ \hline 143 \end{array}$ ✓ $\frac{55}{88} = \frac{5}{8}$ ✓

2. 1. let x = distance run by first tire   <u>11,900 mi.</u>
2. x + 1400 = distance run by second tire   <u>13,300 mi.</u>
3. $\frac{17}{19} = \frac{x}{x + 1400}$
4. $19x = 17x + 23,800$
$2x = 23,800$
$x = 11,900$
5. $\begin{array}{r} 13,300 \\ -11,900 \\ \hline 1,400 \end{array}$ ✓ $\frac{11,900}{13,300} = \frac{119}{133} = \frac{17}{19}$ ✓

III
1. $\frac{g}{g'} = \frac{d}{d'}$ or $\frac{g}{d} = \frac{g'}{d'}$
$\frac{12}{8} = \frac{210}{d'}$ $\frac{12}{210} = \frac{8}{d'}$
$\frac{3}{2} = \frac{210}{d'}$ $\frac{2}{35} = \frac{8}{d'}$
$3d' = 420$ $2d' = 280$
$d' = 140$ mi. $d' = 140$ mi.

2. d = distance between points of smaller star
2d = distance between points of larger star
$\frac{3.6}{A'} = (\frac{d}{2d})^2$
$\frac{3.6}{A'} = (\frac{1}{2})^2$
$\frac{3.6}{A'} = \frac{1}{4}$
$A' = 14.4$ sq. in.

<u>Test B</u>   Page 212

I 1. $\frac{4}{x} = \frac{7}{10}$
$7x = 40$
$x = 5\frac{5}{7}$

2. $\frac{x}{9} = \frac{5}{6}$
$6x = 45$
$x = 7\frac{3}{6} = 7\frac{1}{2}$

3. $\frac{4}{7} = \frac{8}{x + 2}$
$4x + 8 = 56$
$4x = 48$
$x = 12$

4. $\frac{x - 5}{16} = \frac{3}{8}$
$8x - 40 = 48$
$8x = 88$
$x = 11$

II
1. 1. let c = amount of cream produced   <u>150 gal.</u>
2. 700 = c = amount of skim milk produced   550 gal.
3. $\frac{c}{700 - c} = \frac{3}{11}$
4. $11c = 2100 - 3c$
$14c = 2100$
$c = 150$ gal.
5. $\begin{array}{r} 150 \\ +550 \\ \hline 700 \end{array}$ ✓ $\frac{150}{550} = \frac{15}{55} = \frac{3}{11}$ ✓

2. 1. let a = acres in one estate   <u>24 acres</u>
2. a - 9 = acres in other estate   <u>15 acres</u>
3. $\frac{a - 9}{a} = \frac{5}{8}$
4. $8a - 72 = 5a$
$3a = 72$
$a = 24$
5. $\begin{array}{r} 24 \\ -15 \\ \hline 9 \end{array}$ ✓ $\frac{15}{24} = \frac{5}{8}$ ✓

III

1. $\frac{I}{I'} = \frac{t}{t'}$

$\frac{60}{I'} = \frac{4}{18}$

$\frac{60}{I'} = \frac{2}{9}$

$2I' = 540$

$I' = \$270$

2. (a) $\frac{A}{A'} = \frac{d^2}{d'^2} = (\frac{d}{d'})^2$

(b) $\frac{78.5}{A'} = (\frac{10}{20})^2$

$\frac{78.5}{A'} = (\frac{1}{2})^2$

$\frac{78.5}{A'} = \frac{1}{4}$

$A = 314$ sq. ft.

Test C Page 213

1. Answers will vary.

2. 1. let x = the smaller number $7\frac{1}{2}$
   2. 20 - x = the larger number $12\frac{1}{2}$
   3. $\frac{x}{20 - x} = \frac{3}{5}$
   4. $5x = 60 - 3x$

      $8x = 60$

      $x = 7\frac{4}{8} = 7\frac{1}{2}$
   5. $12\frac{1}{2} + 7\frac{1}{2} = 20$ ✓ $\quad \frac{7\frac{1}{2}}{12\frac{1}{2}} \equiv \frac{\frac{15}{2}}{\frac{25}{2}} = \frac{15}{25} = \frac{3}{5}$ ✓

3. $\frac{AD}{DB} = \frac{16}{20} = \frac{4}{5}$;

$\frac{4}{5} = \frac{AD}{27 - AD}$

$5AD = 4(27 - AD)$

$5AD = 108 - 4AD$

$9AD = 108$

$AD = 12$

$DB = 27 - 12 = 15$

4. $\frac{A}{A'} = \frac{b^2}{b'^2} = (\frac{b}{b'})^2$

$\frac{48}{A'} = (\frac{12}{9})^2$

$\frac{48}{A'} = (\frac{4}{3})^2$

$\frac{48}{A'} = \frac{16}{9}$

$16A' = 432$

$A' = 27$ sq. in.

5. 1. let x = amount for son $15,000
   2. 35,000 - x = amount for daughter $20,000
   3. $\frac{x}{35,000 - x} = \frac{3}{4}$
   4. $4x = 3(35,000 - x)$

      $4x = 105,000 - 3x$

      $7x = 105,000$

      $x = 15,000$
   5. $15,000 + 20,000 = $35,000 ✓ $\quad \frac{\$15,000}{\$20,000} = \frac{3}{4}$ ✓

6.
$$\frac{w}{w'} = \frac{d}{d'}$$
$$\frac{6}{8} = \frac{24}{d'}$$
$$\frac{3}{4} = \frac{24}{d'}$$
$$3d' = 96$$
$$d' = 32 \text{ ft.}$$

7.
$$\frac{w}{w'} = \frac{r^3}{r'^3} = \left(\frac{r}{r'}\right)^3$$
$$\frac{w}{1} = \frac{3^3}{(\frac{1}{2})^3}$$
$$\frac{w}{1} = \frac{27}{\frac{1}{8}}$$
$$\frac{1}{8}w = 27$$
$$w = 216 \text{ oz.}$$
or 13.5 lb.

8.
$$\frac{3937}{3600} = \frac{x}{720}$$
$$3600x = 2{,}834{,}640$$
$$x = 787.4 \text{ yd.}$$

9. (a) π; $\frac{1}{6}$ in the volume formula
(b) (1) The circumference of a circle varies as <u>the diameter</u>.
(2) The area of a circle varies as <u>the square of the radius</u>.
(3) The volume of a sphere varies as <u>the cube of the diameter</u>.

10. (a)
$$\frac{A}{A'} = \frac{d^2}{d'^2} = \left(\frac{d}{d'}\right)^2$$

(b)
$$\frac{30}{A'} = \left(\frac{30}{24}\right)^2$$
$$\frac{30}{A'} = \left(\frac{5}{4}\right)^2$$
$$\frac{30}{A'} = \frac{25}{16}$$
$$25A' = 480$$
$$A' = 19.2 \text{ sq. ft.}$$

UNIT 10 — Linear Equations

Exercises 10.1 Pages 215-216

The check is left for the teacher.

1. $8v = 24$
   $v = 3$
2. $9r = 54$
   $r = 6$
3. $\frac{1}{4}r = 1.5$
   $r = 6$
4. $\frac{1}{2}x = 2.5$
   $x = 5$
5. $11 + x = 15$
   $x = 4$
6. $20 + x = 30$
   $x = 10$
7. $7y - 5 = 2$
   $7y = 7$
   $y = 1$
8. $2z + 3 = 9$
   $2z = 6$
   $z = 3$
9. $4h + 3 = 7$
   $4h = 4$
   $h = 1$
10. $6r - 7 = 5$
    $6r = 12$
    $r = 2$
11. $\frac{1}{2}b + 3 = 8$
    $\frac{1}{2}b = 5$
    $b = 10$
12. $\frac{1}{5}x + 2 = 6$
    $\frac{1}{5}x = 4$
    $x = 20$
13. $8x - 7 = 3 + 6x$
    $2x = 10$
    $x = 5$
14. $7x + 6 = 6x + 8$
    $x = 2$
15. $5x - 10 = 2x + 20$
    $3x = 30$
    $x = 10$
16. $4r - 18 = 20 + \frac{1}{5}r$
    $5(4r - 18) = 5(20 + \frac{1}{5}r)$
    $20r - 90 = 100 + r$
    $19r = 190$
    $r = 10$
17. $5n - (2n + 3) = 12$
    $5n - 2n - 3 = 12$
    $3n = 15$
    $n = 5$
18. $17t + 5(2 - 3t) = 18$
    $17t + 10 - 15t = 18$
    $2t = 8$
    $t = 4$
19. $5x - [4 - (6x - 3)] = 26$
    $5x - [4 - 6x + 3] = 26$
    $5x - 4 + 6x - 3 = 26$
    $11x - 7 = 26$
    $11x = 33$
    $x = 3$
20. $(2w - 1)^2 = 4(w - 3)^2$
    $4w^2 - 4w + 1 = 4(w^2 - 6w + 9)$
    $4w^2 - 4w + 1 = 4w^2 - 24w + 36$
    $20w = 35$
    $w = \frac{35}{20} = \frac{7}{4}$
21. $21x + (x - 4)^2 = (5 + x)^2$
    $21x + x^2 - 8x + 16 = 25 + 10x + x^2$
    $13x + 16 = 25 + 10x$
    $3x = 9$
    $x = 3$
22. $(12x + 6) \div 3 = 9 - 3x$
    $\frac{12x + 6}{3} = 9 - 3x$
    $12x + 6 = 27 - 9x$
    $21x = 21$
    $x = 1$
23. $(x + 1)(x + 2) = 11 + x^2$
    $x^2 + 3x + 2 = 11 + x^2$
    $3x = 9$
    $x = 3$
24. $\frac{1}{4}x - 4 + \frac{3}{4}x = 16 + \frac{1}{4}x - 10$
    $4(\frac{1}{4}x - 4 + \frac{3}{4}x) = 4(16 + \frac{1}{4}x - 10)$
    $x - 16 + 3x = 64 + x - 40$
    $4x - 16 = x + 24$
    $3x = 40$
    $x = \frac{40}{3}$

25.
$$\begin{aligned} x(x + 5) - 6 &= x(x - 1) + 12 \\ x^2 + 5x - 6 &= x^2 - x + 12 \\ 6x &= 18 \\ x &= 3 \end{aligned}$$

26.
$$\begin{aligned} 3(2 - x) - 2(x + 3) &= 6 - 2x \\ 6 - 3x - 2x - 6 &= 6 - 2x \\ -5x &= 6 - 2x \\ -3x &= 6 \\ x &= -2 \end{aligned}$$

27.
$$\begin{aligned} x - (2 + 4x) &= 13 - 5(x + 5) \\ x - 2 - 4x &= 13 - 5x - 25 \\ -3x - 2 &= -5x - 12 \\ 2x &= -10 \\ x &= -5 \end{aligned}$$

28.
$$\begin{aligned} 4x - (2x - 2) &= 3x - (3x - 4) \\ 4x - 2x + 2 &= 3x - 3x + 4 \\ 2x + 2 &= 4 \\ 2x &= 2 \\ x &= 1 \end{aligned}$$

29.
$$\begin{aligned} .6x - 1 &= .25x + 1.5x - 3.3 \\ 100(.6x - 1) &= 100(.25x + 1.5x - 3.3) \\ 60x - 100 &= 25x + 150x - 330 \\ 60x - 100 &= 175x - 330 \\ -115x &= -230 \\ x &= 2 \end{aligned}$$

30.
$$\begin{aligned} 36 + 5x - 22 - (7x - 16) &= 5x + 17 - (2x + 22) \\ 36 + 5x - 22 - 7x + 16 &= 5x + 17 - 2x - 22 \\ -2x + 30 &= 3x - 5 \\ -5x &= -35 \\ x &= 7 \end{aligned}$$

31.
$$\begin{aligned} 2(r - 5)(r - 4) &= (r - 4)(r - 3) + (r - 2)(r - 5) \\ (2r - 10)(r - 4) &= r^2 - 7r + 12 + r^2 - 7r + 10 \\ 2r^2 - 18r + 40 &= 2r^2 - 14r + 22 \\ -4r &= -18 \\ r &= \frac{-18}{-4} \\ r &= \frac{9}{2} \end{aligned}$$

32.
$$\begin{aligned} 5(x + 2)^2 - (x - 5)^2 &= (2x - 3)(2x + 3) + 19 \\ 5(x^2 + 4x + 4) - (x^2 - 10x + 25) &= 4x^2 - 9 + 19 \\ 5x^2 + 20x + 20 - x^2 + 10x - 25 &= 4x^2 + 10 \\ 4x^2 + 30x - 5 &= 4x^2 + 10 \\ 30x &= 15 \\ x &= \frac{15}{30} \\ x &= \frac{1}{2} \end{aligned}$$

33.
$$\begin{aligned} 3x - \frac{x}{5} &= 14 \\ 5(3x - \frac{x}{5}) &= 5(14) \\ 15x - x &= 70 \\ 14x &= 70 \\ x &= 5 \end{aligned}$$

34.
$$\begin{aligned} \frac{2x}{3} - \frac{5}{6} &= \frac{x}{4} \\ 12(\frac{2x}{3} - \frac{5}{6}) &= 12(\frac{x}{4}) \\ 8x - 10 &= 3x \\ 5x &= 10 \\ x &= 2 \end{aligned}$$

35.
$$\frac{2x}{3} - \frac{7x}{8} + \frac{5x}{18} + \frac{x}{24} = \frac{4}{9}$$
$$72\left(\frac{2x}{3} - \frac{7x}{8} + \frac{5x}{18} + \frac{x}{24}\right) = 72\left(\frac{4}{9}\right)$$
$$48x - 63x + 20x + 3x = 32$$
$$8x = 32$$
$$x = 4$$

36.
$$\frac{3t - 5}{4} - \frac{7t - 13}{6} = 3 - \frac{t + 3}{2}$$
$$12\left(\frac{3t - 5}{4} - \frac{7t - 13}{6}\right) = 12\left(3 - \frac{t + 3}{2}\right)$$
$$3(3t - 5) - 2(7t - 13) = 36 - 6(t + 3)$$
$$9t - 15 - 14t + 26 = 36 - 6t - 18$$
$$-5t + 11 = -6t + 18$$
$$t = 7$$

37.
$$\frac{r}{2}(2 - r) - \frac{r}{4}(3 - 2r) = \frac{r + 10}{6}$$
$$12\left[\frac{r}{2}(2 - r) - \frac{r}{4}(3 - 2r)\right] = 12\left(\frac{r + 10}{6}\right)$$
$$6r(2 - r) - 3r(3 - 2r) = 2(r + 10)$$
$$12r - \cancel{6r^2} - 9r + \cancel{6r^2} = 2r + 20$$
$$3r = 2r + 20$$
$$r = 20$$

38.
$$\frac{6r + 3}{15} - \frac{3r - 1}{5r - 25} = \frac{2r - 9}{5}$$
$$\frac{2r + 1}{5} - \frac{2r - 9}{5} = \frac{3r - 1}{5r - 25}$$
$$\frac{2r + 1 - 2r + 9}{5} = \frac{3r - 1}{5r - 25}$$
$$2 = \frac{3r - 1}{5r - 25}$$
$$10r - 50 = 3r - 1$$
$$7r = 49$$
$$r = 7$$

39.
$$\frac{x^3 + 1}{x - 1} - \frac{x^3 - 1}{x + 1} = \frac{8}{x^2 - 1} + 2x$$
$$\frac{x^3 + 1}{x - 1} - \frac{x^3 - 1}{x + 1} = \frac{8}{(x + 1)(x - 1)} + 2x$$
$$(x + 1)(x - 1)\left(\frac{x^3 + 1}{x - 1} - \frac{x^3 - 1}{x + 1}\right) = (x + 1)(x - 1)\left[\frac{8}{(x + 1)(x - 1)} + 2x\right]$$
$$(x + 1)(x^3 + 1) - (x - 1)(x^3 - 1) = 8 + 2x(x + 1)(x - 1)$$
$$x^4 + x^3 + x + 1 - (x^4 - x^3 - x + 1) = 8 + 2x(x^2 - 1)$$
$$x^4 + x^3 + x + 1 - x^4 + x^3 + x - 1 = 8 + 2x^3 - 2x$$
$$2x^3 + 2x = 8 + 2x^3 - 2x$$
$$4x = 8$$
$$x = 2$$

40.
$$\frac{5x + 2}{3} - (x - \frac{3x - 1}{2} = \frac{3x + 19}{2} - \left(\frac{x + 1}{6} + 5\right)$$
$$6\left[\frac{5x + 2}{3} - \left(x - \frac{3x - 1}{2}\right)\right] = 6\left[\frac{3x + 19}{2} - \left(\frac{x + 1}{6} + 5\right)\right]$$
$$2(5x + 2) - 6\left(x - \frac{3x - 1}{2}\right) = 3(3x + 19) - 6\left(\frac{x + 1}{6} + 5\right)$$
$$10x + 4 - 6x + 3(3x - 1) = 9x + 57 - (x + 1) - 30$$
$$10x + 4 - 6x + 9x - 3 = 9x + 57 - x - 1 - 30$$
$$13x + 1 = 8x + 26$$
$$5x = 25$$
$$x = 5$$

Exercises 10.2 Pages 218

1.
$$A = \frac{1}{2}bh$$
$$2A = bh$$
$$\frac{2A}{b} = h$$
$$h = \frac{2A}{b}$$

2. (1)
$$A = \frac{1}{2}h(b_1 + b_2)$$
$$2A = h(b_1 + b_2)$$
$$\frac{2A}{b_1 + b_2} = h$$

(2)
$$A = \frac{1}{2}h(b_1 + b_2)$$
$$2A = h(b_1 + b_2)$$
$$2A = hb_1 + hb_2$$
$$2A - hb_2 = hb_1$$
$$\frac{2A - hb_2}{h} = b_1$$
$$\text{or } b_1 = \frac{2A}{h} - b_2$$

(3)
$$A = \frac{1}{2}h(b_1 + b_2)$$
$$2A = h(b_1 + b_2)$$
$$2A = hb_1 + hb_2$$
$$2A - hb_1 = hb_2$$
$$\frac{2A - hb_1}{h} = b_2 \quad \text{or } b_2 = \frac{2A}{h} - b_1$$

3.
$$V = \frac{1}{3}Bh$$
$$3V = Bh$$
$$\frac{3V}{B} = h$$

4. (1)
$$i = prt$$
$$\frac{i}{pr} = t$$
$$t = \frac{i}{pr}$$

(2)
$$i = prt$$
$$\frac{i}{pt} = r$$
$$r = \frac{i}{pt}$$

(3)
$$i = prt$$
$$\frac{i}{rt} = p$$
$$p = \frac{i}{rt}$$

5.
$$C = \frac{5}{9}(F - 32)$$
$$9C = 5(F - 32)$$
$$9C = 5F - 160$$
$$9C + 160 = 5F$$
$$\frac{9C + 160}{5} = F$$
$$F = \frac{9}{5}C + \frac{160}{5}$$
$$F = \frac{9}{5}C + 32^o$$

6.
$$s = \frac{1}{2}gt^2$$
$$2s = gt^2$$
$$\frac{2s}{t^2} = g$$

7.
$$I = \frac{E}{R + r}$$
$$I(R + r) = E$$
$$IR + Ir = E$$
$$Ir = E - IR$$
$$r = \frac{E - IR}{I}$$
$$\text{or } r = \frac{E}{I} - R$$

8.
$$V_1P_1 = V_2P_2$$
$$\frac{V_1P_1}{V_2} = P_2$$

9.
$$\frac{1}{f} = \frac{1}{f_1} - \frac{1}{f_2}$$
$$ff_1f_2(\frac{1}{f}) = ff_1f_2(\frac{1}{f_1} - \frac{1}{f_2})$$
$$f_1f_2 = ff_2 - ff_1$$
$$f_1f_2 + ff_1 = ff_2$$
$$f_1(f_2 + f) = ff_2$$
$$f_1 = \frac{ff_2}{f_2 + f}$$

10.
$$\frac{E}{e} = \frac{R + r}{r}$$
$$e(R + r) = Er$$
$$e = \frac{Er}{R + r}$$

11.
$$S = \frac{a}{1 - r}$$
$$S(1 - r) = a$$
$$S - Sr = a$$
$$-Sr = a - S$$
$$r = \frac{a - S}{-S}$$
$$r = \frac{S - a}{S}$$

12. (1)
$$S = \frac{n}{2}(a + \ell)$$
$$2S = n(a + \ell)$$
$$\frac{2S}{a + \ell} = n$$

(2)
$$S = \frac{n}{2}(a + \ell)$$
$$2S = n(a + \ell)$$
$$2S = an + \ell n$$
$$2S - \ell n = an$$
$$\frac{2S - \ell n}{n} = a \text{ or } a = \frac{2S}{n} - \ell$$

13.
$$W = \frac{Kbd^2}{L}$$
$$WL = Kbd^2$$
$$\frac{WL}{bd^2} = K$$

14.
$$t = \frac{spc^2}{d}$$
$$dt = spc^2$$
$$d = \frac{spc^2}{t}$$

15.
$$D = \frac{n + 2}{p}$$
$$Dp = n + 2$$
$$Dp - 2 = n$$
$$n = Dp - 2$$

16.
$$A = 2\pi r^2 + 2\pi ra$$
$$A - 2\pi r^2 = 2\pi ra$$
$$\frac{A - 2\pi r^2}{2\pi r} = a$$

17.
$$F = \frac{wv}{w + v}$$
$$F(w + v) = wv$$
$$Fw + Fv = wv$$
$$Fw = wv - Fv$$
$$Fw = v(w - F)$$
$$\frac{Fw}{w - F} = v$$

18.
$$\frac{1}{f} + \frac{1}{s} = \frac{1}{b}$$
$$bfs(\frac{1}{f} + \frac{1}{s}) = bfs(\frac{1}{b})$$
$$bs + bf = fs$$
$$bs = fs - bf$$
$$bs = f(s - b)$$
$$\frac{bs}{s - b} = f$$

19.
$$H = \frac{ND^2}{2.5}$$
$$2.5H = ND^2$$
$$\frac{2.5H}{D^2} = N$$

20.
$$S = \frac{r\ell - a}{r - 1}$$
$$S(r - 1) = r\ell - a$$
$$Sr - S = r\ell - a$$
$$Sr - r\ell = -a + S$$
$$r(S - \ell) = S - a$$
$$r = \frac{S - a}{S - \ell}$$

The check is left for the teacher.

21. $x - c = d$
$x = c + d$

22. $t + a = b$
$t = b - a$

23. $w - 6 = a$
$w = a + 6$

24. $ay = d$
$y = \frac{d}{a}$

25. $bz = m + n$
$z = \frac{m + n}{b}$

26. $by - c = d$
$by = c + d$
$y = \frac{c + d}{b}$

27. $cz + d = e$
$cz = e - d$
$z = \frac{e - d}{c}$

28. $r = ax + b$
$r - b = ax$
$\frac{r - b}{a} = x$

29. $m = by + n$
$m - n = by$
$\frac{m - n}{b} = y$

30. $2mx = m + n$
$x = \frac{m + n}{2m}$

31. $by = b^2$
$y = b$

32. $cdx = cd$
$x = 1$

33. $(b + c)x = bc$
$x = \frac{bc}{b + c}$

34. $3aby = 6ab$
$y = 2$

35. $2x - c = d$
$2x = c + d$
$x = \frac{c + d}{2}$

The remaining checks are shown.

36. $x - a = b - x$
$2x = a + b$
$x = \frac{a + b}{2}$

$$\begin{array}{r|l} \frac{a + b}{2} - a & b - \frac{a + b}{2} \\ \frac{a + b - 2a}{2} & \frac{2b - a - b}{2} \\ \frac{-a + b}{2} \;=& \frac{-a + b}{2} \checkmark \end{array}$$

37. $ax + 6a^2 = 2ax + 4a^2$
$ax - 2ax = -2a^2$
$-ax = -2a^2$
$x = 2a$

$$\begin{array}{r|l} a(2a) + 6a^2 & 2a(2a) + 4a^2 \\ 2a^2 + 6a^2 & 4a^2 + 4a^2 \\ 8a^2 \;=& 8a^2 \checkmark \end{array}$$

38. $by - 9b^3 = 4by - 15b^3$
$by - 4by = 9b^3 - 15b^3$
$-3by = -6b^3$
$y = 2b^2$

$$\begin{array}{r|l} b(2b^2) - 9b^3 & 4b(2b^2) - 15b^3 \\ 2b^3 - 9b^3 & 8b^3 - 15b^3 \\ -7b^3 \;=& -7b^3 \checkmark \end{array}$$

39. $ax - a^2 = cx - c^2$
$ax - cx = a^2 - c^2$
$x(a - c) = a^2 - c^2$
$x = \frac{a^2 - c^2}{a - c}$
$x = \frac{(a + c)\cancel{(a - c)}}{\cancel{a - c}}$
$x = a + c$

$$\begin{array}{r|l} a(a + c) - a^2 & c(a + c) - c^2 \\ a^2 + ac - a^2 & ac + c^2 - c^2 \\ ac \;=& ac \checkmark \end{array}$$

40. $rx + s^2 = r^2 - sx$
$rx + sx = r^2 - s^2$
$x(r + s) = r^2 - s^2$
$x = \frac{r^2 - s^2}{r + s}$
$x = \frac{\cancel{(r + s)}(r - s)}{\cancel{r + s}}$
$x = r - s$

$$\begin{array}{r|l} r(r - s) + s^2 & r^2 - s(r - s) \\ r^2 - rs + s^2 \;=& r^2 - rs + s^2 \checkmark \end{array}$$

41. $a^2x - b^4 = b^2x - a^4$
$a^2x - b^2x = b^4 - a^4$
$x(a^2 - b^2) = b^4 - a^4$
$x = \frac{b^4 - a^4}{a^2 - b^2}$
$x = \frac{(b^2 + a^2)\overset{-1}{\cancel{(b^2 - a^2)}}}{\cancel{a^2 - b^2}}$
$x = -(b^2 + a^2)$ or $-b^2 - a^2$

$$\begin{array}{r|l} a^2(-b^2 - a^2) - b^4 & b^2(-b^2 - a^2) - a^4 \\ -a^2b^2 - a^4 - b^4 & -b^4 - a^2b^2 - a^4 \\ -a^2b^2 - a^4 - b^4 \;=& -a^2b^2 - a^4 - b^4 \checkmark \end{array}$$

42. $\frac{x}{b} - 1 = c$
$b(\frac{x}{b} - 1) = bc$
$x - b = bc$
$x = b + bc$

$$\begin{array}{r|l} \frac{b + bc}{b} - 1 & c \\ \frac{b + bc - b}{b} & \\ \frac{bc}{b} & \\ c \;=& c \checkmark \end{array}$$

43.

$$\frac{y}{b + c} - c = b$$

$$b + c\left(\frac{y}{b + c} - c\right) = b(b + c)$$

$$y - c(b + c) = b(b + c)$$

$$y = b(b + c) + c(b + c)$$

$$y = (b + c)(b + c)$$

$$y = (b + c)^2 \text{ or } b^2 + 2bc + c^2$$

$$\frac{b^2 + 2bc + c^2}{b + c} - c \quad \Big| \quad b$$

$$\frac{b^2 + 2bc + c^2}{b + c} - \frac{c(b + c)}{b + c}$$

$$\frac{b^2 + 2bc + c^2 - bc - c^2}{b + c}$$

$$\frac{b^2 + bc}{b + c}$$

$$\frac{b\cancel{(b + c)}}{\cancel{b + c}}$$

$$b = b \checkmark$$

44.

$$\frac{bx}{c} = 2 - \frac{cx}{b}$$

$$bc\left(\frac{bx}{c}\right) = bc\left(2 - \frac{cx}{b}\right)$$

$$b^2x = 2bc - c^2x$$

$$b^2x + c^2x = 2bc$$

$$x(b^2 + c^2) = 2bc$$

$$x = \frac{2bc}{b^2 + c^2}$$

$$\frac{b\left(\frac{2bc}{b^2 + c^2}\right)}{c} \quad \Big| \quad 2 - \frac{c\left(\frac{2bc}{b^2 + c^2}\right)}{b}$$

$$\frac{\frac{2b^2c}{b^2 + c^2}}{c} \quad \Big| \quad 2 - \frac{\frac{2bc^2}{b^2 + c^2}}{b}$$

$$\frac{2b^2}{b^2 + c^2} \quad \Big| \quad 2 - \frac{2c^2}{b^2 + c^2}$$

$$\frac{2(b^2 + c^2)}{b^2 + c^2} - \frac{2c^2}{b^2 + c^2}$$

$$\frac{2b^2 + 2c^2 - 2c^2}{b^2 + c^2}$$

$$\frac{2b^2}{b^2 + c^2} = \frac{2b^2}{b^2 + c^2} \checkmark$$

45. $\dfrac{1}{a - y} = \dfrac{1}{y}$

$y = a - y$

$2y = a$

$y = \dfrac{a}{2}$

$\dfrac{1}{a - \frac{a}{2}} \quad \Big| \quad \dfrac{1}{\frac{a}{2}}$

$\dfrac{1}{\frac{2a - a}{2}}$

$\dfrac{2}{a} = \dfrac{2}{a}$ ✓

46. $\dfrac{1}{y + a} = \dfrac{1}{4a}$

$y + a = 4a$

$y = 3a$

$\dfrac{1}{3a + a} \quad \Big| \quad \dfrac{1}{4a}$

$\dfrac{1}{4a} = \dfrac{1}{4a}$ ✓

47. $\dfrac{a - bx}{ax - b} = \dfrac{a}{b}$

$a(ax - b) = b(a - bx)$

$a^2x - ab = ab - b^2x$

$a^2x + b^2x = ab + ab$

$x(a^2 + b^2) = 2ab$

$x = \dfrac{2ab}{a^2 + b^2}$

$\dfrac{a - b(\frac{2ab}{a^2 + b^2})}{a(\frac{2ab}{a^2 + b^2}) - b} \quad \Big| \quad \dfrac{a}{b}$

$\dfrac{a - \frac{2ab^2}{a^2 + b^2}}{\frac{2a^2b}{a^2 + b^2} - b}$

$\dfrac{\frac{a(a^2 + b^2)}{(a^2 + b^2)} - \frac{2ab^2}{a^2 + b^2}}{\frac{2a^2b}{a^2 + b^2} - \frac{b(a^2 + b^2)}{a^2 + b^2}}$

$\dfrac{\frac{a^3 + ab^2 - 2ab^2}{a^2 + b^2}}{\frac{2a^2b - a^2b - b^3}{a^2 + b^2}}$

$\dfrac{a^3 - ab^2}{a^2b - b^3}$

$\dfrac{a\cancel{(a^2 - b^2)}}{b\cancel{(a^2 - b^2)}}$

$\dfrac{a}{b} = \dfrac{a}{b}$ ✓

48. $b(2x - 9c - 14b) = c(c - x)$

$2bx - 9bc - 14b^2 = c^2 - cx$

$2bx + cx = c^2 + 9bc + 14b^2$

$x(2b + c) = 14b^2 + 9bc + c^2$

$x = \dfrac{14b^2 + 9bc + c^2}{2b + c}$

$x = \dfrac{(7b + c)\cancel{(2b + c)}}{\cancel{2b + c}}$

$x = 7b + c$

$b[2(7b + c) - 9c - 14b] \quad \Big| \quad c[c - (7b + c)]$

$b(14b + 2c - 9c - 14b) \quad \Big| \quad c(c - 7b - c)$

$b(-7c) \quad \Big| \quad c(-7b)$

$-7bc = -7bc$ ✓

49.

$$1 - \frac{ab}{x} = \frac{7}{ab} - \frac{49}{abx}$$
$$abx\left(1 - \frac{ab}{x}\right) = abx\left(\frac{7}{ab} - \frac{49}{abx}\right)$$
$$abx - a^2b^2 = 7x - 49$$
$$abx - 7x = a^2b^2 - 49$$
$$x(ab - 7) = a^2b^2 - 49$$
$$x = \frac{a^2b^2 - 49}{ab - 7}$$
$$x = \frac{(ab + 7)\cancel{(ab - 7)}}{\cancel{ab - 7}}$$
$$x = ab + 7$$

$1 - \frac{ab}{ab + 7}$	$\frac{7}{ab} - \frac{49}{ab(ab + 7)}$
$\frac{ab + 7 - ab}{ab + 7}$	$\frac{7(ab + 7) - 49}{ab(ab + 7)}$
$\frac{7}{ab + 7}$	$\frac{7ab + 49 - 49}{ab(ab + 7)}$
	$\frac{7\cancel{ab}}{\cancel{ab}(ab + 7)}$
$\frac{7}{ab + 7}$ =	$\frac{7}{ab + 7}$ ✓

<u>Exercises 10.3</u> Pages 219-223

1. 1. let x = number Justin caught <u>8</u>
   2. 12 - x = number his father caught <u>4</u>
   3. $3x - 12 = 5(12 - x) - 8$
      $3x - 12 = 60 - 5x - 8$
      $3x - 12 = 52 - 5x$
   4. $8x = 64$
      $x = 8$
   5. $\begin{array}{r} 8 \\ +4 \\ \hline 12 \end{array}$ ✓ $\begin{array}{r} 8 \\ \times 3 \\ \hline 24 \end{array}$ $\begin{array}{r} 24 \\ -12 \\ \hline 12 \end{array}$ $\begin{array}{r} 4 \\ \times 5 \\ \hline 20 \end{array}$ $\begin{array}{r} 20 \\ -8 \\ \hline 12 \end{array}$ ✓

2. 1. let x = winning team's score
   2. 18 - x = losing team's score

   game score = <u>12</u> to <u>6</u>

   3. $\frac{1}{2}x - 5 = \frac{1}{3}(18 - x) - 1$
   4. $6\left(\frac{1}{2}x - 5\right) = 6\left[\frac{1}{3}(18 - x) - 1\right]$
      $3x - 30 = 2(18 - x) - 6$
      $3x - 30 = 36 - 2x - 6$
      $3x - 30 = 30 - 2x$
      $5x = 60$
      $x = 12$
   5. $\frac{1}{2}(12) = 6$ $\begin{array}{r} 6 \\ -5 \\ \hline 1 \end{array}$ ✓

      $\frac{1}{3}(6) = 2$ $\begin{array}{r} 2 \\ -1 \\ \hline 1 \end{array}$

3\. 1. let w = weight of truck 4800 lb.

2\. $\frac{1}{2}w - 200$ = weight of trailer 2200 lb.

3\. $w + \frac{1}{2}w - 200 = 7000$

4\. $2(w + \frac{1}{2}w - 200) = 2(7000)$

$2w + w - 400 = 14{,}000$

$3w = 14{,}400$

$w = 4800$

5\. $4800 + 2200 = 7000$ ✓ $\quad \frac{1}{2}(4800) = 2400 \quad 2400 - 2200 = 200$ ✓

4\. 1. let x = number of necklaces 300

2\.

3\. $\frac{(1500)(2.4)}{12} = x$

4\. $x = 300$

5\. $\frac{300(12)}{2.4} = 1500$ ✓

5\. 1. let x = cost per foot of tubing

2\. 5x = cost of tubing $2.50

12x = cost of pump $6.00

3\. $5x + 12x = 8.50$

4\. $17x = 8.50$

$x = .50$

5\. $6.00 + $2.50 = $8.50 $\quad$ $2.50 ÷ 5 = $.50 $\quad$ $6.00 is 12 times $.50 ✓

6\. 1. let x = number of 500 watt bulbs 5

2\. 2x = number of 250 watt bulbs 10

3\. $500x + 250(2x) = 5000$

4\. $500x + 500x = 5000$

$1000x = 5000$

$x = 5$

5\. $500 \times 5 = 2500 \quad 250 \times 10 = 2500 \quad 2500 + 2500 = 5000$ ✓

7\. 1. let x = gallons per minute for smaller pumps 400

2\. 4x = gallons per minute for larger pumps 1600

3\. $4x + 2(4x) = 4800$

4\. $4x + 8x = 4800$

$12x = 4800$

$x = 400$

5\. $400 \times 4 = 1600 \quad 1600 \times 2 = 3200 \quad 1600 + 3200 = 4800$ $\quad$ 1600 is 4 times 400 ✓

8. 1. let x = number of rounds fired   <u>12</u>
   2. x - 11 = number of misses   1
   3. $\frac{3}{4}x = 9(x - 11)$

   4. $4(\frac{3}{4}x) = (4)(9)(x - 11)$

        $3x = 36(x - 11)$
        $3x = 36x - 396$
     $-33x = -396$
         $x = 12$

   5. 12 shots with 1 miss is 11 hits ✓
     $\frac{3}{4}(12) = 9$ which is 9 times 1 miss ✓

9. 1. let w = width   <u>151 ft.</u>
   2. w + 101 = length   <u>252 ft.</u>
       w - 25 = decreased width
   3. w + 101 = 2(w - 25)
   4. w + 101 = 2w - 50
          -w = -151
           w = 151

   5.   252   151   252 is twice 126 ✓
       -151   -25
        <u>101</u> ✓ <u>126</u>

10. 1. x = amount of capital   <u>$4000</u>
     $\frac{4}{5}x$ = amount at 10.5% $3200

   2. $\frac{1}{5}x$ = amount at 10% $8000

   3. $.105(\frac{4}{5}x) + .1(\frac{1}{5}x) = 416$

   4. $.021(4x) + .1(.2x) = 416$
          $.084x + .02x = 416$
        $84x + 20x = 416,000$
             $104x = 416,000$
                $x = 4000$

   5. $3200 $800 $336
      x.105   x.10   +80
     $ 336 $ 80 $416 ✓

11. 1. let x = number of cases at $10.50   <u>7</u>
   2. 62 - x = number of cases at $8.50   5<u>5</u>
   3. 10.5x + 8.5(62 - x) = 541
   4.   105x + 85(62 - x) = 5410
      105x + 5270 - 85x = 5410
                20x = 140
                 x = 7

   5. $10.50 $ 8.50 $467.50
      x 7   x 55   +73.50
     $73.50 $467.50 $541.00 ✓

12. 1. let x = number of boxes at $27   <u>9</u>
   2. 25 - x = number of boxes at $16.50   <u>16</u>
   3. 27x + 16.5(25 - x) = 507
   4. 270x + 165(25 - x) = 5070
      270x + 4125 - 165x = 5070
               105x = 945
                 x = 9

   5. $ 27 $16.50 $243
     x 9   x 16   +264
     $243 $ 264 $507 ✓

13. 1. let x = total sold

$\frac{1}{4}x$ = number sold at \$18 <u>24</u>

2. $\frac{1}{6}x$ = number sold at \$20 <u>16</u>

$\frac{1}{3}x$ = number sold at \$15 <u>32</u>

$\frac{1}{4}x$ = number sold at \$21 <u>24</u>

3. $\overset{9}{\cancel{18}}(\frac{1}{\underset{2}{\cancel{4}}}x) + \overset{10}{\cancel{20}}(\frac{1}{\underset{3}{\cancel{6}}}x) + \overset{5}{\cancel{15}}(\frac{1}{\cancel{3}}x) + 21(\frac{1}{4}x) = 1440 + 296$

4.
$$\frac{9x}{2} + \frac{10x}{3} + 5x + \frac{21x}{4} = 1736$$
$$12\left[\frac{9x}{2} + \frac{10x}{3} + 5x + \frac{21x}{4}\right] = 12(1736)$$
$$54x + 40x + 60x + 63x = 20,832$$
$$217x = 20,832$$
$$x = 96$$

5.

\$ 18	\$ 20	\$ 15	\$ 21	\$ 432	\$1736
x 24	x 16	x 32	x 24	320	- 296
\$432	\$320	\$480	\$504	480	\$1440 ✓
				+ 504	
				\$1736	

14. 1. let d = distance covered by second balloon <u>650 mi.</u>

2. $\frac{1}{2}d + 50$ = distance covered by first balloon <u>375 mi.</u>

3. $d + \frac{1}{2}d + 50 = 1025$

4.
$$2d + d + 100 = 2050$$
$$3d = 1950$$
$$d = 650$$

5. 650 + 375 = 1025 ✓

15. 1. let x = monthly earnings of secretary <u>\$1400</u>

2. x -200 = monthly earnings of cashier <u>\$1200</u>

3. $\frac{1}{5}(x - 200) - 40 = \frac{1}{7}x$

4.
$$35[\frac{1}{5}(x - 200) - 40] = 35(\frac{1}{7}x)$$
$$7(x - 200) - 1400 = 5x$$
$$7x - 1400 - 1400 = 5x$$
$$2x = 2800$$
$$x = 1400$$

5. $\frac{1}{5}(1200) = \$240$

$\frac{1}{7}(1400) = \$200$

\$240 − \$200 = \$ 40 ✓

16. 1. let n = numerator 20

2. n + 15 = denominator 35

$\frac{n}{n + 15}$ = the fraction $\underline{\frac{20}{35}}$

3. $\frac{n}{n + 15} = \frac{4}{7}$

4. $7n = 4n + 60$
$3n = 60$
$n = 20$

5. $\frac{20}{35} = \frac{4}{7}$ ✓

17. 1. let d = denominator 18

2. $\frac{1}{2}d + 3$ = numerator 12

3. $\frac{\frac{1}{2}d + 3}{d}$ = the fraction $\underline{\frac{12}{18}}$

4. $\frac{\frac{1}{2}d + 3}{d} = \frac{2}{3}$
$2d = \frac{3}{2}d + 9$
$4d = 3d + 18$
$d = 18$

5. $\frac{12}{18} = \frac{2}{3}$ ✓

18. 1. let d = denominator 17

2. d - 8 = numerator 9

$\frac{d - 8}{d}$ = the fraction $\underline{\frac{9}{17}}$

3. $\frac{d - 8 - 5}{d - 5} = \frac{1}{3}$

4. $\frac{d - 13}{d - 5} = \frac{1}{3}$
$3d - 39 = d - 5$
$2d = 34$
$d = 17$

5. $\frac{9 - 5}{17 - 5} = \frac{4}{12} = \frac{1}{3}$ ✓

19. 1. let g = number of pounds of grain 1500

2. g + 2000 = number of pounds of straw 3500

$\frac{g}{60}$ = number of bushels of grain $\underline{25}$

3. $g = .3(g + g + 2000)$

4. $g = .3(2g + 2000)$
$10g = 3(2g + 2000)$
$10g = 6g + 6000$
$4g = 6000$
$g = 1500$
$\frac{g}{60} = \frac{150\not{0}}{6\not{0}} = 25$

5. $3500 - 1500 = 2000$ ✓ $\quad 3500 + 1500 = 5000$

$5000 \times .3 = 1500.0$ ✓ which is the weight of the grain

*20. 1. let x = number sold at 3/$2.50   48
2. 72 - x = number sold at $.70   24
3. $\frac{2.50}{3}$x + .70(72 - x) = 49.00 + 7.80

4.   2.50x + 2.10(72 - x) = 147.00 + 23.40
    2.50x + 151.20 - 2.10x = 170.40
              .4x = 19.20
               x = 48

5.   16 $2.50 $ .70 $40.00 $56.80
   3 $\overline{)48}$ x 16   x 24   +16.80   -49.00
              $40 $16.80 $56.80 $ 7.80 ✓

21. 1. let c = cost/mile of the first car in cents   15¢
2. c + 6 = cost/mile of the second car in cents   21¢
3. 100c + 180 = 80(c + 6)
4. 100c + 180 = 80c + 480
      20c = 300
       c = 15

5.   100   80 $16.80
   x.15   x.21   -15.00
   $ 15 $16.80 $ 1.80 ✓

22. 1. let t = time in days $4\frac{4}{9}$
2.

	Together	1 Day	t Days
John	t	$\frac{1}{8}$	$\frac{t}{8}$
Paul	t	$\frac{1}{10}$	$\frac{t}{10}$

3. $\frac{t}{8} + \frac{t}{10} = 1$

4. $40(\frac{t}{8} + \frac{t}{10}) = 40$
      5t + 4t = 40
        9t = 40
         t = $4\frac{4}{9}$

5. $\dfrac{4\frac{4}{9}}{8} + \dfrac{4\frac{4}{9}}{10}$

  $= \dfrac{\frac{40}{9}}{8} + \dfrac{\frac{40}{9}}{10}$

  $= \frac{5}{9} + \frac{4}{9} = 1$ ✓

23\. 1. let h = hours together $\quad \underline{2\frac{6}{19} \text{ hr.}}$

2.

	Together	1 Hour	h Hours
Luciano	h	$\frac{1}{4}$	$\frac{h}{4}$
Zeithlan	h	$\frac{1}{5\frac{1}{2}}$	$\frac{h}{5\frac{1}{2}}$

3. $\frac{h}{4} + \frac{h}{5\frac{1}{2}} = 1$

4. $\frac{h}{4} + \frac{h}{\frac{11}{2}} = 1$

$$\frac{h}{4} + \frac{2h}{11} = 1$$
$$44\left(\frac{h}{4} + \frac{2h}{11}\right) = 44$$
$$11h + 8h = 44$$
$$19h = 44$$
$$h = 2\frac{6}{19}$$

5. $$\frac{2\frac{6}{19}}{4} + \frac{2\frac{6}{19}}{5\frac{1}{2}}$$
$$= \frac{\frac{44}{19}}{4} + \frac{\frac{44}{19}}{\frac{11}{2}}$$
$$= \frac{11}{19} + \frac{8}{19} = 1 \checkmark$$

24\. 1. let d = number of days together $\quad \underline{3\frac{9}{37}}$

2.

	Together	1 Day	d Days
Patrick	d	$\frac{1}{10}$	$\frac{d}{10}$
Russell	d	$\frac{1}{12}$	$\frac{d}{12}$
Joseph	d	$\frac{1}{8}$	$\frac{d}{8}$

3. $\frac{d}{10} + \frac{d}{12} + \frac{d}{8} = 1$

4. $$120\left(\frac{d}{10} + \frac{d}{12} + \frac{d}{8}\right) = 120$$
$$12d + 10d + 15d = 120$$
$$37d = 120$$
$$d = 3\frac{9}{37}$$

5. $$\frac{3\frac{9}{37}}{10} + \frac{3\frac{9}{37}}{12} + \frac{3\frac{9}{37}}{8}$$
$$= \frac{\frac{120}{37}}{10} + \frac{\frac{120}{37}}{12} + \frac{\frac{120}{37}}{8}$$
$$= \frac{12}{37} + \frac{10}{37} + \frac{15}{37} = 1 \checkmark$$

25. 1. let h = number of hours working together $\underline{3\frac{3}{7}}$

2.

	Together	1 Hour	h Hours
Machine I	h	$\frac{1}{8}$	$\frac{h}{8}$
Machine II	h	$\frac{1}{6}$	$\frac{h}{6}$

3. $\frac{h}{8} + \frac{h}{6} = 1$

4.
$$24\left(\frac{h}{8} + \frac{h}{6}\right) = 24$$
$$3h + 4h = 24$$
$$7h = 24$$
$$h = 3\frac{3}{7}$$

5.
$$\frac{3\frac{3}{7}}{8} + \frac{3\frac{3}{7}}{6}$$
$$= \frac{\frac{24}{7}}{8} + \frac{\frac{24}{7}}{6}$$
$$= \frac{3}{7} + \frac{4}{7} = 1 \checkmark$$

*26. let x = time for Blake alone

	Hours Together	Part Done in 1 Hour	Part Done in Given Time
Blake	$\frac{7}{4}$	$\frac{1}{x}$	$\frac{7}{4x}$
Carlos	$\frac{7}{4}$	$\frac{1 - \frac{7}{4x}}{\frac{7}{4}} = \boxed{\frac{4}{7} - \frac{1}{x}}$	$1 - \frac{7}{4x}$
Blake	$\frac{7}{3}$	$\frac{1}{x}$	$\frac{7}{3x}$
Chuck	$\frac{7}{3}$	$\frac{1 - \frac{7}{3x}}{\frac{7}{3}} = \boxed{\frac{3}{7} - \frac{1}{x}}$	$1 - \frac{7}{3x}$
Carlos	$\frac{5}{2}$	$\frac{4}{7} - \frac{1}{x}$	$\frac{5}{2}\left(\frac{4}{7} - \frac{1}{x}\right)$
Chuck	$\frac{5}{2}$	$\frac{3}{7} - \frac{1}{x}$	$\frac{5}{2}\left(\frac{3}{7} - \frac{1}{x}\right)$

$$\frac{5}{2}\left(\frac{4}{7} - \frac{1}{x}\right) + \frac{5}{2}\left(\frac{3}{7} - \frac{1}{x}\right) = 1$$
$$\frac{20}{14} - \frac{5}{2x} + \frac{15}{14} - \frac{5}{2x} = 1$$
$$\frac{35}{14} - \frac{10}{2x} = 1$$
$$14x\left(\frac{35}{14} - \frac{10}{2x}\right) = 14x$$
$$35x - 70 = 14x$$
$$21x = 70$$
$$x = \frac{70}{21}$$
$$x = \frac{10}{3}$$

<u>Blake</u> $x = 3\frac{1}{3}$ hr.

<u>Carlos</u>
$$\left(\frac{4}{7} - \frac{1}{\frac{10}{3}}\right)h = 1$$
$$\left(\frac{4}{7} - \frac{3}{10}\right)h = 1$$
$$\left(\frac{40 - 21}{70}\right)h = 1$$
$$19h = 70$$
$$h = 3\frac{13}{19} \text{ hr.}$$

<u>Chuck</u>
$$\left(\frac{3}{7} - \frac{1}{\frac{10}{3}}\right)h = 1$$
$$\left(\frac{3}{7} - \frac{3}{10}\right)h = 1$$
$$\left(\frac{30}{70} - \frac{21}{70}\right)h = 1$$
$$9h = 70$$
$$h = 7\frac{7}{9} \text{ hr.}$$

let h = time to do job alone

26. (continued)

Blake and Carlos

$$(1\frac{3}{4})(\frac{1}{3\frac{1}{3}}) + (1\frac{3}{4})(\frac{1}{3\frac{13}{19}}) = (\frac{7}{4})(\frac{3}{10}) + (\frac{7}{4})(\frac{19}{70}) = \frac{21}{40} + \frac{19}{40} = 1 \checkmark$$

Carlos and Chuck

$$(2\frac{1}{2})(\frac{1}{3\frac{13}{19}}) + (2\frac{1}{2})(\frac{1}{7\frac{7}{9}}) = (\frac{5}{2})(\frac{19}{70}) + (\frac{5}{2})(\frac{9}{70}) = \frac{19}{28} + \frac{9}{28} = 1 \checkmark$$

Blake and Chuck

$$(2\frac{1}{3})(\frac{1}{3\frac{1}{3}}) + (2\frac{1}{3})(\frac{1}{7\frac{7}{9}}) = (\frac{7}{3})(\frac{3}{10}) + (\frac{7}{3})(\frac{9}{70}) = \frac{7}{10} + \frac{3}{10} = 1 \checkmark$$

27. 1. let t = time until they meet <u>4 hr.</u>

2.

	Rate	Time	Distance
Walker	$3\frac{1}{2}$	t	$3\frac{1}{2}t$
Bicycler	9	t	9t

3. $3\frac{1}{2}t + 9t = 50$

4. $\frac{7}{2}t + 9t = 50$

$$7t + 18t = 100$$
$$25t = 100$$
$$t = 4$$

5. $3.5 \times 4 = 14.0$ $\qquad 9 \times 4 = 36$ $\qquad 36 + 14 = 50 \checkmark$

28. 1. let x = number of trips for larger aircraft 4
2. 3x = number of trips for smaller aircraft 12

Together	Per Trip	3 Trips
3 trips	$\frac{1}{x}$	$\frac{3}{x}$
3 trips	$\frac{1}{3x}$	$\frac{3}{3x}$

3. $\frac{3}{x} + \frac{3}{3x} = 1$

4. $\frac{3}{x} + \frac{1}{x} = 1$

$\frac{4}{x} = 1$

$x = 4$

$3x = 12$

5. $\frac{3}{4} + \frac{3}{12} = 1$

$\frac{3}{4} + \frac{1}{4} = 1$

$1 - 1$ ✓

29. 1. let t = time for both together 2 hr.

2.

	Together	1 Hour	t Hours
Experienced	t	$\frac{1}{3}$	$\frac{t}{3}$
Trainee	t	$\frac{1}{6}$	$\frac{t}{6}$

3. $\frac{t}{3} + \frac{t}{6} = 1$

4. $6(\frac{t}{3} + \frac{t}{6}) = 6$

$2t + t = 6$

$3t = 6$

$t = 2$

5. $\frac{2}{3} + \frac{2}{6}$

$= \frac{2}{3} + \frac{1}{3} = 1$ ✓

30. 1. let x = amount at 8% $500
2. 800 - x = amount at 7.5% $300
3. $.08x + .075(800 - x) = 62.5$
4. $80x + 75(800 - x) = 62,500$

$80x + 60,000 - 75x = 62,500$

$5x = 2500$

$x = 500$

5.

$500	$ 300	$40.00
x.08	x.075	+22.50
$ 40	$22.50	$62.50 ✓

31. 1. let x = number of liters of water 15

2.

	Liters	Percent Acid	Liters of Acid
First	30	30	.3(30)
Second	30 + x	20	.2(30 + x)

3. $.3(30) = .2(30 + x)$
4. $9 = 6 + .2x$

$3 = .2x$

$15 = x$

Alternate Solution

	Liters	Percent Water	Liters of Water
First	30	70	.7(30)
Second	30 + x	80	.8(30 + x)

$.7(30) + x = .8(30 + x)$

$21 + x = 24 + .8x$

$210 + 10x = 240 + 8x$

$2x = 30$

$x = 15$

1. let x = the smaller number 7
2. x + 35 = the larger number 42
3. $\dfrac{x + 35}{x} = 6$
4. 6x = x + 35
    5x = 35
    x = 7

5. $\dfrac{42}{7} = 6$ ✓

33.
1. let x = amount of good investment $2750
2. 4330 - x = amount of bad investment $1580
3. .12x - .05(4330 - x) = 251
4. 12x - 5(4330 - x) = 25,100
    12x - 21,650 + 5x = 25,100
    17x = 46,750
    x = 2750

5.
$2750	$1580	$330
x.12	x.05	-79
$ 330	$ 79	$251 ✓

34.
1. let x = amount Mr. Bailey loaned at 9% $6000
2. $\dfrac{4}{5}x$ = amount Mr. Day loaned at 12% $4800
3. $.09x + 36 = .12(\dfrac{4}{5}x)$
4. $5(.09x + 36) = 5(.12)(\dfrac{4}{5}x)$
    .45x + 180 = .48x
    45x + 18,000 = 48x
    -3x = -18,000
    x = 6000

5.
$6000	$4800	$576
x.09	x.12	-540
$ 540	$ 576	$ 36 ✓

35.
1. let r = rate of slower truck 50.3 mph
   r + 3 = rate of faster truck 53.3 mph
2.
	Rate	Time	Distance
First	r	$\dfrac{905.4}{r}$	905.4
Second	r + 3	$\dfrac{905.4 + 54}{r + 3}$	905.4 + 54

3. $\dfrac{905.4}{r} = \dfrac{905.4 + 54}{r + 3}$

4. $r(r + 3)(\dfrac{905.4}{r}) = r(r + 3)(\dfrac{959.4}{r + 3})$
    905.4(r + 3) = 959.4r
    905.4r + 2716.2 = 959.4r
    -54r = -2716.2
    r = 50.3

5. $\dfrac{905.4}{50.3} = 18$ ✓

    $\dfrac{959.4}{53.3} = 18$

36. 1. let s = speed of merchant ship   <u>18 knots</u>

2.

	Speed	Time	Distance
Warship	30	$1\frac{36}{60}$	$30(1\frac{36}{60})$
Merchant ship	s	$1\frac{4}{60}+1\frac{36}{60}$	$s(2\frac{40}{60})$

3. $30(1\frac{36}{60}) = s(2\frac{40}{60})$

4. $30(1.6) = s(2\frac{2}{3})$

$$48 = \frac{8}{3}s$$

$$\frac{3}{8}(48) = \frac{3}{8}\cdot\frac{8}{3}s$$

$$18 = s$$

5. $30(1\frac{36}{60}) = 48$ ✓

$18(2\frac{40}{60}) = 48$

37. 1. let r = rate per minute   <u>3 mi./min.</u>

2.

	Rate	Time	Distance
Now	r	6 min.	6r
If	$r+\frac{6}{10}$	5 min.	$5(r + \frac{6}{10})$

3. $5(r + \frac{6}{10}) = 6r$

4. $5r + \frac{30}{10} = 6r$

$$5r + 3 = 6r$$

$$r = 3$$

5.
```
 3     3.6
x6     x 5
18     18  ✓
```

38. 1. let x = original depth   <u>18 ft.</u>
2. 2x + 4 = final depth   <u>40 ft.</u>
3. 2x + 4 = x + 22
4.   x = 18

5.
```
18      40
x2     -18
36      22 ✓
+4
40 ✓
```

*39. 1. let c = cost <u>$8</u>
2. 2c + 11 = selling price
3. (2c + .11) - (c) = 1.01375c
4.   c + .11 = 1.01375c
         -.01375c = -.11
            1375c = 11,000
                c = 8

5.
```
$ 8.00    $16.11    $8.11
  x 2     -8.00     ─────  = 1.01375
─────────  ───────   $8
$16.00    $ 8.11           = 101.375%
  +.11                     = 101 3/8 %  ✓
─────────
$16.11
```

40. n = monthly rental
12n = yearly rental
$\frac{12n}{a}$ = fractional part of cost
$\frac{1200n}{a}$ = percentage of cost

41. 1. let r = rate of bicycle 15 mph
4r = rate of motorcycle 60 mph

2.

	Rate	Time	Distance
Bicycle	r	6	6r
Motorcycle	4r	6	24r

3. $6r + 24r = 450$
4. $30r = 450$
$r = 15$

5. 15 × 6 = 90; 60 × 6 = 360; 360 + 90 = 450 ✓

42. 1. let x = total value $15,000
2.
3. $.13(\frac{2}{5}x) + .12(\frac{1}{3}x) + .08(x - \frac{2}{5}x - \frac{1}{3}x) = 1700$
4. $\frac{.26x}{5} + .04x + .08(\frac{15x}{15} - \frac{6x}{15} - \frac{5x}{15}) = 1700$
$\frac{26x}{5} + 4x + 8(\frac{4x}{15}) = 170{,}000$
$15(\frac{26x}{5} + 4x + \frac{32x}{15}) = 15(170{,}000)$
$78x + 60x + 32x = 2{,}550{,}000$
$170x = 2{,}550{,}000$
$x = 15{,}000$

5. $\frac{2}{5}(15{,}000) =$ $6000 × .13 = $ 780; $\frac{1}{3}(15{,}000) =$ $5000 × .12 = $ 600; $4000 × .08 = $ 320; $ 780 + 600 + 320 = $1700 ✓

Test A Page 223

The check is left for the teacher.

I 1. $9 - 9x = 1 - 7x$
$-2x = -8$
$x = 4$

2. $3x - 4(5x - 6) = 40 - 3(6x + 4)$
$3x - 20x + 24 = 40 - 18x - 12$
$-17x + 24 = 28 - 18x$
$x = 4$

3. $(x - 3)(x + 3) - (x - 4)(4 + x) = 2x$
$x^2 - 9 - (x^2 - 16) = 2x$
$x^2 - 9 + (4 - x)(4 + x) = 2x$
$x^2 - 9 + 16 - x^2 = 2x$
$7 = 2x$
$x = \frac{7}{2}$

4.
$$\frac{4x + 2}{6} - \frac{8x}{3} = \frac{2}{3} - 3x$$
$$6\left(\frac{4x + 2}{6} - \frac{8x}{3}\right) = 6\left(\frac{2}{3} - 3x\right)$$
$$4x + 2 - 16x = 4 - 18x$$
$$-12x + 2 = 4 - 18x$$
$$6x = 2$$
$$x = \frac{1}{3}$$

5.
$$\frac{2x^2 + 2x}{x^2 - 4} - \frac{x - 2}{x + 2} = \frac{x + 2}{x - 2}$$
$$(x + 2)(x - 2)\left[\frac{2x^2 + 2x}{(x + 2)(x - 2)} - \frac{x - 2}{x + 2}\right] = (x + 2)\cancel{(x - 2)}\left(\frac{x + 2}{\cancel{x - 2}}\right)$$
$$2x^2 + 2x - (x - 2)^2 = (x + 2)^2$$
$$2x^2 + 2x - (x^2 - 4x + 4) = x^2 + 4x + 4$$
$$2x^2 + 2x - x^2 + 4x - 4 = x^2 + 4x + 4$$
$$x^2 + 6x - 4 = x^2 + 4x + 4$$
$$2x = 8$$
$$x = 4$$

6.
$$x(x - 5) - 4(x + 6) = 3x + 4$$
$$x^2 - 5x - 4x - 24 = 3x + 4$$
$$x^2 - 9x - 24 = 3x + 4$$
$$x^2 - 12x - 28 = 0$$
$$(x - 14)(x + 2) = 0$$
$$x - 14 = 0 \qquad x + 2 = 0$$
$$x = 14 \qquad x = -2$$

7.
$$3mx - 2n = 6m - nx$$
$$nx + 3mx = 6m + 2n$$
$$x(n + 3m) = 6m + 2n$$
$$x = \frac{6m + 2n}{n + 3m}$$
$$x = \frac{2\cancel{(3m + n)}}{\cancel{n + 3m}}$$
$$x = 2$$

8.
$$s = \frac{uv}{g} + \frac{v^2}{2g}$$
$$2gs = 2g\left(\frac{uv}{g} + \frac{v^2}{2g}\right)$$
$$2gs = 2uv + v^2$$
$$g = \frac{2uv + v^2}{2s}$$

II 1.
1. let a = number of apples
2.
3. $.25a + .35 = .27a - .55$

2.
1. let x = amount in bonds
2. $16{,}000 - x$ = amount in bank
3. $.08x + 315 = .065(16{,}000 - x)$

3.
1. let s = speed of slower car
   s + 8 = speed of faster car
2.

	Speed	Time	Distance
Slower	s	5.5	5.5s
Faster	s + 8	5.5	5.5(s + 8)

3. $5.5s + 5.5(s + 8) = 704$

4.
1. let x = number of days worked
2. $10 - x$ = number of days idle
3. $100x - 20(10 - x) = 760$

Test B   Pages 223-224

I

The check is left for the teacher.

1. $$\begin{aligned} 21 + 9x &= 5x - 7 \\ 4x &= -28 \\ x &= -7 \end{aligned}$$

2. $$\begin{aligned} 2(4x - 1) - 3(8x - 3) &= 19 - 5(6x + 1) \\ 8x - 2 - 24x + 9 &= 19 - 30x - 5 \\ -16x + 7 &= 14 - 30x \\ 14x &= 7 \\ x &= \frac{1}{2} \end{aligned}$$

3. $$\begin{aligned} (x + 5)(x - 5) - (x + 2)^2 &= 1 - 2x \\ x^2 - 25 - (x^2 + 4x + 4) &= 1 - 2x \\ x^2 - 25 - x^2 - 4x - 4 &= 1 - 2x \\ -4x - 29 &= 1 - 2x \\ -2x &= 30 \\ x &= -15 \end{aligned}$$

4. $$\begin{aligned} \frac{11x + 7}{6} - \frac{x}{4} &= x + 1\frac{3}{4} \\ \frac{11x + 7}{6} - \frac{6x}{6} &= \frac{7}{4} + \frac{x}{4} \\ \frac{5x + 7}{6} &= \frac{7 + x}{4} \\ 20x + 28 &= 42 + 6x \\ 14x &= 14 \\ x &= 1 \end{aligned}$$

5. $$\begin{aligned} \frac{2x^2 - 15}{x^2 - 5x + 6} - \frac{x + 3}{x - 2} &= \frac{x + 4}{x - 3} \\ \frac{2x^2 - 15}{(x - 3)(x - 2)} - \frac{x + 3}{x - 2} &= \frac{x + 4}{x - 3} \\ (x - 3)(x - 2)\left[\frac{2x^2 - 15}{(x - 3)(x - 2)} - \frac{x + 3}{x - 2}\right] &= \cancel{(x - 3)}(x - 2)\left(\frac{x + 4}{\cancel{x - 3}}\right) \\ 2x^2 - 15 - (x - 3)(x + 3) &= (x - 2)(x + 4) \\ 2x^2 - 15 - (x^2 - 9) &= x^2 + 2x - 8 \\ 2x^2 - 15 - x^2 + 9 &= x^2 + 2x - 8 \\ x^2 - 6 &= x^2 + 2x - 8 \\ -2x &= -2 \\ x &= 1 \end{aligned}$$

6. $$\begin{aligned} 8a^2 - 5bx &= 2ax - 20ab \\ -2ax - 5bx &= -8a^2 - 20ab \\ 2ax + 5bx &= 8a^2 + 20ab \\ x(2a + 5b) &= 4a(2a + 5b) \\ x &= \frac{4a\cancel{(2a + 5b)}}{\cancel{2a + 5b}} \\ x &= 4a \end{aligned}$$

7. $$\begin{aligned} q &= \frac{D}{d} - \frac{r}{3d} \\ 3dq &= 3d\left(\frac{D}{d} - \frac{r}{3d}\right) \\ 3dq &= 3D - r \\ d &= \frac{3D - r}{3q} \end{aligned}$$

II

1. 1. let x = number of games lost
   $4x - 1$ = number of games won
   2. $x - 2$ = number of games tied
   3. $x + (4x - 1) + (x - 2) = 21$

2. 1. let x = amount invested at 9%
   2. $x + 3000$ = possible amount at 8.5%
   3. $.09x + .08(3000) = .085(x + 3000)$

3. 1. let m = time to catch up in minutes
   2.
   3. $30(40) + 40m = 50m$

4. 1. let x = number of years
   2.
   3. $36 + x = 2(9 + x)$

Test C   Pages 224-225

I 1.

$$\frac{x-1}{x-2} = 2 - \frac{x}{x-1}$$
$$(x-1)\cancel{(x-2)}\left(\frac{x-1}{\cancel{x-2}}\right) = (x-1)(x-2)\left(2 - \frac{x}{x-1}\right)$$
$$(x-1)^2 = 2(x^2 - 3x + 2) - x(x-2)$$
$$x^2 - 2x + 1 = 2x^2 - 6x + 4 - x^2 + 2x$$
$$x^2 - 2x + 1 = x^2 - 4x + 4$$
$$2x = 3$$
$$x = \frac{3}{2}$$

$\dfrac{\frac{3}{2} - 1}{\frac{3}{2} - 2}$	$2 - \dfrac{\frac{3}{2}}{\frac{3}{2} - 1}$
$\dfrac{\frac{1}{2}}{\frac{-1}{2}}$	$2 - \dfrac{\frac{3}{2}}{\frac{1}{2}}$
-1	$2 - 3$
$-1 =$	-1 ✓

2.

$$\frac{x^2 + a^2}{4x^2 - a^2} + \frac{1}{4} = \frac{x}{2x + a}$$
$$\frac{x^2 + a^2}{(2x + a)(2x - a)} + \frac{1}{4} = \frac{x}{2x + a}$$
$$4(2x + a)(2x - a)\left[\frac{x^2 + a^2}{(2x + a)(2x - a)} + \frac{1}{4}\right] = 4\cancel{(2x + a)}(2x - a)\left(\frac{x}{\cancel{2x + a}}\right)$$
$$4(x^2 + a^2) + (2x + a)(2x - a) = 4x(2x - a)$$
$$4x^2 + 4a^2 + 4x^2 - a^2 = 8x^2 - 4ax$$
$$8x^2 + 3a^2 = 8x^2 - 4ax$$
$$4ax = -3a^2$$
$$x = -\frac{3a^2}{4a}$$
$$x = -\frac{3a}{4}$$

$\dfrac{(\frac{-3a}{4})^2 + a^2}{4(\frac{-3a}{4})^2 - a^2} + \frac{1}{4}$	$\dfrac{\frac{-3a}{4}}{2(\frac{-3a}{4}) + a}$
$\dfrac{\frac{9a^2 + 16a^2}{16}}{\frac{36a^2 - 16a^2}{16}} + \frac{1}{4}$	$\dfrac{\frac{-3a}{4}}{\frac{-6a + 4a}{4}}$
$\dfrac{25a^2}{20a^2} + \frac{1}{4}$	$\dfrac{\frac{-3a}{4}}{\frac{-2a}{4}}$
$\frac{5}{4} + \frac{1}{4}$	$\frac{3}{2}$
$\frac{3}{2} =$	$\frac{3}{2}$ ✓

3.
$$\frac{x^2 - x + 1}{x - 1} + \frac{x^2 + x + 1}{x + 1} = 2x$$
$$(x - 1)(x + 1)\left(\frac{x^2 - x + 1}{x - 1} + \frac{x^2 + x + 1}{x + 1}\right) = 2x(x - 1)(x + 1)$$
$$(x + 1)(x^2 - x + 1) + (x - 1)(x^2 + x + 1) = 2x(x^2 - 1)$$
$$x^3 + 1 + x^3 - 1 = 2x^3 - 2x$$
$$\cancel{2x^3} = \cancel{2x^3} - 2x$$
$$2x = 0$$
$$x = 0$$

$$\frac{(0)^2 - 0 + 1}{0 - 1} + \frac{(0)^2 + 0 + 1}{0 + 1} \;\Big|\; 2(0)$$
$$\frac{1}{-1} + \frac{1}{1} \;\Big|\; 0$$
$$0 = 0 \checkmark$$

4.
$$\frac{2y - 3}{2} - \frac{4y - 33}{10} = \frac{3y + 4}{5} - \frac{4}{y}$$
$$\left(\frac{2y - 3}{2} - \frac{4y - 33}{10} - \frac{3y + 4}{5}\right) = -\frac{4}{y}$$
$$\frac{10y - 15 - 4y + 33 - 6y - 8}{10} = -\frac{4}{y}$$
$$1 = -\frac{4}{y}$$
$$y = -4$$

$$\frac{2(-4) - 3}{2} - \frac{4(-4) - 33}{10} \;\Big|\; \frac{3(-4) + 4}{5} - \frac{4}{-4}$$
$$\frac{-11}{2} + \frac{49}{10} \;\Big|\; -\frac{8}{5} + 1$$
$$\frac{-55}{10} + \frac{49}{10} \;\Big|\; -\frac{3}{5}$$
$$-\frac{3}{5} = -\frac{3}{5} \checkmark$$

5. (1)
$$C = \frac{nE}{R + nr}$$
$$C(R + nr) = nE$$
$$CR + Cnr = nE$$
$$Cnr - nE = -CR$$
$$n(Cr - E) = -CR$$
$$n = \frac{-CR}{Cr - E}$$
$$n = \frac{CR}{E - Cr}$$

(2)
$$n = \frac{CR}{E - CR}$$
$$n = \frac{(4)(4)}{6 - (4)(.5)}$$
$$n = \frac{16}{6 - 2}$$
$$n = \frac{16}{4}$$
$$n = 4$$

6. (1)
$$S = \frac{n}{2}[2a + (n - 1)d]$$
$$2S = n[2a + (n - 1)d]$$
$$2S = 2an + dn(n - 1)$$
$$2S - 2an = dn(n - 1)$$
$$\frac{2S - 2an}{n(n - 1)} = d$$

(2)
$$d = \frac{2S - 2an}{n(n - 1)}$$
$$d = \frac{2(80) - 2(3)(8)}{8(8 - 1)}$$
$$d = \frac{160 - 48}{8(7)}$$
$$d = \frac{112}{56}$$
$$d = 2$$

II 1. 1. let x = number of pounds of bluegrass seed <u>24</u>

2.

3. $\frac{3}{5}(40) + x = \frac{3}{4}(40 + x)$

4. $24 + x = 30 + \frac{3}{4}x$

$4(24 + x) = 4(30 + \frac{3}{4}x)$

$96 + 4x = 120 + 3x$

$x = 24$

5. $\frac{3}{5}(40) + 24 = 48$

$\frac{3}{4}(40 + 24) = 48$ ✓

2. 1. let r = number of rows <u>18</u>

2. $\frac{432}{r}$ = number in each row <u>24</u>

3. $(r - 2)(\frac{432}{r} + 3) = 432$

4. $r(r - 2)(\frac{432}{r} + 3) = 432r$

$432(r - 2) + 3r(r - 2) = 432r$

~~432r~~ $- 864 + 3r^2 - 6r =$ ~~432r~~

$3r^2 - 6r - 864 = 0$

$r^2 - 2r - 288 = 0$

$(r - 18)(r + 16) = 0$

$r - 18 = 0$ ~~r + 16 = 0~~

$r = 18$ ~~r = -16~~

Reject since negative.

5. $\begin{array}{r} 27 \\ \times 16 \\ \hline 432 \end{array}$

3. 1. let r = rate of first player <u>6 yd./sec.</u>

r + 2 = rate of opponent <u>8 yd./sec.</u>

2.

	Rate	Time	Distance
Player	r	$\frac{24}{r}$	24
Opponent	$r + 2$	$\frac{32}{r + 2}$	32

3. $\frac{24}{r} = \frac{32}{r + 2}$

4. $32r = 24r + 48$

$8r = 48$

$r = 6$

5. $\frac{24}{6} = 4$

$\frac{32}{8} = 4$ ✓

4. 1. let a = number of adult tickets <u>250</u>

2. 423 - a = number of children's tickets <u>173</u>

3. $4a + 1.5(423 - a) = 1259.50$

4. $40a + 15(423 - a) = 12{,}595$

$40a + 6345 - 15a = 12{,}595$

$25a = 6250$

$a = 250$

5. $\begin{array}{r} 250 \\ \times\ 4 \\ \hline \$1000 \end{array}$ $\begin{array}{r} 173 \\ \times\ 1.50 \\ \hline \$259.50 \end{array}$ $\begin{array}{r} \$1000.00 \\ +\ 259.50 \\ \hline \$1259.50 \end{array}$ ✓

UNIT 11 — Linear Systems of Equations

Exercises 11.1   Page 229

1.-12.

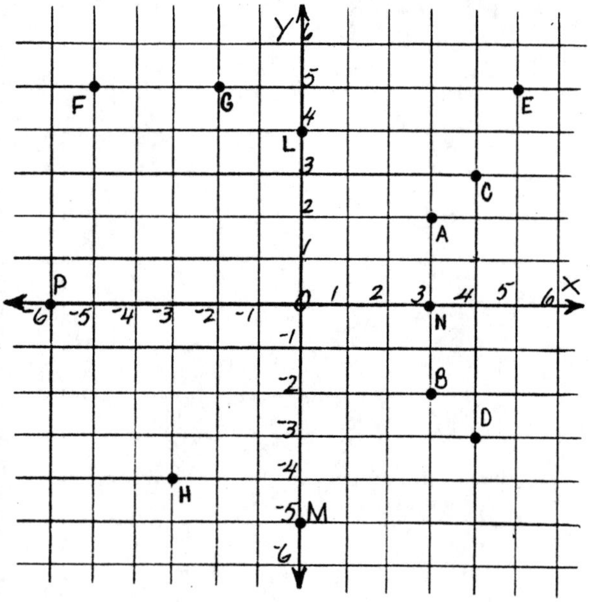

13. On the y-axis; on the x-axis

14. (0, 0)

15. $y = 3x - 7$

x	y
0	-7
1	-4
2	-1
3	2
4	5

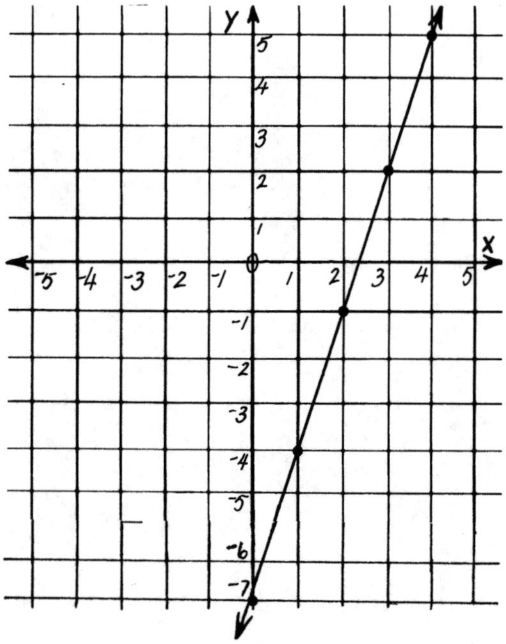

16. $x - 2y = 2$

$$-2y = -x + 2$$

$$y = \frac{1}{2}x - 1$$

x	y
0	-1
2	0
4	1
6	2
-2	-2
-4	-3
-6	-4

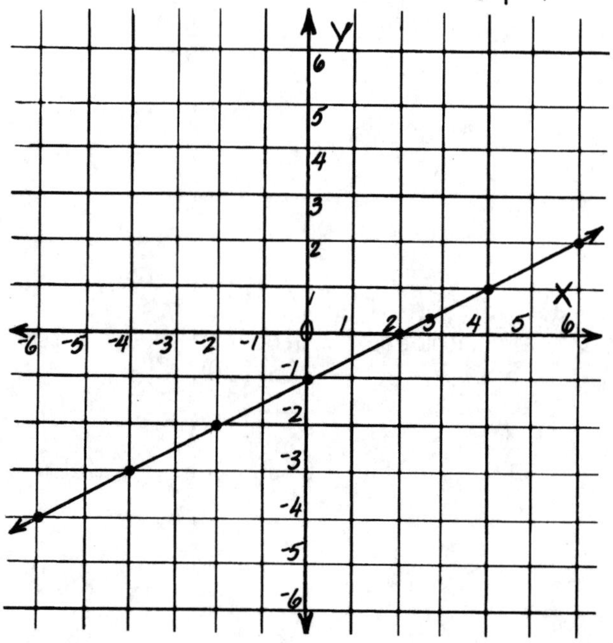

17. $y = 2x + 1$

x	y
0	1
1	3
2	5
3	7
-1	-1
-2	-3
-3	-5
-4	-7

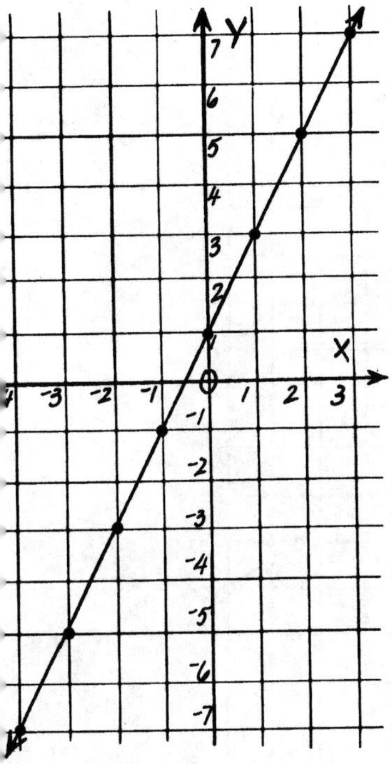

18. $3x = 2y$
$2y = 3x$
$y = \frac{3}{2}x$

x	y
0	0
2	3
4	6
-2	-3
-4	-6

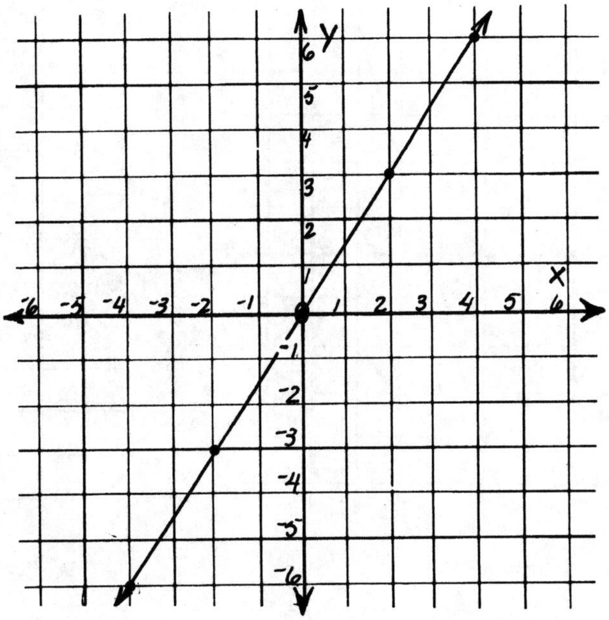

19. $y = 2x - 1$

x	y
0	-1
1	1
2	3
3	5
4	7
-1	-3
-2	-5

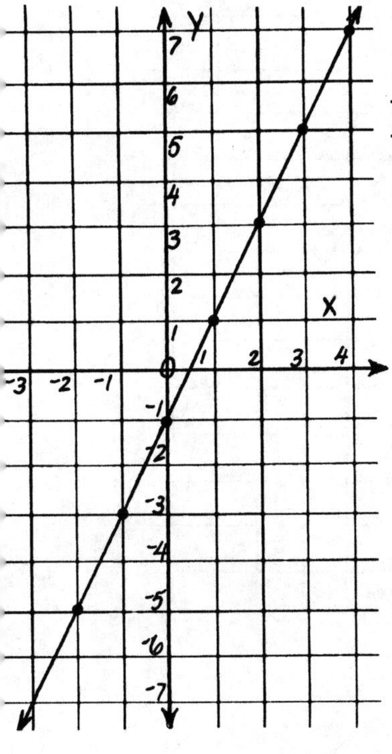

20. $2x + y = 1$
$y = -2x + 1$

x	y
0	1
1	-1
2	-3
3	-5
-1	3
-2	5
-3	7

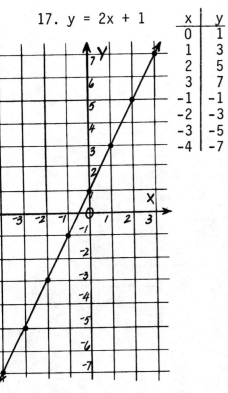

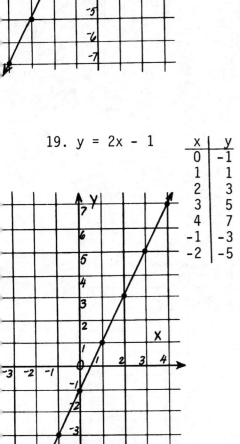

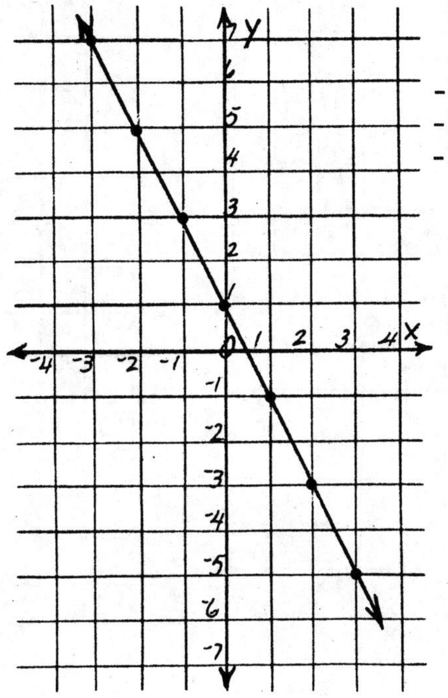

21. $3x - y = 4$
$-y = -3x + 4$
$y = 3x - 4$

x	y
0	-4
1	-1
2	2
3	5

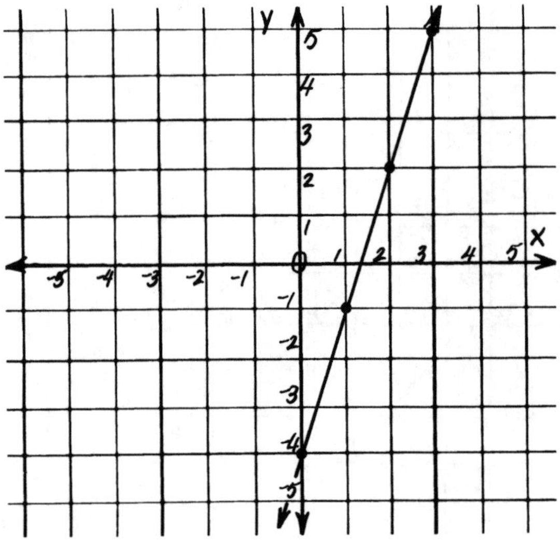

22. $2x + 3y = 6$
$3y = -2x + 6$
$y = \frac{-2}{3}x + 2$

x	y
-6	6
-3	4
0	2
3	0
6	-2

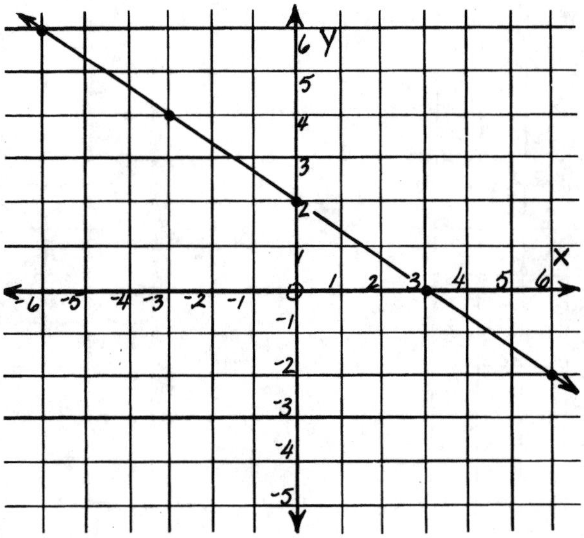

23. $4x - y = 10$
$-y = -4x + 10$
$y = 4x - 10$

x	y
1	-6
2	-2
3	2
4	6

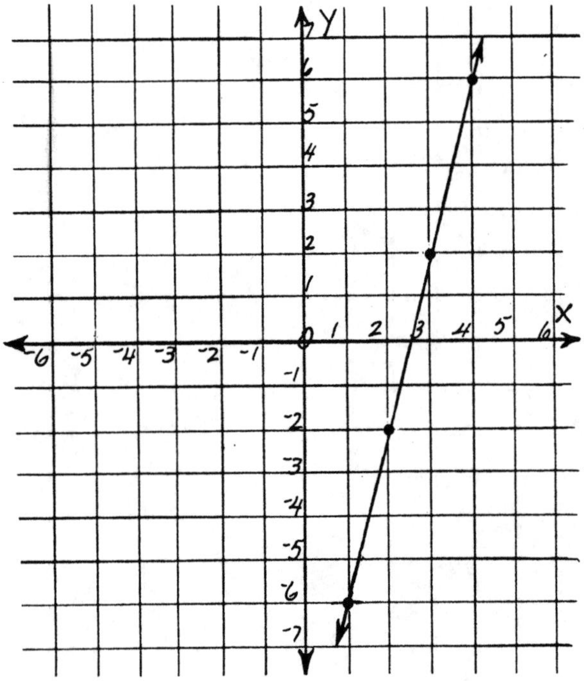

24. $3x + 2y = 12$
$2y = -3x + 12$
$y = \frac{-3}{2}x + 6$

x	y
0	6
2	3
4	0
6	-3

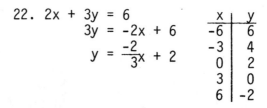

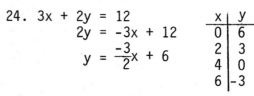

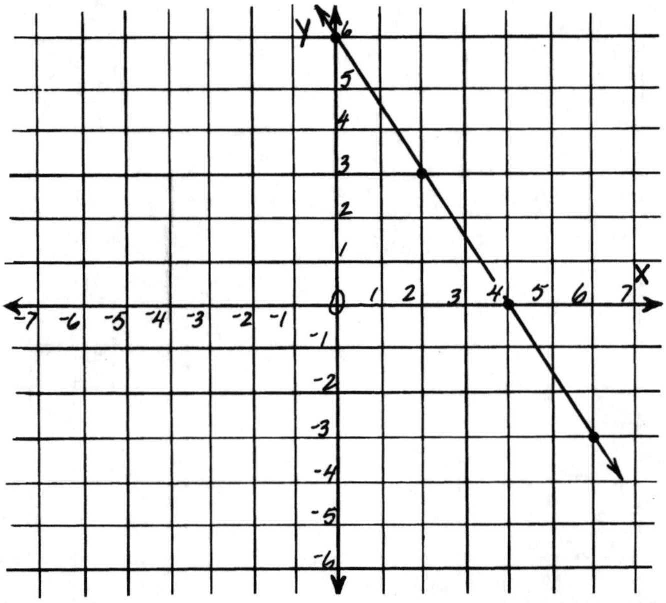

<u>Exercises 11.2</u> Page 230

1. $2x - 3y = 6$

$-3y = -2x + 6$

$y = \frac{2}{3}x - 2$

x	y
-6	-6
-3	-4
0	-2
3	0
6	2

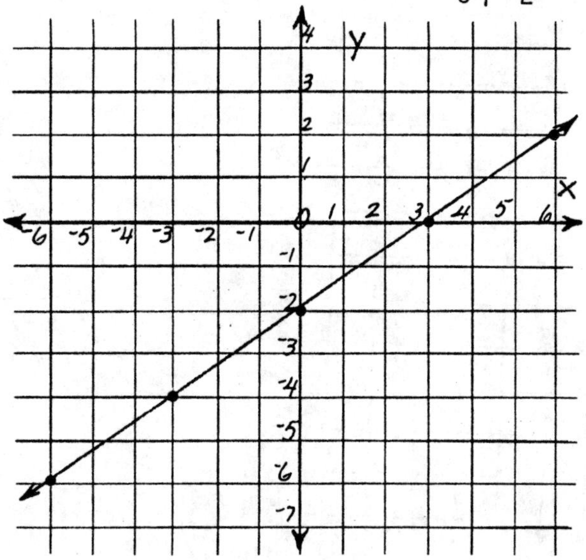

2. $2x + 3y = 0$

$3y = -2x$

$y = \frac{-2}{3}x$

x	y
-6	4
-3	2
0	0
3	-2
6	-4

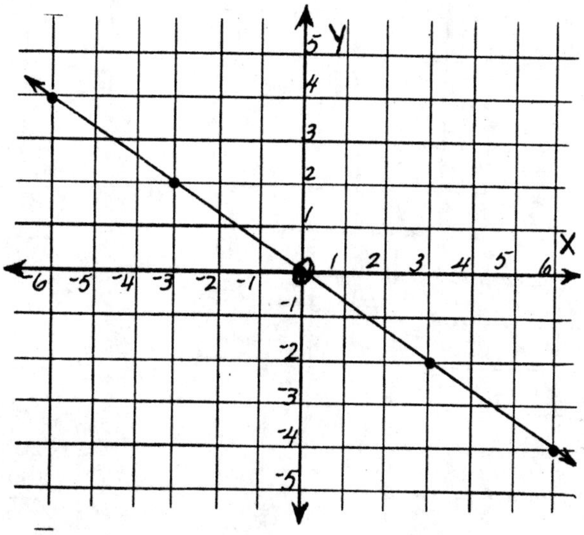

3. $3x + 4y = 12$

$4y = -3x + 12$

$y = \frac{-3}{4}x + 3$

x	y
-4	6
0	3
4	0

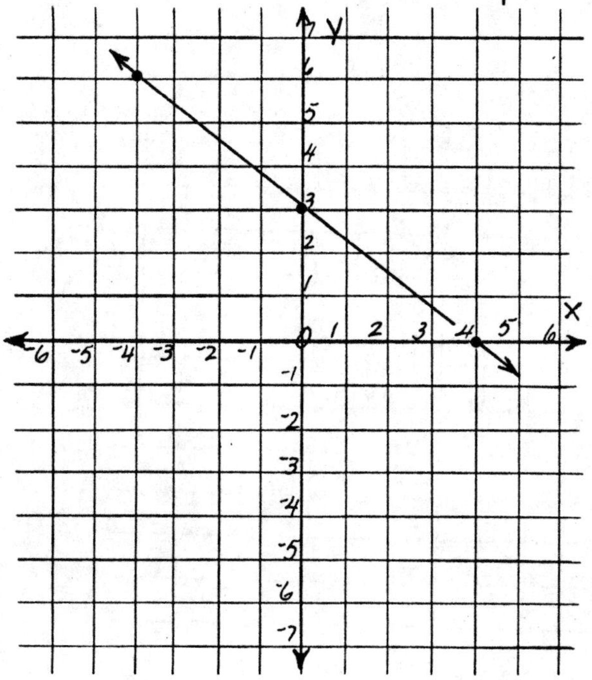

4. $5x - 2y = 10$

$-2y = -5x + 10$

$y = \frac{5}{2}x - 5$

x	y
0	-5
2	0
4	5

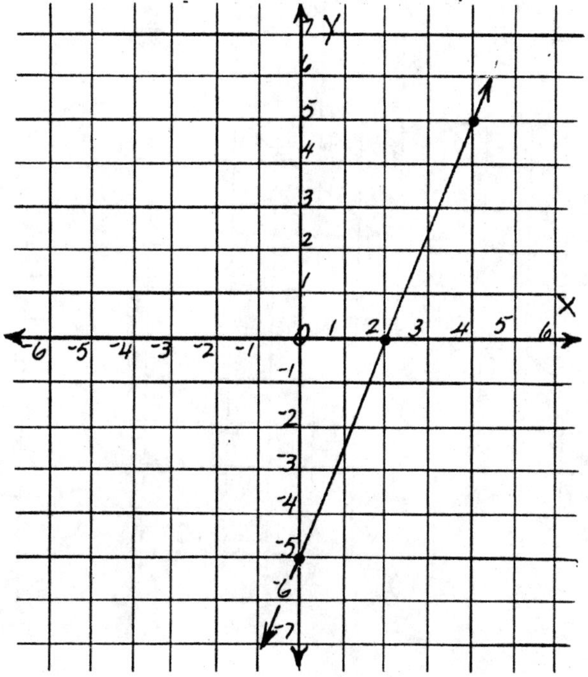

5. $8x - 3y = -6$

$-3y = -8x - 6$

$y = \frac{8}{3}x + 2$

x	y
-3	-6
0	2
1.5	6

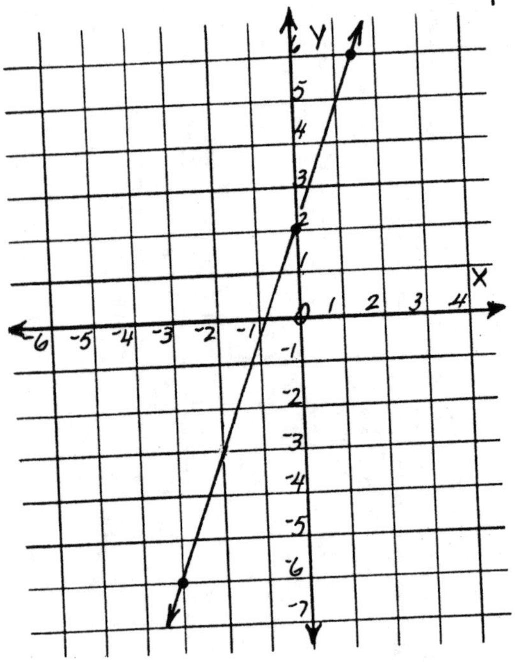

6. $-2x + y = -3$

$y = 2x - 3$

x	y
-1	-5
0	-3
1	-1
2	1
3	3
4	5
5	7

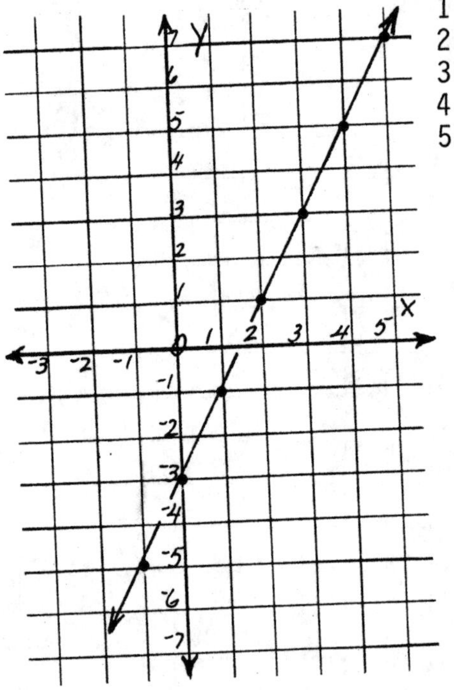

7. $-3x + 4y = 8$

$4y = 3x + 8$

$y = \frac{3}{4}x + 2$

x	y
-4	-1
0	2
4	5

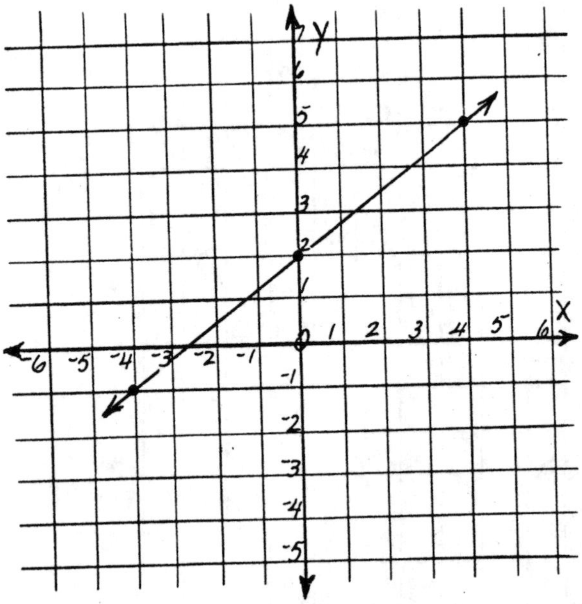

8. $5x + 3y = 7\frac{1}{2}$

$2(5x + 3y) = 2(7\frac{1}{2})$

$10x + 6y = 15$

$6y = -10x + 15$

$y = \frac{-5}{3}x + \frac{5}{2}$

x	y
0	2.5
1.5	0
3	-2.5

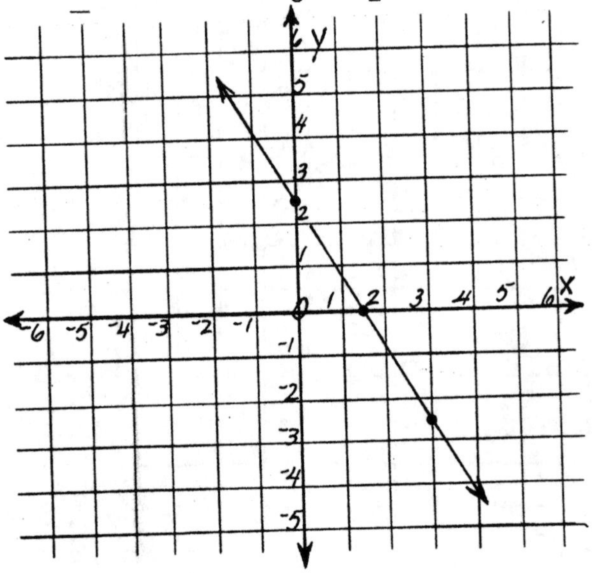

9.

$$x - \frac{1}{2}y = 3$$

$$2(x - \frac{1}{2}y) = 2(3)$$

$$2x - y = 6$$

$$-y = -2x + 6$$

$$y = 2x - 6$$

x	y
0	-6
1	-4
2	-2
3	0
4	2
5	4
6	6

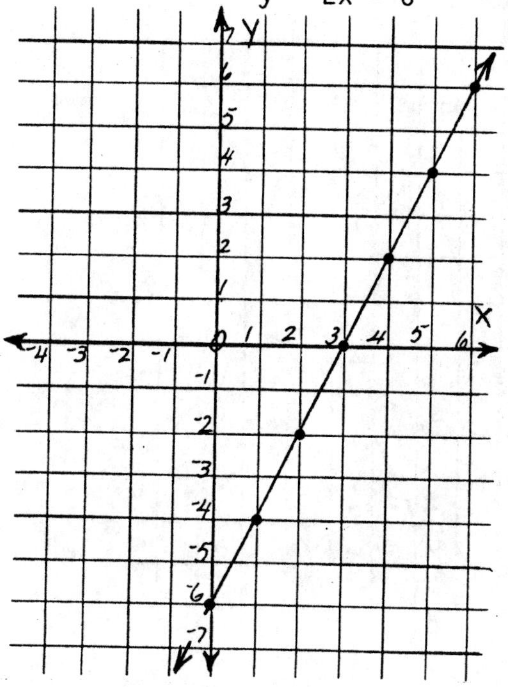

10.

$$\frac{1}{2}x + \frac{1}{3}y = 2$$

$$6(\frac{1}{2}x + \frac{1}{3}y) = 6(2)$$

$$3x + 2y = 12$$

$$2y = -3x + 12$$

$$y = \frac{-3}{2}x + 6$$

x	y
0	6
2	3
4	0
6	-3

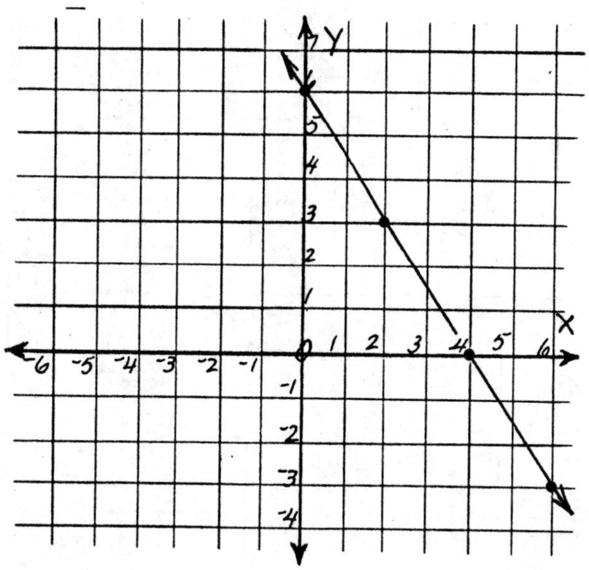

Exercises 11.4 Pages 233-234

1. $x - y = 1$ $x + y = 9$

x	y
1	0
0	-1
6	5

x	y
3	6
6	3
7	2

Solution (5, 4)

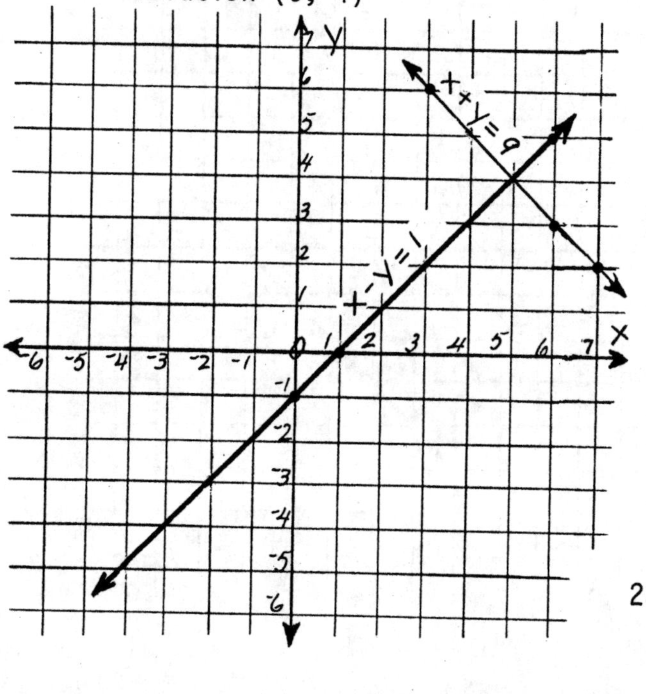

2. $x + y = 3$ $x + 2y = 4$

x	y
0	3
3	0
6	-3

x	y
4	0
0	2
-6	5

Solution (2, 1)

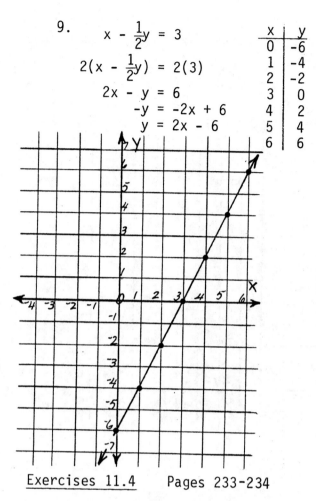

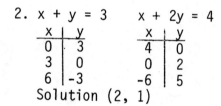

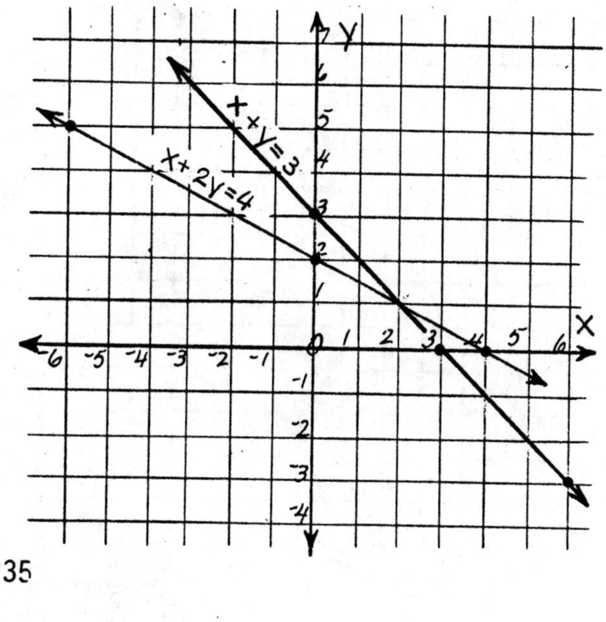

3. $x = 4 + y$

x	y
4	0
0	-4
6	2

$y = 3 + x$

x	y
0	3
-3	0
-6	-3

No solution; inconsistent system (parallel lines)

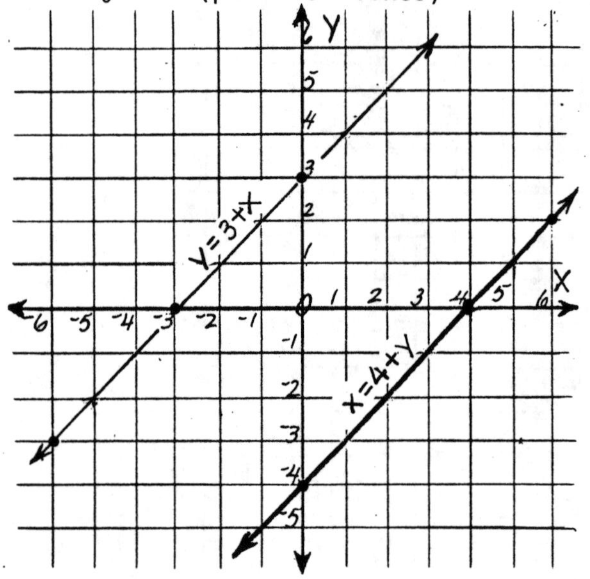

4. $2x - y = 5$

x	y
2.5	0
0	-5
5	5

$4x + y = 16$

x	y
4	0
5	-4
2.5	6

Solution (3.5, 2)

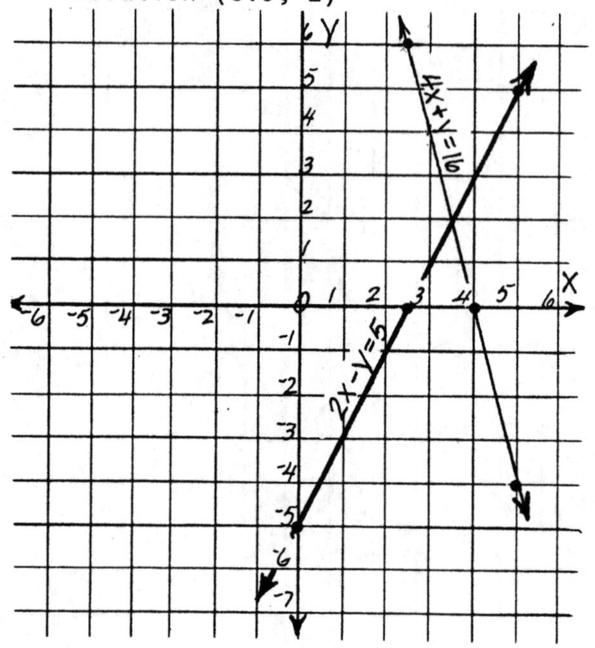

5. $3x = y + 9$

x	y
3	0
2	-3
5	6

$2y = 6x - 18$

x	y
3	0
5	6
1	-6

Indeterminate; dependent system (same line)

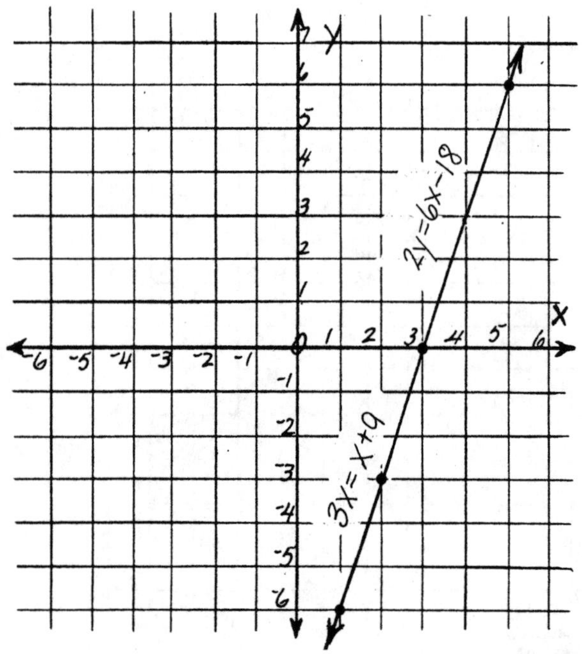

6. $y = 4x$

x	y
0	0
1	4
-1	-4

$x - y = 3$

x	y
3	0
0	-3
6	3

Solution (-1, -4)

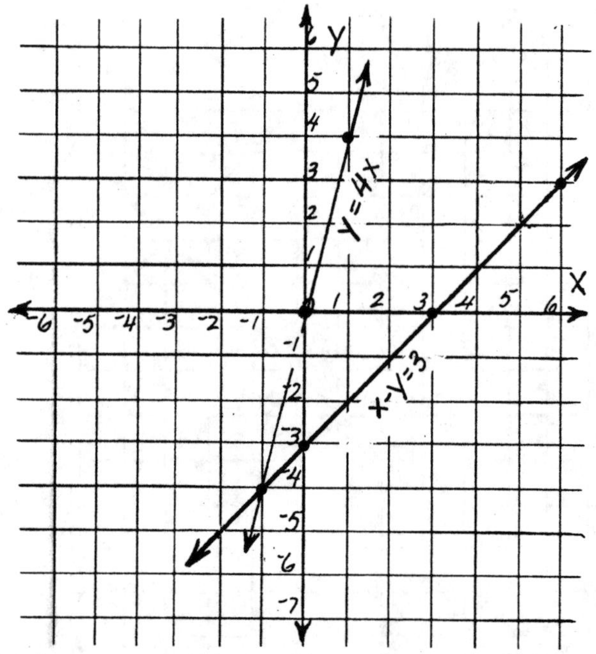

7. $x = \frac{1}{2}(y + 4)$

x	y
2	0
5	6
-1	-6

$y = 2(x - 2)$

x	y
0	-4
5	6
-1	-6

Indeterminate; dependent system (same line)

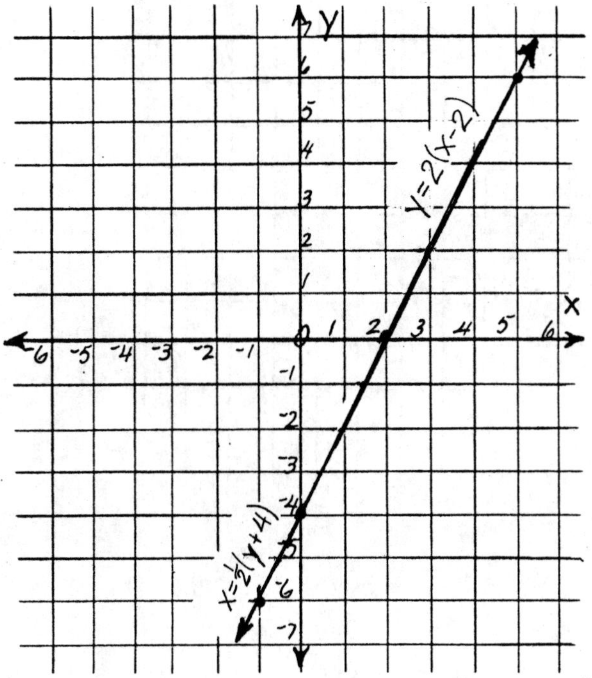

8. $x + y = -3$

x	y
-3	0
0	-3
4	-7

$x - 2y = -12$

x	y
0	6
-2	5
-6	3

Solution (-6, 3)

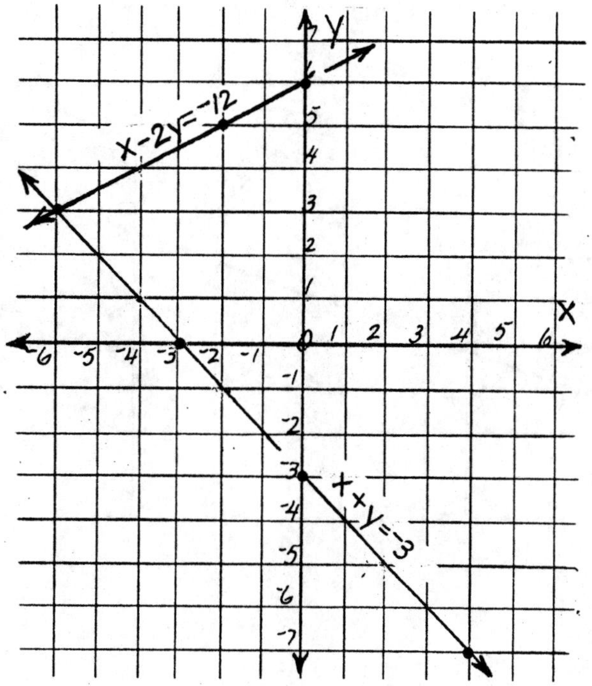

9. $x + y = 4$

x	y
0	4
4	0
6	-2

$y = 2 - x$

x	y
0	2
2	0
6	-4

No solution; inconsistent system (parallel lines)

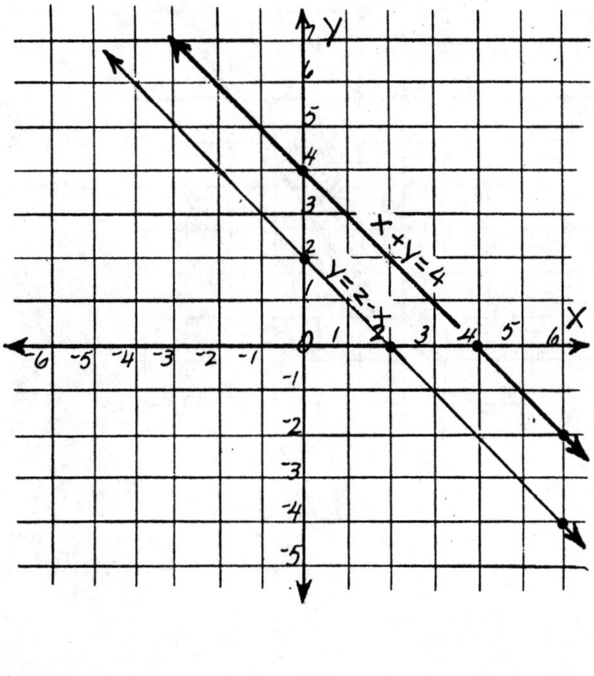

10. $x = 2(y + 1)$

x	y
2	0
0	-1
-6	-4

$21 = 2(2x + y)$

$4x + 2y = 21$

$2y = 21 - 4x$

$y = 10.5 - 2x$

x	y
5	.5
2	6.5
6	-1.5

Solution (4.6, 1.3)

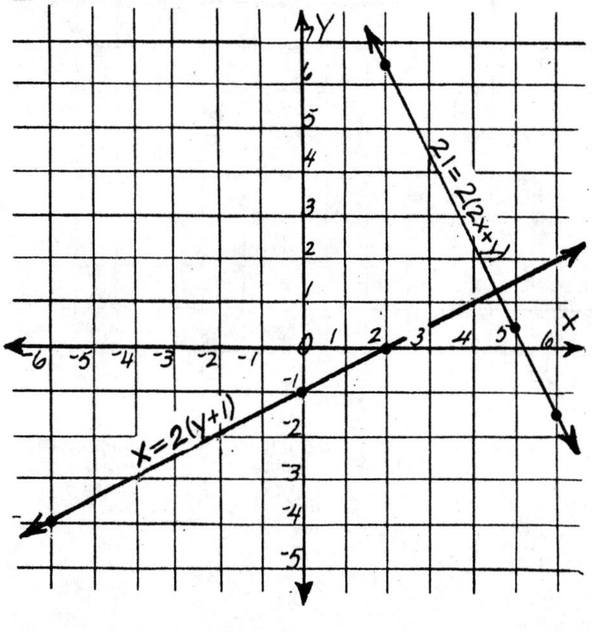

11. x + y = 8

x	y
6	2
4	4
2	6

2x - 6y = -9

x	y
-4.5	0
0	1.5
6	3.5

Solution (4.9, 3.1)
(nearest tenth)

12. 2x - 5y = 5

x	y
0	-1
2.5	0
-5	-3

10y = 2x + 1

x	y
-.5	0
4.5	1
-5.5	-1

Solution (5.5, 1.2)

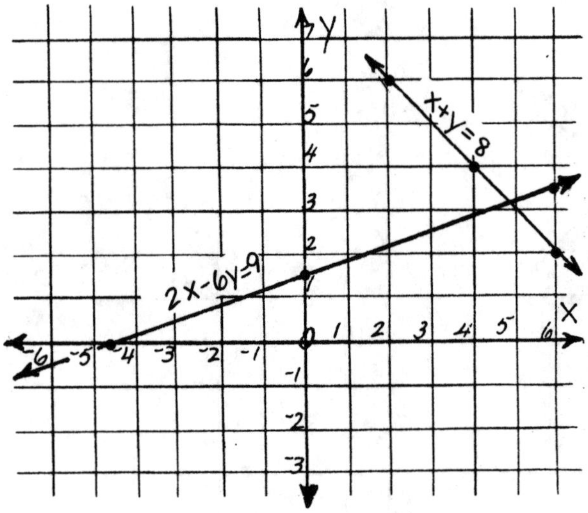

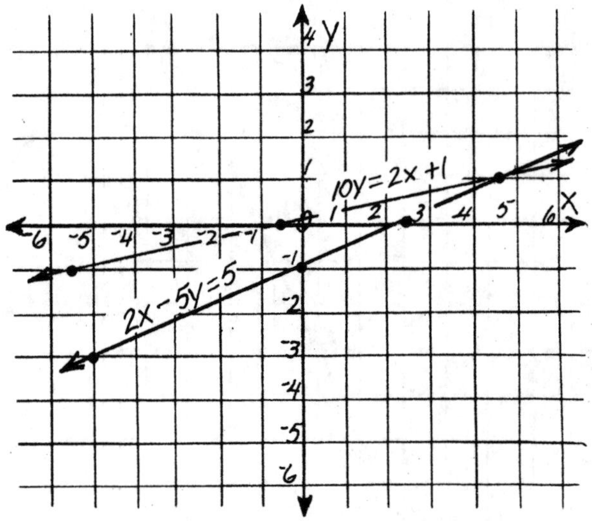

13. 3y = 2x - 7

x	y
2	-1
5	1
-1	-3

2x = 6 + 3y

x	y
3	0
6	2
-6	-6

No solution; inconsistent system (parallel lines)

14. 3(x - 4) = 2y

x	y
0	-6
2	-3
4	0

6(y + 6) = 9x

x	y
4	0
6	3
0	-6

Indeterminate; dependent system (same line)

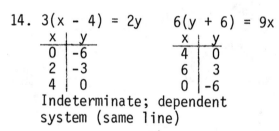

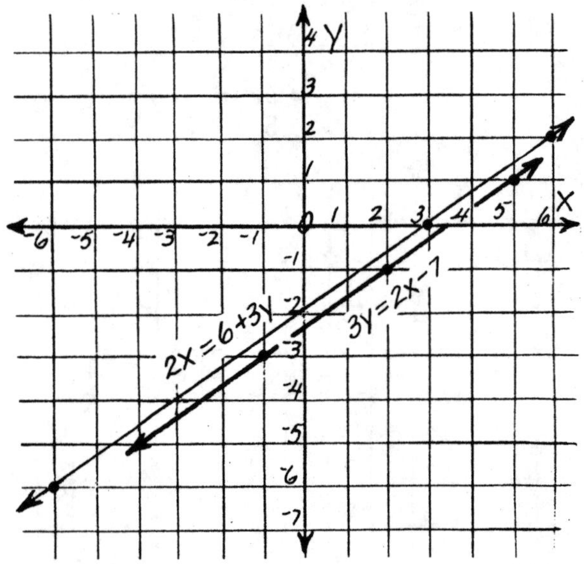

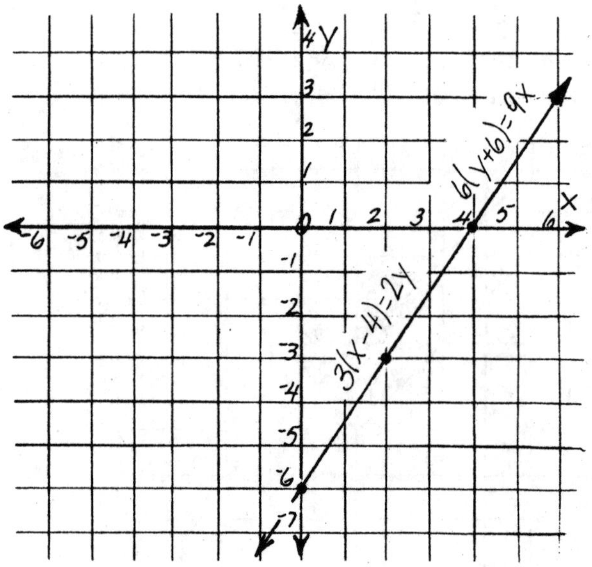

15. $10x + y = 14$

x	y
1	4
2	-6
1.5	-1

$8x - 5y = -2$

x	y
1	2
3.5	6
-4	-6

Solution (1.2, 2.3)
(nearest tenth)

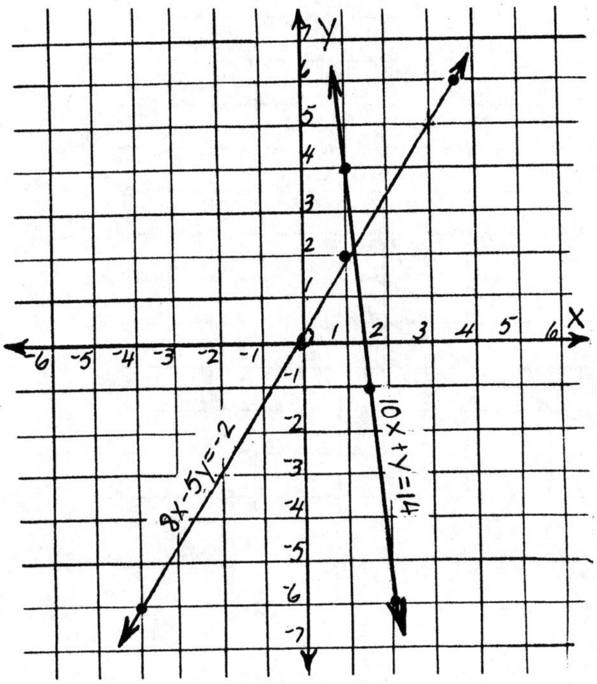

16. $2x + 3y = 8$

x	y
4	0
1	2
7	-2

$3x + 2y = 8$

x	y
0	4
2	1
4	-2

Solution (1.6, 1.6)

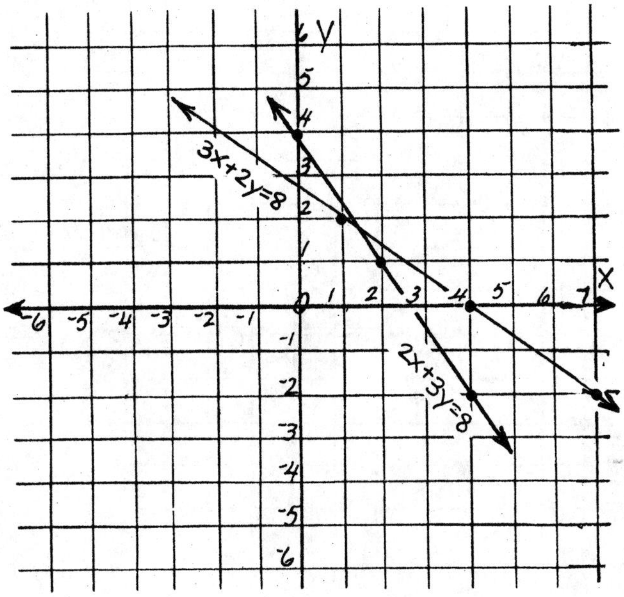

17. $4y + 3x = 5$

x	y
.5	1
3.5	-3
-2.5	5

$4x - 3y = 3$

x	y
0	-1
3	3
6	7

Solution (1.1, .4)
(nearest tenth)

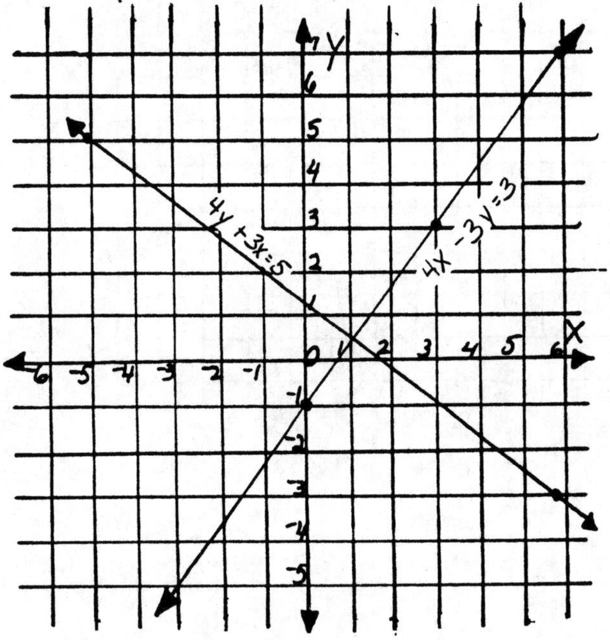

18. $x + 3y = -6$

x	y
-6	0
0	-2
6	-4

$2x - 4y = -12$

x	y
-6	0
0	3
6	6

Solution (-6, 0)

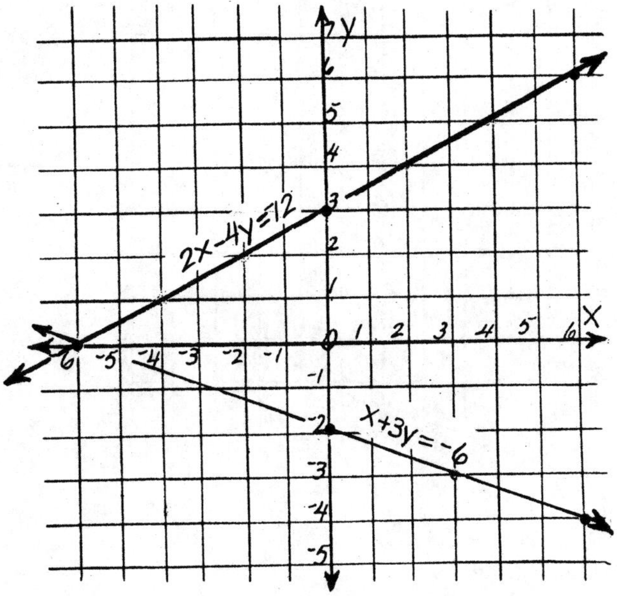

19. $4x - 10y = 0$ $\qquad$ $2x + y = 12$

x	y
0	0
5	2
-5	-2

x	y
6	0
3	6
5	2

Solution (5, 2)

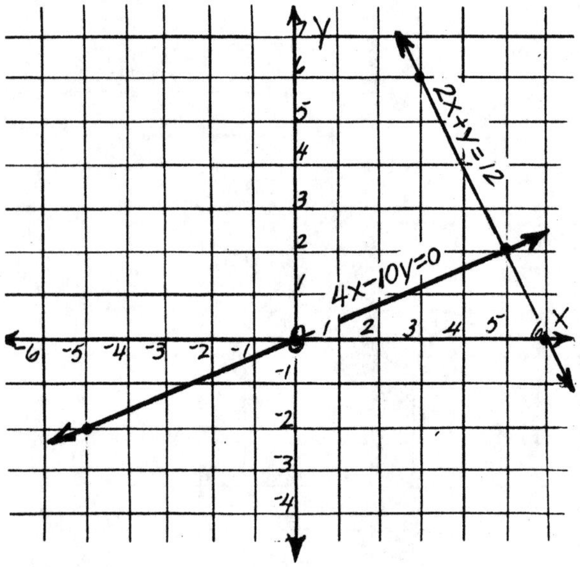

20. $x - 2y = 2$ $\qquad$ $2y - 6x = 3$

x	y
2	0
0	-1
6	2

x	y
-.5	0
1.5	6
1	4.5

Solution (-1, -1.5)

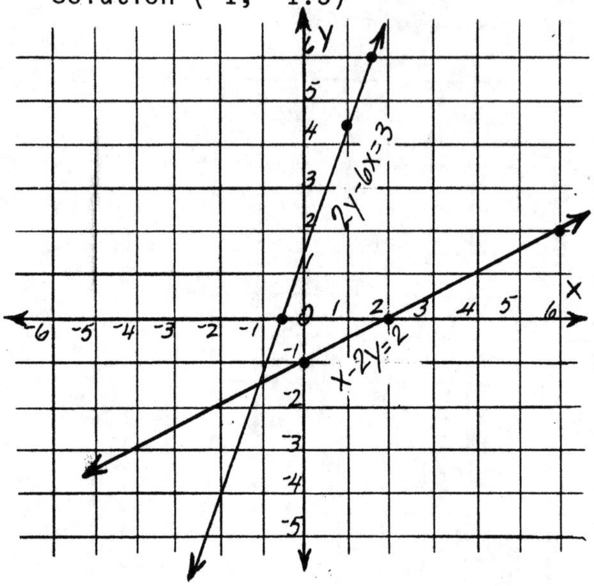

21. $3x + 4y = 10$ $\qquad$ $6x + 8y = 20$

x	y
2	1
4	-.5
0	2.5

x	y
2	1
-2	4
6	-2

Indeterminate; dependent system (same line)

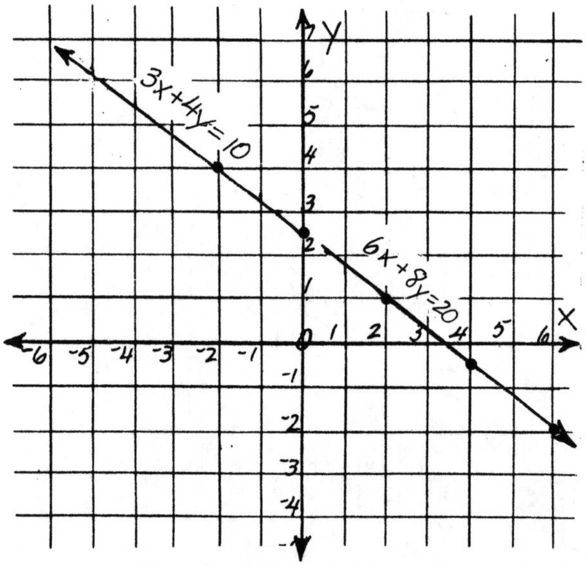

22. $\frac{3}{2}x + \frac{5}{2}y = 3\frac{1}{2}$ $\qquad$ $10x - 2y = 14$

x	y
4	-1
-1	2
-6	5

x	y
1	-2
2	3
2.5	5.5

Solution (1.5, .5)

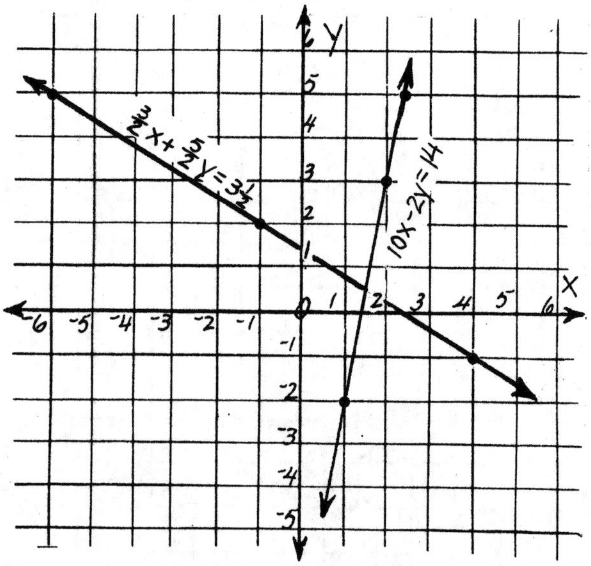

Exercises 11.6 Pages 235-236

The check is left for the teacher.

1. $\begin{cases} 7x - 5y = 52 \\ 2x + 5y = 47 \end{cases}$ (+)

$$9x = 99$$
$$x = 11$$

$$7(11) - 5y = 52$$
$$77 - 5y = 52$$
$$-5y = -25$$
$$y = 5$$

Solution (11, 5)

2. $\begin{cases} 3x + 2y = 23 \\ x + y = 8 \quad (2) \end{cases}$

$\begin{cases} 3x + 2y = 23 \\ 2x + 2y = 16 \end{cases}$ (-)

$$x = 7$$

$$7 + y = 8$$
$$y = 1$$

Solution (7, 1)

3. $\begin{cases} 3x - 4y = 7 \\ x + 10y = 25 \quad (3) \end{cases}$

$\begin{cases} 3x - 4y = 7 \\ 3x + 30y = 75 \end{cases}$ (-)

$$-34y = -68$$
$$y = 2$$

$$3x - 4(2) = 7$$
$$3x - 8 = 7$$
$$3x = 15$$
$$x = 5$$

Solution (5, 2)

4. $\begin{cases} 2x - 10y = 15 \\ 2x - 4y = 18 \end{cases}$ (-)

$$-6y = -3$$
$$y = \frac{3}{6} = \frac{1}{2} = .5$$

$$2x - 10(\tfrac{1}{2}) = 15$$
$$2x - 5 = 15$$
$$2x = 20$$
$$x = 10$$

Solution (10, .5)

5. $\begin{cases} 2a + 3b = 17 \quad (2) \\ 3a + 2b = 18 \quad (3) \end{cases}$

$\begin{cases} 4a + 6b = 34 \\ 9a + 6b = 54 \end{cases}$ (-)

$$-5a = -20$$
$$a = 4$$

$$2(4) + 3b = 17$$
$$8 + 3b = 17$$
$$3b = 9$$
$$b = 3$$

Solution (4, 3)

6. $\begin{cases} 3d + 4y = 25 \quad (3) \\ 4d + 3y = 31 \quad (4) \end{cases}$

$\begin{cases} 9d + 12y = 75 \\ 16d + 12y = 124 \end{cases}$ (-)

$$-7d = -49$$
$$d = 7$$

$$3(7) + 4y = 25$$
$$21 + 4y = 25$$
$$4y = 4$$
$$y = 1$$

Solution (7, 1)

7. $\begin{cases} 5p + 6q = 32 \\ 7p - 3q = 22 \quad (2) \end{cases}$

$\begin{cases} 5p + 6q = 32 \\ 14p - 6q = 44 \end{cases}$ (+)

$$19p = 76$$
$$p = 4$$

$$5(4) + 6q = 32$$
$$20 + 6q = 32$$
$$6q = 12$$
$$q = 2$$

Solution (4, 2)

8. $\begin{cases} 3a + 6z = 39 & (3) \\ 9a - 4z = 51 \end{cases}$

$$\begin{aligned} &\begin{cases} 9a + 18z = 117 \\ 9a - 4z = 51 \end{cases} \quad (-) \\ &22z = 66 \\ &z = 3 \end{aligned}$$

$$\begin{aligned} 3a + 6(3) &= 39 \\ 3a + 18 &= 39 \\ 3a &= 21 \\ a &= 7 \end{aligned}$$

Solution (7, 3)

9. $\begin{cases} 6x - 5y = 33 & (4) \\ 4x + 4y = 44 & (5) \end{cases}$

$$\begin{aligned} &\begin{cases} 24x - 20y = 132 \\ 20x + 20y = 220 \end{cases} \quad (+) \\ &44x = 352 \\ &x = 8 \end{aligned}$$

$$\begin{aligned} 6(8) - 5y &= 33 \\ 48 - 5y &= 33 \\ -5y &= -15 \\ y &= 3 \end{aligned}$$

Solution (8, 3)

10. $\begin{cases} 3m + 11n = 67 & (3) \\ 5m - 3n = 5 & (11) \end{cases}$

$$\begin{aligned} &\begin{cases} 9m + 33n = 201 \\ 55m - 33n = 55 \end{cases} \quad (+) \\ &64m = 256 \\ &m = 4 \end{aligned}$$

$$\begin{aligned} 3(4) + 11n &= 67 \\ 12 + 11n &= 67 \\ 11n &= 55 \\ n &= 5 \end{aligned}$$

Solution (4, 5)

Exercises 11.7   Page 236

The check is left for the teacher.

1. $\begin{cases} x - y = 4 \\ 4y - x = 14 \end{cases}$ $x = 4 + y$ Solution (10, 6)

$$\begin{aligned} 4y - (4 + y) &= 14 \\ 4y - 4 - y &= 14 \\ 3y &= 18 \\ y &= 6 \end{aligned}$$

$$\begin{aligned} x &= 4 + 6 \\ x &= 10 \end{aligned}$$

2. $\begin{cases} 3x - 4y = 26 \\ x - 8y = 22 \end{cases}$ $x = 22 + 8y$ Solution (6, -2)

$$\begin{aligned} 3(22 + 8y) - 4y &= 26 \\ 66 + 24y - 4y &= 26 \\ 20y &= -40 \\ y &= -2 \end{aligned}$$

$$\begin{aligned} x &= 22 + 8(-2) \\ x &= 22 - 16 \\ x &= 6 \end{aligned}$$

3. $\begin{cases} x + y = 10 \\ 6x - 7y = 34 \end{cases}$ $x = 10 - y$

$$\begin{aligned} 6(10 - y) - 7y &= 34 \\ 60 - 6y - 7y &= 34 \\ -13y &= -26 \\ y &= 2 \end{aligned}$$

$$\begin{aligned} x &= 10 - 2 \\ x &= 8 \end{aligned}$$

Solution (8, 2)

4. $\begin{cases} 6y - 10x = 14 \\ y - x = 3 \end{cases}$ $y = 3 + x$

$$\begin{aligned} 6(3 + x) - 10x &= 14 \\ 18 + 6x - 10x &= 14 \\ 18 - 4x &= 14 \\ -4x &= -4 \\ x &= 1 \end{aligned}$$

$$\begin{aligned} y &= 3 + 1 \\ y &= 4 \end{aligned}$$

Solution (1, 4)

5. $\begin{cases} y + 1 = 3x \\ 5x + 9 = 3y \end{cases}$ $y = 3x - 1$

$$\begin{aligned} 5x + 9 &= 3(3x - 1) \\ 5x + 9 &= 9x - 3 \\ -4x &= -12 \\ x &= 3 \end{aligned}$$

$$\begin{aligned} y &= 3(3) - 1 \\ y &= 9 - 1 \\ y &= 8 \end{aligned}$$

Solution (3, 8)

6. $\begin{cases} 7z - 3x = 18 \\ 2z - 5x = 1 \end{cases}$

$$\begin{aligned} 7z &= 18 + 3x \\ z &= \frac{18 + 3x}{7} \end{aligned}$$

$$\begin{aligned} 2\left(\frac{18 + 3x}{7}\right) - 5x &= 1 \\ \frac{36 + 6x}{7} - 5x &= 1 \\ 7\left(\frac{36 + 6x}{7} - 5x\right) &= 7(1) \\ 36 + 6x - 35x &= 7 \\ -29x &= -29 \\ x &= 1 \end{aligned}$$

$$\begin{aligned} z &= \frac{18 + 3(1)}{1} \\ z &= \frac{21}{7} \\ z &= 3 \end{aligned}$$

Solution (1, 3)

7. $\begin{cases} 17 = 3x + z \\ 7 = 3z - 2x \end{cases}$ $z = 17 - 3x$

$$\begin{aligned} 7 &= 3(17 - 3x) - 2x \\ 7 &= 51 - 9x - 2x \\ -44 &= -11x \\ x &= 4 \end{aligned}$$

$$\begin{aligned} z &= 17 - 3(4) \\ z &= 17 - 12 \\ z &= 5 \end{aligned}$$

Solution (4, 5)

8. $\begin{cases} 3 - 15y = -x \\ 3 + 15y = 4x \end{cases}$ $x = 15y - 3$

$$\begin{aligned} 3 + 15y &= 4(15y - 3) \\ 3 + 15y &= 60y - 12 \\ -45y &= -15 \\ y &= \frac{-15}{-45} = \frac{1}{3} \end{aligned}$$

$$\begin{aligned} x &= 15(\tfrac{1}{3}) - 3 \\ x &= 5 - 3 \\ x &= 2 \end{aligned}$$

Solution $(2, \frac{1}{3})$

9. $\begin{cases} 4y = 10 - x \\ y - x = 5 \end{cases}$ $y = 5 + x$

$$\begin{aligned} 4(5 + x) &= 10 - x \\ 20 + 4x &= 10 - x \\ 5x &= -10 \\ x &= -2 \end{aligned}$$

$$\begin{aligned} y &= 5 + (-2) \\ y &= 3 \end{aligned}$$

Solution (-2, 3)

10. $\begin{cases} 1 - x = 3y \\ 3(1 - x) = 40 - y \end{cases}$ $1 - 3y = x$

$$\begin{aligned} 3[1 - (1 - 3y)] &= 40 - y \\ 3[1 - 1 + 3y] &= 40 - y \\ 3(3y) &= 40 - y \\ 9y &= 40 - y \\ 10y &= 40 \\ y &= 4 \end{aligned}$$

$$\begin{aligned} x &= 1 - 3(4) \\ x &= 1 - 12 \\ x &= -11 \end{aligned}$$

Solution (-11, 4)

<u>Exercises 11.8</u> Pages 237-238

The check is left for the teacher.

1. $$\begin{aligned} &\begin{cases} x + z = 1.3 \\ x - z = .5 \end{cases} \quad (+) \\ &2x = 1.8 \\ &x = .9 \end{aligned}$$

$$\begin{aligned} .9 + z &= 1.3 \\ z &= .4 \end{aligned}$$

Solution (.9, .4)

2. $\begin{cases} 3x + y = 10 \\ x + 3y = 6 \end{cases}$ $x = 6 - 3y$

$$\begin{aligned} 3(6 - 3y) + y &= 10 \\ 18 - 9y + y &= 10 \\ -8y &= -8 \\ y &= 1 \end{aligned}$$

$$\begin{aligned} x &= 6 - 3(1) \\ x &= 6 - 3 \\ x &= 3 \end{aligned}$$

Solution (3, 1)

3.
$$\begin{cases} 4x + 5y = -2 & (4) \\ 5x + 4y = 2 & (5) \end{cases}$$

$$(-)\begin{cases} 16x + 20y = -8 \\ 25x + 20y = 10 \end{cases}$$
$$-9x = -18$$
$$x = 2$$

$$4(2) + 5y = -2$$
$$8 + 5y = -2$$
$$5y = -10$$
$$y = -2$$

Solution (2, -2)

4.
$$\begin{cases} .5x - y = 2.8 & (5) \\ .3x + 5y = 2.8 \end{cases}$$

$$(+)\begin{cases} 2.5x - 5y = 14 \\ .3x + 5y = 2.8 \end{cases}$$
$$2.8x = 16.8$$
$$28x = 168$$
$$x = 6$$

$$.5(6) - y = 2.8$$
$$3 - y = 2.8$$
$$-y = -.2$$
$$y = .2$$

Solution (6, .2)

5.
$$\begin{cases} x + 3 = y - 3 \\ 2(x + 3) = 6 - y \end{cases} \qquad x = y - 6$$

$$2(y - 6 + 3) = 6 - y$$
$$2(y - 3) = 6 - y$$
$$2y - 6 = 6 - y$$
$$3y = 12$$
$$y = 4$$

$$x = 4 - 6$$
$$x = -2$$

Solution (-2, 4)

6.
$$\begin{cases} 5x - y = 12 & (3) \\ x + 3y = 12 \end{cases}$$

$$(+)\begin{cases} 15x - 3y = 36 \\ x + 3y = 12 \end{cases}$$
$$16x = 48$$
$$x = 3$$

$$3 + 3y = 12$$
$$3y = 9$$
$$y = 3$$

Solution (3, 3)

7.
$$4(2 - x) = 3y$$
$$2(2 - x) = 2(y - 2) \quad (2)$$

$$4(2 - x) = 3y$$
$$(-)\ 4(2 - x) = 4(y - 2)$$
$$0 = 3y - 4(y - 2)$$
$$0 = 3y - 4y + 8$$
$$0 = -y + 8$$
$$y = 8$$

$$4(2 - x) = 3(8)$$
$$8 - 4x = 24$$
$$-4x = 16$$
$$x = -4$$

Solution (-4, 8)

8.
$$(-)\begin{cases} (x + 1) + (y - 2) = 7 \\ (x + 1) - (y - 2) = 5 \end{cases}$$
$$2(y - 2) = 2$$
$$y - 2 = 1$$
$$y = 3$$

$$(x + 1) + (3 - 2) = 7$$
$$x + 1 + 1 = 7$$
$$x + 2 = 7$$
$$x = 5$$

Solution (5, 3)

9. $\begin{cases} x + \frac{y}{3} = 11 & (27) \\ \frac{x}{3} + 3y = 21 & (3) \end{cases}$

$$(-)\begin{cases} 27x + 9y = 297 \\ x + 9y = 63 \end{cases}$$
$$26x = 234$$
$$x = 9$$

$$9 + \frac{y}{3} = 11$$
$$\frac{y}{3} = 2$$
$$y = 6$$

Solution (9, 6)

10. $\begin{cases} \frac{3x}{4} + \frac{4y}{5} = 21 & (20) \\ \frac{2x}{3} + \frac{3y}{5} = 17 & (15) \end{cases}$

$$\begin{cases} 15x + 16y = 420 & (2) \\ 10x + 9y = 255 & (3) \end{cases}$$

$$(-)\begin{cases} 30x + 32y = 840 \\ 30x + 27y = 765 \end{cases}$$
$$5y = 75$$
$$y = 15$$

$$\frac{3}{4}x + \frac{4}{5}(15) = 21$$
$$\frac{3}{4}x + 12 = 21$$
$$\frac{3}{4}x = 9$$
$$3x = 36$$
$$x = 12$$

Solution (12, 15)

11. $\begin{cases} \frac{x}{2} - \frac{2y}{3} = -2 \\ \frac{5x}{2} + \frac{y}{3} = 12 & (2) \end{cases}$

$$(+)\begin{cases} \frac{x}{2} - \frac{2y}{3} = -2 \\ \frac{10x}{2} + \frac{2y}{3} = 24 \end{cases}$$
$$\frac{11x}{2} = 22$$
$$11x = 44$$
$$x = 4$$

$$\frac{4}{2} - \frac{2y}{3} = -2$$
$$2 - \frac{2y}{3} = -2$$
$$\frac{-2y}{3} = -4$$
$$-2y = -12$$
$$y = 6$$

Solution (4, 6)

12. $\begin{cases} \frac{x + y}{2} - \frac{x - y}{3} = 8 & (6) \\ \frac{x + y}{3} + \frac{x - y}{4} = 11 & (12) \end{cases}$

$$\begin{cases} 3(x + y) - 2(x - y) = 48 \\ 4(x + y) + 3(x - y) = 132 \end{cases}$$

$$\begin{cases} 3x + 3y - 2x + 2y = 48 \\ 4x + 4y + 3x - 3y = 132 \end{cases}$$

$$\begin{cases} x + 5y = 48 \\ 7x + y = 132 & (5) \end{cases}$$

$$(-)\begin{cases} x + 5y = 48 \\ 35x + 5y = 660 \end{cases}$$
$$-34x = -612$$
$$x = 18$$

$$\frac{18 + y}{2} - \frac{18 - y}{3} = 8$$
$$6\left(\frac{18 + y}{2} - \frac{18 - y}{3}\right) = 6(8)$$

$$3(18 + y) - 2(18 - y) = 48$$
$$54 + 3y - 36 + 2y = 48$$
$$5y + 18 = 48$$
$$5y = 30$$
$$y = 6$$

Solution (18, 6)

13.
$$\begin{cases} x + \frac{1}{2}(3x - y - 1) = \frac{1}{4} + \frac{3}{4}(y - 1) & (4) \\ \frac{1}{5}(4x + 3y) = \frac{1}{10}(7y + 24) & (10) \end{cases}$$

$$\begin{cases} 4x + 2(3x - y - 1) = 1 + 3(y - 1) \\ 2(4x + 3y) = 7y + 24 \end{cases}$$

$$\begin{cases} 4x + 6x - 2y - 2 = 1 + 3y - 3 \\ 8x + 6y = 7y + 24 \end{cases}$$

$$\begin{cases} 10x - 2y - 2 = 3y - 2 \\ 8x - y = 24 \end{cases}$$

$$\begin{cases} 10x - 5y = 0 \\ 8x - y = 24 \quad (5) \end{cases}$$

$$(-)\begin{cases} 10x - 5y = 0 \\ 40x - 5y = 120 \end{cases}$$
$$-30x = -120$$
$$x = 4$$

$$4 + \frac{1}{2}[3(4) - y - 1] = \frac{1}{4} + \frac{3}{4}(y - 1)$$
$$4 + \frac{1}{2}(11 - y) = \frac{1}{4} + \frac{3}{4}(y - 1) \quad (4)$$
$$16 + 2(11 - y) = 1 + 3(y - 1)$$
$$16 + 22 - 2y = 1 + 3y - 3$$
$$38 - 2y = 3y - 2$$
$$-5y = -40$$
$$y = 8$$

Solution (4, 8)

14.
$$\begin{cases} \frac{5}{x} - \frac{3}{y} = -2 \\ \frac{25}{x} + \frac{1}{y} = 6 \quad (3) \end{cases}$$

$$(+)\begin{cases} \frac{5}{x} - \frac{3}{y} = -2 \\ \frac{75}{x} + \frac{3}{y} = 18 \end{cases}$$
$$\frac{80}{x} = 16$$
$$\frac{1}{\cancel{80}}\left(\frac{\cancel{80}}{x}\right) = \frac{16}{80}$$
$$\frac{1}{x} = \frac{1}{5}$$
$$x = 5$$

$$\frac{25}{5} + \frac{1}{y} = 6$$
$$5 + \frac{1}{y} = 6$$
$$\frac{1}{y} = 1$$
$$y = 1$$

Solution (5, 1)

15.
$$\begin{cases} \frac{7}{x} - \frac{8}{y} = -1 & (3) \\ \frac{1}{x} + \frac{3}{y} = \frac{25}{28} & (8) \end{cases}$$

$$(+)\begin{cases} \frac{21}{x} - \frac{24}{y} = -\frac{84}{28} \\ \frac{8}{x} + \frac{24}{y} = \frac{200}{28} \end{cases}$$
$$\frac{29}{x} = \frac{116}{28}$$
$$\frac{1}{\cancel{29}}\left(\frac{\cancel{29}}{x}\right) = \frac{1}{\cancel{29}}\left(\frac{\overset{4}{\cancel{116}}}{28}\right)$$
$$\frac{1}{x} = \frac{4}{28} = \frac{1}{7}$$
$$x = 7$$

$$\frac{4}{28} + \frac{3}{y} = \frac{25}{28}$$
$$\frac{3}{y} = \frac{21}{28}$$
$$\frac{3}{y} = \frac{3}{4}$$
$$y = 4$$

Solution (7, 4)

16. $\begin{cases} \frac{3}{2x} - \frac{1}{y} = -3 & (3) \\ \frac{5}{2x} + \frac{3}{y} = 23 \end{cases}$

$$(+)\begin{cases} \frac{9}{2x} - \frac{3}{y} = -9 \\ \frac{5}{2x} + \frac{3}{y} = 23 \end{cases}$$

$$\frac{14}{2x} = 14$$

$$2x = 1$$

$$x = \frac{1}{2}$$

$$\frac{5}{2}(2) + \frac{3}{y} = 23$$

$$5 + \frac{3}{y} = 23$$

$$\frac{3}{y} = 18$$

$$\frac{1}{3}\left(\frac{3}{y}\right) = \frac{1}{3}(18)$$

$$\frac{1}{y} = 6$$

$$y = \frac{1}{6}$$

Solution $(\frac{1}{2}, \frac{1}{6})$

17. $\begin{cases} \frac{2}{x} - \frac{3}{y} = 5 & (2) \\ \frac{5}{x} - \frac{2}{y} = 7 & (3) \end{cases}$

$$(-)\begin{cases} \frac{4}{x} - \frac{6}{y} = 10 \\ \frac{15}{x} - \frac{6}{y} = 21 \end{cases}$$

$$-\frac{11}{x} = -11$$

$$x = 1$$

$$\frac{2}{1} - \frac{3}{y} = 5$$

$$-\frac{3}{y} = 3$$

$$-3 = 3y$$

$$y = -1$$

Solution (1, -1)

18. $\begin{cases} \frac{4}{x} + \frac{3}{y} = \frac{9}{8} & (4) \\ \frac{3}{x} + \frac{4}{y} = \frac{11}{12} & (3) \end{cases}$

$$(-)\begin{cases} \frac{16}{x} + \frac{12}{y} = \frac{36}{8} = \frac{9}{2} = \frac{54}{12} \\ \frac{9}{x} + \frac{12}{y} = \frac{33}{12} \end{cases}$$

$$\frac{7}{x} = \frac{21}{12} = \frac{7}{4}$$

$$x = 4$$

$$\frac{3}{4} + \frac{4}{y} = \frac{11}{12}$$

$$\frac{9}{12} + \frac{4}{y} = \frac{11}{12}$$

$$\frac{4}{y} = \frac{2}{12} = \frac{1}{6}$$

$$y = 24$$

Solution (4, 24)

19. $\begin{cases} \frac{5}{3x} + \frac{4}{y} = 3 & (7) \\ \frac{-1}{6x} + \frac{7}{y} = 2\frac{1}{6} & (4) \end{cases}$

$$\begin{cases} \frac{35}{3x} + \frac{28}{y} = 21 \\ -\frac{4}{6x} + \frac{28}{y} = 4\left(\frac{13}{6}\right) \end{cases}$$

$$(-)\begin{cases} \frac{35}{3x} + \frac{28}{y} = \frac{63}{3} \\ -\frac{2}{3x} + \frac{28}{y} = \frac{26}{3} \end{cases}$$

$$\frac{37}{3x} = \frac{37}{3}$$

$$3x = 3$$

$$x = 1$$

$$\frac{5}{3} + \frac{4}{y} = 3$$

$$\frac{4}{y} = \frac{9}{3} - \frac{5}{3}$$

$$\frac{4}{y} = \frac{4}{3}$$

$$y = 3$$

Solution (1, 3)

Exercises 11.9 Pages 239-240

1.
$$\begin{cases} ax + by = m & (a) \\ bx - ay = c & (b) \end{cases}$$

$$(+)\begin{cases} a^2x + aby = am \\ b^2x - aby = bc \end{cases}$$
$$a^2x + b^2x = am + bc$$
$$x(a^2 + b^2) = am + bc$$
$$x = \frac{am + bc}{a^2 + b^2}$$

$$\begin{cases} ax + by = m & (b) \\ bx - ay = c & (a) \end{cases}$$

$$(-)\begin{cases} abx + b^2y = bm \\ abx - a^2y = ac \end{cases}$$
$$b^2y + a^2y = bm - ac$$
$$y(b^2 + a^2) = bm - ac$$
$$y = \frac{bm - ac}{a^2 + b^2}$$

2.
$$\begin{cases} ax - by = m & (d) \\ cx - dy = r & (b) \end{cases}$$

$$(-)\begin{cases} adx - bdy = dm \\ bcx - bdy = br \end{cases}$$
$$adx - bcx = dm - br$$
$$x(ad - bc) = dm - br$$
$$x = \frac{dm - br}{ad - bc}$$

$$\begin{cases} ax - by = m & (c) \\ cx - dy = r & (a) \end{cases}$$

$$(-)\begin{cases} acx - bcy = cm \\ acx - ady = ar \end{cases}$$
$$-bcy + ady = cm - ar$$
$$y(ad - bc) = cm - ar$$
$$y = \frac{cm - ar}{ad - bc}$$

3.
$$\begin{cases} ax = by \\ x + y = ab \end{cases}$$

$$\begin{cases} ax - by = 0 & \\ x + y = ab & (b) \end{cases}$$

$$(+)\begin{cases} ax - by = 0 \\ bx + by = ab^2 \end{cases}$$
$$ax + bx = ab^2$$
$$x(a + b) = ab^2$$
$$x = \frac{ab^2}{a + b}$$

$$\begin{cases} ax - by = 0 & \\ x + y = ab & (a) \end{cases}$$

$$(-)\begin{cases} ax - by = 0 \\ ax + ay = a^2b \end{cases}$$
$$-by - ay = -a^2b$$
$$-y(a + b) = -a^2b$$
$$-y = \frac{-a^2b}{a + b}$$
$$y = \frac{a^2b}{a + b}$$

4.
$$\begin{cases} m(x + y) = a \\ n(x - y) = 2a \end{cases}$$

$$(+)\begin{cases} mx + my = a & (n) \\ nx - ny = 2a & (m) \end{cases}$$

$$(+)\begin{cases} mnx + mny = an \\ mnx - mny = 2am \end{cases}$$
$$2mnx = an + 2am$$
$$x = \frac{an + 2am}{2mn}$$

$$(-)\begin{array}{l} mnx + mny = an \\ mnx - mny = 2am \end{array}$$
$$2mny = an - 2am$$
$$y = \frac{an - 2am}{2mn}$$

5. $\begin{cases} a(x - y) = 5 \\ bx - cy = n \end{cases}$

$\begin{cases} ax - ay = 5 & (c) \\ bx - cy = n & (a) \end{cases}$

$(-)\begin{cases} acx - acy = 5c \\ abx - acy = an \end{cases}$

$acx - abx = 5c - an$

$x(ac - ab) = 5c - an$

$x = \dfrac{5c - an}{ac - ab}$ or $\dfrac{an - 5c}{ab - ac}$

$\begin{cases} ax - ay = 5 & (b) \\ bx - cy = n & (a) \end{cases}$

$(-)\begin{cases} abx - aby = 5b \\ abx - acy = an \end{cases}$

$-aby + acy = 5b - an$

$y(ac - ab) = 5b - an$

$y = \dfrac{5b - an}{ac - ab}$ or $\dfrac{an - 5b}{ab - ac}$

6. $\begin{cases} a(a - x) = b(y - b) \\ ax = by \end{cases}$

$x = \dfrac{by}{a}$

$a(a - \dfrac{by}{a}) = b(y - b)$

$a^2 - by = by - b^2$

$-2by = -a^2 - b^2$

$y = \dfrac{a^2 + b^2}{2b}$

$x = \dfrac{b}{a}(\dfrac{a^2 + b^2}{2b})$

$x = \dfrac{a^2 + b^2}{2a}$

7. $\begin{cases} x + y = b - a & (a) \\ bx - ay + 2ab = 0 \end{cases}$

$(+)\begin{cases} ax + ay = ab - a^2 \\ bx - ay = -2ab \end{cases}$

$ax + bx = -a^2 - ab$

$x(a + b) = -a(a + b)$

$x = \dfrac{-a(a + b)}{a + b}$

$x = -a$

$-a + y = b - a$

$y = b$

8. $\begin{cases} x - y = a - b & (b) \\ ax + by = a^2 - b^2 \end{cases}$

$(+)\begin{cases} bx - by = ab - b^2 \\ ax + by = a^2 - b^2 \end{cases}$

$bx + ax = a^2 + ab - 2b^2$

$x(a + b) = a^2 + ab - 2b^2$

$x = \dfrac{(a + 2b)(a - b)}{a + b}$

$\begin{cases} x - y = a - b & (a) \\ ax + by = a^2 - b^2 \end{cases}$

$(-)\begin{cases} ax - ay = a^2 - ab \\ ax + by = a^2 - b^2 \end{cases}$

$-ay - by = -ab + b^2$

$ay + by = ab - b^2$

$y(a + b) = b(a - b)$

$y = \dfrac{b(a - b)}{a + b}$

9.

$$\begin{cases} \frac{x}{a} + \frac{y}{b} - 2 = 0 \\ bx - ay = 0 \quad \left(\frac{1}{ab}\right) \end{cases}$$

$$\begin{array}{rl} (+) & \begin{cases} \frac{x}{a} + \frac{y}{b} = 2 \\ \frac{x}{a} - \frac{y}{b} = 0 \end{cases} \\ \hline & \frac{2x}{a} = 2 \end{array}$$

$$2x = 2a$$
$$x = a$$

$$\begin{array}{rl} (-) & \begin{cases} \frac{x}{a} + \frac{y}{b} = 2 \\ \frac{x}{a} - \frac{y}{b} = 0 \end{cases} \\ \hline & \frac{2y}{b} = 2 \end{array}$$

$$2y = 2b$$
$$y = b$$

*10.

$$\begin{array}{rl} (+) & \begin{cases} \frac{1}{x} + \frac{1}{y} = \frac{1}{a} \\ \frac{1}{x} - \frac{1}{y} = \frac{1}{b} \end{cases} \\ \hline & \frac{2}{x} = \frac{1}{a} + \frac{1}{b} \end{array}$$

$$\frac{1}{2}\left(\frac{2}{x}\right) = \frac{1}{2}\left(\frac{1}{a} + \frac{1}{b}\right)$$
$$\frac{1}{x} = \frac{1}{2a} + \frac{1}{2b}$$
$$\frac{1}{x} = \frac{b}{2ab} + \frac{a}{2ab} = \frac{a + b}{2ab}$$
$$x = \frac{2ab}{a + b}$$

$$\begin{array}{rl} (-) & \begin{cases} \frac{1}{x} + \frac{1}{y} = \frac{1}{a} \\ \frac{1}{x} - \frac{1}{y} = \frac{1}{b} \end{cases} \\ \hline & \frac{2}{y} = \frac{1}{a} - \frac{1}{b} \end{array}$$

$$\frac{1}{2}\left(\frac{2}{y}\right) = \frac{1}{2}\left(\frac{1}{a} - \frac{1}{b}\right)$$
$$\frac{1}{y} = \frac{1}{2a} - \frac{1}{2b}$$
$$\frac{1}{y} = \frac{b}{2ab} - \frac{a}{2ab}$$
$$\frac{1}{y} = \frac{b - a}{2ab}$$
$$y = \frac{2ab}{b - a}$$

*11.

$$\begin{cases} \frac{a}{x} - \frac{b}{y} = -1 \quad (a) \\ \frac{b}{x} - \frac{a}{y} = -1 \quad (b) \end{cases}$$

$$\begin{array}{rl} (-) & \begin{cases} \frac{a^2}{x} - \frac{ab}{y} = -a \\ \frac{b^2}{x} - \frac{ab}{y} = -b \end{cases} \\ \hline & \frac{a^2}{x} - \frac{b^2}{x} = -a + b \end{array}$$

$$\frac{1}{x}(a^2 - b^2) = b - a$$

$$\frac{1}{x} = \frac{b - a}{a^2 - b^2} = \frac{-1(\cancel{a - b})}{(a + b)(\cancel{a - b})} = \frac{-1}{a + b}$$
$$x = -(a + b)$$

$$\begin{cases} \frac{a}{x} - \frac{b}{y} = -1 \quad (b) \\ \frac{b}{x} - \frac{a}{y} = -1 \quad (a) \end{cases}$$

$$\begin{array}{rl} (-) & \begin{cases} \frac{ab}{x} - \frac{b^2}{y} = -b \\ \frac{ab}{x} - \frac{a^2}{y} = -a \end{cases} \\ \hline & \frac{-b^2}{y} + \frac{a^2}{y} = -b + a \end{array}$$

$$\frac{1}{y}(a^2 - b^2) = a - b$$
$$\frac{1}{y} = \frac{a - b}{(a + b)(a - b)}$$
$$\frac{1}{y} = \frac{1}{a + b}$$
$$y = a + b$$

*12. $\begin{cases} \dfrac{x+1}{y+1} = \dfrac{a+b+1}{a-b+1} \\ x - y = 2b \end{cases}$

Product of means and extremes in first equation gives:

$$ax - bx + x + a - b + 1 = ay + by + y + a + b + 1$$
$$ax - bx + x - ay - by - y = -a + b + 1 + a + b - 1$$
$$\begin{cases} (a - b + 1)x - (a + b + 1)y = 2b \\ x - y = 2b \qquad (a + b + 1) \end{cases}$$

$$\begin{aligned} &\begin{cases} (a - b + 1)x - (a + b + 1)y = 2b \\ (a + b + 1)x - (a + b + 1)y = 2ab + 2b^2 + 2b \end{cases} \quad (-) \\ &(a - b + 1 - a - b - 1)x = 2b - 2ab - 2b^2 - 2b \\ &-2bx = -2ab - 2b^2 \\ &-2bx = -2b(a + b) \\ &x = \frac{-2b(a + b)}{-2b} \\ &x = a + b \end{aligned}$$

Substituting in second equation

$$\begin{aligned} a + b - y &= 2b \\ -y &= 2b - a - b \\ -y &= b - a \\ y &= a - b \end{aligned}$$

*13. $\begin{cases} \dfrac{1}{x-a} = \dfrac{1}{a-y} \\ \dfrac{x+y}{x-y} = \dfrac{a}{1} \end{cases}$ Product of means and extremes taken on each equation

$$\begin{cases} x - a = a - y \\ x + y = ax - ay \end{cases}$$

$$\begin{cases} x + y = 2a \\ -ax + x + y + ay = 0 \end{cases}$$

$$\begin{cases} x + y = 2a \qquad (1 + a) \\ (1 - a)x + (1 + a)y = 0 \end{cases}$$

$$\begin{aligned} &\begin{cases} (1 + a)x + (1 + a)y = 2a + 2a^2 \\ (1 - a)x + (1 + a)y = 0 \end{cases} \quad (-) \\ &(1 + a - 1 + a)x = 2a + 2a^2 \\ &2ax = 2a^2 + 2a \\ &x = \frac{2a(a + 1)}{2a} \\ &x = a + 1 \end{aligned}$$

$$\begin{cases} x + y = 2a \qquad (1 - a) \\ (1 - a)x + (1 + a)y = 0 \end{cases}$$

$$\begin{aligned} &\begin{cases} (1 - a)x + (1 - a)y = 2a - 2a^2 \\ (1 - a)x + (1 + a)y = 0 \end{cases} \quad (-) \\ &(1 - a - 1 - a)y = 2a - 2a^2 \\ &-2ay = 2a(1 - a) \\ &y = \frac{2a(1 - a)}{-2a} \\ &y = -(1 - a) \\ &y = a - 1 \end{aligned}$$

*14. $\begin{cases} \dfrac{x}{a} + \dfrac{y}{b} = c & (ab) \\ \dfrac{x}{b} + \dfrac{y}{c} = d & (bc) \end{cases}$

$\begin{cases} ab(\dfrac{x}{a} + \dfrac{y}{b}) = abc \\ bc(\dfrac{x}{b} + \dfrac{y}{c}) = bcd \end{cases}$

$\begin{cases} bx + ay = abc & (b) \\ cx + by = bcd & (a) \end{cases}$

$(-)\begin{cases} b^2x + aby = ab^2c \\ acx + aby = abcd \end{cases}$

$b^2x - acx = ab^2c - abcd$

$x(b^2 - ac) = abc(b - d)$

$x = \dfrac{abc(b - d)}{b^2 - ac}$

or $x = \dfrac{abcd - ab^2c}{ac - b^2}$

$\begin{cases} bx + ay = abc & (c) \\ cx + by = bcd & (b) \end{cases}$

$(-)\begin{cases} bcx + acy = abc^2 \\ bcx + b^2y = b^2cd \end{cases}$

$acy - b^2y = abc^2 - b^2cd$

$y(ac - b^2) = bc(ac - bd)$

$y = \dfrac{bc(ac - bd)}{ac - b^2}$

or $y = \dfrac{abc^2 - b^2cd}{ac - b^2}$

Exercises 11.10 Page 240

1. $(+)\begin{cases} x - y = 1 \\ x + y = 9 \end{cases}$

$2x = 10$

$x = 5$

$5 + y = 9$

$y = 4$

Solution (5, 4)

2. $(+)\begin{cases} 2x - y = 5 \\ 4x + y = 16 \end{cases}$

$6x = 21$

$x = \dfrac{21}{6} = \dfrac{7}{2} = 3.5$

$4(3.5) + y = 16$

$14 + y = 16$

$y = 2$

Solution (3.5, 2)

3. $\begin{cases} 3x = y + 9 \\ 2y = 6x - 18 \end{cases}$

$y = 3x - 9$

$2(3x - 9) = 6x - 18$

$6x - 18 = 6x - 18$

$0 = 0$

Indeterminate; dependent (same line)

4. $\begin{cases} y = 4x \\ x - y = 3 \end{cases}$

$x - 4x = 3$

$-3x = 3$

$x = -1$

$y = 4(-1)$

$y = -4$

Solution (-1, -4)

5. $\begin{cases} x + y = 4 \\ y = 2 - x \end{cases}$

$x + 2 - x = 4$

$0 = 2$

No solution; inconsistent (lines are parallel)

6. $\begin{cases} 2x - 5y = 5 \\ 10y = 2x + 1 \end{cases}$

$$\begin{array}{rl} & \begin{cases} 2x - 5y = 5 \\ -2x + 10y = 1 \end{cases} \\ (+) & \\ \hline & 5y = 6 \end{array}$$

$$y = \frac{6}{5} = 1.2$$

$$2x - 5(1.2) = 5$$
$$2x - 6 = 5$$
$$2x = 11$$
$$x = \frac{11}{2} = 5.5$$

Solution (5.5, 1.2)

7. $\begin{cases} 2x + 3y = 8 & (2) \\ 3x + 2y = 8 & (3) \end{cases}$

$$\begin{array}{rl} & 4x + 6y = 16 \\ (-) & 9x + 6y = 24 \\ \hline & -5x = -8 \end{array}$$

$$x = \frac{8}{5} = 1.6$$

$$2(1.6) + 3y = 8$$
$$3.2 + 3y = 8$$
$$3y = 4.8$$
$$y = 1.6$$

Solution (1.6, 1.6)

8. $\begin{cases} 4y + 3x = 5 \\ 4x - 3y = 3 \end{cases}$

$\begin{cases} 3x + 4y = 5 & (3) \\ 4x - 3y = 3 & (4) \end{cases}$

$$\begin{array}{rl} & \begin{cases} 9x + 12y = 15 \\ 16x - 12y = 12 \end{cases} \\ (+) & \\ \hline & 25x = 27 \\ & x = 1.08 \end{array}$$

$$4(1.08) - 3y = 3$$
$$4.32 - 3y = 3$$
$$-3y = -1.32$$
$$y = .43$$

Solution to the nearest tenth (1.1, .4)

9. $\begin{cases} x + 3y = -6 \\ 2x - 4y = -12 & (\div 2) \end{cases}$

$$\begin{array}{rl} & \begin{cases} x + 3y = -6 \\ x - 2y = -6 \end{cases} \\ (-) & \\ \hline & 5y = 0 \\ & y = 0 \end{array}$$

$$x + 3(0) = -6$$
$$x = -6$$

Solution (-6, 0)

10. $\begin{cases} 3x + 4y = 10 \\ 6x + 8y = 20 & (\div 2) \end{cases}$

$$\begin{array}{rl} & \begin{cases} 3x + 4y = 10 \\ 3x + 4y = 10 \end{cases} \\ (-) & \\ \hline & 0 = 0 \end{array}$$

Indeterminate;
dependent (same line)

Exercises 11.11   Pages 240-246

1. let l = number of yards in length of lot <u>100</u>
   w = number of yards in width of lot <u>80</u>

$$\begin{cases} l - w = 20 & (2) \\ 2l + 2w = 360 \end{cases}$$

$$\begin{cases} 2l - 2w = 40 \\ 2l + 2w = 360 \end{cases}$$
$$\overline{4l \quad\quad = 400}$$
$$l \quad\quad = 100$$

100 - w = 20
-w = -80
w = 80

```
100      100
-80      100
 20✓      80
         +80
         360✓
```

2. let x = number of $24 hats <u>10</u>
   y = number of $12 hats <u>8</u>

$$\begin{cases} 24x + 12y = 336 & \div 12 \\ x + y = 18 \end{cases}$$

$$(-)\begin{cases} 2x + y = 28 \\ x + y = 18 \end{cases}$$
$$\overline{x \quad\quad = 10}$$

10 + y = 18
y = 8

```
10     $ 24     $12      $240
+8       x10    x 8      +96
18✓    $240     $96     $336✓
```

3. let r = price per carton of raspberries <u>$2.10</u>
   c = price per carton of cherries <u>$1.80</u>

$$\begin{cases} 2r + 3c = 9.60 & (2) \\ 3r + 2c = 9.90 & (3) \end{cases}$$

```
      4r + 6c = 19.20
(-)   9r + 6c = 29.70
     -5r      = -10.50
      r       = 2.10
```

2(2.10) + 3c = 9.60
4.20 + 3c = 9.60
3c = 5.40
c = 1.80

```
$2.10    $1.80     $4.20
 x 2      x 3      +5.40
$4.20    $5.40     $9.60✓

$2.10    $1.80     $6.30
 x 3      x 2      +3.60
$6.30    $3.60     $9.90✓
```

4. let x = number at \$.75 <u>500</u>
   y = number at \$.90 <u>350</u>

$$\begin{cases} .75x + .90y = 690 \ (\frac{100}{5}) \\ x + y = 850 \ (18) \end{cases}$$

$$(-)\begin{cases} 15x + 18y = 13{,}800 \\ 18x + 18y = 15{,}300 \end{cases}$$
$$-3x = -1500$$
$$x = 500$$

$$500 + y = 850$$
$$y = 350$$

500	\$ .75	\$ .90	\$375
+350	x 500	x 350	+315
850 ✓	2500	\$315.00	\$690 ✓
	3500		
	\$375.00		

5. let x = number sold at \$1.60 <u>16</u>
   y = number sold at \$1.80 <u>20</u>

$$\begin{cases} 1.6x + 1.8y = 61.6 \quad (10) \\ x + y = 36 \quad (18) \end{cases}$$

$$(-)\begin{cases} 16x + 28y = 616 \\ 18x + 18y = 648 \end{cases}$$
$$-2x = -32$$
$$x = 16$$

$$16 + y = 36$$
$$y = 20$$

16	\$ 1.60	\$ 1.80	\$25.60
+20	x 16	x 20	+36.00
36 ✓	960	\$36.00	\$61.60 ✓
	160		
	\$25.60		

6. let a = number of adult tickets <u>200</u>
   c = number of student tickets <u>100</u>

$$\begin{cases} a + c = 300 \quad (15) \\ 2.5a + 1.5c = 650 \quad (10) \end{cases}$$

$$(-)\begin{cases} 15a + 15c = 4500 \\ 25a + 15c = 6500 \end{cases}$$
$$-10a = -2000$$
$$a = 200$$

$$200 + c = 300$$
$$c = 100$$

200	\$ 2.50	\$ 1.50	\$500
+100	x 200	x 100	+150
300 ✓	\$500.00	\$150.00	\$650 ✓

7. let b = capacity of a barrel __75__
    c = capacity of a case __225__

$$\begin{cases} 6b + 6c = 1800 & (7) \\ 9b + 7c = 2250 & (6) \end{cases}$$

$$(-)\begin{cases} 42b + 42c = 12{,}600 \\ 54b + 42c = 13{,}500 \end{cases}$$
$$\begin{array}{rl} -12b &= -900 \\ b &= 75 \end{array}$$

$$\begin{array}{r} 6(75) + 6c = 1800 \\ 450 + 6c = 1800 \\ 6c = 1350 \\ c = 225 \end{array}$$

75	225	1350
x 6	x 6	+450
450	1350	1800 ✓

75	225	675
x 9	x 7	+1575
675	1575	2250 ✓

8. let s = length of span __325 ft.__
    h = height of span __265 ft.__

$$\begin{cases} s = h + 60 \\ h - 200 = \frac{1}{5}s \end{cases}$$

$$h - 200 = \frac{1}{5}(h + 60)$$
$$5h - 1000 = h + 60$$
$$4h = 1060$$
$$h = 265$$

$$s = 265 + 60$$
$$s = 325$$

325	265
-265	-200
60 ✓	65 is $\frac{1}{5}(325)$ ✓

9. let d = height of Detroit chimney __100 ft.__
    c = height of Chicago chimney __150 ft.__

$$\begin{cases} d + 50 = c \\ \frac{1}{3}c - 25 = \frac{1}{4}d \end{cases}$$

$$\frac{1}{3}(d + 50) - 25 = \frac{1}{4}d$$
$$12[\frac{1}{3}(d + 50) - 25] = 12(\frac{1}{4}d)$$
$$4(d + 50) - 300 = 3d$$
$$4d + 200 - 300 = 3d$$
$$4d - 100 = 3d$$
$$d = 100$$

$$c = 100 + 50$$
$$c = 150$$

150	$\frac{1}{3}(150) = 50$
-100	$\frac{1}{4}(100) = 25$
50	25 ✓

10. let x = number of one-dollar bills 26
y = number of five-dollar bills 12

$$(-)\begin{cases} x + y = 38 \\ x + 5y = 86 \end{cases}$$
$$-4y = -48$$
$$y = 12$$

$$x + 12 = 38$$
$$x = 26$$

26	$ 1	$ 5	$26
+12	x26	x12	+60
38 ✓	$26	$60	$86 ✓

11. let x = boxes of small oranges 3
y = boxes of large oranges 7

$$360x + 48y = 1416$$
$$x + y = 10 \quad (48)$$

$$360x + 48y = 1416$$
$$(-)\ 48x + 48y = 480$$
$$312x = 936$$
$$x = 3$$

$$3 + y = 10$$
$$y = 7$$

3	360	48	1080
+7	x 3	x 7	+336
10 ✓	1080	336	1416 ✓

12. let x = amount invested at 10% $500
y = amount invested at 14% $800

$$y = x + 300$$
$$.14y = .10x + 62$$

$$.14(x + 300) = .10x + 62$$
$$14(x + 300) = 10x + 6200$$
$$14x + 4200 = 10x + 6200$$
$$4x = 2000$$
$$x = 500$$

$$y = 500 + 300$$
$$y = 800$$

$800	$ 500	$ 800	$112
-500	x .10	x .14	- 50
$300 ✓	$50.00	$112.00	$ 62 ✓

13. let x = number won by champion 107
y = number lost by champion 45

Records: First place team 107 - 45
Second place team 91 - 63

$$\begin{cases} x = y + 62 \\ x - 16 + y + 18 = 154 \end{cases}$$

$$(y + 62) - 16 + y + 18 = 154$$
$$2y + 64 = 154$$
$$2y = 90$$
$$y = 45$$

$$x = 45 + 62$$
$$x = 107$$

$$x - 16 = 107 - 16 = 91$$
$$y + 18 = 45 + 18 = 63$$

107	91
-45	+63
62 ✓	154 ✓

14. let p = diameter of pipe <u>8 in.</u>
c = diameter of casing <u>12 in.</u>

$$\begin{cases} p = \frac{2}{3}c \quad (3) \\ \frac{c}{2} + 2 = p \end{cases}$$

$$\frac{c}{2} + 2 = \frac{2}{3}c$$
$$6\left(\frac{c}{2} + 2\right) = 6\left(\frac{2}{3}c\right)$$
$$3c + 12 = 4c$$
$$-c = -12$$
$$c = 12$$

$$p = \frac{2}{3}(12)$$
$$p = 8$$

8 is $\frac{2}{3}$ of 12 ✓
6 is 2 less than 8 ✓

15. let a = number of adults <u>85</u>
t = number of teenagers <u>15</u>

$$\begin{cases} a + t = 100 \\ 98.40a + 52.80t = 9156 \end{cases}$$

$$(-)\begin{cases} 52.80a + 52.80t = 5280 \quad (1) \times 52.80 \\ 98.40a + 52.80t = 9156 \end{cases}$$
$$-45.60a = -3876$$
$$a = 85$$
$$85 + t = 100$$
$$t = 15$$

85	$98.40	$52.80	$8364
+15	x 85	x 15	+ 792
100 ✓	$ 8364	$ 792	$9156 ✓

16. let ℓ = length <u>18 in.</u>
w = width <u>12 in.</u>

$$\begin{cases} 2\ell + 2w = 60 \\ \ell = w + 6 \end{cases}$$

$$2(w + 6) + 2w = 60$$
$$2w + 12 + 2w = 60$$
$$4w = 48$$
$$w = 12$$

$$\ell = 12 + 6$$
$$\ell = 18$$

18
-12
6 ✓

18
18
12
+12
60 ✓

17. let c = number of cars <u>725</u>
t = number of trucks <u>650</u>

$$\begin{cases} c + t = 1375 \\ t + 50 = c - 25 \end{cases}$$

$$(+)\begin{cases} c + t = 1375 \\ -c + t = -75 \end{cases}$$
$$2t = 1300$$
$$t = 650$$

$$c + 650 = 1375$$
$$c = 725$$

$$\begin{array}{r} 725 \\ +650 \\ \hline 1375 \checkmark \end{array} \quad \begin{array}{r} 650 \\ +50 \\ \hline 700 \end{array} \quad \begin{array}{r} 725 \\ -25 \\ \hline 700 \checkmark \end{array}$$

18. let A = number of Americans <u>1700</u>
B = number of British <u>1094</u>

$$\begin{cases} A + B = 2794 \quad (3) \\ 2A + 3B = 6682 \end{cases}$$

$$(-)\begin{cases} 3A + 3B = 8382 \\ 2A + 3B = 6682 \end{cases}$$
$$A = 1700$$
$$1700 + B = 2794$$
$$B = 1094$$

$$\begin{array}{r} 1700 \\ +1094 \\ \hline 2794 \checkmark \end{array} \quad \begin{array}{r} 1700 \\ \times 2 \\ \hline 3400 \end{array} \quad \begin{array}{r} 1094 \\ \times 3 \\ \hline 3282 \end{array} \quad \begin{array}{r} 3400 \\ +3282 \\ \hline 6682 \checkmark \end{array}$$

19. let e = number at eastern U. <u>9000</u>
w = number at western U. <u>6000</u>

$$\begin{cases} e = w + 3000 \\ \frac{1}{2}e + \frac{1}{3}w = 6500 \end{cases}$$

$$\frac{1}{2}(w + 3000) + \frac{1}{3}w = 6500$$
$$\frac{1}{2}w + 1500 + \frac{1}{3}w = 6500$$
$$6(\frac{1}{2}w + 1500 + \frac{1}{3}w) = 6(6500)$$
$$3w + 9000 + 2w = 39,000$$

$$5w = 30,000$$
$$w = 6000$$

$$e = 6000 + 3000$$
$$e = 9000$$

$$\begin{array}{r} 9000 \\ -6000 \\ \hline 3000 \checkmark \end{array} \quad \begin{array}{r} \frac{1}{2}(9000) = 4500 \\ + \frac{1}{3}(6000) = 2000 \\ \hline 6500 \checkmark \end{array}$$

20. let x = annual cost of streetlight under previous contract <u>$32.85</u>
y = annual cost of streetlight under present contract <u>$57.00</u>

$$\begin{cases} y = x + 24.15 \\ 9x + 46.35 = 6y \end{cases}$$

$$\begin{aligned} 9x + 46.35 &= 6(x + 24.15) \\ 9x + 46.35 &= 6x + 144.90 \\ 3x &= 98.55 \\ x &= 32.85 \end{aligned}$$

$$\begin{aligned} y &= 32.85 + 24.15 \\ y &= 57 \end{aligned}$$

$$\begin{array}{r} \$57.00 \\ -32.85 \\ \hline \$24.15 \checkmark \end{array} \quad \begin{array}{r} \$\ 32.85 \\ \times\ 9 \\ \hline \$295.65 \end{array} \quad \begin{array}{r} \$\ 57 \\ \times\ 6 \\ \hline \$342 \end{array} \quad \begin{array}{r} \$342.00 \\ -295.65 \\ \hline \$\ 46.35 \checkmark \end{array}$$

21. let x = amount invested at 9% <u>$1500</u>
y = amount invested at 8% <u>$2500</u>

$$\begin{cases} x + y = 4000 & (8) \\ .09x + .08y = 335 & (100) \end{cases}$$

$$\begin{array}{rrcl} & 8x + 8y &=& 32{,}000 \\ (-) & 9x + 8y &=& 33{,}500 \\ \hline & -x &=& -1500 \\ & x &=& 1500 \end{array}$$

$$\begin{aligned} 1500 + y &= 4000 \\ y &= 2500 \end{aligned}$$

$$\begin{array}{r} 1500 \\ +2500 \\ \hline 4000 \checkmark \end{array} \quad \begin{array}{r} \$\ 1500 \\ \times\ .09 \\ \hline \$135.00 \end{array} \quad \begin{array}{r} \$\ 2500 \\ \times\ .08 \\ \hline \$200.00 \end{array} \quad \begin{array}{r} \$200 \\ +135 \\ \hline \$335 \checkmark \end{array}$$

22. let x = price of first painting <u>$975</u>
y = price of second painting <u>$950</u>

$$\begin{cases} x + y = 1925 \\ x - 15 = y + 10 \end{cases}$$

$$\begin{array}{rcl} x + y &=& 1925 \\ x - y &=& 25 \\ \hline 2x &=& 1950 \\ x &=& 975 \end{array}$$

$$\begin{aligned} 975 + y &= 1925 \\ y &= 950 \end{aligned}$$

$$\begin{array}{r} \$\ 975 \\ +\ 950 \\ \hline \$1925 \end{array} \quad \begin{array}{r} \$975 \\ -\ 15 \\ \hline \$960 \end{array} \quad \begin{array}{r} \$950 \\ +\ 10 \\ \hline \$960 \end{array} \checkmark$$

23. let w = number of WWII vintage rifles <u>6</u>
c = number of Civil War vintage rifles <u>4</u>

$$\begin{cases} w + c = 10 \\ 600(w - 3) + 1500(c + 3) = 12{,}300 \end{cases}$$

$$\begin{aligned} w &= 10 - c \\ 600(10 - c - 3) + 1500(c + 3) &= 12{,}300 \\ 6000 - 600c - 1800 + 1500c + 4500 &= 12{,}300 \\ 8700 + 900c &= 12{,}300 \\ 900c &= 3600 \\ c &= 4 \end{aligned}$$

$w = 10 - 4$
$w = 6$

6	\$ 600	\$ 1500	\$10,500
+4	x 3	x 7	+1,800
10 ✓	\$1800	\$10,500	\$12,300 ✓

24. let a = number of admission tickets <u>1200</u>
g = number of game tickets <u>160</u>

$$\begin{cases} 1.50a + 1.25g = 2000 \quad (100) \\ 1.50a + 1.25(2g) = 2200 \quad (100) \end{cases}$$

$$(-)\begin{cases} 150a + 125g = 200{,}000 \\ 150a + 250g = 220{,}000 \end{cases}$$

$$\begin{aligned} -125g &= -20{,}000 \\ g &= 160 \end{aligned}$$

$$\begin{aligned} 1.50a + 1.25(160) &= 2000 \\ 1.50a + 200 &= 2000 \\ 1.50a &= 1800 \\ 15a &= 18{,}000 \\ a &= 1200 \end{aligned}$$

\$1.50	\$1.25	\$1800
x1200	x 160	+ 200
\$1800	\$ 200	\$2000 ✓

\$1.25	\$1800
x 320	+ 400
\$ 400	\$2200 ✓

25. let o = quantity of oranges sold <u>2250 lb.</u>
a = quantity of apples sold <u>900 lb.</u>

$$\begin{cases} o = a + 1350 \\ \frac{1}{5}o = \frac{1}{2}a \end{cases}$$

$$\begin{aligned} \frac{1}{5}(a + 1350) &= \frac{1}{2}a \\ \frac{1}{5}a + 270 &= \frac{1}{2}a \\ 10\left(\frac{1}{5}a + 270\right) &= 10\left(\frac{1}{2}a\right) \\ 2a + 2700 &= 5a \\ -3a &= -2700 \\ a &= 900 \end{aligned}$$

$o = 900 + 1350$
$o = 2250$

2250	$\frac{1}{5}(2250) = 450$
-900	✓
1350 ✓	$\frac{1}{2}(900) = 450$

26. let c = capacity of a car <u>48 T</u>
p = capacity of a pocket <u>160 T</u>

$$\begin{cases} 7.5p = 25c & (10) \\ 2c - 16 = \frac{1}{2}p & (2) \end{cases}$$

$$\begin{cases} 75p = 250c \\ 4c - 32 = p \end{cases}$$

$$75(4c - 32) = 250c$$
$$300c - 2400 = 250c$$
$$50c = 2400$$
$$c = 48$$

$$p = 4(48) - 32$$
$$p = 192 - 32$$
$$p = 160$$

$$\begin{array}{r} 48 \\ \times 25 \\ \hline 1200 \end{array} \quad \begin{array}{r} 160 \\ \times 7.5 \\ \hline 1200 \end{array} \checkmark$$

27. let x = pounds evaporated by 1 lb. of coal <u>6.5</u>
y = pounds evaporated by 1 gal. of oil <u>100</u>

$$\begin{cases} 100x - 50 = 6y \\ 60x + 10 = 4y \end{cases}$$

$$\begin{cases} 100x - 6y = 50 & (4) \\ 60x - 4y = -10 & (6) \end{cases}$$

$$\begin{array}{rl} & 400x - 24y = 200 \\ (-) & 360x - 24y = -60 \\ \hline & 40x = 260 \\ & x = 6.5 \end{array}$$

$$60(6.5) + 10 = 4y$$
$$390 + 10 = 4y$$
$$400 = 4y$$
$$y = 100$$

$$\begin{array}{r} 100 \\ \times 6.5 \\ \hline 650 \end{array} \quad \begin{array}{r} 100 \\ \times 6 \\ \hline 600 \end{array} \quad \begin{array}{r} 650 \\ -600 \\ \hline 50 \end{array} \checkmark \quad \begin{array}{r} 60 \\ \times 6.5 \\ \hline 390 \end{array} \quad \begin{array}{r} 100 \\ \times 4 \\ \hline 400 \end{array} \quad \begin{array}{r} 400 \\ -390 \\ \hline 10 \end{array} \checkmark$$

28. See page 243 in text.

29. let t = tens' digit 9
u = units' digit 3
10t + u = the number <u>93</u>

$$\begin{cases} t = 3u \\ \frac{10t + u - 33}{t - u} = 10 \end{cases}$$

$$10t + u - 33 = 10(t - u)$$
$$10t + u - 33 = 10t - 10u$$
$$11u = 33$$
$$u = 3$$
$$t = 3(3) = 9$$

9 is 3(3) ✓

$$\begin{array}{r} 93 \\ -33 \\ \hline 60 \end{array} \quad \begin{array}{r} 9 \\ -3 \\ \hline 6 \end{array} \quad 6\overline{)60} = 10 \checkmark$$

30. let t = tens digit 6
u = units digit 7
10t + u = the number 67

$$\begin{cases} t + u = 13 \\ 10t + u + 9 = 10u + t \end{cases}$$

$$\begin{cases} t + u = 13 \\ 9t - 9u = -9 \quad (\div 9) \end{cases}$$

$$(+)\begin{cases} t + u = 13 \\ t - u = -1 \end{cases}$$
$$2t = 12$$
$$t = 6$$

$$6 + u = 13$$
$$u = 7$$

7 + 6 = 13 ✓

76 - 9 = 67, and 76 is 67 written in reverse order. ✓

31. let x = pounds of \$2.88 coffee 60
y = pounds of \$3.78 coffee 40

$$\begin{cases} x + y = 100 & (378) \\ 2.88x + 3.78y = 3.24(100) & (100) \end{cases}$$

$$(-)\begin{cases} 378x + 378y = 37{,}800 \\ 288x + 378y = 32{,}400 \end{cases}$$
$$90x = 5400$$
$$x = 60$$

$$60 + y = 100$$
$$y = 40$$

60 + 40 = 100 ✓ $\quad$ \$2.88 × 60 = \$172.80 $\quad$ \$3.78 × 40 = \$151.20

\$3.24 × 100 = \$324.00 $\quad$ \$172.80 + 151.20 = \$324.00 ✓

32. let x = number of peach trees 78
y = number of plum trees 42

$$\begin{cases} x + y = 120 \\ 2x - 30 = 3y \end{cases}$$

$$\begin{cases} x + y = 120 \quad (3) \\ 2x - 3y = 30 \end{cases}$$

$$(+)\begin{cases} 3x + 3y = 360 \\ 2x - 3y = 30 \end{cases}$$
$$5x = 390$$
$$x = 78$$

$$78 + y = 120$$
$$y = 42$$

78 + 42 = 120 ✓ $\quad$ 2(78) = 156, -3(42) = 126, 30 ✓

33. let x = amount of 9% investment <u>$11,027.03</u>
y = amount of $9\frac{1}{2}\%$ investment <u>$6,027.05</u>

$$\begin{cases} .09x + .095y = 1565 & \left(\frac{1000}{5}\right) \\ .095x + .09y = 1565 + 25 & \left(\frac{1000}{5}\right) \end{cases}$$

$$\begin{cases} 18x + 19y = 313{,}000 & (18) \\ 19x + 18y = 318{,}000 & (19) \end{cases}$$

$$\begin{array}{rl} & 324x + 342y = 5{,}634{,}000 \\ (-) & \underline{361x + 342y = 6{,}042{,}000} \\ & -37x = -408{,}000 \\ & x \approx 11{,}027.03 \end{array}$$

$$\begin{array}{r} \$11{,}027.03 \\ \underline{x\ .09} \\ \$\ 992.43 \end{array} \quad \begin{array}{r} \$6027.05 \\ \underline{x\ .095} \\ \$\ 572.57 \end{array} \quad \begin{array}{r} \$\ 992.43 \\ \underline{+572.57} \\ \$1565.00 \checkmark \end{array}$$

$$\begin{aligned} .09(11{,}027.03) + .095y &= 1565 \\ 992.43 + .095y &= 1565 \\ .095y &= 572.57 \\ y &= 6{,}027.05 \end{aligned}$$

$$\begin{array}{r} \$11{,}027.03 \\ \underline{x\ .095} \\ \$\ 1047.57 \end{array} \quad \begin{array}{r} \$6027.05 \\ \underline{x\ .09} \\ \$\ 542.43 \end{array} \quad \begin{array}{r} \$1047.57 \\ \underline{+542.43} \\ \$1590.00 \end{array} \quad \begin{array}{r} \$1590 \\ \underline{-1565} \\ \$\ 25 \checkmark \end{array}$$

34. let x = rate at which $10,000 is invested <u>9%</u>
y = rate at which $8000 is invested <u>8%</u>

$$\begin{cases} 10{,}000x + 8000y = 1540 & \left(\frac{6}{10}\right) \\ 12{,}000x + 6000y = 1540 + 20 & \left(\frac{8}{10}\right) \end{cases}$$

$$\begin{array}{rl} & \begin{cases} 6000x + 4800y = 924 \\ \underline{9600x + 4800y = 1248} \end{cases} \\ (-) & \\ & -3600x = -324 \\ & x = .09 = 9\% \end{array}$$

$$\begin{aligned} 10{,}000(.09) + 8000y &= 1540 \\ 900 + 8000y &= 1540 \\ 8000y &= 640 \\ y &= .08 = 8\% \end{aligned}$$

$$\begin{array}{r} \$10{,}000 \\ \underline{x\ .09} \\ \$\ 900 \end{array} \quad \begin{array}{r} \$8000 \\ \underline{x\ .08} \\ \$\ 640 \end{array} \quad \begin{array}{r} \$\ 900 \\ \underline{+640} \\ \$1540 \checkmark \end{array} \quad \begin{array}{r} \$12{,}000 \\ \underline{x\ .09} \\ \$\ 1080 \end{array} \quad \begin{array}{r} \$6000 \\ \underline{x\ .08} \\ \$\ 480 \end{array} \quad \begin{array}{r} \$1080 \\ \underline{+\ 480} \\ \$1560 \end{array} \quad \begin{array}{r} \$1560 \\ \underline{-1540} \\ \$\ 20 \checkmark \end{array}$$

35. let n = numerator 5
d = denominator 8
$\frac{n}{d}$ = the fraction $\underline{\frac{5}{8}}$

$$\begin{cases} \frac{n+1}{d} = \frac{3}{4} \\ \frac{n}{d+2} = \frac{1}{2} \end{cases}$$

$$\begin{cases} 4n + 4 = 3d \\ 2n = d + 2 \end{cases}$$

$$\begin{cases} 4n - 3d = -4 \\ 2n - d = 2 \quad (3) \end{cases}$$

$$\begin{array}{rl} & 4n - 3d = -4 \\ (-) & \underline{6n - 3d = 6} \\ & -2n = -10 \\ & n = 5 \end{array}$$

$$\frac{5+1}{d} = \frac{3}{4}$$
$$\frac{6}{d} = \frac{3}{4}$$
$$3d = 24$$
$$d = 8$$

$$\frac{5+1}{8} = \frac{6}{8} = \frac{3}{4} \checkmark$$
$$\frac{5}{8+2} = \frac{5}{10} = \frac{1}{2} \checkmark$$

36. let n = numerator 5
d = denominator 4
$\frac{n}{d}$ = the fraction $\underline{\frac{5}{4}}$

$$\begin{cases} \frac{n-2}{d} = \frac{n}{d} - \frac{1}{2} \\ \frac{n}{d+4} = \frac{n}{d} - \frac{5}{8} \end{cases}$$

$$2d\left(\frac{n-2}{d}\right) = 2d\left(\frac{n}{d} - \frac{1}{2}\right)$$
$$2(n - 2) = 2n - d$$
$$2n - 4 = 2n - d$$
$$d = 4$$

$$\frac{n}{4+4} = \frac{n}{4} - \frac{5}{8}$$
$$8\left(\frac{n}{8}\right) = 8\left(\frac{n}{4} - \frac{5}{8}\right)$$
$$n = 2n - 5$$
$$-n = -5$$
$$n = 5$$

$$\frac{5-2}{4} = \frac{3}{4}$$
$$\frac{5}{4} - \frac{3}{4} = \frac{1}{2} \checkmark$$
$$\frac{5}{4+4} = \frac{5}{8}$$
$$\frac{5}{4} - \frac{5}{8} = \frac{5}{8} \checkmark$$

37. let t = tens digit 6
u = units digit 3
10t + u = the number $\underline{63}$

$$\begin{cases} 10t + u = 7(t + u) \\ 10t + u - 27 = 10u + t \end{cases}$$

$$\begin{cases} 3t - 6u = 0 \\ 9t - 9u = 27 \quad (\div 3) \end{cases}$$

$$\begin{array}{rl} & \begin{cases} 3t - 6u = 0 \\ \underline{3t - 3u = 9} \end{cases} \\ (-) & -3u = -9 \\ & u = 3 \end{array}$$

$$10t + 3 = 7(t + 3)$$
$$10t + 3 = 7t + 21$$
$$3t = 18$$
$$t = 6$$

63 is 7 times (6 + 3) ✓

$$\begin{array}{r} 63 \\ \underline{-27} \\ 36 \end{array}$$

36 is 63 with the digits reversed ✓

38. let s = tons of steel $\underline{2200 \text{ tons}}$
i = tons of cast iron $\underline{3400 \text{ tons}}$

$$\begin{cases} s + i = 5600 \quad (11) \\ 17s = 11i \end{cases}$$

$$\begin{array}{rl} & \begin{cases} 11s + 11i = 61{,}600 \\ \underline{17s - 11i = \phantom{61{,}60}0} \end{cases} \\ (+) & 28s = 61{,}600 \\ & s = 2200 \end{array}$$

$$2200 + i = 5600$$
$$i = 3400$$

$$\begin{array}{r} 2200 \\ \underline{+3400} \\ 5600 \checkmark \end{array} \qquad \begin{array}{r} 2200 \\ \underline{\times 17} \\ 37{,}400 \end{array} \qquad \begin{array}{r} 3400 \\ \underline{\times 11} \\ 37{,}400 \checkmark \end{array}$$

39. let x = number of one-dollar bills $\underline{19}$
     y = number of five-dollar bills $\underline{16}$

$$(-)\begin{cases} x + y = 35 \\ x + 5y = 99 \end{cases}$$

$$-4y = -64$$
$$y = 16$$

$$x + 16 = 35$$
$$x = 19$$

$$\begin{array}{cc} 19 & 16 \\ +16 & \times 5 \\ \hline 35\checkmark & \overline{80} \\ & +19 \\ & \overline{\$99}\checkmark \end{array}$$

40. s = weight of smaller apple $\underline{30\ oz.}$
     ℓ = weight of larger apple $\underline{34\ oz.}$

$$\begin{cases} s + \ell = 64 & (2) \\ s - 13 = \tfrac{1}{2}\ell & (2) \end{cases}$$

$$\begin{cases} 2s + 2\ell = 128 \\ 2s - 26 = \ell \end{cases}$$

$$(-)\begin{cases} 2s + 2\ell = 128 \\ 2s - \ell = 26 \end{cases}$$
$$3\ell = 102$$
$$\ell = 34$$

$$s + 34 = 64$$
$$s = 30$$

$$\begin{array}{cc} 30 & 30 \\ +34 & -13 \\ \hline 64\checkmark & \overline{17} \end{array} \text{ is } \tfrac{1}{2} \text{ of } 34 \checkmark$$

41. let A = Alan's earnings $\underline{\$48}$
     R = Robert's earnings $\underline{\$30}$

$$\begin{cases} A - 18 = R \\ 5A = 8R \end{cases}$$

$$\begin{cases} A - R = 18 & (5) \\ 5A - 8R = 0 \end{cases}$$

$$(-)\begin{cases} 5A - 5R = 90 \\ 5A - 8R = 0 \end{cases}$$
$$3R = 90$$
$$R = 30$$

$$A - 18 = 30$$
$$A = 48$$

$$\begin{array}{ccc} \$48 & \$48 & \$30 \\ -30 & \times 5 & \times 8 \\ \hline \$18\checkmark & \$240 & \$240 \checkmark \end{array}$$

42. let b = rate of bird in still air <u>40 mph</u>
w = rate of lighter wind <u>5 mph</u>
2w = rate of stronger wind <u>10 mph</u>

$$(-)\begin{cases} b + w = 45 \\ b - 2w = 30 \end{cases}$$
$$3w = 15$$
$$w = 15$$

$$b + (5) = 45$$
$$b = 40$$

$$\begin{array}{r} 40 \\ +5 \\ \hline 45 \end{array} ✓ \qquad \begin{array}{r} 40 \\ -10 \\ \hline 30 \end{array} ✓$$

43. let x = rate in still water <u>4 mph</u>
y = rate of current <u>2 mph</u>

$$\begin{cases} 2(x + y) = 12 \\ 6(x - y) = 12 \end{cases} \qquad d = rt$$

$$\begin{cases} 2x + 2y = 12 \quad (3) \\ 6x - 6y = 12 \end{cases}$$

$$(+)\begin{cases} 6x + 6y = 36 \\ 6x - 6y = 12 \end{cases}$$
$$12x = 48$$
$$x = 4$$

$$2(4 + y) = 12$$
$$4 + y = 6$$
$$y = 2$$

$$\begin{array}{r} 2 \\ 6\overline{)12} \end{array} ✓ \qquad \begin{array}{r} 6 \\ 2\overline{)12} \end{array} ✓$$

$$4 - 2 = 2 \qquad 4 + 2 = 6$$

*44. let x = rate in still water $\underline{\frac{cm + dm}{2cd} \text{ mph}}$

y = rate of current $\underline{\frac{dm - cm}{2cd} \text{ mph}}$

$$\begin{cases} c(x + y) = m \\ d(x - y) = m \end{cases}$$

$$\begin{cases} cx + cy = m \quad (d) \\ dx - dy = m \quad (c) \end{cases}$$

$$(+)\begin{cases} cdx + cdy = dm \\ cdx - cdy = cm \end{cases}$$
$$2cdx = cm + dm$$
$$x = \frac{cm + dm}{2cd}$$

$$c\left(\frac{cm + dm}{2cd} + \frac{dm - cm}{2cd}\right) = m$$
$$\cancel{c}\left(\frac{\cancel{2}\cancel{d}m}{\cancel{2}\cancel{c}\cancel{d}}\right) = m$$
$$m = m$$

$$(-)\begin{cases} cdx + cdy = dm \\ cdx - cdy = cm \end{cases}$$
$$2cdy = dm - cm$$
$$y = \frac{dm - cm}{2cd}$$

$$d\left(\frac{cm + dm}{2cd} - \frac{dm - cm}{2cd}\right) = m$$
$$\cancel{d}\left(\frac{\cancel{2}\cancel{c}m}{\cancel{2}\cancel{c}\cancel{d}}\right) = m$$
$$m = m$$

45. let x = one number $\underline{8}$

y = other number $\dfrac{1}{4}$

$$\begin{cases} \dfrac{1}{x} + \dfrac{1}{y} = 4\dfrac{1}{8} \\ x = 32y \end{cases}$$

$$\frac{1}{32y} + \frac{1}{y} = \frac{33}{8}$$

$$32y\left(\frac{1}{32y} + \frac{1}{y}\right) = 32y\left(\frac{33}{8}\right)$$

$$1 + 32 = 132y$$

$$132y = 33$$

$$y = \frac{33}{132} = \frac{1}{4}$$

$$x = 32\left(\frac{1}{4}\right) = 8$$

8 is $32(\frac{1}{4})$ ✓

$$\frac{1}{8} + \frac{1}{\frac{1}{4}} = \frac{1}{8} + 4 = 4\frac{1}{8}\ ✓$$

*46. let x = one number $\dfrac{1+\ell}{m}$

y = other number $\dfrac{1+\ell}{\ell m}$

$$\begin{cases} \dfrac{1}{x} + \dfrac{1}{y} = m \\ x = \ell y \end{cases}$$

$$\frac{1}{\ell y} + \frac{1}{y} = m$$

$$\ell y\left(\frac{1}{\ell y} + \frac{1}{y}\right) = \ell y(m)$$

$$1 + \ell = \ell m y$$

$$y = \frac{1+\ell}{\ell m}$$

$$x = \ell\left(\frac{1+\ell}{\ell m}\right) = \frac{1+\ell}{m}$$

$$\frac{1}{\frac{1+\ell}{m}} + \frac{1}{\frac{1+\ell}{\ell m}} = m$$

$$\frac{m}{1+\ell} + \frac{\ell m}{1+\ell} = m$$

$$\frac{m+\ell m}{1+\ell} = m$$

$$\frac{m\cancel{(1+\ell)}}{\cancel{1+\ell}} = m$$

$$m \stackrel{?}{=} m\ ✓$$

$$\frac{1+\ell}{m} = \ell\left(\frac{1+\ell}{\cancel{\ell}m}\right)$$

$$\frac{1+\ell}{m} \stackrel{?}{=} \frac{1+\ell}{m}\ ✓$$

47. let x = one number $\underline{3}$
y = other number $\underline{2}$

$$\begin{cases} 3\left(\frac{1}{x}\right) + 6\left(\frac{1}{y}\right) = 4 \\ x = \frac{3}{2}y \end{cases}$$

$$\frac{3}{x} + \frac{6}{y} = 4$$

$$\frac{3}{\frac{3y}{2}} + \frac{6}{y} = 4$$

$$\frac{2}{y} + \frac{6}{y} = 4$$

$$\frac{8}{y} = 4$$

$$4y = 8$$

$$y = 2$$

$$x = \frac{3}{2}(2)$$

$$x = 3$$

$3\left(\frac{1}{3}\right) + 6\left(\frac{1}{2}\right) = 1 + 3 = 4$ ✓

3 is $1\frac{1}{2}(2)$ ✓

48. See page 245 in text.

49. let x = time for first pipe $\underline{18 \text{ min.}}$
y = time for second pipe $\underline{36 \text{ min.}}$

$$\begin{cases} 12\left(\frac{1}{x} + \frac{1}{y}\right) = 1 \\ 5\left(\frac{1}{x}\right) + 26\left(\frac{1}{y}\right) = 1 \end{cases}$$

$$\begin{cases} \frac{12}{x} + \frac{12}{y} = 1 \quad (5) \\ \frac{5}{x} + \frac{26}{y} = 1 \quad (12) \end{cases}$$

$$\begin{cases} \frac{60}{x} + \frac{60}{y} = 5 \\ (-)\ \frac{60}{x} + \frac{312}{y} = 12 \end{cases}$$

$$\frac{-252}{y} = -7$$

$$-7y = -252$$

$$y = 36$$

$$\frac{12}{x} + \frac{12}{36} = 1$$

$$\frac{12}{x} + \frac{1}{3} = 1$$

$$\frac{12}{x} = \frac{2}{3}$$

$$2x = 36$$

$$x = 18$$

$$12\left(\frac{1}{18} + \frac{1}{36}\right) \;\Big|\; 1$$

$$\frac{2}{3} + \frac{1}{3} \;\Big|$$

$1 = 1$ ✓

$$5\left(\frac{1}{18}\right) + 26\left(\frac{1}{36}\right) \;\Big|\; 1$$

$$\frac{5}{18} + \frac{13}{18} \;\Big|$$

$1 = 1$ ✓

50. let x = time for one press 75 hr.
y = time for other press 50 hr.

$$\begin{cases} 30(\frac{1}{x}) + 30(\frac{1}{y}) = 1 \\ 18(\frac{1}{x}) + 18(\frac{1}{y}) + 20(\frac{1}{y}) = 1 \end{cases}$$

$$\begin{cases} \frac{30}{x} + \frac{30}{y} = 1 \quad (12) \\ \frac{18}{x} + \frac{38}{y} = 1 \quad (20) \end{cases}$$

$$\begin{array}{r} \begin{cases} \frac{360}{x} + \frac{360}{y} = 12 \\ (-)\ \frac{360}{x} + \frac{760}{y} = 20 \end{cases} \\ \hline \frac{-400}{y} = -8 \\ -8y = -400 \\ y = 50 \end{array}$$

$$\frac{30}{x} + \frac{30}{50} = 1$$
$$\frac{30}{x} = \frac{2}{5}$$
$$2x = 150$$
$$x = 75$$

$$\frac{30}{75} + \frac{30}{50} \;\Big|\; 1$$
$$\frac{2}{5} + \frac{3}{5} \;\Big|$$
$$1 = 1 \checkmark$$

$$\frac{18}{75} + \frac{18}{50} + \frac{20}{50} \;\Big|\; 1$$
$$\frac{18}{75} + \frac{38}{50} \;\Big|$$
$$\frac{36 + 114}{150} \;\Big|\; 1$$
$$1 = 1 \checkmark$$

*51. let x = number of quarts of 20% solution 4.8
y = number of quarts of 10% solution 3.2

$$\begin{cases} .20x + .10y = .16(x + y) \\ x + y = 8 \end{cases}$$

$$20x + 10y = 16x + 16y$$

$$\begin{cases} 4x - 6y = 0 \\ x + y = 8 \quad (6) \end{cases}$$

$$\begin{array}{r} \begin{cases} 4x - 6y = 0 \\ (+)\ 6x + 6y = 48 \end{cases} \\ \hline 10x = 48 \\ x = 4.8 \end{array}$$

$$4.8 + y = 8$$
$$y = 3.2$$

4.8	4.8	3.2	.96	.16
+3.2	x.2	x.1	+.32	x 8
8.0 ✓	.96	.32	1.28	1.28 ✓

52. let c = price per yard of corduroy $\underline{\$7}$
d = price per yard of denim $\underline{\$2}$

$$\begin{cases} 3c + 12d = 45 & (5) \\ 5c + 8d = 51 & (3) \end{cases}$$

$$\begin{array}{r} \begin{cases} 15c + 60d = 225 \\ 15c + 24d = 153 \end{cases} (-) \\ \hline 36d = 72 \\ d = 2 \end{array}$$

$$\begin{aligned} 3c + 12(2) &= 45 \\ 3c + 24 &= 45 \\ 3c &= 21 \\ c &= 7 \end{aligned}$$

$$\begin{array}{r} \$\,7 \\ \times\ 3 \\ \hline \$21 \end{array} \quad \begin{array}{r} \$\,2 \\ \times 12 \\ \hline \$24 \end{array} \quad \begin{array}{r} \$21 \\ +24 \\ \hline \$45 \checkmark \end{array} \quad \begin{array}{r} \$\,7 \\ \times\ 5 \\ \hline \$35 \end{array} \quad \begin{array}{r} \$\,2 \\ \times\ 8 \\ \hline \$16 \end{array} \quad \begin{array}{r} \$35 \\ +16 \\ \hline \$51 \checkmark \end{array}$$

53. let x = number of days for faster machine $\underline{6.5}$
y = number of days for slower machine $\underline{13}$

$$\begin{cases} 4\left(\frac{1}{x}\right) + 5\left(\frac{1}{y}\right) = 1 & (7) \\ 3\left(\frac{1}{x}\right) + 7\left(\frac{1}{y}\right) = 1 & (5) \end{cases}$$

$$\begin{array}{r} (-)\begin{cases} \frac{28}{x} + \frac{35}{y} = 7 \\ \frac{15}{x} + \frac{35}{y} = 5 \end{cases} \\ \hline \frac{13}{x} \qquad = 2 \end{array}$$

$$\begin{aligned} 2x &= 13 \\ x &= 6.5 \end{aligned}$$

$$\begin{aligned} \frac{4}{6.5} + \frac{5}{y} &= 1 \\ 6.5y\left(\frac{4}{6.5} + \frac{5}{y}\right) &= 6.5y \\ 4y + 32.5 &= 6.5y \\ -2.5y &= -32.5 \\ 25y &= 325 \\ y &= 13 \end{aligned}$$

$$\begin{array}{r|l} 4\left(\frac{1}{6.5}\right) + 5\left(\frac{1}{13}\right) & 1 \\ \frac{8}{13} + \frac{5}{13} & 1 \\ 1 & = 1 \end{array}$$

$$\begin{array}{r|l} 3\left(\frac{1}{6.5}\right) + 7\left(\frac{1}{13}\right) & 1 \\ \frac{6}{13} + \frac{7}{13} & 1 \\ 1 & = 1 \end{array}$$

*54. let t = tens digit 7
u = units digit 5
10t + u = the number 75

$$\begin{cases} t + u = 6(t - u) \\ 10t + u - 6(t + u) = 3 \end{cases}$$

$$\begin{cases} t + u = 6t - 6u \\ 10t + u - 6t - 6u = 3 \end{cases}$$

$$\begin{cases} -5t + 7u = 0 \quad (5) \\ 4t - 5u = 3 \quad (7) \end{cases}$$

$$(+)\begin{cases} -25t + 35u = 0 \\ 28t - 35u = 21 \end{cases}$$
$$3t = 21$$
$$t = 7$$

$$7 + u = 6(7 - u)$$
$$7 + u = 42 - 6u$$
$$7u = 35$$
$$u = 5$$

Note: If assumption is made that $u > t$, rather than $t > u$, the resulting value of u is fractional and t is negative. Thus $t > u$ provides the only solution.

$7 + 5 = 6(7 - 5)$ ✓
75 is 3 greater than 6(12) ✓

55. let x = number of bushels in 22% oat bin 10 bu.
y = number of bushels in 30% oat bin 30 bu.

$$\begin{cases} .22x + .30y = .28(40) \quad (100) \\ x + y = 40 \quad (22) \end{cases}$$

$$(-)\begin{cases} 22x + 30y = 1120 \\ 22x + 22y = 880 \end{cases}$$
$$8y = 240$$
$$y = 30$$

$$x + 30 = 40$$
$$x = 10$$

10	30	2.2	40	10
x.22	x.30	+9.0	x.28	+30
2.2	9.00	11.2 ✓	11.2	40 ✓

Time Test Page 246

1.
$$(-)\begin{cases} 3x + 4y = 29 \\ 3x - y = 4 \end{cases}$$
$$5y = 25$$
$$y = 5$$

$$3x + 4(5) = 29$$
$$3x + 20 = 29$$
$$3x = 9$$
$$x = 3$$

Solution (3, 5)

2.
$$\begin{cases} 2x + y = -2 \quad (3) \\ 5x + 3y = -3 \end{cases}$$

$$(-)\begin{cases} 6x + 3y = -6 \\ 5x + 3y = -3 \end{cases}$$
$$x = -3$$

$$2(-3) + y = -2$$
$$-6 + y = -2$$
$$y = 4$$

Solution (-3, 4)

3. $\begin{cases} 6x + 5y = 13 & (4) \\ 4x + 2y = 10 & (6) \end{cases}$

$$(-)\begin{cases} 24x + 20y = 52 \\ 24x + 12y = 60 \end{cases}$$
$$8y = -8$$
$$y = -1$$

$$6x + 5(-1) = 13$$
$$6x - 5 = 13$$
$$6x = 18$$
$$x = 3$$

Solution (3, -1)

4. $\begin{cases} 4x + y = 7 & (2) \\ 6x + 2y = 13 \end{cases}$

$$(-)\begin{cases} 8x + 2y = 14 \\ 6x + 2y = 13 \end{cases}$$
$$2x = 1$$
$$x = \frac{1}{2}$$

$$4(\tfrac{1}{2}) + y = 7$$
$$2 + y = 7$$
$$y = 5$$

Solution $(\frac{1}{2}, 5)$

5. $\begin{cases} x + y = -5 & (2) \\ 3x + 2y = -13 \end{cases}$

$$(-)\begin{cases} 2x + 2y = -10 \\ 3x + 2y = -13 \end{cases}$$
$$-x = 3$$
$$x = -3$$

$$-3 + y = -5$$
$$y = -2$$

Solution (-3, -2)

6. $\begin{cases} 2x - 4y = 5 & (2) \\ 5x + 8y = 17 \end{cases}$

$$(+)\begin{cases} 4x - 8y = 10 \\ 5x + 8y = 17 \end{cases}$$
$$9x = 27$$
$$x = 3$$

$$2(3) - 4y = 5$$
$$6 - 4y = 5$$
$$-4y = -1$$
$$y = \frac{1}{4}$$

Solution $(3, \frac{1}{4})$

7. $\begin{cases} 3a - 6 = 2b \\ 4a - 3 = 3b \end{cases}$

$\begin{cases} 3a - 2b = 6 & (3) \\ 4a - 3b = 3 & (2) \end{cases}$

$$(-)\begin{cases} 9a - 6b = 18 \\ 8a - 6b = 6 \end{cases}$$
$$a = 12$$

$$3(12) - 6 = 2b$$
$$36 - 6 = 2b$$
$$2b = 30$$
$$b = 15$$

Solution (12, 15)

8. $\begin{cases} .5x + .2y = 2 & (10) \\ x - y = 18 & (2) \end{cases}$

$$(+)\begin{cases} 5x + 2y = 20 \\ 2x - 2y = 36 \end{cases}$$
$$7x = 56$$
$$x = 8$$

$$.5(8) + .2y = 2$$
$$4 + .2y = 2$$
$$.2y = -2$$
$$y = \frac{-2}{.2}$$
$$y = -\frac{20}{2}$$
$$y = -10$$

Solution (8, -10)

9.

$$\begin{cases} 3m + 6n = 5 \\ 6m + 4 = 9n \end{cases}$$

$$\begin{cases} 3m + 6n = 5 & (2) \\ 6m - 9n = -4 \end{cases}$$

$$\begin{aligned} &\begin{cases} 6m + 12n = 10 \\ 6m - 9n = -4 \end{cases} \quad (-) \\ &21n = 14 \\ &n = \frac{2}{3} \end{aligned}$$

$$\begin{aligned} 3m + 6\left(\frac{2}{3}\right) &= 5 \\ 3m + 4 &= 5 \\ 3m &= 1 \\ m &= \frac{1}{3} \end{aligned}$$

Solution $\left(\frac{1}{3}, \frac{2}{3}\right)$

10.

$$\begin{cases} .4r - .3s = -1 & (10) \\ .6r - .3s = 0 & (10) \end{cases}$$

$$\begin{aligned} &\begin{cases} 4r - 3s = -10 \\ 6r - 3s = 0 \end{cases} \quad (-) \\ &-2r = -10 \\ &r = 5 \end{aligned}$$

$$\begin{aligned} .4(5) - .3s &= -1 \\ 2 - .3s &= -1 \\ -.3s &= -3 \\ s &= \frac{-3}{-.3} \\ s &= \frac{30}{3} \\ s &= 10 \end{aligned}$$

Solution (5, 10)

11.

$$\begin{cases} 3p + 4q = 100 & (3) \\ 8p - 3q = 48 & (4) \end{cases}$$

$$\begin{aligned} &\begin{cases} 9p + 12q = 300 \\ 32p - 12q = 192 \end{cases} \quad (+) \\ &41p = 492 \\ &p = 12 \end{aligned}$$

$$\begin{aligned} 3(12) + 4q &= 100 \\ 36 + 4q &= 100 \\ 4q &= 64 \\ q &= 16 \end{aligned}$$

Solution (12, 16)

12.

$$\begin{cases} 8a + 8\ell = -5b \\ 4a + 23 = b \end{cases}$$

$$\begin{cases} 8a + 5b = -8\ell \\ 4a - b = -23 & (5) \end{cases}$$

$$\begin{aligned} &\begin{cases} 8a + 5b = -8\ell \\ 20a - 5b = -115 \end{cases} \quad (+) \\ &28a = -196 \\ &a = -7 \end{aligned}$$

$$\begin{aligned} 8(-7) + 8\ell &= -5b \\ -56 + 8\ell &= -5b \\ 25 &= -5b \\ b &= -5 \end{aligned}$$

Solution (-7, -5)

<u>Review of Linear Systems</u> Pages 246-247

1. Fractional equations contain variables in the denominator; integral equations do not. Integral equations may have fractional coefficients, however. Dependent equations are two equations which express one relation between the variables and can be reduced to the same equation. Independent equations are two equations which express different relations between the variables and cannot be reduced to the same equation.

2. The root or roots of an equation refer to the value or values that make the equation true. To solve an equation is to find the root(s).

3. Equivalent equations are different equations having the same root or roots. Illustrations will vary.

4. A formula is a computational rule written using variables. Formulas will vary.

5. Answers will vary. The equation is a linear equation because all variables contained are of the first degree.

6. A system of equations is two or more equations, all of which must be satisfied by the same values of the variables. Elimination refers to getting an equivalent system of equations in which one of the variables is eliminated from all the equations. The same quantity may be added to both sides of an equation and equality retained. Equal quantities may be substituted for one another in an equation without losing equality.

7. Multiply one or both of a set of two linear equations by whatever constant or constants will make the coefficients on one of the variables the same or opposites; then add or subtract corresponding members of the equations making one variable drop out. To solve by substitution, solve one equation for a particular variable and substitute the result for that variable in the other equation.

8. A graph is a picture of the relation between two variables. Graphs teach by the eye, giving a better picture than just number pairs, equations, or formulas by themselves.

9. Coordinates are the x-distance and y-distance from the intersection of perpendicular axes. The origin is the point where the axes intersect.

10. Positive values of x are located to the right of the origin and positive values of y above the origin. Negative values of x are located to the left of the origin and negative values of y below the origin. Point A = (-4, 3) is four units left and three above the origin.

11. Zero; zero; (0, 0)

12. Linear equations in two variables graph as lines.

13.

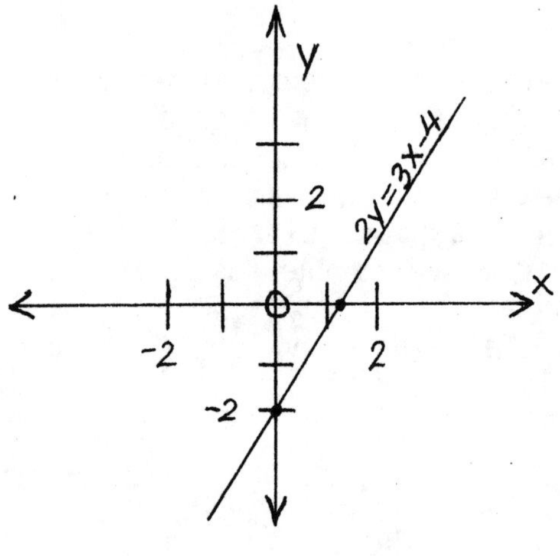

x	y
0	-2
$\frac{4}{3}$	0

14. Two; two points determine a line.

15. Set y = 0 in the equation; set x = 0 in the equation.

16. Only one point is found. Pick a non-zero value for x or y and substitute it into the equation.

17. A point where the lines representing the equations intersect.

18.

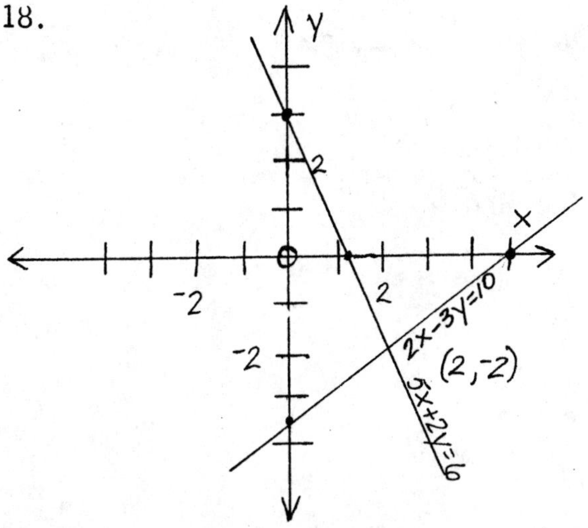

$2x - 3y = 10$

x	y
5	0
0	$-3\frac{1}{3}$

$5x + 2y = 6$

x	y
$1\frac{1}{5}$	0
0	3

$$\begin{cases} 2x - 3y = 10 & (2) \\ 5x + 2y = 6 & (3) \end{cases}$$

$$\begin{aligned} &\begin{cases} 4x - 6y = 20 \\ 15x + 6y = 18 \end{cases} \quad (+) \\ &19x = 38 \\ &x = 2 \end{aligned}$$

$$\begin{aligned} 2(2) - 3y &= 10 \\ -3y &= 6 \\ y &= -2 \end{aligned}$$

Solution (2, -2)

19. Both equations will graph as the same line.

20.

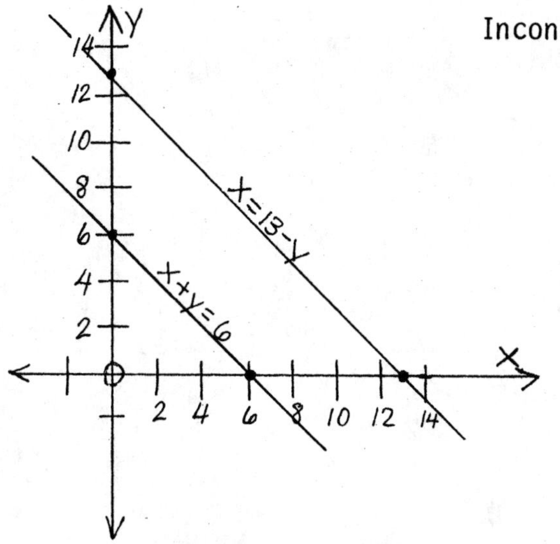

Inconsistent; no solution

21. integral equations a, c, d, e
fractional equations b, f
numerical equations a, b, d, e
literal equations c, f
indeterminate equations a, f

22. a) $\begin{cases} 3x = 18 \\ x + 5 = 11 \end{cases}$ Equivalent equations as x = 6 in each.

b) $\begin{cases} x + y = 7 \\ x + y = 11 \end{cases}$ Inconsistent system of equations. They graph as parallel lines and have no solution.

c) $\begin{cases} x + y = 6 \\ 3x - y = 2 \end{cases}$ Consistent independent system of equations; solution is (2, 4).

d) $\begin{cases} x - y = 2 \\ 3x - 3y = 6 \end{cases}$ Dependent system of equations; solution is indeterminate.

23.

$$\begin{cases} \frac{x}{y} = \frac{2}{3} \\ \frac{x + 5}{x - y} = \frac{3}{1} \end{cases}$$

$$\begin{cases} 3x = 2y \\ 3x - 3y = x + 5 \end{cases}$$

$$\begin{cases} 3x - 2y = 0 & (3) \\ 2x - 3y = 5 & (2) \end{cases}$$

$$\begin{array}{rl} & 9x - 6y = 0 \\ (-) & \underline{4x - 6y = 10} \\ & 5x = -10 \\ & x = -2 \end{array}$$

$$3(-2) = 2y$$
$$2y = -6$$
$$y = -3$$

Solution (-2, -3)

24. let x = one angle $\quad 56\frac{1}{4}^\circ$

let y = other angle $\quad 33\frac{3}{4}^\circ$

$$\begin{cases} x + y = 90 \\ \frac{5}{3} = \frac{x}{y} \end{cases}$$

$$3x = 5y$$

$$\begin{cases} 3x - 5y = 0 \\ x + y = 90 & (5) \end{cases}$$

$$\begin{array}{rl} & 3x - 5y = 0 \\ (+) & \underline{5x + 5y = 450} \\ & 8x = 450 \\ & x = 56\frac{2}{8} = 56\frac{1}{4} \end{array}$$

$$56\frac{1}{4} + y = 90$$
$$y = 33\frac{3}{4}$$

$$\begin{array}{r} 56\frac{1}{4}^\circ \\ +33\frac{3}{4}^\circ \\ \hline 90^\circ \checkmark \end{array} \qquad \frac{56\frac{1}{4}}{33\frac{3}{4}} = \frac{\frac{225}{4}}{\frac{135}{4}} = \frac{225}{135} = \frac{5}{3} \checkmark$$

25. let A = amount received by Andrew $8.10
let P = amount received by Paul $9.00

$$\begin{cases} A + P = 17.10 \\ \dfrac{13.5}{15} = \dfrac{A}{P} \end{cases}$$

$$15A = 13.5P$$
$$15A - 13.5P = 0$$

$$\begin{cases} 15A - 13.5P = 0 \\ A + P = 17.10 \quad (13.5) \end{cases}$$

$$\begin{array}{rl} & 15A - 13.5P = 0 \\ (+) & 13.5A + 13.5P = 230.85 \\ \hline & 28.5A = 230.85 \\ & A = 8.10 \end{array}$$

$$8.10 + P = 17.10$$
$$P = 9.00$$

$$\begin{array}{r} \$\ 8.10 \\ +\ 9.00 \\ \hline \$17.10 \end{array} \checkmark$$

$$\frac{13.5}{15} = \frac{135}{150} = \frac{81}{90} = \frac{8.10}{9.00} \checkmark$$

Test A   Page 248

The check is left for the teacher.

1.
$$\begin{array}{rl} & m - 2n = 7 \\ (-) & m + 3n = -3 \\ \hline & -5n = 10 \\ & n = -2 \end{array}$$

$$m - 2(-2) = 7$$
$$m + 4 = 7$$
$$m = 3$$

Solution (3, -2)

2.
$$\begin{array}{rl} & 3x - y = 1 \\ (+) & 5x + y = 15 \\ \hline & 8x = 16 \\ & x = 2 \end{array}$$

$$3(2) - y = 1$$
$$6 - y = 1$$
$$-y = -5$$
$$y = 5$$

Solution (2, 5)

3.
$$\begin{cases} 3a - 4f = 0 \\ a + 2f = 10 \quad (2) \end{cases}$$

$$\begin{array}{rl} & 3a - 4f = 0 \\ (+) & 2a + 4f = 20 \\ \hline & 5a = 20 \\ & a = 4 \end{array}$$

$$4 + 2f = 10$$
$$2f = 6$$
$$f = 3$$

Solution (4, 3)

4.
$$\begin{cases} 6x + 2y = 8 \quad (3) \\ 7x + 3y = 6 \quad (2) \end{cases}$$

$$\begin{array}{rl} & 18x + 6y = 24 \\ (-) & 14x + 6y = 12 \\ \hline & 4x = 12 \\ & x = 3 \end{array}$$

$$6(3) + 2y = 8$$
$$18 + 2y = 8$$
$$2y = -10$$
$$y = -5$$

Solution (3, -5)

5.
$$\begin{array}{rl} & \dfrac{1}{x} - \dfrac{1}{y} = 1 \\ (+) & \dfrac{2}{x} + \dfrac{1}{y} = 8 \\ \hline & \dfrac{3}{x} = 9 \\ & 3 = 9x \\ & x = \dfrac{3}{9} = \dfrac{1}{3} \end{array}$$

$$\frac{1}{\frac{1}{3}} - \frac{1}{y} = 1$$
$$3 - \frac{1}{y} = 1$$
$$-\frac{1}{y} = -2$$
$$-2y = -1$$
$$y = \frac{1}{2}$$

Solution $(\frac{1}{3}, \frac{1}{2})$

6. $$\begin{cases} \dfrac{r + t}{r - t} = 4 \\ \dfrac{5t - 3}{6} = \dfrac{r + t}{4} \end{cases}$$

$r + t = 4(r - t)$ $\qquad$ $6(r + t) = 4(5t - 3)$

$r + t = 4r - 4t$ $\qquad$ $6r + 6t = 20t - 12$

$$\begin{cases} -3r + 5t = 0 \quad (2) \\ 6r - 14t = -12 \end{cases}$$

$$(+)\begin{cases} -6r + 10t = 0 \\ 6r - 14t = -12 \end{cases}$$

$-4t = -12$

$t = 3$

$\dfrac{r + 3}{r - 3} = 4$

$r + 3 = 4(r - 3)$

$r + 3 = 4r - 12$

$-3r = -15$

$r = 5$

Solution (5, 3)

7. $$\begin{cases} 2x - y = 16 \\ x + 3y = -6 \end{cases}$$

$2x - y = 16$

x	y
8	0
5	-6
4	-8

$x + 3y = -6$

x	y
-6	0
0	-2
3	-3

Solution (6, -4)

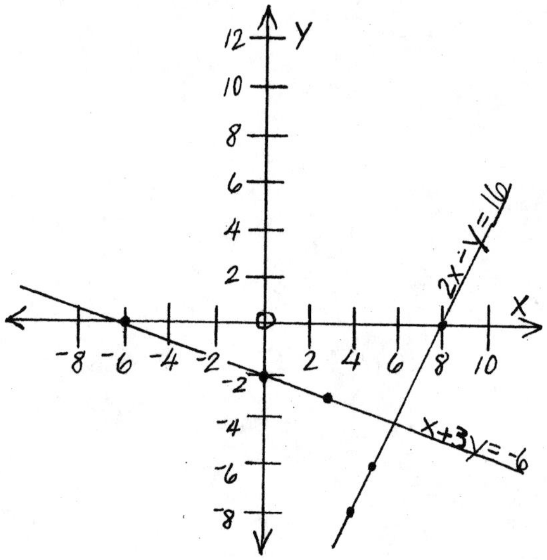

Test B   Page 248

The check is left for the teacher.

1.
$$(-)\begin{cases} x + y = 5 \\ x - 2y = -1 \end{cases}$$
$$3y = 6$$
$$y = 2$$
$$x + 2 = 5$$
$$x = 3$$

Solution (3, 2)

2.
$$\begin{cases} 5a + 3b = 42 \\ 4a - b = 20 \end{cases}$$
$$(+)\begin{cases} 5a + 3b = 42 \\ 12a - 3b = 60 \end{cases}$$
$$17a = 102$$
$$a = 6$$
$$5(6) + 3b = 42$$
$$30 + 3b = 42$$
$$3b = 12$$
$$b = 4$$

Solution (6, 4)

3.
$$\begin{cases} 2x - 3y = 2 \quad (2) \\ 3x - 2y = 8 \quad (3) \end{cases}$$
$$(-)\begin{cases} 4x - 6y = 4 \\ 9x - 6y = 24 \end{cases}$$
$$-5x = -20$$
$$x = 4$$
$$2(4) - 3y = 2$$
$$8 - 3y = 2$$
$$-3y = -6$$
$$y = 2$$

Solution (4, 2)

4.
$$(+)\begin{cases} 6m - n = -1 \\ 5m + n = 12 \end{cases}$$
$$11m = 11$$
$$m = 1$$
$$6(1) - n = -1$$
$$-n = -7$$
$$n = 7$$

Solution (1, 7)

5.
$$(+)\begin{cases} \frac{2}{x} + \frac{1}{y} = \frac{1}{6} \\ \frac{1}{x} + \frac{1}{y} = \frac{5}{6} \end{cases}$$
$$\frac{1}{x} = \frac{2}{3}$$
$$x - 2x = 3$$
$$x = \frac{3}{-2}$$
$$\frac{2}{\frac{3}{-2}} + \frac{1}{y} = \frac{1}{6}$$
$$-\frac{4}{3} + \frac{1}{y} = \frac{1}{6}$$
$$\frac{1}{y} = \frac{1}{6} + \frac{8}{6}$$
$$\frac{1}{y} = \frac{9}{6}$$
$$9y = 6$$
$$y = \frac{6}{9} \text{ or } \frac{2}{3}$$

Solution $(-\frac{3}{2}, \frac{2}{3})$

6.
$$\begin{cases} \frac{a}{4} + \frac{b+1}{3} = 5 \quad (12) \\ \frac{a}{3} - \frac{3b+1}{4} = 0 \quad (12) \end{cases}$$
$$\begin{cases} 3a + 4(b + 1) = 60 \\ 4a - 3(3b + 1) = 0 \end{cases}$$
$$\begin{cases} 3a + 4b = 56 \quad (9) \\ 4a - 9b = 3 \quad (4) \end{cases}$$
$$(+)\begin{cases} 27a + 36b = 504 \\ 16a - 36b = 12 \end{cases}$$
$$43a = 516$$
$$a = 12$$
$$\frac{12}{4} + \frac{b+1}{3} = 5$$
$$3 + \frac{b+1}{3} = 5$$
$$\frac{b+1}{3} = 2$$
$$b + 1 = 6$$
$$b = 5$$

Solution (12, 5)

7. $3x + y = 7$

x	y
0	7
2	1
3	-2

$2x - y = 3$

x	y
$\frac{3}{2}$	0
0	-3
2	1

Solution (2, 1)

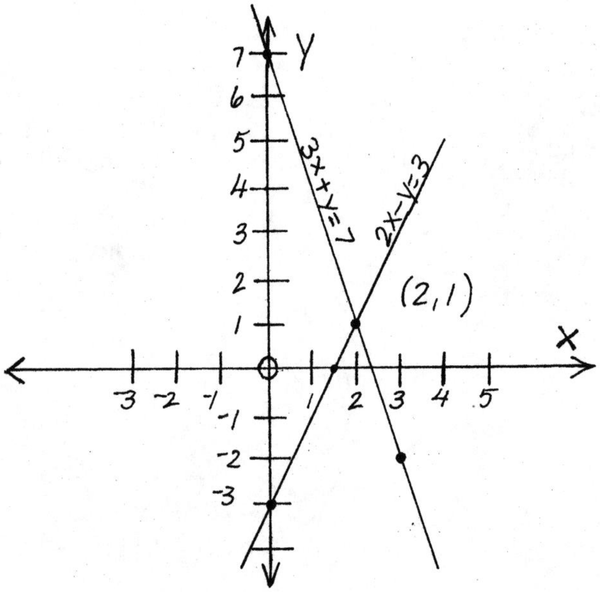

Test C Pages 248-249

I 1. $2x - y = 4$

x	y
2	0
0	-4
3	2

$4x - 2y = -2$

x	y
0	1
1	3
2	5

The lines are parallel; the system is inconsistent.

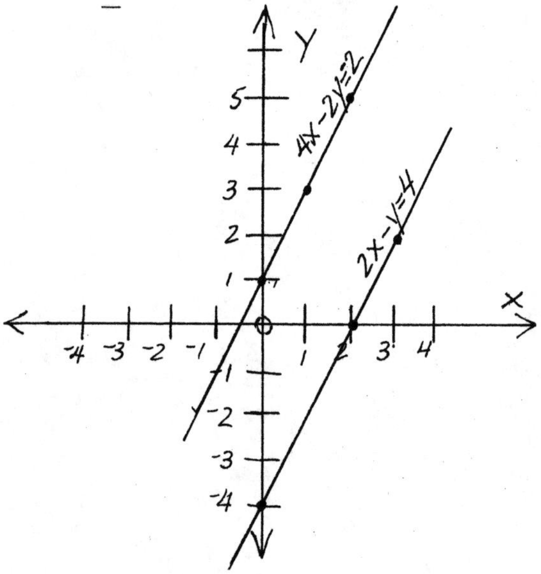

2. $x + 5y = 2$ $3x + 15y = 6$

x	y
2	0
-3	1
-8	2

The solution is indeterminate. Dividing each term of the second equation by 3 gives the first equation. The system is dependent; that is, both graph as the same line.

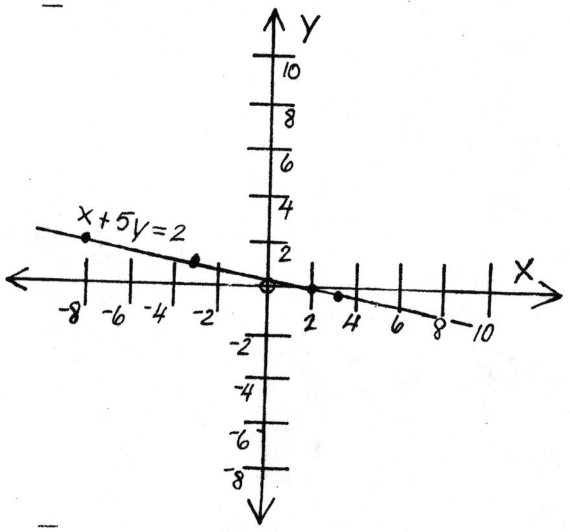

II 1. let f = father's wages
s = son's wages

$$\left.\begin{aligned} 6f + 6s &= 900 \\ 8f + 8s &= 1200 \end{aligned}\right\}$$ Dependent system, solution indeterminate; solutions will vary.

2. let x = price of first candy <u>$1.80</u>
y = price of second candy <u>$2.70</u>

$$\begin{cases} 6x + 5y = 24.3 & (3) \\ 9x + 3y = 24.3 & (5) \end{cases}$$

$$(-)\begin{cases} 18x + 15y = 72.9 \\ 45x + 15y = 121.5 \end{cases}$$
$$-27x = -48.6$$
$$x = 1.8$$

$$6(1.8) + 5y = 24.3$$
$$10.8 + 5y = 24.3$$
$$5y = 13.5$$
$$y = 2.7$$

$ 1.80	$ 2.70	$10.80
x 6	x 5	+13.50
$10.80	$13.50	$24.30 ✓
$ 1.80	$2.70	$16.20
x 9	x 3	+ 8.10
$16.20	$8.10	$24.30 ✓

3. let x = rate of first man <u>5.5 mph</u>
y = rate of second man <u>4 mph</u>

$$\begin{cases} 6x + 4y = 49 \\ 3x - 2y = 8.5 & (2) \end{cases}$$

$$(+)\begin{cases} 6x + 4y = 49 \\ 6x - 4y = 17 \end{cases}$$
$$12x = 66$$
$$x = 5.5$$

$$6(5.5) + 4y = 49$$
$$33 + 4y = 49$$
$$4y = 16$$
$$y = 4$$

5.5	4	33.0	5.5	4	16.5
x 6	x4	+16	x 3	x2	-8
33.0	16	49.0 ✓	16.5	8	8.5 ✓

UNIT 12 — Powers and Roots

Exercises 12.1   Page 253

1. $(ab^2c^3)^2 = a^2b^4c^6$
2. $(a^3b^2c)^4 = a^{12}b^8c^4$
3. $(2a^2c)^3 = 8a^6c^3$
4. $(7a^2m^5)^2 = 49a^4m^{10}$
5. $(-4c^2y^5)^3 = -64c^6y^{15}$
6. $(-2a^3n^5)^4 = 16a^{12}n^{20}$
7. $(abcx)^m = a^mb^mc^mx^m$
8. $(2e^2x^c)^6 = 64e^{12}x^{6c}$
9. $(-1)^9 = -1$
10. $(-1)^{10} = 1$
11. $(3bc)^n = 3^nb^nc^n$
12. $(2a^2x^3)^n = 2^na^{2n}x^{3n}$

Exercises 12.2   Page 254

1. $(\frac{1}{4b})^2 = \frac{1}{16b^2}$
2. $(\frac{2x}{7y})^2 = \frac{4x^2}{49y^2}$
3. $(\frac{3x^2}{10y^3})^2 = \frac{9x^4}{100y^6}$
4. $(\frac{-5}{ab})^2 = \frac{25}{a^2b^2}$
5. $(-\frac{2}{3x})^4 = \frac{16}{81x^4}$
6. $(-\frac{3x}{2y})^3 = -\frac{27x^3}{8y^3}$
7. $(-\frac{2a}{b})^6 = \frac{64a^6}{b^6}$
8. $(-\frac{b^3c^2}{a^2x})^2 = \frac{b^6c^4}{a^4x^2}$
9. $(\frac{a^2b^3}{xy^4})^n = \frac{a^{2n}b^{3n}}{x^ny^{4n}}$
10. (1) $(\frac{2a}{3})^2 = \frac{4a^2}{9}$ (2) $(\frac{3b}{c})^2 = \frac{9b^2}{c^2}$ (3) $(\frac{4a}{5b})^2 = \frac{16a^2}{25b^2}$

    (4) $(\frac{2}{3b})^2 = \frac{4}{9b^2}$ (5) $(\frac{7a}{8m})^2 = \frac{49a^2}{64m^2}$

Exercises 12.3   Page 256

1. $(3x + 4y)^2 = (3x)^2 + 2(3x)(4y) + (4y)^2 = 9x^2 + 24xy + 16y^2$
2. $(5m - 4n)^2 = (5m)^2 + 2(5m)(-4n) + (-4n)^2 = 25m^2 - 40mn + 16n^2$
3. $(5m^2 - 6)^2 = (5m^2)^2 + 2(5m^2)(-6) + (-6)^2 = 25m^4 - 60m^2 + 36$
4. $(4r^2 + s^2) = (4r^2)^2 + 2(4r^2)(s^2) + (s^2)^2 = 16r^4 + 8r^2s^2 + s^4$
5. $(2a + b + c)^2 = (2a)^2 + b^2 + c^2 + 2(2a)(b) + 2(2a)(c) + 2(b)(c)$
   $= 4a^2 + b^2 + c^2 + 4ab + 4ac + 2bc$
6. $(3a + 2b - 4c)^2 = (3a)^2 + (2b)^2 + (-4c)^2 + 2(3a)(2b) + 2(3a)(-4c) + 2(2b)(-4c)$
   $= 9a^2 + 4b^2 + 16c^2 + 12ab - 24ac - 16bc$

7. $(5a - 2c - 3e)^2 = (5a)^2 + (-2c)^2 + (-3e)^2 + 2(5a)(-2c) + 2(5a)(-3e) + 2(-2c)(-3e)$
$= 25a^2 + 4c^2 + 9e^2 - 20ac - 30ae + 12ce$

8. $(3r^2 + 2s + t^4)^2 = (3r^2)^2 + (2s)^2 + (t^4)^2 + 2(3r^2)(2s) + 2(3r^2)(t^4) + 2(2s)(t^4)$
$= 9r^4 + 4s^2 + t^8 + 12r^2s + 6r^2t^4 + 4st^4$

9. $(2x^2 + 3y + z^3)^2 = (2x^2)^2 + (3y)^2 + (z^3)^2 + 2(2x^2)(3y) + 2(2x^2)(z^3) + 2(3y)(z^3)$
$= 4x^4 + 9y^2 + z^6 + 12x^2y + 4x^2z^3 + 6yz^3$

10. $(x + y)^3 = (x + y)^2(x + y) = (x^2 + 2xy + y^2)(x + y)$
$= x^3 + x^2y + 2x^2y + 2xy^2 + xy^2 + y^3$
$= x^3 + 3x^2y + 3xy^2 + y^3$

11. $(x - y)^3 = (x - y)^2(x - y) = (x^2 - 2xy + y^2)(x - y)$
$= x^3 - x^2y - 2x^2y + 2xy^2 + xy^2 - y^3$
$= x^3 - 3x^2y + 3xy^2 - y^3$

12. $(a + b)^4 = [(a + b)^2]^2 = (a^2 + 2ab + b^2)^2$
$= (a^2)^2 + (2ab)^2 + (b^2)^2 + 2(a^2)(2ab) + 2(a^2)(b^2) + 2(2ab)(b^2)$
$= a^4 + 4a^2b^2 + b^4 + 4a^3b + 2a^2b^2 + 4ab^3$
$= a^4 + 4a^3b + 6a^2b^2 + 4ab^3 + b^4$

13. $(a - b)^4 = [(a - b)^2]^2 = (a^2 - 2ab + b^2)^2$
$= (a^2)^2 + (-2ab)^2 + (b^2)^2 + 2(a^2)(-2ab) + 2(a^2)(b^2) + 2(-2ab)(b^2)$
$= a^4 + 4a^2b^2 + b^4 - 4a^3b + 2a^2b^2 - 4ab^3$
$= a^4 - 4a^3b + 6a^2b^2 - 4ab^3 + b^4$

14. (See number 12 for $(a + b)^4$)
$(a + b)^5 = (a + b)^4(a + b)$
$= (a^4 + 4a^3b + 6a^2b^2 + 4ab^3 + b^4)(a + b)$
$= a^5 + 4a^4b + 6a^3b^2 + 4a^2b^3 + ab^4 = (a + b)^4a$
(+) $\quad a^4b + 4a^3b^2 + 6a^2b^3 + 4ab^4 + b^5 = (a + b)^4b$
$a^5 + 5a^4b + 10a^3b^2 + 10a^2b^3 + 5ab^4 + b^5 = (a + b)^4(a + b)$

15. (See number 13 for $(a - b)^4$)
$(a - b)^5 = (a - b)^4(a - b)$
$= (a^4 - 4a^3b + 6a^2b^2 - 4ab^3 + b^4)(a - b)$
$= a^5 - 4a^4b + 6a^3b^2 - 4a^2b^3 + ab^4 = (a - b)^4a$
(+) $\quad - a^4b + 4a^3b^2 - 6a^2b^3 + 4ab^4 - b^5 = (a - b)^4(-b)$
$a^5 - 5a^4b + 10a^3b^2 - 10a^2b^3 + 5ab^4 - b^5 = (a - b)^4[a + (-b)]$

16. The volume of a cube is equal to the cube of the length of an edge.

17. (a) $(a + b)^3 = (a + b)^2(a + b) = (a^2 + 2ab + b^2)(a + b)$
$= a^3 + 2a^2b + ab^2 + a^2b + 2ab^2 + b^3$
$= a^3 + 3a^2b + 3ab^2 + b^3$

(b) $(a - b)^3 = (a - b)^2(a - b) = (a^2 - 2ab + b^2)(a - b)$
$= a^3 - 2a^2b + ab^2 - a^2b + 2ab^2 - b^3$
$= a^3 - 3a^2b + 3ab^2 - b^3$

18. $(a + 2b)^3 = (a + 2b)^2(a + 2b)$
$= (a^2 + 4ab + 4b^2)(a + 2b) = a^3 + 4a^2b + 4ab^2 + 2a^2b + 8ab^2 + 8b^3$
$= a^3 + 6a^2b + 12ab^2 + 8b^3$

19. $(2a - b)^3 = (2a - b)^2(2a - b)$
$= (4a^2 - 4ab + b^2)(2a - b) = 8a^3 - 8a^2b + 2ab^2 - 4a^2b + 4ab^2 - b^3$
$= 8a^3 - 12a^2b + 6ab^2 - b^3$

20. See table, page 267, for cubes of numbers 1 to 10.

<u>Exercises 12.5</u> Page 257

1. $\sqrt{625} = 25$
2. $\sqrt[3]{729} = 9$
3. $\sqrt[3]{343} = 7$
4. $\sqrt{441} = 21$
5. $\sqrt{484} = 22$
6. $\sqrt[3]{512} = 8$
7. $\sqrt{576} = 24$
8. $\sqrt[3]{216} = 6$
9. $\sqrt{289} = 17$
10. $\sqrt[3]{1000} = 10$
11. $\sqrt[4]{81} = 3$
12. $\sqrt[5]{1} = 1$

<u>Exercises 12.6a</u> Page 259

1. $\sqrt[3]{a^3b^6c^9} = a^{\frac{3}{3}}b^{\frac{6}{3}}c^{\frac{9}{3}} = ab^2c^3$

2. $\sqrt{a^6b^4c^8} = a^{\frac{6}{2}}b^{\frac{4}{2}}c^{\frac{8}{2}} = a^3b^2c^4$

3. $\sqrt[5]{a^{10}x^5y^{15}} = a^{\frac{10}{5}}x^{\frac{5}{5}}y^{\frac{15}{5}} = a^2xy^3$

4. $\sqrt[4]{a^{4n}b^8c^{12}} = a^{\frac{4n}{4}}b^{\frac{8}{4}}c^{\frac{12}{4}} = a^nb^2c^3$

5. $\sqrt{x^{4n}y^8z^{2m}} = x^{\frac{4n}{2}}y^{\frac{8}{2}}z^{\frac{2m}{2}} = x^{2n}y^4z^m$

6. $\sqrt[3]{-8a^6a^{15}} = (-8)^{\frac{1}{3}}a^{\frac{6}{3}}b^{\frac{15}{3}} = -2a^2b^5$

7. $\sqrt[5]{-32x^{10}y^{10}} = (-32)^{\frac{1}{5}}x^{\frac{10}{5}}y^{\frac{10}{5}} = -2x^2y^2$

8. $\sqrt{16x^4y^2} = 16^{\frac{1}{2}}x^{\frac{4}{2}}y^{\frac{2}{2}} = 4x^2y$

9. $\sqrt[7]{-a^7b^{14}x^7} = -a^{\frac{7}{7}}b^{\frac{14}{7}}x^{\frac{7}{7}} = -ab^2x$

10. $\sqrt[5]{-243y^{5n}} = (-243)^{\frac{1}{5}}y^{\frac{5n}{5}} = -3y^n$

11. $\sqrt{(-mb^3)^2} = (-mb^3)^{\frac{2}{2}} = -mb^3$ Notice ± is not used when the root is taken, as clearly it is the "negative" root being squared. The following procedure fails to use this knowledge. $\sqrt{(-mb^3)^2} = \sqrt{m^2b^6} = mb^3$

12. $\sqrt[3]{(-a^2b)^9} = (-a^2b)^{\frac{9}{3}}$
$= (-a^2b)^3$
$= -a^6b^3$

13. $-\sqrt[9]{a^{18}b^9c^{27}} = -(a^{\frac{18}{9}}b^{\frac{9}{9}}c^{\frac{27}{9}})$
$= -a^2bc^3$

14. $-\sqrt[3]{-27p^9r^3} = -(-27^{\frac{1}{3}}p^{\frac{9}{3}}r^{\frac{3}{3}})$
$= -(-3p^3r)$
$= 3p^3r$

15. $\sqrt[3]{8a^6c^9d^9} = 8^{\frac{1}{3}}a^{\frac{6}{3}}c^{\frac{9}{3}}d^{\frac{9}{3}} = 2a^2c^3d^3$

Exercises 12.6b   Page 260

1. $\sqrt[3]{\frac{-8x^9y^6}{27m^3n^{12}}} = \frac{\sqrt[3]{-8x^9y^6}}{\sqrt[3]{27m^3n^{12}}} = \frac{(-8)^{\frac{1}{3}}x^{\frac{9}{3}}y^{\frac{6}{3}}}{27^{\frac{1}{3}}m^{\frac{3}{3}}n^{\frac{12}{3}}} = -\frac{2x^3y^2}{3mn^4}$

2. $\sqrt{\frac{64a^4b^6}{81m^2n^8}} = \frac{\sqrt{64a^4b^6}}{\sqrt{81m^2n^8}} = \pm\frac{64^{\frac{1}{2}}a^{\frac{4}{2}}b^{\frac{6}{2}}}{81^{\frac{1}{2}}m^{\frac{2}{2}}n^{\frac{8}{2}}} = \pm\frac{8a^2b^3}{9mn^4}$

3. $\sqrt[7]{\frac{(x-y)^{14}}{128x^{14}}} = \frac{\sqrt[7]{(x-y)^{14}}}{\sqrt[7]{128x^{14}}} = \frac{(x-y)^{\frac{14}{7}}}{128^{\frac{1}{7}}x^{\frac{14}{7}}} = \frac{(x-y)^2}{2x^2}$

4. $\sqrt[3]{-125\frac{x^3}{y^9}} = \frac{\sqrt[3]{-125x^3}}{\sqrt[3]{y^9}} = \frac{(-125)^{\frac{1}{3}}x^{\frac{3}{3}}}{y^{\frac{9}{3}}} = -\frac{5x}{y^3}$

5. $\sqrt[5]{\frac{-32a^5x^{10}}{243y^{15}}} = \frac{\sqrt[5]{-32a^5x^{10}}}{\sqrt[5]{243y^{15}}} = \frac{(-32)^{\frac{1}{5}}a^{\frac{5}{5}}x^{\frac{10}{5}}}{243^{\frac{1}{5}}y^{\frac{15}{5}}} = -\frac{2ax^2}{3y^3}$

6. $\sqrt[3]{\left(\frac{-27a^3}{64b^6}\right)^2} = \frac{\sqrt[3]{(-27a^3)^2}}{\sqrt[3]{(64b^6)^2}} = \frac{(-27a^3)^{\frac{2}{3}}}{(64b^6)^{\frac{2}{3}}} = \frac{(-27)^{\frac{2}{3}}a^2}{64^{\frac{2}{3}}b^4} = \frac{9a^2}{16b^4}$

7. $\sqrt[3]{\frac{125x^{12}y^{12}}{1728c^3}} = \frac{\sqrt[3]{125x^{12}y^{12}}}{\sqrt[3]{1728c^3}} = \frac{(125)^{\frac{1}{3}}x^{\frac{12}{3}}y^{\frac{12}{3}}}{1728^{\frac{1}{3}}c^{\frac{3}{3}}} = \frac{5x^4y^4}{12c}$

Exercises 12.7a   Page 261

1.

	$4x^2 + 12x + 9$	$2x + 3$
$(2x)^2 = $	$4x^2$	$\pm(2x + 3)$
	$12x + 9$	
$2(2x) = 4x + 3$	$12x + 9$	

2.

	$x^2 + 2x + 1$	$x + 1$
$(x)^2 = $	x^2	$\pm(x + 1)$
	$2x + 1$	
$2(x) = 2x + 1$	$2x + 1$	

3.

$$\begin{array}{l}4m^2 - 4m + 1 \;\Big|\; 2m - 1 \\ \pm(2m - 1)\end{array}$$

$(2m)^2 = 4m^2$

$-4m + 1$

$2(2m) = 4m - 1$ $\quad -4m + 1$

4.

$$c^2 - 12c + 36 \;\Big|\; c - 6 \qquad \pm(c - 6)$$

$(c)^2 = c^2$

$-12c + 36$

$2(c) = 2c - 6$ $\quad -12c + 36$

5.

$$4x^2 + 4x + 1 \;\Big|\; 2x + 1 \qquad \pm(2x + 1)$$

$(2x)^2 = 4x^2$

$4x + 1$

$2(2x) = 4x + 1$ $\quad 4x + 1$

6.

$$\frac{4a^2}{b^2} + 8 + \frac{4b^2}{a^2} \;\Big|\; \frac{2a}{b} + \frac{2b}{a} \qquad \pm\left(\frac{2a}{b} + \frac{2b}{a}\right)$$

$\left(\frac{2a}{b}\right)^2 = \frac{4a^2}{b^2}$

$2\left(\frac{2a}{b}\right) = \frac{4a}{b} + \frac{2b}{a}$ $\quad 8 + \frac{4b^2}{2}$

$8 + \frac{4b^2}{a^2}$

Note: $8 \div \frac{4a}{b} = \overset{2}{\cancel{8}} \cdot \frac{b}{\cancel{4}a} = \frac{2b}{a}$

7.

$$\frac{x^2}{b^2} + 4 + \frac{4b^2}{x^2} \;\Big|\; \frac{x}{b} + \frac{2b}{x} \qquad \pm\left(\frac{x}{b} + \frac{2b}{x}\right)$$

$\left(\frac{x}{b}\right)^2 = \frac{x^2}{b^2}$

$4 + \frac{4b^2}{x^2}$

$2\left(\frac{x}{b}\right) = \frac{2x}{b} + \frac{2b}{x}$ $\quad 4 + \frac{4b^2}{x^2}$

$4 \div \frac{2x}{b} = \overset{2}{\cancel{4}} \cdot \frac{b}{\cancel{2}x} = \frac{2b}{x}$

*8.

$$a^4 - 2a^3 + \frac{3a^2}{2} - \frac{a}{2} + \frac{1}{16} \;\Big|\; a^2 - a + \frac{1}{4} \qquad \pm\left(a^2 - a + \frac{1}{4}\right)$$

$(a^2)^2 = a^4$

$2(a^2) = 2a^2 - a$ $\quad -2a^3 + \frac{3a^2}{2}$

$-2a^3 + a^2$

$\frac{a^2}{2} - \frac{a}{2} + \frac{1}{16}$

$2(a^2 - a) = 2a^2 - 2a + \frac{1}{4}$ $\quad \frac{a^2}{2} - \frac{a}{2} + \frac{1}{16}$

$\frac{a^2}{2} \div 2a^2 = \frac{\cancel{a^2}}{2} \cdot \frac{1}{2\cancel{a^2}} = \frac{1}{4}$

$\frac{1}{4}\left(2a^2 - 2a + \frac{1}{4}\right) = \frac{2a^2}{4} - \frac{2a}{4} + \frac{1}{16}$

$= \frac{a^2}{2} - \frac{a}{2} + \frac{1}{16}$

Exercises 12.7b   Page 265

1.

$$\begin{array}{rl} & 5'29 \quad \underline{|\,2\;3} \\ 2^2 = & 4 \\ 2(20) = 40 & \overline{1\,29} \\ \underline{3} & 1\,29 \\ 43 & \end{array}$$

estimate: 22

$$\begin{array}{r} 24 \\ 22\,\overline{)529} \\ \underline{44} \\ 89 \\ \underline{88} \\ 1 \end{array}$$

estimate

$$\begin{array}{r} 23 \\ 23\,\overline{)529} \\ \underline{46} \\ 69 \\ \underline{69} \end{array}$$

23

2.

$$\begin{array}{rl} & 22'09 \quad \underline{|\,4\;7} \\ 4^2 = & 16 \\ 2(40) = 80 & \overline{6\,09} \\ \underline{7} & 6\,09 \\ 87 & \end{array}$$

estimate: 49

$$\begin{array}{r} 45 \\ 49\,\overline{)2209} \\ \underline{196} \\ 249 \\ \underline{245} \\ 4 \end{array}$$

estimate

$$\begin{array}{r} 47 \\ 47\,\overline{)2209} \\ \underline{188} \\ 329 \\ \underline{329} \end{array}$$

47

3.

$$\begin{array}{rl} & 47'61 \quad \underline{|\,6\;9} \\ 6^2 = & 36 \\ 2(60) = 120 & \overline{11\,61} \\ \underline{9} & 11\,61 \\ 129 & \end{array}$$

$$\begin{aligned} \sqrt{4761} &= \sqrt{3^2 \cdot 23^2} \\ &= \sqrt{3^2} \cdot \sqrt{23^2} \\ &= 3 \cdot 23 \\ &= 69 \end{aligned}$$

$$\begin{array}{r|l} 3 & 4761 \\ 3 & 1587 \\ & 529 \end{array}$$

See number 1.

4.

$$\begin{array}{rl} & 90'25 \quad \underline{|\,9\;5} \\ 9^2 = & 81 \\ 2(90) = 180 & \overline{9\,25} \\ \underline{5} & 9\,25 \\ 185 & \end{array}$$

$$\begin{aligned} \sqrt{9025} &= \sqrt{25 \cdot 19^2} \\ &= \sqrt{25}\,\sqrt{19^2} \\ &= 5 \cdot 19 \\ &= 95 \end{aligned}$$

$$\begin{array}{r|l} 25 & 9025 \\ 19 & 361 \\ & 19 \end{array}$$

5.

$$\begin{array}{rl} & 94'09 \quad \underline{|\,9\;7} \\ 9^2 = & 81 \\ 2(90) = 180 & \overline{13\,09} \\ \underline{7} & 13\,09 \\ 187 & \end{array}$$

estimate: 95

$$\begin{array}{r} 99 \\ 95\,\overline{)9409} \\ \underline{855} \\ 859 \\ \underline{855} \\ 4 \end{array}$$

estimate: 97

$$\begin{array}{r} 97 \\ 97\,\overline{)9409} \\ \underline{873} \\ 679 \\ \underline{679} \end{array}$$

6.

$$\begin{array}{rl} & 98'01 \quad \underline{|\,9\;9} \\ 9^2 = & 81 \\ 2(90) = 180 & \overline{17\,01} \\ \underline{9} & 17\,01 \\ 189 & \end{array}$$

$$\begin{aligned} \sqrt{9801} &= \sqrt{3^2 \cdot 3^2 \cdot 11^2} \\ &= \sqrt{3^2}\,\sqrt{3^2}\,\sqrt{11^2} \\ &= 3 \cdot 3 \cdot 11 \\ &= 99 \end{aligned}$$

$$\begin{array}{r|l} 3 & 9801 \\ 3 & 3267 \\ 3 & 1089 \\ 3 & 363 \\ 11 & 121 \\ & 11 \end{array}$$

7.

$79'21 \quad \underline{|\,8\ 9}$

$8^2 = 64$

$2(80) = 160 \qquad 15\ 21$

$\underline{\quad 9} \qquad \underline{15\ 21}$

169

estimate: 84

$$\begin{array}{r} 94 \\ 84\,\overline{)7921} \\ \underline{756} \\ 361 \\ \underline{336} \\ 25 \end{array}$$

estimate: 89

$$\begin{array}{r} 89 \\ 89\,\overline{)7921} \\ \underline{712} \\ 801 \\ \underline{801} \end{array}$$

89

8.

$65'61 \quad \underline{|\,8\ 1}$

$8^2 = 64$

$2(80) = 160 \qquad 1\ 61$

$\underline{\quad 1} \qquad \underline{1\ 61}$

161

$$\begin{aligned} \sqrt{6561} &= \sqrt{3^4 \cdot 81} \\ &= \sqrt{3^4}\,\sqrt{81} \\ &= 3^2 \cdot 9 \\ &= 9 \cdot 9 \\ &= 81 \end{aligned}$$

$$\begin{array}{r|l} 3 & 6561 \\ 3 & 2187 \\ 3 & 729 \\ 3 & 243 \\ & 81 \end{array}$$

9.

$68'89 \quad \underline{|\,8\ 3}$

$8^2 = 64$

$2(80) = 160 \qquad 4\ 89$

$\underline{\quad 3} \qquad \underline{4\ 89}$

163

estimate: 80

$$\begin{array}{r} 86 \\ 80\,\overline{)6889} \\ \underline{640} \\ 489 \\ \underline{480} \\ 9 \end{array}$$

$$\begin{array}{r} 83 \\ 83\,\overline{)6889} \\ \underline{664} \\ 249 \\ \underline{249} \end{array}$$

83

10.

$50'41 \quad \underline{|\,7\ 1}$

$7^2 = 49$

$2(70) = 140 \qquad 1\ 41$

$\underline{\quad 1} \qquad \underline{1\ 41}$

141

estimate:

$$\begin{array}{r} 72 \\ 70\,\overline{)5041} \\ \underline{490} \\ 141 \\ \underline{140} \\ 1 \end{array}$$

$$\begin{array}{r} 71 \\ 71\,\overline{)5041} \\ \underline{497} \\ 71 \\ 71 \end{array}$$

71

11.

$75'69 \quad \underline{|\,8\ 7}$

$8^2 = 64$

$2(80) = 160 \qquad 11\ 69$

$\underline{\quad 7} \qquad \underline{11\ 69}$

167

12.

$9^2 = 96'04 \quad \underline{|\,9\ 8}$

$2(90) = 180 \qquad 81$

$\underline{\quad 8} \qquad 15\ 04$

$188 \qquad \underline{15\ 04}$

13. $\sqrt{\dfrac{625}{729}} = \dfrac{25}{\sqrt{9}\,\sqrt{81}} = \dfrac{25}{27}$

14. $\sqrt{\dfrac{576}{841}} = \dfrac{\sqrt{4}\cdot\sqrt{144}}{(\sqrt{29})^2} = \dfrac{24}{29}$

15. $\sqrt{\dfrac{169}{225}} = \dfrac{13}{15}$

16. $\sqrt{\dfrac{196}{1156}} = \dfrac{\sqrt{\not{4}}\cdot\sqrt{49}}{\sqrt{\not{4}}\cdot\sqrt{289}} = \dfrac{7}{17}$

17. $\sqrt{\dfrac{289}{324}} = \dfrac{\sqrt{17^2}}{\sqrt{4}\cdot\sqrt{81}} = \dfrac{17}{18}$

18. $\sqrt{\dfrac{361}{400}} = \dfrac{19}{20}$

19. $\sqrt{\dfrac{576}{784}} = \dfrac{\sqrt{4}\ \sqrt{144}}{\sqrt{16}\sqrt{49}} = \dfrac{24}{28} = \dfrac{6}{7}$

20. $\sqrt{\dfrac{289}{961}} = \dfrac{\sqrt{17^2}}{\sqrt{31^2}} = \dfrac{17}{31}$

```
21.                      13´32. 25   |3 6 . 5 0 0
                3² =  9
      2(30) = 60      4 32
               6      3 96
              66        36  25
     2(360) = 720       36  25
               5
             725

22.                      24´80. 04   |4 9 . 8 0 0
                4² = 16
      2(40) = 80      8 80
               9      8 01
              89        79  04
     2(490) = 980       79  04
               8
             988

23.                      10. 95´61    |3 . 3 1 0
                3² =  9
      2(30) = 60      1  95
               3      1  89
              63           6 61
     2(330) = 660          6 61
               1
             661

24.                    .00´12´25    | . 0 3 5
             3² =            9
     2(30) = 60            3 25
              5            3 25
             65

25.                       .09´16´01        | . 3 0 2 6 ≈ .303
                 3² =      9
       2(30) = 60              16
                0              00
               60              16 01
      2(300) = 600             12 04
                 2              3 97 00
               602              3 62 76
     2(3020) = 6040
                  6
               6046
```

26. $.95'48'14'00 \quad \lfloor .\ 9\ 7\ 7\ 1 \approx .977$

$9^2 = 81$

	.95′48′14′00
9^2 =	81
2(90) = 180	14 48
7	13 09
187	1 39 14
2(970) = 1940	1 36 29
7	2 85 00
1947	1 95 41
2(.9770) = 19,540	89 59
1	
19,541	

27. $\sqrt{\frac{3}{4}} = \sqrt{.75}$

$.75'00'00'00 \quad \lfloor .\ 8\ 6\ 6\ 0 \approx .866$

8^2 =	64
2(80) = 160	11 00
6	9 96
166	1 04 00
2(860) = 1720	1 03 56
6	44 00
1726	
2(8660) = 17,320	

28. $\sqrt{\frac{4}{5}} = \sqrt{.8}$

$.80'00'00'00 \quad \lfloor .\ 8\ 9\ 4\ 4 \approx .894$

8^2 =	64
2(80) = 160	16 00
9	15 21
169	79 00
2(890) = 1780	71 36
4	7 64 00
1784	7 15 36
2(8940) = 17,880	48 64
4	
17,884	

29. $\sqrt{\frac{5}{8}} = \sqrt{.625}$

estimate: .78

.78) .6250 = .80
624
10

estimate: .79

.79) .625000 = .7911
553
720
711
90
79
110
79
31

estimate: .791

.7905) .6250000 = .7905 ≈ .791
55335
71650
71145
50500
39525

30. $\sqrt{\frac{2}{9}} = \frac{\sqrt{2}}{\sqrt{9}} = \frac{\sqrt{2}}{3}$

```
                      2. 00'00'00        | 1. 4 1 4 2  ≈ 1.414
              1² = 1                                     .471
     2(10) = 20     1 00                            3 |1.4142
              4       96                               1 2
             24      4 00                                21
    2(140) = 280     2 81                                21
              1      1 19 00                              4
            281      1 12 96                              3
   2(1410) = 2820       6 04 00                           1
              4         5 65 64
           2824           38 36
 2(14,140) = 28,280
              2
          28,282
```

$\sqrt{\frac{2}{9}} \approx .471$

31. $\sqrt{\frac{5}{16}} = \frac{\sqrt{5}}{\sqrt{16}} = \frac{\sqrt{5}}{4}$

```
                      5. 00'00           | 2. 2 3 6 0       .559
              2² = 4                                     4 |2.2360
     2(20) = 40     1 00                                   2 0
              2       84                                     23
             42      16 00                                   20
    2(220) = 440     13 29                                    36
              3       2 71 00                                 36
            443       2 67 96
   2(2230) = 4460        3 04 00
              6
           4466
 2(22,360) = 44,720
```

.559

32. $\sqrt{\frac{5}{12}} = \frac{\sqrt{5}}{\sqrt{12}} = \frac{\sqrt{5}}{\sqrt{4}\,\sqrt{3}} = \frac{\sqrt{5}}{2\sqrt{3}}$

$\sqrt{5} = 2.236$ See number 31.

```
                      3. 00'00           | 1. 7 3 2 0    2 √3 = 2(1.732) = 3.464
              1² = 1                                              .6454
     2(10) = 20     2 00                  √5
              7     1 89                 ----- = 3.464^ |2.236^00000
             27      11 00               2 √3            2 0784
    2(170) = 340     10 29                                 15760
              3         71 00                              13856
            343         69 24                               19040
   2(1730) = 3460       1 76 00                             17320
              2                                              17200
           3462
 2(17,320) = 34,640
```

$\sqrt{\frac{5}{12}} \approx .645$

33. $c^2 = 6^2 + 8^2$
$c^2 = 36 + 64$
$c^2 = 100$
$c = \sqrt{100}$
$c = 10$

34. $30^2 = a^2 + 18^2$
$900 = a^2 + 324$
$576 = a^2$
$a = \sqrt{576}$
$a = 24$

35. ABC is a right triangle; b^2

36. $d^2 = (1.5)^2 + 2^2$
$d^2 = 2.25 + 4$
$d^2 = 6.25$
$d = \sqrt{6.25}$
$d = 2.5$

37.

$$\begin{array}{rr}
 & 1'10.\ 25 \\
1^2 = & \underline{1} \\
2(10) = 20 & 10 \\
\underline{0} & \underline{0} \\
20 & 10\ \ 25 \\
2(100) = 200 & \underline{10\ \ 25} \\
\underline{5} & \\
205 &
\end{array}$$

10 .5 ft.

Exercises 12.8 Page 266

1. $\sqrt[3]{512} = \sqrt[3]{2^3 \cdot 2^3 \cdot 2^3} = 2 \cdot 2 \cdot 2 = 8$
2. $\sqrt[3]{1000} = \sqrt[3]{10^3} = 10$
3. $\sqrt[3]{1728} = \sqrt[3]{2^3 \cdot 2^3 \cdot 3^3} = 2 \cdot 2 \cdot 3 = 12$
4. $\sqrt[3]{2744} = \sqrt[3]{2^3 \cdot 7^3} = 2 \cdot 7 = 14$
5. $\sqrt[3]{8000} = \sqrt[3]{2^3 \cdot 10^3} = 2 \cdot 10 = 20$
6. $\sqrt[3]{3375} = \sqrt[3]{3^3 \cdot 5^3} = 3 \cdot 5 = 15$
7. $\sqrt[3]{4096} = \sqrt[3]{2^{12}} = 2^{\frac{12}{3}} = 2^4 = 16$
8. $\sqrt[3]{125{,}000} = \sqrt[3]{125}\ \sqrt[3]{1000} = 5 \cdot 10 = 50$
9. $\sqrt[3]{13{,}824} = \sqrt[3]{2^3}\ \sqrt[3]{1728} = 2(12) = 24$
10. $\sqrt[3]{4096a^6b^9} = 16a^2b^3$
11. $\sqrt[3]{216} = \sqrt[3]{2^3 \cdot 3^3} = 2 \cdot 3 = 6$ in.
12. $\sqrt[3]{1728} = \sqrt[3]{12^3} = 12$

Exercises 12.9 Page 268

1. $7.2^2 = (\frac{72}{10})2 = \frac{72^2}{10^2} = \frac{5184}{100} = 51.84$
2. $840^2 = (84 \cdot 10)^2 = (84^2)(10^2) = (7056)(100) = 705{,}600$
3. $9.8^3 = (\frac{98}{10})^3 = \frac{98^3}{10^3} = \frac{941{,}192}{1000} = 941.192$
4. $\sqrt{26.01} = \sqrt{\frac{2601}{100}} = \frac{\sqrt{2601}}{\sqrt{100}} = \frac{51}{10} = 5.1$
5. $\sqrt{.9409} = \sqrt{\frac{9409}{10{,}000}} = \frac{\sqrt{9409}}{\sqrt{10{,}000}} = \frac{97}{100} = .97$
6. $9.7^2 = (\frac{97}{10})^2 = \frac{97^2}{10^2} = \frac{9409}{100} = 94.09$

7. $\sqrt{98.01} = \sqrt{\frac{9801}{100}} = \frac{\sqrt{9801}}{\sqrt{100}} = \frac{99}{10} = 9.9$

8. $\sqrt{.6889} = \sqrt{\frac{6889}{10,000}} = \frac{\sqrt{6889}}{\sqrt{10,000}} = \frac{83}{100} = .83$

9. $\sqrt[3]{456.533} = \frac{\sqrt[3]{456,533}}{1000} = \frac{\sqrt[3]{456,533}}{\sqrt[3]{1000}} = \frac{77}{10} = 7.7$

10. $\sqrt[3]{474.552} = \sqrt{\frac{474,552}{1000}} = \frac{\sqrt{474,552}}{\sqrt{1000}} = \frac{78}{10} = 7.8$

11. $\sqrt[3]{551.368} = \sqrt[3]{\frac{551,368}{1000}} = \frac{\sqrt[3]{551,368}}{\sqrt[3]{1000}} = \frac{82}{10} = 8.2$

12. $.79^2 = \left(\frac{79}{100}\right)^2 = \frac{79^2}{100^2} = \frac{6241}{10,000} = .6241$

13. $\sqrt{.9216} = \sqrt{\frac{9216}{10,000}} = \frac{\sqrt{9216}}{\sqrt{10,000}} = \frac{96}{100} = .96$

14. $.94^3 = \left(\frac{94}{100}\right)^3 = \frac{94^3}{100^3} = \frac{830,584}{1,000,000} = .830584$

15. $\sqrt[3]{132.651} = \sqrt[3]{\frac{132,651}{1000}} = \frac{\sqrt[3]{132,651}}{\sqrt[3]{1000}} = \frac{51}{10} = 5.1$

16. $\sqrt[3]{753.571} = \sqrt[3]{\frac{753,571}{1000}} = \frac{\sqrt[3]{753,571}}{\sqrt[3]{1000}} = \frac{91}{10} = 9.1$

<u>Test A</u> Page 268

I 1.

$$\begin{array}{rrl}
 & 1'74'24 & \underline{|\,132} \\
1^2 = 1 & \underline{1} & \\
2(10) = 20 & 74 & \\
\underline{3} & \underline{69} & \\
23 & 5\ 24 & \\
2(130) = 260 & \underline{5\ 24} & \\
\underline{2} & & \\
262 & &
\end{array}$$

2.

$$\begin{array}{rrl}
 & 2'19.'00'00 & \underline{|\,14.79} \\
1^2 = 1 & \underline{1} & \approx 14.8 \\
2(10) = 20 & 1\ 19 & \\
\underline{4} & \underline{96} & \\
24 & 23\ 00 & \\
2(140) = 280 & \underline{20\ 09} & \\
\underline{7} & 2\ 91\ 00 & \\
287 & \underline{2\ 65\ 41} & \\
2(1470) = 2940 & 25\ 59 & \\
\underline{9} & & \\
2949 & &
\end{array}$$

3.

$$\begin{array}{rl}
 & 40.\ 00'00'00 \quad \underline{|6.324} \approx 6.32 \\
6^2 = & \underline{36} \\
2(60) = 120 & 4\ 00 \\
\underline{3} & \underline{3\ 69} \\
123 & 31\ 00 \\
2(630) = 1260 & \underline{25\ 24} \\
\underline{2} & 5\ 76\ 00 \\
1262 & \underline{5\ 05\ 76} \\
2(6320) = 12640 & 70\ 24 \\
\underline{4} & \\
12644 &
\end{array}$$

II 1. $.62^2 = (\frac{62}{100})^2 = \frac{62^2}{100^2} = \frac{3844}{10{,}000} = .3844$

2. $1.7^3 = (\frac{17}{10})^3 = \frac{17^3}{10^3} = \frac{4913}{1000} = 4.913$

3. $\sqrt{0.2116} = \sqrt{\frac{2116}{10{,}000}} = \frac{\sqrt{2116}}{\sqrt{10{,}000}} = \frac{46}{100} = .46$

4. $\sqrt[3]{35.937} = \sqrt[3]{\frac{35{,}937}{1000}} = \frac{\sqrt[3]{35{,}937}}{\sqrt[3]{1000}} = \frac{33}{10} = 3.3$

III

1. $(3a^2b^3)^4 = 3^4a^8b^{12} = 81a^8b^{12}$

2. $(-5xy^2)^3 = (-5)^3x^3y^6 = -125x^3y^6$

3. $(\frac{-2}{3a^2})^2 = \frac{(-2)^2}{(3a^2)^2} = \frac{4}{9a^4}$

4. $(\frac{ab^2}{4c})^3 = \frac{a^3b^6}{4^3c^3} = \frac{a^3b^6}{64c^3}$

5. $\sqrt[5]{32x^{10}y^{20}} = 32^{\frac{1}{5}}x^{\frac{10}{5}}y^{\frac{20}{5}} = 2x^2y^4$

6. $\sqrt[6]{64m^{18}} = 64^{\frac{1}{6}}m^{\frac{18}{6}} = 2m^3$

7. $\sqrt{a^{2m}b^{6n}} = a^{\frac{2m}{2}}b^{\frac{6n}{2}} = a^m b^{3n}$

8. $\sqrt[3]{-216a^6b^3} = (-216)^{\frac{1}{3}}a^{\frac{6}{3}}b^{\frac{3}{5}} = -6a^2b$

9. $(\frac{-2x}{y^3})^5 = \frac{(-2)^5x^5}{y^{15}} = -\frac{32x^5}{y^{15}}$

Test B Page 268

I 1.

$$\begin{array}{rl}
 & 5'61'69 \quad \underline{|237} \\
2^2 = & \underline{4} \\
2(20) = 40 & 1\ 61 \\
\underline{3} & \underline{1\ 29} \\
43 & 32\ 69 \\
2(230) = 460 & \underline{32\ 69} \\
\underline{7} & \\
467 &
\end{array}$$

2.

$$
\begin{array}{rl}
 & 3'42.\ 00'00 \quad \underline{|\,18.49} \approx 18.5 \\
1^2 = & \underline{1} \\
2(10) = 20 & 2\ 42 \\
\underline{8} & \underline{2\ 24} \\
28 & 18\ 00 \\
2(180) = 360 & \underline{14\ 56} \\
\underline{4} & 3\ 44\ 00 \\
364 & \underline{3\ 32\ 01} \\
2(1840) = 3680 & 11\ 99 \\
\underline{9} & \\
3689 &
\end{array}
$$

3.

$$
\begin{array}{rl}
 & 78.\ 00'00'00 \quad \underline{|\,8.831} \approx 8.83 \\
8^2 = & \underline{64} \\
2(80) = 160 & 14\ 00 \\
\underline{8} & \underline{13\ 44} \\
168 & 56\ 00 \\
2(880) = 1760 & \underline{52\ 89} \\
\underline{3} & 3\ 11\ 00 \\
1763 & \underline{1\ 76\ 61} \\
2(8830) = 17660 & 1\ 34\ 39 \\
\underline{1} & \\
17661 &
\end{array}
$$

II 1. $0.31^2 = (\frac{31}{100})^2 = \frac{31^2}{100^2} = \frac{961}{10,000} = .0961$

2. $2.3^3 = (\frac{23}{10})^3 = \frac{23^3}{10^3} = \frac{12,167}{1000} = 12.167$

3. $\sqrt{0.3969} = \sqrt{\frac{3969}{10,000}} = \frac{\sqrt{3969}}{\sqrt{10,000}} = \frac{63}{100} = .63$

4. $\sqrt[3]{12.167} = \sqrt[3]{\frac{12,167}{1000}} = \frac{\sqrt[3]{12,167}}{\sqrt[3]{1000}} = \frac{23}{10} = 2.3$

III

1. $(2x^3y^2)^4 = 2^4x^{12}y^8 = 16x^{12}y^8$

2. $(-5ab^4)^3 = (-5)^3a^3b^{12} = -125a^3b^{12}$

3. $(\frac{-3^2}{5x^3}) = \frac{(-3)^2}{(5x^3)^2} = \frac{9}{5^2x^6} = \frac{9}{25x^6}$

4. $(\frac{m^2n}{3p})^3 = \frac{(m^2n)^3}{(3p)^3} = \frac{m^6n^3}{3^3p^3} = \frac{m^6n^3}{27p^3}$

5. $\sqrt[4]{81x^8y^{16}} = 81^{\frac{1}{4}}x^{\frac{8}{4}}y^{\frac{16}{4}} = 3x^2y^4$

6. $\sqrt[5]{32a^{20}} = 32^{\frac{1}{5}}a^{\frac{20}{5}} = 2a^4$

7. $\sqrt{a^{4m}b^{2n}} = a^{\frac{4m}{2}}b^{\frac{2n}{2}} = a^{2m}b^n$

8. $\sqrt[3]{-125x^9y^{15}} = (-125)^{\frac{1}{3}}x^{\frac{9}{3}}y^{\frac{15}{3}} = -5x^3y^5$

9. $(-\frac{3a}{b^2})^5 = \frac{(-3a)^5}{(b^2)^5} = \frac{(-3)^5a^5}{b^{10}} = -\frac{243a^5}{b^{10}}$

Test C   Page 269

1. $(AC)^2 = 36^2 + 40^2$
   $(AC)^2 = 1296 + 1600$
   $(AC)^2 = 2896$
   $AC = \sqrt{2896}$

	28´96. 00´00 ⌊53.81 ≈ 53.8
5^2 =	25
2(50) = 100	3 96
3	3 09
103	87 00
2(530) = 1060	85 44
8	1 56 00
1068	1 07 61
2(5380) = 10760	48 39
1	
10761	

2. let w = width 10 ft.
   3w - 6 = length 24 ft.

$2w + 2(3w - 6) = 68$
$2w + 6w - 12 = 68$
$8w = 80$
$w = 10$

10
10
24
+24
68

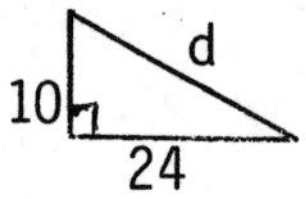

$d^2 = 10^2 + 24^2$
$d^2 = 100 + 576$
$d^2 = 676$
$d = \sqrt{676}$
$d = 26$ ft.

3. 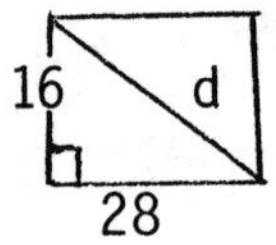

$d^2 = 16^2 + 28^2$
$d^2 = 256 + 784$
$d^2 = 1040$
$d = \sqrt{1040}$
$d = \sqrt{4 \cdot 4 \cdot 65}$
$d = \sqrt{4^2}\sqrt{65}$
$d = 4(8.062)$
$d = 32.248 \approx 32.2$ in.

4. $\frac{22}{7}r^2 = 1320$
   $22r^2 = 9240$
   $r^2 = 420$
   $r = \sqrt{420}$

	4´20. 00´00 ⌊20.49 ≈ 20.5 in.
2^2 =	4
2(20) = 40	20
0	0
40	20 00
2(200) = 400	16 16
4	3 84 00
404	3 68 01
2(2040) = 4080	15 99
9	
4089	

5. Since triangle is equilateral, the length of a side is $\frac{108}{3} = 36$, and one leg of the triangle is 18.

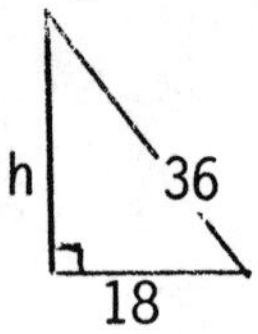

$h^2 + 18^2 = 36^2$
$h^2 + 324 = 1296$
$h^2 = 972$
$h = \sqrt{972}$
$h = \sqrt{9 \cdot 9 \cdot 12}$
$h = \sqrt{9^2}\sqrt{12}$
$h = 9(3.464)$
$h = 31.176 \approx 31.2$ in.

6.

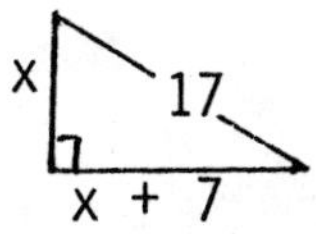

let x = one leg $\underline{8}$
x + 7 = other leg $\underline{15}$

$$x^2 + (x + 7)^2 = 17^2$$
$$x^2 + x^2 + 14x + 49 = 289$$
$$2x^2 + 14x - 240 = 0$$
$$x^2 + 7x - 120 = 0$$
$$(x + 15)(x - 8) = 0$$

~~$x + 15 = 0$~~
~~$x = -15$~~
Reject since negative.

$x - 8 = 0$
$x = 8$

$8^2 + 15^2 \stackrel{?}{=} 17^2$
$64 + 225 \stackrel{?}{=} 289$
$289 = 289$ ✓

7.(a) $v = \sqrt{2gd} = \sqrt{2(32)d} = \sqrt{64d} = 8\sqrt{d}$

d	$8\sqrt{d}$	=	v
1	$8\sqrt{1}$	=	8
4	$8\sqrt{4}$	=	16
9	$8\sqrt{9}$	=	24
16	$8\sqrt{16}$	=	32
25	$8\sqrt{25}$	=	40
36	$8\sqrt{36}$	=	48
49	$8\sqrt{49}$	=	56
64	$8\sqrt{64}$	=	64

(b) 1) about 44 ft./sec.
2) about 20 ft.

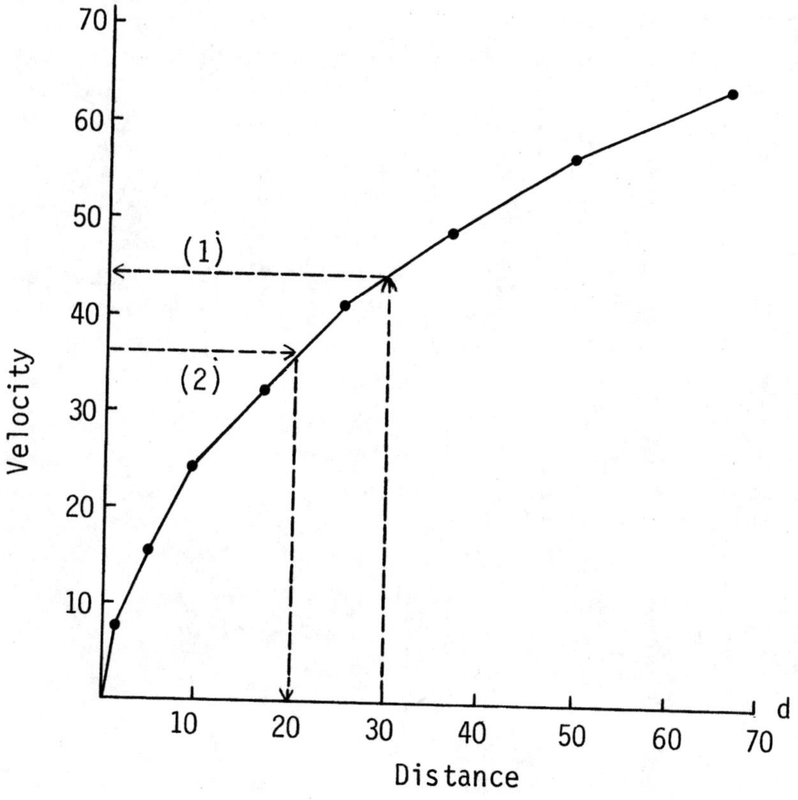

UNIT 13 — Exponents

Exercises 13.1 Page 272

1. $5^0 = 1$

2. $4^{-2} = \frac{1}{4^2} = \frac{1}{16}$

3. $2^{-5} = \frac{1}{2^5} = \frac{1}{32}$

4. $3^{-3} = \frac{1}{3^3} = \frac{1}{27}$

5. $(-3)^0 = 1$

6. $(-6)^{-2} = \frac{1}{(-6)^2} = \frac{1}{36}$

7. $(a^n b^2 q)^0 = 1$

8. $(-\frac{1}{3})^{-2} = (-3)^2 = 9$

9. $(\frac{1}{5})^2 = \frac{1}{25}$; $(\frac{1}{5})^3 = \frac{1}{125}$; $(\frac{1}{5})^2$ is greater
$(\frac{1}{5})^{-2} = 5^2 = 25$
$(\frac{1}{5})^{-3} = 5^3 = 125$; $(\frac{1}{5})^{-3}$ is greater

10. $2x^{-1} = \frac{2}{x}$

11. $5a^{-5} = \frac{5}{a^5}$

12. $a^{-1}b^{-1} = \frac{1}{ab}$

13. $x^{-3}y^{-2} = \frac{1}{x^3y^2}$

14. $4^{-2}a^2c^{-2} = \frac{a^2}{4^2c^2} = \frac{a^2}{16c^2}$

15. $3^{-3}ax^{-2} = \frac{a}{3^3x^2} = \frac{a}{27x^2}$

16. $\frac{ax}{by} = ab^{-1}xy^{-1}$

17. $\frac{mn}{a^2} = a^{-2}mn$

18. $\frac{1}{a^{-2}b^2} = a^2b^{-2}$

19. $(\frac{x}{y})^2 = \frac{x^2}{y^2} = x^2y^{-2}$

20. $8^{\frac{1}{3}} = \sqrt[3]{8} = 2$

21. $8^{\frac{2}{3}} = \sqrt[3]{8^2} = (\sqrt[3]{8})^2 = 2^2 = 4$

22. $64^{\frac{2}{3}} = \sqrt[3]{64^2} = (\sqrt[3]{64})^2 = 4^2 = 16$

23. $-32^{\frac{3}{5}} = -\sqrt[5]{32^3} = -(\sqrt[5]{32})^3 = -(2^3) = -8$

24. $-64^{-\frac{2}{3}} = -\sqrt[3]{(64)^{-2}} = -\sqrt[3]{(\frac{1}{64})^2} = -(\sqrt[3]{\frac{1}{64}})^2 = -(\frac{1}{4})^2 = -\frac{1}{16}$

25. $(-8)^{\frac{4}{3}} = \sqrt[3]{(-8)^{-4}} = (\sqrt[3]{-8})^{-4} = (-2)^{-4} = \frac{1}{(-2)^4} = \frac{1}{16}$

26. $27^{\frac{2}{3}} = (27^{\frac{1}{3}})^2 = 3^2 = 9$

$(-27)^{-\frac{2}{3}} = [(-27)^{\frac{1}{3}}]^{-2} = (-3)^{-2} = \frac{1}{(-3)^2} = \frac{1}{9}$

$27^{\frac{2}{3}}$ is greater

$(\frac{1}{4})^{\frac{3}{2}} = \sqrt{(\frac{1}{4})^3} = (\sqrt{\frac{1}{4}})^3 = (\frac{1}{2})^3 = \frac{1}{8}$

$(\frac{1}{4})^{-\frac{3}{2}} = \sqrt{(\frac{1}{4})^{-3}} = \sqrt{4^3} = \sqrt{64} = 8$

$(\frac{1}{4})^{-\frac{3}{2}}$ is greater

27. $\sqrt{ab^3} = a^{\frac{1}{2}}b^{\frac{3}{2}}$

28. $\sqrt{xy} = x^{\frac{1}{2}}y^{\frac{1}{2}}$

29. $(\sqrt{x})^3 = (x^{\frac{1}{2}})^3 = x^{\frac{3}{2}}$

30. $(\sqrt[5]{y})^4 = (y^{\frac{1}{5}})^4 = y^{\frac{4}{5}}$

31. $(\sqrt[3]{xy})^{-2} = [(xy)^{\frac{1}{3}}]^{-2} = (xy)^{-\frac{2}{3}} = \frac{1}{(xy)^{\frac{2}{3}}} = \frac{1}{x^{\frac{2}{3}}y^{\frac{2}{3}}}$

32. $5\sqrt{x^{-1}y^{-1}} = 5x^{-\frac{1}{2}}y^{-\frac{1}{2}} = \frac{5}{x^{\frac{1}{2}}y^{\frac{1}{2}}}$

33. $a^{\frac{2}{5}} = \sqrt[5]{a^2}$

34. $-x^{\frac{4}{5}} = -\sqrt[5]{x^4}$

35. $-x^{\frac{5}{4}} = -\sqrt[4]{x^5} = -x\sqrt[4]{x}$

36. $a^{\frac{1}{3}}b^{\frac{2}{3}} = \sqrt[3]{ab^2}$

37. $x^{\frac{5}{6}}y^{\frac{1}{6}} = \sqrt[6]{x^5y}$

38. $a^{\frac{1}{4}}b^{-\frac{3}{4}} = \sqrt[4]{ab^{-3}} = \sqrt[4]{\frac{a}{b^3}}$

39. $a^{\frac{1}{2}} \div x^{\frac{1}{2}} = (a \div x)^{\frac{1}{2}} = \sqrt{a \div x}$

40. $x^{\frac{2}{3}} \div y^{\frac{4}{3}} = \frac{x^{\frac{2}{3}}}{y^{\frac{4}{3}}} = \sqrt[3]{\frac{x^2}{y^4}}$

41. $a^3(a^{-2}) = a^{3+(-2)} = a$

42. $a^2 \cdot a^{-1} = a^{2+(-1)} = a$

43. $a^4(a^{-4}) = a^{4+(-4)} = a^0 = 1$

44. $a(a^{-3}) = a^{1+(-3)} = a^{-2}$ or $\frac{1}{a^2}$

45. $a^2(a^0) = a^{2+0} = a^2$

46. $x^{\frac{1}{2}}(x^{\frac{1}{2}}) = x^{\frac{1}{2}+\frac{1}{2}} = x^1 = x$

47. $\frac{a^5}{a^6} = a^{5-6} = a^{-1}$ or $\frac{1}{a}$

48. $\frac{a^3}{a^0} = \frac{a^3}{1} = a^3$

49. $\frac{a^2}{a^{-2}} = a^{2-(-2)} = a^4$

50. $\frac{x^{\frac{5}{2}}}{x^{-\frac{1}{2}}} = x^{\frac{5}{2}-(-\frac{1}{2})} = x^{\frac{6}{2}} = x^3$

51. $\frac{x^{\frac{1}{2}}}{x^{\frac{1}{3}}} = x^{\frac{1}{2}-\frac{1}{3}} = x^{\frac{3}{6}-\frac{2}{6}} = x^{\frac{1}{6}}$

52. $\frac{x^{n-\frac{3}{2}}}{x^{n-2}} = x^{n-\frac{3}{2}-(n-2)} = x^{n-\frac{3}{2}-n+2}$

$= x^{\frac{1}{2}}$

53.

$x^{\frac{1}{2}} = 7$

$(x^{\frac{1}{2}})^2 = 7^2$

$x = 49$

54.

$x^{\frac{3}{4}} = 8$

$(x^{\frac{3}{4}})^4 = 8^4$

$x^3 = 8^4$

$x = \sqrt[3]{8^4}$

$x = (\sqrt[3]{8})^4$

$x = 2^4$

$x = 16$

55.

$x^{\frac{4}{3}} = 81$

$(x^{\frac{1}{3}})^4 = 3^4$

$x^{\frac{1}{3}} = 3$

$(x^{\frac{1}{3}})^3 = 3^3$

$x = 27$

56.

$\frac{1}{3}x^{\frac{3}{2}} = 72$

$x^{\frac{3}{2}} = 216$

$(x^{\frac{3}{2}})2 = 216^2$

$x^3 = 216^2$

$x = \sqrt[3]{216^2}$

$x = (\sqrt[3]{216})^2$

$x = 6^2$

$x = 36$

57.

$x^{-\frac{1}{2}} = 6$

$(x^{-\frac{1}{2}})^{-2} = 6^{-2}$

$x = 6^{-2}$

$x = \frac{1}{6^2}$

$x = \frac{1}{36}$

58.

$x^{-\frac{2}{3}} = 144$

$(x^{-\frac{2}{3}})^3 = 144^3$

$x^{-2} = 144^3$

$(x^{-2})^{-\frac{1}{2}} = (144^3)^{-\frac{1}{2}}$

$x = 144^{-\frac{3}{2}}$

$x = (\sqrt{144})^{-3}$

$x = 12^{-3}$

$x = \frac{1}{12^3}$

$x = \frac{1}{1728}$

59.

$$25x^{-\frac{2}{3}} = 1$$
$$x^{-\frac{2}{3}} = \frac{1}{25}$$
$$(x^{-\frac{2}{3}})^3 = (\frac{1}{25})^3$$
$$x^{-2} = \frac{1}{25^3}$$
$$\frac{1}{x^2} = \frac{1}{25^3}$$
$$x^2 = 25^3$$
$$x = \sqrt{25^3}$$
$$x = (\sqrt{25})^3$$
$$x = 5^3$$
$$x = 125$$

60.

$$x^{\frac{5}{3}} + 32 = 0$$
$$x^{\frac{5}{3}} = -32$$
$$(x^{\frac{5}{3}})^3 = (-32)^3$$
$$x^5 = (-32)^3$$
$$x = \sqrt[5]{(-32)^3}$$
$$x = (\sqrt[5]{-32})^3$$
$$x = (-2)^3$$
$$x = -8$$

Exercises 13.3 Page 274

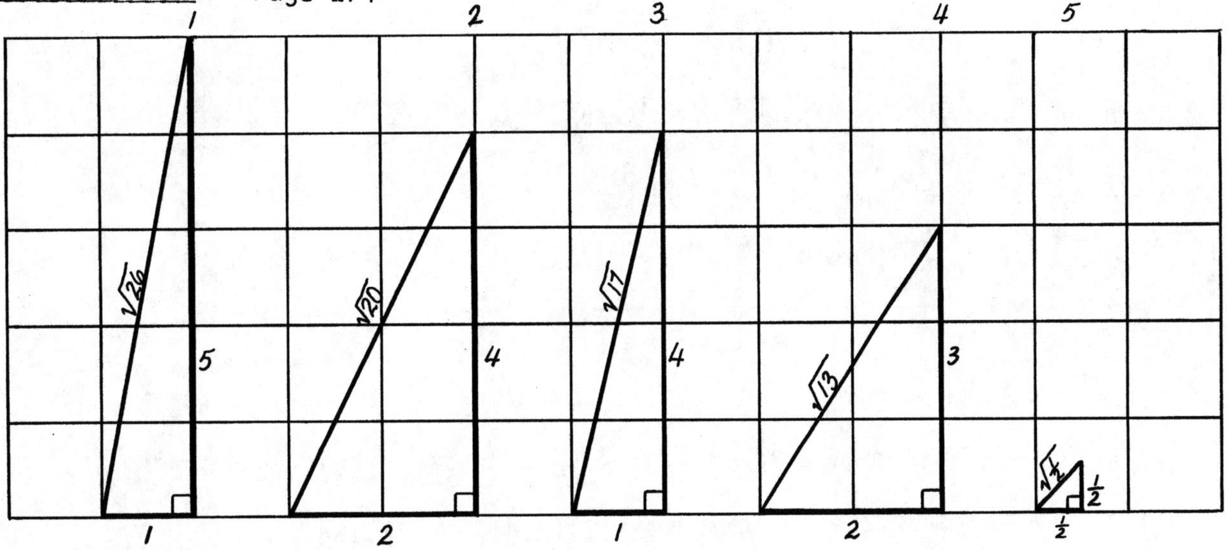

Exercises 13.5 Page 276

1. $\sqrt{12} = \sqrt{4\cdot3} = \sqrt{4}\sqrt{3} = 2\sqrt{3}$

2. $\sqrt{75} = \sqrt{25\cdot3} = \sqrt{25}\sqrt{3} = 5\sqrt{3}$

3. $\sqrt[3]{16} = \sqrt[3]{8\cdot2} = \sqrt[3]{8}\sqrt[3]{2} = 2\sqrt[3]{2}$

4. $\sqrt{128} = \sqrt{64\cdot2} = \sqrt{64}\sqrt{2} = 8\sqrt{2}$

5. $\sqrt[3]{250} = \sqrt[3]{125\cdot2} = \sqrt[3]{125}\sqrt[3]{2} = 5\sqrt[3]{2}$

6. $\sqrt{54} = \sqrt{9\cdot6} = \sqrt{9}\sqrt{6} = \sqrt[3]{6}$

7. $\sqrt{80} = \sqrt{16\cdot5} = \sqrt{16}\sqrt{5} = 4\sqrt{5}$

8. $\sqrt{125} = \sqrt{25\cdot5} = \sqrt{25}\sqrt{5} = 5\sqrt{5}$

9. $\sqrt{45} = \sqrt{9\cdot5} = \sqrt{9}\sqrt{5} = 3\sqrt{5}$

10. $3\sqrt{108} = 3\sqrt{36\cdot3} = 3\sqrt{36}\sqrt{3} = 3\cdot6\sqrt{3} = 18\sqrt{3}$

11. $4\sqrt{175} = 4\sqrt{25\cdot7} = 4\sqrt{25}\sqrt{7} = 4\cdot5\sqrt{7} = 20\sqrt{7}$

12. $2\sqrt{160} = 2\sqrt{16\cdot 10} = 2\sqrt{16}\sqrt{10} = 2\cdot 4\sqrt{10} = 8\sqrt{10}$

13. $3\sqrt{162} = 3\sqrt{81\cdot 2} = 3\sqrt{81}\sqrt{2} = 3\cdot 9\sqrt{2} = 27\sqrt{2}$

14. $5\sqrt{72} = 5\sqrt{36\cdot 2} = 5\sqrt{36}\sqrt{2} = 5\cdot 6\sqrt{2} = 30\sqrt{2}$

15. $2(98)^{\frac{1}{2}} = 2\sqrt{98} = 2\sqrt{49\cdot 2} = 2\sqrt{49}\sqrt{2} = 2\cdot 7\sqrt{2} = 14\sqrt{2}$

16. $4(128)^{\frac{1}{2}} = 4\sqrt{128} = 4\sqrt{64\cdot 2} = 4\sqrt{64}\sqrt{2} = 4\cdot 8\sqrt{2} = 32\sqrt{2}$

17. $3(180)^{\frac{1}{2}} = 3\sqrt{180} = 3\sqrt{36\cdot 5} = 3\sqrt{36}\sqrt{5} = 3\cdot 6\sqrt{5} = 18\sqrt{5}$

18. $\sqrt[4]{32} = \sqrt[4]{16\cdot 2} = \sqrt[4]{16}\sqrt[4]{2} = 2\sqrt[4]{2}$

19. $\sqrt{a^2b} = \sqrt{a^2}\sqrt{b} = a\sqrt{b}$

20. $(25b)^{\frac{1}{2}} = \sqrt{25b} = \sqrt{25}\sqrt{b} = 5\sqrt{b}$

21. $\sqrt{98c^3} = \sqrt{49c^2\cdot 2c} = \sqrt{49c^2}\sqrt{2c} = 7c\sqrt{2c}$

22. $(50a)^{\frac{1}{2}} = \sqrt{50a} = \sqrt{25\cdot 2a} = \sqrt{25}\sqrt{2a} = 5\sqrt{2a}$

23. $75a^4x^{10} = \sqrt{25a^4x^{10}\cdot 3} = \sqrt{25a^4x^{10}}\sqrt{3} = 5a^2x^5\sqrt{3}$

24. $(72a^6b^3)^{\frac{1}{3}} = \sqrt[3]{72a^6b^3} = \sqrt[3]{8a^6b^3.9} = \sqrt[3]{8a^6b^3}\sqrt[3]{9} = 2a^2b\sqrt[3]{9}$

25. $\sqrt{20a^4b} = \sqrt{4a^4\cdot 5b} = \sqrt{4a^4}\sqrt{5b} = 2a^2\sqrt{5b}$

*26. $\sqrt{18x - 9} = \sqrt{9(2x - 1)} = \sqrt{9}\sqrt{2x - 1} = 3\sqrt{2x - 1}$

*27. $\sqrt[3]{x^6 - x^3} = \sqrt[3]{x^3(x^3 - 1)} = \sqrt[3]{x^3}\sqrt[3]{x^3 - 1} = x\sqrt[3]{x^3 - 1}$

28. Given: $a = 9$, $b = 25$, $c = 4$, $x = 10$

(19) $a\sqrt{b} = 9\sqrt{25} = 9(5) = 45$ (20) $5\sqrt{b} = 5\sqrt{25} = 5(5) = 25$

(21) $7c\sqrt{2c} = 7\cdot 4\sqrt{2\cdot 4} = 28\sqrt{4}\sqrt{2} = 28(2)(1.414) = 79.184$

(22) $5\sqrt{2a} = 5\sqrt{2\cdot 9} = 5\sqrt{9}\sqrt{2} = 5(3)(1.414) = 21.21$

(23) $5a^2x^5\sqrt{3} = 5(9)^2(10)^5(1.732) = 5(81)(100{,}000)(1.732) = 70{,}146{,}000$

(24) $2a^2b\sqrt[3]{9} = 2(9)^2(25)(2.080) = 8424$

(25) $2a^2\sqrt{5b} = 2(9)^2\sqrt{5\cdot 25} = 162\sqrt{25}\sqrt{5} = 162(5)(2.236) = 1811.16$

(26) $3\sqrt{2x - 1} = 3\sqrt{2\cdot 10 - 1} = 3\sqrt{19} = 3(4.358) = 13.074$

*(27) $x\sqrt[3]{x^3 - 1} = 10\sqrt[3]{10^3 - 1} = 10\sqrt[3]{999} = 10\sqrt[3]{27}\sqrt[3]{37} = 10(3)\sqrt[3]{37}$
$= 30(3.332) = 99.96$

29. 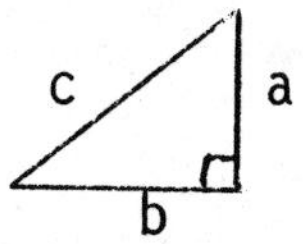

(1) $c^2 = 3^2 + 4^2$
$c^2 = 9 + 16$
$c^2 = 25$
$c = 5$

(2) $c^2 = 3^2 + 6^2$
$c^2 = 9 + 36$
$c^2 = 45$
$c = \sqrt{45} = 6.708$

(3) $c^2 = 4^2 + 8^2$
$c^2 = 16 + 64$
$c^2 = 80$
$c = \sqrt{80}$
$c = 8.944$

(4) $a^2 + 8^2 = 10^2$
$a^2 + 64 = 100$
$a^2 = 36$
$a = 6$

(5) $3^2 + b^2 = 5^2$
$9 + b^2 = 25$
$b^2 = 16$
$b = 4$

30. $h = \frac{1}{2}(12)\sqrt{3}$ $\quad h = \frac{1}{2}(24)\sqrt{3}$ $\quad h = \frac{1}{2}(15)\sqrt{3}$ $\quad h = \frac{1}{2}(\frac{2}{3})\sqrt{3}$ $\quad h = \frac{1}{2}m\sqrt{3}$

$h = 6\sqrt{3}$ $\quad h = 12\sqrt{3}$ $\quad h = \frac{15}{2}\sqrt{3}$ $\quad h = \frac{1}{3}\sqrt{3}$ $\quad h = \frac{m}{2}\sqrt{3}$

$h = \frac{1}{2}(4m)\sqrt{3}$ $\quad h = \frac{1}{2}(\frac{2}{3}m)\sqrt{3}$

$h = 2m\sqrt{3}$ $\quad h = \frac{1}{3}m\sqrt{3}$

31. $s = \frac{1}{2}at^2$
$12 = \frac{1}{2}(3)t^2$
$24 = 3t^2$
$t^2 = 8$
$t = \sqrt{8}$
$t = \sqrt{4}\sqrt{2}$
$t = 2\sqrt{2}$

32. $a = \frac{y^2}{r}$
$6 = \frac{y^2}{4}$
$y^2 = 24$
$y = \sqrt{24}$
$y = \sqrt{4}\sqrt{6}$
$y = 2\sqrt{6}$

33. $F = \frac{mv^2}{r}$
$40 = \frac{12v^2}{6}$
$40 = 2v^2$
$20 = v^2$
$v = \sqrt{20}$
$v = \sqrt{4}\sqrt{5}$
$v = 2\sqrt{5}$

<u>Exercises 13.6</u> Page 278

1. $\sqrt{\frac{1}{2}} = \sqrt{\frac{1\cdot 2}{2\cdot 2}} = \sqrt{\frac{2}{4}} = \frac{\sqrt{2}}{\sqrt{4}} = \frac{\sqrt{2}}{2}$

2. $\sqrt{\frac{2}{3}} = \sqrt{\frac{2\cdot 3}{3\cdot 3}} = \sqrt{\frac{6}{9}} = \frac{\sqrt{6}}{\sqrt{9}} = \frac{\sqrt{6}}{3}$

3. $\sqrt{\frac{3}{8}} = \sqrt{\frac{3\cdot 2}{8\cdot 2}} = \sqrt{\frac{6}{16}} = \frac{\sqrt{6}}{\sqrt{16}} = \frac{\sqrt{6}}{4}$

4. $\sqrt{\frac{2}{5}} = \sqrt{\frac{2\cdot 5}{5\cdot 5}} = \sqrt{\frac{10}{25}} = \frac{\sqrt{10}}{\sqrt{25}} = \frac{\sqrt{10}}{5}$

5. $\sqrt{\frac{5}{12}} = \sqrt{\frac{5\cdot 3}{12\cdot 3}} = \sqrt{\frac{15}{36}} = \frac{\sqrt{15}}{\sqrt{36}} = \frac{\sqrt{15}}{6}$

6. $\sqrt{\frac{2}{7}} = \sqrt{\frac{2\cdot 7}{7\cdot 7}} = \sqrt{\frac{14}{49}} = \frac{\sqrt{14}}{\sqrt{49}} = \frac{\sqrt{14}}{7}$

7. $\sqrt{\frac{5}{6}} = \sqrt{\frac{5\cdot 6}{6\cdot 6}} = \sqrt{\frac{30}{36}} = \frac{\sqrt{30}}{\sqrt{36}} = \frac{\sqrt{30}}{6}$

8. $\sqrt{\frac{25}{32}} = \frac{\sqrt{25}}{\sqrt{32}} = \frac{5}{\sqrt{32}} = \frac{5\sqrt{2}}{\sqrt{32}\sqrt{2}} = \frac{5\sqrt{2}}{\sqrt{64}} = \frac{5\sqrt{2}}{8}$

9. $\sqrt{\frac{4}{7}} = \frac{\sqrt{4}}{\sqrt{7}} = \frac{2}{\sqrt{7}} = \frac{2\sqrt{7}}{\sqrt{7}\sqrt{7}} = \frac{2\sqrt{7}}{7} = \frac{2\sqrt{7}}{7}$

10. $\sqrt{\frac{9}{10}} = \frac{\sqrt{9}}{\sqrt{10}} = \frac{3}{\sqrt{10}} = \frac{3\sqrt{10}}{\sqrt{10}\sqrt{10}} = \frac{3\sqrt{10}}{10} = \frac{3\sqrt{10}}{10}$

11. $\sqrt[3]{\frac{4}{5}} = \sqrt[3]{\frac{4\cdot 5^2}{5\cdot 5^2}} = \sqrt[3]{\frac{100}{5^3}} = \frac{\sqrt[3]{100}}{\sqrt[3]{5^3}} = \frac{\sqrt[3]{100}}{5}$

12. $\sqrt[3]{\frac{5}{12}} = \sqrt[3]{\frac{5\cdot 12^2}{12\cdot 12^2}} = \sqrt[3]{\frac{720}{12^3}} = \frac{\sqrt[3]{720}}{\sqrt[3]{12^3}} = \frac{\sqrt[3]{8}\sqrt[3]{90}}{12} = \frac{2\sqrt[3]{90}}{12} = \frac{\sqrt[3]{90}}{6}$

Exercises 13.7 Page 279

1. $\sqrt[4]{36} = 36^{\frac{1}{4}} = (6^2)^{\frac{1}{4}} = 6^{\frac{2}{4}} = 6^{\frac{1}{2}} = \sqrt{6}$

2. $\sqrt[4]{25} = 25^{\frac{1}{4}} = (5^2)^{\frac{1}{4}} = 5^{\frac{2}{4}} = 5^{\frac{1}{2}} = \sqrt{5}$

3. $\sqrt[4]{1600} = (1600)^{\frac{1}{4}} = (40^2)^{\frac{1}{4}} = 40^{\frac{2}{4}} = 40^{\frac{1}{2}} = \sqrt{40} = \sqrt{4}\sqrt{10} = 2\sqrt{10}$

4. $\sqrt[6]{27a^3} = (3^3a^3)^{\frac{1}{6}} = 3^{\frac{3}{6}}a^{\frac{3}{6}} = 3^{\frac{1}{2}}a^{\frac{1}{2}} = \sqrt{3a}$

5. $\sqrt[4]{9a^2b^2c^6} = (3^2a^2b^2c^6)^{\frac{1}{4}} = 3^{\frac{2}{4}}a^{\frac{2}{4}}b^{\frac{2}{4}}c^{\frac{6}{4}} = 3^{\frac{1}{2}}a^{\frac{1}{2}}b^{\frac{1}{2}}c^{\frac{3}{2}} = c(3abc)^{\frac{1}{2}} = c\sqrt{3abc}$

6. $\sqrt[4]{121a^6x^4} = (11^2a^6x^4)^{\frac{1}{4}} = 11^{\frac{2}{4}}a^{\frac{6}{4}}x = 11^{\frac{1}{2}}a^{\frac{3}{2}}x = ax(11^{\frac{1}{2}}a^{\frac{1}{2}}) = ax\sqrt{11a}$

7. $\sqrt{600} = \sqrt{100}\sqrt{6} = 10\sqrt{6}$

8. $\sqrt{500} = \sqrt{100}\sqrt{5} = 10\sqrt{5}$

9. $\sqrt[5]{160} = \sqrt[5]{32}\sqrt[5]{5} = 2\sqrt[5]{5}$

10. $\sqrt[3]{3000} = \sqrt[3]{1000}\sqrt[3]{3} = 10\sqrt[3]{3}$

11. $\sqrt[3]{189} = \sqrt[3]{27}\sqrt[3]{7} = 3\sqrt[3]{7}$

12. $\sqrt{84} = \sqrt{4}\sqrt{21} = 2\sqrt{21}$

13. $\sqrt[3]{72} = \sqrt[3]{8}\sqrt[3]{9} = 2\sqrt[3]{9}$

14. $\sqrt[3]{192} = \sqrt[3]{64}\sqrt[3]{3} = 4\sqrt[3]{3}$

15. $\sqrt[4]{144} = \sqrt[4]{16}\sqrt[4]{9} = 2(3^2)^{\frac{1}{4}} = 2(3^{\frac{2}{4}}) = 2(3^{\frac{1}{2}}) = 2\sqrt{3}$

16. $\sqrt[6]{81} = \sqrt[6]{3^4} = 3^{\frac{4}{6}} = 3^{\frac{2}{3}} = \sqrt[3]{3^2} = \sqrt[3]{9}$

17. $\sqrt[6]{343} = \sqrt[6]{7^3} = 7^{\frac{3}{6}} = 7^{\frac{1}{2}} = \sqrt{7}$

18. $\sqrt[4]{289} = \sqrt[4]{17^2} = 17^{\frac{2}{4}} = 17^{\frac{1}{2}} = \sqrt{17}$

19. $\frac{1}{3} = \frac{1}{\sqrt{3}} = \frac{1}{\sqrt{3}}\left(\frac{\sqrt{3}}{\sqrt{3}}\right) = \frac{1}{3}\sqrt{3}$

20. $\sqrt{\frac{1}{x^3}} = \sqrt{\frac{1}{x^3}\cdot\frac{x}{x}} = \sqrt{\frac{x}{x^4}} = \frac{\sqrt{x}}{\sqrt{x^4}} = \frac{\sqrt{x}}{x^2}$

21. $\sqrt[3]{16m^5n^4} = \sqrt[3]{8m^3n^3}\sqrt[3]{2m^2n} = 2mn\sqrt[3]{2m^2n}$

22. $\sqrt{405a^5y^2} = \sqrt{81a^4y^2}\sqrt{5a} = 9a^2y\sqrt{5a}$

23. $(135x^4y^5)^{\frac{1}{3}} = \sqrt[3]{135x^4y^5} = \sqrt[3]{27x^3y^3}\ \sqrt[3]{5xy^2} = 3xy\ \sqrt[3]{5xy^2}$

24. $\sqrt[6]{a^4b^2c^4d^8} = (a^4b^2c^4d^8)^{\frac{1}{6}} = a^{\frac{4}{6}}b^{\frac{2}{6}}c^{\frac{4}{6}}d^{\frac{8}{6}} = a^{\frac{2}{3}}b^{\frac{1}{3}}c^{\frac{2}{3}}d^{\frac{4}{3}}$

$= d^{\frac{3}{3}}(a^{\frac{2}{3}}b^{\frac{1}{3}}c^{\frac{2}{3}}d^{\frac{1}{3}}) = d\ \sqrt[3]{a^2bc^2d}$

25. $\sqrt[4]{132a^5b^5c^5} = \sqrt[4]{a^4b^4c^4}\ \sqrt[4]{132abc} = abc\ \sqrt[4]{132abc}$

26. $\sqrt[5]{32a^4b^2c^5} = \sqrt[5]{32c^5}\ \sqrt[5]{a^4b^2} = 2c\ \sqrt[5]{a^4b^2}$

27.
$A = \pi r^2$
$44 = \frac{22}{7}r^2$
$308 = 22r^2$
$r^2 = 14$
$r = \sqrt{14}$

28.
$h = \frac{a}{2}\sqrt{3}$
$h = \frac{18}{2}\sqrt{3}$
$h = 9\sqrt{3}$ in.

$A = \frac{a^2}{4}\sqrt{3}$
$A = \frac{18^2}{4}\sqrt{3}$
$A = \frac{324}{4}\sqrt{3}$
$A = 81\sqrt{3}$ sq. in.

29. (a)
$h = \frac{a}{2}\sqrt{3}$
$h = \frac{8}{2}\sqrt{3}$
$h = 4\sqrt{3}$ in.

$A = \frac{a^2}{4}\sqrt{3}$
$A = \frac{8^2}{4}\sqrt{3}$
$A = \frac{64}{4}\sqrt{3}$
$A = 16\sqrt{3}$ sq. in.

(b)
$h = \frac{a}{2}\sqrt{3}$
$h = \frac{12}{2}\sqrt{3}$
$h = 6\sqrt{3}$ in.

$A = \frac{a^2}{4}\sqrt{3}$
$A = \frac{12^2}{4}\sqrt{3}$
$A = \frac{144}{4}\sqrt{3}$
$A = 36\sqrt{3}$ sq. in.

(c)
$h = \frac{a}{2}\sqrt{3}$
$h = \frac{24}{2}\sqrt{3}$
$h = 12\sqrt{3}$ in.

$A = \frac{a^2}{4}\sqrt{3}$
$A = \frac{24^2}{4}\sqrt{3}$
$A = \frac{576}{4}\sqrt{3}$
$A = 144\sqrt{3}$ sq. in.

(d)
$h = \frac{a}{2}\sqrt{3}$
$h = \frac{\frac{1}{2}}{2}\sqrt{3}$
$h = \frac{1}{4}\sqrt{3}$ in.

$A = \frac{a^2}{4}\sqrt{3}$
$A = \frac{(\frac{1}{2})^2}{4}\sqrt{3}$
$A = \frac{\frac{1}{4}}{4}\sqrt{3}$
$A = \frac{1}{16}\sqrt{3}$ sq. in.

(e)
$h = \frac{a}{2}\sqrt{3}$
$h = \frac{\frac{3}{4}}{2}\sqrt{3}$
$h = \frac{3}{8}\sqrt{3}$ in.

$A = \frac{a^2}{4}\sqrt{3}$
$A = \frac{(\frac{3}{4})^2}{4}\sqrt{3}$
$A = \frac{\frac{9}{16}}{4}\sqrt{3}$
$A = \frac{9}{64}\sqrt{3}$ sq. in.

(f)
$h = \frac{a}{2}\sqrt{3}$
$h = \frac{2\frac{1}{2}}{2}\sqrt{3}$
$h = \frac{\frac{5}{2}}{2}\sqrt{3}$
$h = \frac{5}{4}\sqrt{3}$ in.

$A = \frac{a^2}{4}\sqrt{3}$
$A = \frac{(2\frac{1}{2})^2}{4}\sqrt{3}$
$A = \frac{(\frac{5}{2})^2}{4}\sqrt{3}$
$A = \frac{\frac{25}{4}}{4}\sqrt{3}$
$A = \frac{25}{16}\sqrt{3}$ sq. in.

30. $A = \pi r^2$

$100 = \frac{22}{7}r^2$

$700 = 22r^2$

$r^2 = \frac{700}{22}$

$r = \sqrt{\frac{700}{22}}$

$r = \frac{\sqrt{700}}{\sqrt{22}} = \frac{\sqrt{100}\sqrt{7}}{\sqrt{22}} = \frac{10\sqrt{7}}{\sqrt{22}}$

$r = \frac{10\sqrt{7}}{\sqrt{22}}\left(\frac{\sqrt{22}}{\sqrt{22}}\right) = \frac{10\sqrt{154}}{22} = \frac{5}{11}\sqrt{154}$ in.

Exercises 13.8 Page 280

1. $\sqrt{8} = \sqrt{4 \cdot 2} = \sqrt{4}\sqrt{2} = 2\sqrt{2}$

2. $\sqrt{45} = \sqrt{9 \cdot 5} = \sqrt{9}\sqrt{5} = 3\sqrt{5}$

3. $\sqrt{50} = \sqrt{25 \cdot 2} = \sqrt{25}\sqrt{2} = 5\sqrt{2}$

4. $\sqrt[3]{81} = \sqrt[3]{27 \cdot 3} = \sqrt[3]{27}\sqrt[3]{3} = 3\sqrt[3]{3}$

5. $\sqrt{80} = \sqrt{16 \cdot 5} = \sqrt{16}\sqrt{5} = 4\sqrt{5}$

6. $\frac{1}{2}\sqrt{8} = \frac{1}{2}\sqrt{4 \cdot 2} = \frac{1}{2}\sqrt{4}\sqrt{2} = \frac{1}{2}2\sqrt{2} = \sqrt{2}$

7. $\frac{1}{2}\sqrt{32} = \frac{1}{2}\sqrt{16 \cdot 2} = \frac{1}{2}\sqrt{16}\sqrt{2} = \frac{1}{2}4\sqrt{2} = 2\sqrt{2}$

8. $\sqrt{x^5} = \sqrt{x^4 \cdot x} = \sqrt{x^4}\sqrt{x} = x^2\sqrt{x}$

9. $\frac{1}{2}\sqrt{4b^2c} = \frac{1}{2}\sqrt{4b^2 \cdot c} = \frac{1}{2}\sqrt{4b^2}\sqrt{c} = \frac{1}{2}2b\sqrt{c} = b\sqrt{c}$

10. $\frac{4}{3}\sqrt{45} = \frac{4}{3}\sqrt{9 \cdot 5} = \frac{4}{3}\sqrt{9}\sqrt{5} = \frac{4}{3}3\sqrt{5} = 4\sqrt{5}$

11. $\frac{3}{2}\sqrt{25a^3} = \frac{3}{2}\sqrt{25a^2 \cdot a} = \frac{3}{2}\sqrt{25a^2}\sqrt{a} = \frac{3}{2}5a\sqrt{5} = \frac{15a}{2}\sqrt{a}$

12. $\frac{2}{3}\sqrt[3]{64a^2} = \frac{2}{3}\sqrt[3]{4^3a^2} = \frac{2}{3}\sqrt[3]{4^3}\sqrt[3]{a^2} = \frac{2}{3}4\sqrt[3]{a^2} = \frac{8}{3}\sqrt[3]{a^2}$

Exercises 13.9 Page 281

1. $\sqrt{2} = 2^{\frac{1}{2}} = 2^{\frac{2}{4}} = \sqrt[4]{2^2} = \sqrt[4]{4}$

$\sqrt[4]{3} = 3^{\frac{1}{4}} = \sqrt[4]{3}$

2. $\sqrt{5} = 5^{\frac{1}{2}} = 5^{\frac{3}{6}} = \sqrt[6]{5^3} = \sqrt[6]{125}$

$\sqrt[3]{6} = 6^{\frac{1}{3}} = 6^{\frac{2}{6}} = \sqrt[6]{6^2} = \sqrt[6]{36}$

3. $\sqrt[4]{7} = 7^{\frac{1}{4}} = \sqrt[4]{7}$

$\sqrt{10} = 10^{\frac{1}{2}} = 10^{\frac{2}{4}} = \sqrt[4]{10^2} = \sqrt[4]{100}$

4. $\sqrt[6]{10} = 10^{\frac{1}{6}} = \sqrt[6]{10}$

$\sqrt{2} = 2^{\frac{1}{2}} = 2^{\frac{3}{6}} = \sqrt[6]{2^3} = \sqrt[6]{8}$

$\sqrt[3]{5} = 5^{\frac{1}{3}} = 5^{\frac{2}{6}} = \sqrt[6]{5^2} = \sqrt[6]{25}$

5. $\sqrt[6]{4} = 4^{\frac{1}{6}} = 4^{\frac{2}{12}} = \sqrt[12]{4^2} = \sqrt[12]{16}$

$\sqrt[4]{2} = 2^{\frac{1}{4}} = 2^{\frac{3}{12}} = \sqrt[12]{2^3} = \sqrt[12]{8}$

$\sqrt{3} = 3^{\frac{1}{2}} = 3^{\frac{6}{12}} = \sqrt[12]{3^6} = \sqrt[12]{729}$

6. $\sqrt[10]{13} = 13^{\frac{1}{10}} = \sqrt[10]{13}$

$\sqrt{5} = 5^{\frac{1}{2}} = 5^{\frac{5}{10}} = \sqrt[10]{5^5} = \sqrt[10]{3125}$

$\sqrt[5]{4} = 4^{\frac{1}{5}} = 4^{\frac{2}{10}} = \sqrt[10]{4^2} = \sqrt[10]{16}$

7. $\sqrt{3} = 3^{\frac{1}{2}} = 3^{\frac{6}{12}} = \sqrt[12]{3^6} = \sqrt[12]{729}$

$\sqrt[3]{5} = 5^{\frac{1}{3}} = 5^{\frac{4}{12}} = \sqrt[12]{5^4} = \sqrt[12]{625}$

$\sqrt[4]{\frac{1}{27}} = (\frac{1}{27})^{\frac{1}{4}} = (\frac{1}{27})^{\frac{3}{12}} = \sqrt[12]{\frac{1}{27^3}} = \sqrt[12]{\frac{1}{19,683}}$

8. $\sqrt{ab} = (ab)^{\frac{1}{2}} = (ab)^{\frac{6}{12}} = \sqrt[12]{(ab)^6} = \sqrt[12]{a^6b^6}$

$\sqrt[3]{ab^2} = (ab^2)^{\frac{1}{3}} = (ab^2)^{\frac{4}{12}} = \sqrt[12]{(ab^2)^4} = \sqrt[12]{a^4b^8}$

$\sqrt[4]{2} = 2^{\frac{1}{4}} = 2^{\frac{3}{12}} = \sqrt[12]{2^3} = \sqrt[12]{8}$

9. $\sqrt{a} = a^{\frac{1}{2}} = a^{\frac{6}{12}} = \sqrt[12]{a^6}$

$\sqrt[3]{b} = b^{\frac{1}{3}} = b^{\frac{4}{12}} = \sqrt[12]{b^4}$

$\sqrt[4]{x} = x^{\frac{1}{4}} = x^{\frac{3}{12}} = \sqrt[12]{x^3}$

$\sqrt[6]{y} = y^{\frac{1}{6}} = y^{\frac{2}{12}} = \sqrt[12]{y^2}$

10. $\sqrt[3]{a+b} = (a+b)^{\frac{1}{3}} = (a+b)^{\frac{2}{6}} = \sqrt[6]{(a+b)^2}$

$\sqrt{x+y} = (x+y)^{\frac{1}{2}} = (x+y)^{\frac{3}{6}} = \sqrt[6]{(x+y)^3}$

11. $\sqrt[5]{5} = 5^{\frac{1}{5}} = 5^{\frac{2}{10}} = \sqrt[10]{5^2} = \sqrt[10]{25}$

$\sqrt{2} = 2^{\frac{1}{2}} = 2^{\frac{5}{10}} = \sqrt[10]{2^5} = \sqrt[10]{32}$

$\sqrt[10]{32}$ is greater than $\sqrt[10]{25}$; therefore $\sqrt{2}$ is greater than $\sqrt[5]{5}$.

$\sqrt[3]{4} = 4^{\frac{1}{3}} = 4^{\frac{2}{6}} = \sqrt[6]{4^2} = \sqrt[6]{16}$

$\sqrt{3} = 3^{\frac{1}{2}} = 3^{\frac{3}{6}} = \sqrt[6]{3^3} = \sqrt[6]{27}$

$\sqrt[6]{27}$ is greater than $\sqrt[6]{16}$; therefore $\sqrt{3}$ is greater than $\sqrt[3]{4}$.

12. $\sqrt[3]{3} = 3^{\frac{1}{3}} = 3^{\frac{4}{12}} = \sqrt[12]{3^4} = \sqrt[12]{81}$ $\quad$ $\sqrt[3]{3}$ is greater.

$\sqrt[4]{4} = 4^{\frac{1}{4}} = 4^{\frac{3}{12}} = \sqrt[12]{4^3} = \sqrt[12]{64}$

$3\sqrt{2} = 3(2)^{\frac{1}{2}} = 3(2)^{\frac{3}{6}} = 3\sqrt[6]{2^3} = 3\sqrt[6]{8}$ $\quad$ $3\sqrt[3]{4}$ is greater.

$3\sqrt[3]{4} = 3(4)^{\frac{1}{3}} = 3(4)^{\frac{2}{6}} = 3\sqrt[6]{4^2} = 3\sqrt[6]{16}$

13. $\sqrt[3]{3} = 3^{\frac{1}{3}} = 3^{\frac{4}{12}} = \sqrt[12]{3^4} = \sqrt[12]{81}$ $\quad$ Solution $\sqrt[6]{7}$, $\sqrt{2}$, $\sqrt[3]{3}$

$\sqrt{2} = 2^{\frac{1}{2}} = 2^{\frac{6}{12}} = \sqrt[12]{2^6} = \sqrt[12]{64}$

$\sqrt[6]{7} = 7^{\frac{1}{6}} = 7^{\frac{2}{12}} = \sqrt[12]{7^2} = \sqrt[12]{49}$

14. $\sqrt{2} = 2^{\frac{1}{2}} = 2^{\frac{6}{12}} = \sqrt[12]{2^6} = \sqrt[12]{64}$ $\quad$ Solution $\sqrt{2}$, $\sqrt[4]{5}$, $\sqrt[3]{4}$

$\sqrt[3]{4} = 4^{\frac{1}{3}} = 4^{\frac{4}{12}} = \sqrt[12]{4^4} = \sqrt[12]{256}$

$\sqrt[4]{5} = 5^{\frac{1}{4}} = 5^{\frac{3}{12}} = \sqrt[12]{5^3} = \sqrt[12]{125}$

15. $\sqrt[3]{2} = 2^{\frac{1}{3}} = 2^{\frac{5}{15}} = \sqrt[15]{2^5} = \sqrt[15]{32}$ $\quad$ Solution $\sqrt[5]{3}$, $\sqrt[15]{30}$, $\sqrt[3]{2}$

$\sqrt[5]{3} = 3^{\frac{1}{5}} = 3^{\frac{3}{15}} = \sqrt[15]{3^3} = \sqrt[15]{27}$

$\sqrt[15]{30}$

16. $\sqrt{2} = 2^{\frac{1}{2}} = 2^{\frac{3}{6}} = \sqrt[6]{2^3} = \sqrt[6]{8}$ $\quad$ Solution $\sqrt{2}$, $\sqrt{2\frac{1}{2}}$, $\sqrt[3]{4}$, $\sqrt[3]{5}$

$\sqrt[3]{5} = 5^{\frac{1}{3}} = 5^{\frac{2}{6}} = \sqrt[6]{5^2} = \sqrt[6]{25}$

$\sqrt{2\frac{1}{2}} = (\frac{5}{2})^{\frac{1}{2}} = (\frac{5}{2})^{\frac{3}{6}} = \sqrt[6]{(\frac{5}{2})^3} = \sqrt[6]{\frac{125}{8}} = \sqrt[6]{15\frac{5}{8}}$

$\sqrt[3]{4} = 4^{\frac{1}{3}} = 4^{\frac{2}{6}} = \sqrt[6]{4^2} = \sqrt[6]{16}$

17. $\sqrt{7} = 7^{\frac{1}{2}} = 7^{\frac{6}{12}} = \sqrt[12]{7^6} = \sqrt[12]{117,649}$ $\quad$ Solution $\sqrt[3]{4}$, $\sqrt[6]{63}$, $\sqrt[4]{48}$, $\sqrt{7}$

$\sqrt[4]{48} = 48^{\frac{1}{4}} = 48^{\frac{3}{12}} = \sqrt[12]{48^3} = \sqrt[12]{110,592}$

$\sqrt[3]{4} = 4^{\frac{1}{3}} = 4^{\frac{4}{12}} = \sqrt[12]{4^4} = \sqrt[12]{256}$

$\sqrt[6]{63} = 63^{\frac{1}{6}} = 63^{\frac{2}{12}} = \sqrt[12]{63^2} = \sqrt[12]{3969}$

18. $\sqrt[3]{4} = 4^{\frac{1}{3}} = 4^{\frac{4}{12}} = \sqrt[12]{4^4} = \sqrt[12]{256}$ Solution $\sqrt[4]{5}$, $\sqrt[12]{150}$, $\sqrt[6]{13}$, $\sqrt[3]{4}$

$\sqrt[4]{5} = 5^{\frac{1}{4}} = 5^{\frac{3}{12}} = \sqrt[12]{5^3} = \sqrt[12]{125}$

$\sqrt[6]{13} = 13^{\frac{1}{6}} = 13^{\frac{2}{12}} = \sqrt[12]{13^2} = \sqrt[12]{169}$

$\sqrt[12]{150} = \sqrt[12]{150}$

Exercises 13.10 Page 282

1. $\sqrt{50} = \sqrt{25}\sqrt{2} = 5\sqrt{2}$
$\sqrt{18} = \sqrt{9}\sqrt{2} = 3\sqrt{2}$
$\sqrt{98} = \sqrt{49}\sqrt{2} = 7\sqrt{2}$
$15\sqrt{2}$

2. $\sqrt{27} = \sqrt{9}\sqrt{3} = 3\sqrt{3}$
$\sqrt{12} = \sqrt{4}\sqrt{3} = 2\sqrt{3}$
$\sqrt{75} = \sqrt{25}\sqrt{3} = 5\sqrt{3}$
$10\sqrt{3}$

3. $\sqrt{20} = \sqrt{4}\sqrt{5} = 2\sqrt{5}$
$\sqrt{80} = \sqrt{16}\sqrt{5} = 4\sqrt{5}$
$\sqrt{45} = \sqrt{9}\sqrt{5} = 3\sqrt{5}$
$9\sqrt{5}$

4. $\sqrt{28} = \sqrt{4}\sqrt{7} = 2\sqrt{7}$
$\sqrt{63} = \sqrt{9}\sqrt{7} = 3\sqrt{7}$
$\sqrt{700} = \sqrt{100}\sqrt{7} = 10\sqrt{7}$
$15\sqrt{7}$

5. $\sqrt[3]{250} = \sqrt[3]{125}\sqrt[3]{2} = 5\sqrt[3]{2}$
$\sqrt[3]{16} = \sqrt[3]{8}\sqrt[3]{2} = 2\sqrt[3]{2}$
$\sqrt[3]{54} = \sqrt[3]{27}\sqrt[3]{2} = 3\sqrt[3]{2}$
$10\sqrt[3]{2}$

6. $\sqrt[3]{128} = \sqrt[3]{64}\sqrt[3]{2} = 4\sqrt[3]{2} = \frac{8}{2}\sqrt[3]{2}$
$\sqrt[3]{686} = \sqrt[3]{343}\sqrt[3]{2} = 7\sqrt[3]{2} = \frac{14}{2}\sqrt[3]{2}$
$\sqrt[3]{\frac{1}{4}} = \sqrt[3]{\frac{1}{8}}\sqrt[3]{2} = \frac{1}{2}\sqrt[3]{2} = \frac{1}{2}\sqrt[3]{2}$
$\frac{23}{2}\sqrt[3]{2}$

7. $\sqrt[3]{135} = \sqrt[3]{27}\sqrt[3]{5} = 3\sqrt[3]{5}$
$\sqrt[3]{320} = \sqrt[3]{64}\sqrt[3]{5} = 4\sqrt[3]{5}$
$\sqrt[3]{625} = \sqrt[3]{125}\sqrt[3]{5} = 5\sqrt[3]{5}$
$12\sqrt[3]{5}$

8. $\sqrt[3]{500} = \sqrt[3]{125}\sqrt[3]{4} = 5\sqrt[3]{4}$
$\sqrt[3]{108} = \sqrt[3]{27}\sqrt[3]{4} = 3\sqrt[3]{4}$
$\sqrt[3]{-32} = \sqrt[3]{-8}\sqrt[3]{4} = -2\sqrt[3]{4}$
$6\sqrt[3]{4}$

9. $\sqrt{\frac{1}{2}} = \frac{1}{\sqrt{2}}\frac{(\sqrt{2})}{(\sqrt{2})} = \frac{1}{2}\sqrt{2} = \frac{2}{4}\sqrt{2}$
$\sqrt{12\frac{1}{2}} = \sqrt{\frac{25}{2}} = \frac{5}{\sqrt{2}}\frac{(\sqrt{2})}{(\sqrt{2})} = \frac{5}{2}\sqrt{2} = \frac{10}{4}\sqrt{2}$
$\sqrt{\frac{1}{8}} = \frac{1}{\sqrt{8}}\frac{(\sqrt{2})}{(\sqrt{2})} = \frac{1}{4}\sqrt{2} = \frac{1}{4}\sqrt{2}$
$\sqrt{1\frac{1}{8}} = \sqrt{\frac{9}{8}} = \frac{3}{\sqrt{8}}\frac{(\sqrt{2})}{(\sqrt{2})} = \frac{3}{4}\sqrt{2} = \frac{3}{4}\sqrt{2}$
$\frac{16}{4}\sqrt{2} = 4\sqrt{2}$

10. $\sqrt{\frac{1}{3}} = \frac{1}{\sqrt{3}}\frac{(\sqrt{3})}{(\sqrt{3})} = \frac{1}{3}\sqrt{3}$
$\sqrt{75} = \sqrt{25}\sqrt{3} = 5\sqrt{3}$
$\frac{2}{3}\sqrt{3} = \frac{2}{3}\sqrt{3}$
$\sqrt{12} = \sqrt{4}\sqrt{3} = 2\sqrt{3}$
$8\sqrt{3}$

11. $\sqrt{\frac{3}{4}} = \frac{\sqrt{3}}{\sqrt{4}} = \frac{1}{2}\sqrt{3} = \frac{3}{6}\sqrt{3}$

$\frac{1}{3}\sqrt{3} = \frac{2}{6}\sqrt{3}$

$\frac{7}{6}\sqrt[4]{9} = \frac{7}{6}(3^2)^{\frac{1}{4}} = \frac{7}{6}(3)^{\frac{2}{4}} = \frac{7}{6}\sqrt{3}$

$\sqrt{147} = \sqrt{49}\sqrt{3} = 7\sqrt{3} = \frac{42}{6}\sqrt{3}$

$\frac{54}{6}\sqrt{3} = 9\sqrt{3}$

12. $\sqrt[3]{40} = \sqrt[3]{8}\sqrt[3]{5} = 2\sqrt[3]{5}$

$\sqrt{28} = \sqrt{4}\sqrt{7} = 2\sqrt{7}$

$\sqrt[6]{25} = (5^2)^{\frac{1}{6}} = \sqrt[3]{5}$

$\sqrt{175} = \sqrt{25}\sqrt{7} = 5\sqrt{7}$

$3\sqrt[3]{5} + 7\sqrt{7}$

13. $\sqrt{147} = \sqrt{49}\sqrt{3} = 7\sqrt{3}$

$4\sqrt{20} = 4\sqrt{4}\sqrt{5} = 8\sqrt{5}$

$\sqrt{75} = \sqrt{25}\sqrt{3} = 5\sqrt{3}$

$\sqrt{605} = \sqrt{121}\sqrt{5} = 11\sqrt{5}$

$12\sqrt{3} + 19\sqrt{5}$

14. $\sqrt[3]{192} = \sqrt[3]{64}\sqrt[3]{3} = 4\sqrt[3]{3}$

$\sqrt{80} = \sqrt{16}\sqrt{5} = 4\sqrt{5}$

$4\sqrt{45} = 4\sqrt{9}\sqrt{5} = 12\sqrt{5}$

$5\sqrt[3]{24} = 5\sqrt[3]{8}\sqrt[3]{3} = 10\sqrt[3]{3}$

$14\sqrt[3]{3} + 16\sqrt{5}$

15. $\sqrt{245} - \sqrt{405} + \sqrt{45} = \sqrt{49}\sqrt{5} - \sqrt{81}\sqrt{5} + \sqrt{9}\sqrt{5}$
$= 7\sqrt{5} - 9\sqrt{5} + 3\sqrt{5}$
$= \sqrt{5}$

16. $\sqrt{12} + 3\sqrt{75} - 2\sqrt{27} = \sqrt{4}\sqrt{3} + 3\sqrt{25}\sqrt{3} - 2\sqrt{9}\sqrt{3}$
$= 2\sqrt{3} + 3(5)\sqrt{3} - 2(3)\sqrt{3}$
$= 2\sqrt{3} + 15\sqrt{3} - 6\sqrt{3}$
$= 11\sqrt{3}$

17. $5\sqrt{72} + 3\sqrt{18} - \sqrt{50} = 5\sqrt{36}\sqrt{2} + 3\sqrt{9}\sqrt{2} - \sqrt{25}\sqrt{2}$
$= 5(6)\sqrt{2} + 3(3)\sqrt{2} - 5\sqrt{2}$
$= 30\sqrt{2} + 9\sqrt{2} - 5\sqrt{2}$
$= 34\sqrt{2}$

18. $\sqrt[3]{128} + \sqrt[3]{686} - \sqrt[3]{54} = \sqrt[3]{64}\sqrt[3]{2} + \sqrt[3]{343}\sqrt[3]{2} - \sqrt[3]{27}\sqrt[3]{2}$
$= 4\sqrt[3]{2} + 7\sqrt[3]{2} - 3\sqrt[3]{2}$
$= 8\sqrt[3]{2}$

19. $\sqrt{112} - \sqrt{343} + \sqrt{448} = \sqrt{16}\sqrt{7} - \sqrt{49}\sqrt{7} + \sqrt{64}\sqrt{7}$
$= 4\sqrt{7} - 7\sqrt{7} + 8\sqrt{7}$
$= 5\sqrt{7}$

20. $\sqrt{(a + b)^2c} - \sqrt{(a - b)^2c} = \sqrt{(a + b)^2}\sqrt{c} - \sqrt{(a - b)^2}\sqrt{c}$
$= (a + b)\sqrt{c} - (a - b)\sqrt{c}$
$= (a + b - a + b)\sqrt{c}$
$= 2b\sqrt{c}$

Exercises 13.11   Page 283

1. $\sqrt{2}\,\sqrt{8} = \sqrt{16} = 4$

2. $\sqrt{2}\,\sqrt{6} = \sqrt{12} = \sqrt{4}\,\sqrt{3} = 2\sqrt{3}$

3. $\sqrt{3}\,\sqrt{15} = \sqrt{45} = \sqrt{9}\,\sqrt{5} = 3\sqrt{5}$

4. $2\sqrt{5}(3\sqrt{10}) = 2\cdot 3\sqrt{5\cdot 10} = 6\sqrt{50} = 6\sqrt{25}\,\sqrt{2} = 6\cdot 5\sqrt{2} = 30\sqrt{2}$

5. $3\sqrt{20}(2\sqrt{2}) = 3\cdot 2\sqrt{20\cdot 2} = 6\sqrt{40} = 6\sqrt{4}\,\sqrt{10} = 6\cdot 2\sqrt{10} = 12\sqrt{10}$

6. $2\sqrt[3]{3}(3\sqrt[3]{45}) = 2.3\sqrt[3]{3\cdot 45} = 6\sqrt[3]{135} = 6\sqrt[3]{27}\,\sqrt[3]{5} = 6\cdot 3\sqrt[3]{5} = 18\sqrt[3]{5}$

7. $2\sqrt[3]{24}(\sqrt[3]{18}) = 2\sqrt[3]{8}\,\sqrt[3]{3}\,\sqrt[3]{18} = 2\cdot 2\sqrt[3]{54} = 4\sqrt[3]{27}\,\sqrt[3]{2} = 4\cdot 3\sqrt[3]{2} = 12\sqrt[3]{2}$

8. $5\sqrt[3]{5}(\sqrt[3]{25}) = 5\sqrt[3]{5\cdot 25} = 5\sqrt[3]{125} = 5\cdot 5 = 25$

9. $\sqrt{\frac{2}{3}}\sqrt{\frac{4}{5}}\sqrt{\frac{3}{4}} = \sqrt{\frac{2\cdot \cancel{4}\cdot \cancel{3}}{\cancel{3}\cdot 5\cdot \cancel{4}}} = \sqrt{\frac{2}{5}} = \frac{\sqrt{2}}{\sqrt{5}} = \frac{\sqrt{2}}{\sqrt{5}}\,\frac{(\sqrt{5})}{(\sqrt{5})} = \frac{\sqrt{10}}{5}$

10.
$$\begin{array}{lrrr}
 & \sqrt{5} & +\ \sqrt{3} & \\
 & \sqrt{5} & -\ \sqrt{3} & \\
\hline
 & 5 & +\ \sqrt{15} & \\
 & & -\ \sqrt{15} & -\ 3 \\
\hline
 & 5 & & -\ 3 = 2
\end{array}$$

11.
$$\begin{array}{lrrr}
 & \sqrt{7} & +\ \sqrt{2} & \\
 & \sqrt{7} & -\ \sqrt{2} & \\
\hline
 & 7 & +\ 7\sqrt{2} & \\
 & & -\ 7\sqrt{2} & -\ 2 \\
\hline
 & 7 & & -\ 2 = 5
\end{array}$$

12.
$$\begin{array}{lrrr}
 & \sqrt{6} & -\ \sqrt{5} & \\
 & \sqrt{6} & -\ \sqrt{5} & \\
\hline
 & 6 & -\ \sqrt{30} & \\
 & & -\ \sqrt{30} & +\ 5 \\
\hline
 & 6 & -2\sqrt{30} & +\ 5 = 11 - 2\sqrt{30}
\end{array}$$

13.
$$\begin{array}{rrr}
5 & -\ \sqrt{5} & \\
1 & +\ \sqrt{5} & \\
\hline
5 & -\ \sqrt{5} & \\
 & 5\sqrt{5} & -\ 5 \\
\hline
5 & +\ 4\sqrt{5} & -\ 5 = 4\sqrt{5}
\end{array}$$

14.
$$\begin{array}{rrr}
4\sqrt{7} & +\ 1 & \\
4\sqrt{7} & -\ 1 & \\
\hline
112 & +\ 4\sqrt{7} & \\
 & -\ 4\sqrt{7} & -\ 1 \\
\hline
112 & & -\ 1 = 111
\end{array}$$

15.
$$\begin{array}{rrr}
3\sqrt{3} & +\ 2\sqrt{6} & \\
3\sqrt{3} & -\ 5\sqrt{6} & \\
\hline
27 & +\ 6\sqrt{18} & \\
 & -\ 15\sqrt{18} & -\ 60 \\
\hline
27 & -\ 9\sqrt{18} & -\ 60
\end{array}$$

$= -33 - 9\sqrt{9}\,\sqrt{2}$
$= -33 - 9.3\sqrt{2}$
$= -33 - 27\sqrt{2}$

16.
$$\begin{array}{rrr}
3a & +\ \sqrt{5} & \\
2a & -\ \sqrt{5} & \\
\hline
6a^2 & +\ 2a\sqrt{5} & \\
 & -\ 3a\sqrt{5} & -\ 5 \\
\hline
6a^2 & -\ a\sqrt{5} & -\ 5
\end{array}$$

17.
$$\begin{array}{llllll}
x & -\ \sqrt{xyz} & +\ yz & & & \\
 & \sqrt{x} & +\ \sqrt{yz} & & & \\
\hline
x\sqrt{x} & -\ \sqrt{x^2yz} & +\ yz\sqrt{x} & & & \\
 & & & +\ x\sqrt{yz} & -\ \sqrt{xy^2z^2} & +\ yz\sqrt{yz} \\
\hline
x\sqrt{x} & -\ \sqrt{x^2yz} & +\ yz\sqrt{x} & +\ x\sqrt{yz} & -\ \sqrt{xy^2z^2} & +\ yz\sqrt{yz}
\end{array}$$

$= x\sqrt{x} - x\sqrt{yz} + yz\sqrt{x} + x\sqrt{yz} - yz\sqrt{x} + yz\sqrt{yz}$
$= x\sqrt{x} + yz\sqrt{yz}$

18. $x\sqrt{x} - y\sqrt{y}$

$\underline{\quad\sqrt{x} + \sqrt{y}\quad}$

$x^2 - y\sqrt{xy}$

$\underline{\quad x\sqrt{xy} - y^2}$

$x^2 + (x - y)\sqrt{xy} - y^2$

Exercises 13.12 Page 284

1. $\dfrac{\sqrt{50}}{\sqrt{8}} = \sqrt{\dfrac{50}{8}} = \sqrt{\dfrac{25}{4}} = \dfrac{\sqrt{25}}{\sqrt{4}} = \dfrac{5}{2}$

2. $\dfrac{\sqrt{72}}{2\sqrt{6}} = \dfrac{1}{2}\sqrt{\dfrac{72}{6}} = \dfrac{1}{2}\sqrt{12} = \dfrac{1}{2}\sqrt{4}\,\sqrt{3} = \dfrac{1}{2}(2)\sqrt{3} = \sqrt{3}$

3. $\dfrac{4\sqrt{5}}{\sqrt{40}} = 4\sqrt{\dfrac{5}{40}} = 4\sqrt{\dfrac{1}{8}} = 4\sqrt{\dfrac{1}{4}}\sqrt{\dfrac{1}{2}} = 4(\tfrac{1}{2})\sqrt{\dfrac{1}{2}} = 2\sqrt{\dfrac{1}{2}} = \dfrac{2}{\sqrt{2}} = \dfrac{2}{\sqrt{2}}\dfrac{(\sqrt{2})}{(\sqrt{2})}$

$= \dfrac{2\sqrt{2}}{2} = \sqrt{2}$

4. $\dfrac{6\sqrt{7}}{\sqrt{126}} = 6\sqrt{\dfrac{7}{126}} = 6\sqrt{\dfrac{1}{18}} = 6\sqrt{\dfrac{1}{9}}\sqrt{\dfrac{1}{2}} = 6(\tfrac{1}{3})\dfrac{1}{\sqrt{2}} = \dfrac{2}{\sqrt{2}} = \dfrac{2}{\sqrt{2}}\dfrac{(\sqrt{2})}{(\sqrt{2})} = \dfrac{2\sqrt{2}}{2} = \sqrt{2}$

5. $\dfrac{7\sqrt{75}}{5\sqrt{28}} = \dfrac{7}{5}\sqrt{\dfrac{75}{28}} = \dfrac{7}{5}\sqrt{\dfrac{25}{4}}\sqrt{\dfrac{3}{7}} = \dfrac{7\cdot 5\sqrt{3}}{5\cdot 2\sqrt{7}} = \dfrac{35\sqrt{3}}{10\sqrt{7}} = \dfrac{7\sqrt{3}}{2\sqrt{7}}\dfrac{(\sqrt{7})}{(\sqrt{7})} = \dfrac{7\sqrt{21}}{14} = \dfrac{\sqrt{21}}{2}$

6. $\dfrac{\sqrt{a - b}}{\sqrt{a + b}} = \dfrac{\sqrt{a - b}}{\sqrt{a + b}}\dfrac{(\sqrt{a + b})}{(\sqrt{a + b})} = \dfrac{\sqrt{a^2 - b^2}}{a + b}$

Exercises 13.13 Page 286

1. $(3\sqrt{ab})^2 = (3a^{\frac{1}{2}}b^{\frac{1}{2}})^2 = 9ab$

2. $(2\sqrt[3]{3x})^2 = (2\cdot 3^{\frac{1}{3}}x^{\frac{1}{3}})^2 = 4\cdot 3^{\frac{2}{3}}x^{\frac{2}{3}} = 4\sqrt[3]{3^2x^2}$

$= 4\sqrt[3]{9x^2}$

3. $(x\sqrt[3]{2x^3})^2 = (x^2\sqrt[3]{2})^2 = (x^2\cdot 2^{\frac{1}{3}})^2 = x^4\cdot 2^{\frac{2}{3}} = x^4\sqrt[3]{2^2} = x^4\sqrt[3]{4}$

4. $(n^2\sqrt{4b})^2 = (n^2\cdot 4^{\frac{1}{2}}b^{\frac{1}{2}})^2 = n^4\cdot 4\cdot b = 4bn^4$

5. $(2\sqrt{5})^3 = (2\cdot 5^{\frac{1}{2}})^3 = 2^3\cdot 5^{\frac{3}{2}} = 8\cdot 5^{\frac{2}{2}}\cdot 5^{\frac{1}{2}} = 8\cdot 5\sqrt{5} = 40\sqrt{5}$

6. $(3\sqrt{2})^3 = (3\cdot 2^{\frac{1}{2}})^3 = 3^3\cdot 2^{\frac{3}{2}} = 27\cdot 2^{\frac{2}{2}}\cdot 2^{\frac{1}{2}} = 27\cdot 2\sqrt{2} = 54\sqrt{2}$

7. $(2\sqrt[3]{a^2})^3 = (2\cdot a^{\frac{2}{3}})^3 = 2^3a^2 = 8a^2$

8. $(\sqrt[4]{a^2b^3})^3 = (a^{\frac{2}{4}}b^{\frac{3}{4}})^3 = a^{\frac{6}{4}}b^{\frac{9}{4}} = a^{\frac{4}{4}}b^{\frac{8}{4}}a^{\frac{2}{4}}b^{\frac{1}{4}} = ab^2\sqrt[4]{a^2b}$

Exercises 13.14

1. $\sqrt{\frac{2.0}{3.0}} = \frac{\sqrt{2.0}}{\sqrt{3.0}} = \frac{\sqrt{2.0}}{\sqrt{3.0}}\left(\frac{\sqrt{3.0}}{\sqrt{3.0}}\right) = \frac{\sqrt{6.0}}{3.0} = \frac{2.449}{3} = .816 \approx .8$

2. $\frac{2.0}{\sqrt{5.0}} = \frac{2.0}{\sqrt{5.0}}\left(\frac{\sqrt{5.0}}{\sqrt{5.0}}\right) = \frac{2.0\sqrt{5.0}}{5.0} = .4(2.236) = .8944 \approx .9$

3. $\frac{3.0}{\sqrt{6.0}} = \frac{3.0}{\sqrt{6.0}}\left(\frac{\sqrt{6.0}}{\sqrt{6.0}}\right) = \frac{3.0\sqrt{6.0}}{6.0} = \frac{\sqrt{6.0}}{2.0} = \frac{2.449}{2.0} = 1.225 \approx 1.2$

4. $\frac{6.0}{\sqrt{8.0}} = \frac{6.0}{\sqrt{8.0}}\left(\frac{\sqrt{2.0}}{\sqrt{2.0}}\right) = \frac{6.0\sqrt{2.0}}{\sqrt{16.0}} = \frac{6.0\sqrt{2.0}}{4.0} = 1.5(1.414) = 2.121 \approx 2.1$

5. $\frac{4.0}{\sqrt{12}} = \frac{4.0}{\sqrt{12}}\left(\frac{\sqrt{3}}{\sqrt{3}}\right) = \frac{4.0\sqrt{3}}{\sqrt{36}} = \frac{4.0\sqrt{3}}{6} = \frac{2.0(1.732)}{3} = 1.155 \approx 1.2$

6. $\frac{10}{\sqrt{45}} = \frac{10}{\sqrt{45}}\frac{(\sqrt{5})}{(\sqrt{5})} = \frac{10\sqrt{5}}{\sqrt{225}} = \frac{10\sqrt{5}}{15} = \frac{2(2.236)}{3} = \frac{4.472}{3} \approx 1.491 \approx 1.5$

7. $\frac{15}{\sqrt{50}} = \frac{15}{\sqrt{50}}\frac{(\sqrt{2})}{(\sqrt{2})} = \frac{15\sqrt{2}}{\sqrt{100}} = \frac{15\sqrt{2}}{10} = 1.5(1.414) \approx 2.1$

8. $\frac{1.0}{\sqrt{125}} = \frac{1.0}{\sqrt{125}}\frac{(\sqrt{5})}{(\sqrt{5})} = \frac{\sqrt{5}}{\sqrt{625}} = \frac{\sqrt{5}}{25} = \frac{2.236}{25} = .089 \approx .1$

9. $\frac{1}{\sqrt[3]{16}} = \frac{1}{\sqrt[3]{16}}\frac{(\sqrt[3]{4})}{(\sqrt[3]{4})} = \frac{\sqrt[3]{4}}{\sqrt[3]{64}} = \frac{1.587}{4} = .397 \approx .4$

10. $\frac{1}{\sqrt[3]{5^2}} = \frac{1}{\sqrt[3]{5^2}}\frac{(\sqrt[3]{5})}{(\sqrt[3]{5})} = \frac{\sqrt{5}}{\sqrt[3]{5^3}} = \frac{\sqrt[3]{5}}{5} = \frac{1.709}{5} = .342 \approx .3$

11. $\frac{\sqrt{a}}{\sqrt{b}} = \frac{\sqrt{a}}{\sqrt{b}}\frac{(\sqrt{b})}{(\sqrt{b})} = \frac{\sqrt{ab}}{b}$

12. $\frac{1}{\sqrt{x^7}} = \frac{1}{\sqrt{x^7}}\frac{(\sqrt{x})}{(\sqrt{x})} = \frac{\sqrt{x}}{\sqrt{x^8}} = \frac{\sqrt{x}}{x^4}$

13. $\frac{ax}{\sqrt{2a^3x}} = \frac{ax}{\sqrt{2a^3x}}\frac{(\sqrt{2ax})}{(\sqrt{2ax})} = \frac{ax\sqrt{2ax}}{\sqrt{4a^4x^2}} = \frac{ax\sqrt{2ax}}{2a^2x} = \frac{\sqrt{2ax}}{2a}$

14. $\frac{\sqrt{63x}}{\sqrt{8b^2}} = \frac{\sqrt{63x}}{\sqrt{8b^2}} \frac{(\sqrt{2})}{(\sqrt{2})} = \frac{\sqrt{126x}}{\sqrt{16b^2}} = \frac{\sqrt{9}\sqrt{14x}}{4b} = \frac{3\sqrt{14x}}{4b}$

15. $\frac{2\sqrt{a}}{\sqrt{by}} = \frac{2\sqrt{a}}{\sqrt{by}} \frac{(\sqrt{by})}{(\sqrt{by})} = \frac{2\sqrt{aby}}{by}$

16. $\frac{\sqrt[3]{6}}{\sqrt[3]{12}} = \sqrt[3]{\frac{6}{12}} = \sqrt[3]{\frac{1}{2}} = \frac{1}{\sqrt[3]{2}} = \frac{1}{\sqrt[3]{2}} \frac{(\sqrt[3]{4})}{(\sqrt[3]{4})} = \frac{\sqrt[3]{4}}{\sqrt[3]{8}} = \frac{\sqrt[3]{4}}{2}$

17. $\frac{\sqrt[3]{a}}{\sqrt[3]{ax^2}} = \sqrt[3]{\frac{a}{ax^2}} = \sqrt[3]{\frac{1}{x^2}} = \frac{1}{\sqrt[3]{x^2}} \frac{(\sqrt[3]{x})}{(\sqrt[3]{x})} = \frac{\sqrt[3]{x}}{\sqrt[3]{x^3}} = \frac{\sqrt[3]{x}}{x}$

18. $\sqrt{\frac{x^2y}{3xy^2}} = \sqrt{\frac{x}{3y}} = \frac{\sqrt{x}}{\sqrt{3y}} = \frac{\sqrt{x}}{\sqrt{3y}} \frac{(\sqrt{3y})}{(\sqrt{3y})} = \frac{\sqrt{3xy}}{3y}$

19. $\frac{\sqrt{r-1}}{\sqrt{r+1}} = \frac{\sqrt{r-1}}{\sqrt{r+1}} \frac{(\sqrt{r+1})}{(\sqrt{r+1})} = \frac{\sqrt{r^2-1}}{r+1}$

20. $\frac{\sqrt{a+b}}{\sqrt{a-b}} = \frac{\sqrt{a+b}}{\sqrt{a-b}} \frac{(\sqrt{a-b})}{(\sqrt{a-b})} = \frac{\sqrt{a^2-b^2}}{a-b}$

21. $\sqrt{\frac{x-2}{x+2}} = \frac{\sqrt{x-2}}{\sqrt{x+2}} \frac{(\sqrt{x+2})}{(\sqrt{x+2})} = \frac{\sqrt{x^2-4}}{x+2}$

22. $\sqrt{\frac{a-b}{a^2-b^2}} = \sqrt{\frac{\cancel{a-b}}{(a+b)\cancel{(a-b)}}} = \sqrt{\frac{1}{a+b}} = \frac{1}{\sqrt{a+b}} \frac{(\sqrt{a+b})}{(\sqrt{a+b})} = \frac{\sqrt{a+b}}{a+b}$

<u>Review Exercises</u> Pages 287-288

1. A power is the product resulting from multiplying a quantity by itself two or more times. A root is a quantity which, when multiplied by itself a specified number of times, produces a given quantity.

2. $(a^m)^n = a^{mn}$ $\sqrt[n]{a^m} = a^{\frac{m}{n}}$

3. 2, 4, 6, 8, 10; 3, 5, 7, 9, 11; positive

4. $(\frac{a}{b})^m = \frac{a^m}{b^m}$ $\sqrt[n]{\frac{a}{b}} = \frac{\sqrt[n]{a}}{\sqrt[n]{b}}$ $(\frac{9}{16})^2 = \frac{9^2}{16^2} = \frac{81}{256}$ $\sqrt{\frac{9}{16}} = \frac{\sqrt{9}}{\sqrt{16}} = \frac{3}{4}$

5. $(ab)^n = a^nb^n$; $\sqrt[n]{ab} = \sqrt[n]{a}\sqrt[n]{b}$

6. The taking of a root; by fractional exponents $\sqrt{6} = 6^{\frac{1}{2}}$

7. There are two square roots of 25, ±5. The principal square root of 25 is 5 and the principal cube root of -8 is -2.

8. An index tells how many times the root must be used as a factor to produce the radicand; the square root.

9. The same as the radicand; positive or negative

10. $x^0 = 1$; $x^{-2} = \frac{1}{x^2}$

11. The number of times the number is used as a factor; the root being taken.

12. By changing the sign of the exponent; $a^3b^{-1}x^2$

13. Radical - an indicated root of a number, $\sqrt{a}$
    Radicand - number whose root is required, a in $\sqrt{a}$
    (examples will vary)

14. The order of a radical is the numerical root being taken. $\sqrt[3]{5}$ is a third order radical; $\sqrt[4]{3}$ is a fourth order radical.

15. By using the pythagorean theorem. Let the legs of a right triangle be two numbers, the sum of whose squares is the radicand. The length of the hypotenuse will be the desired square root.

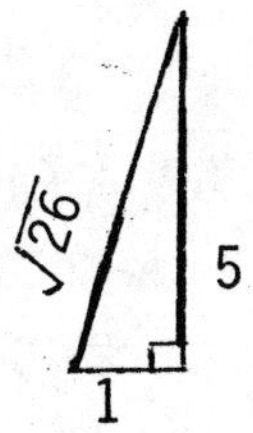

16. Rational number - a number that can be expressed as an integer or as a fraction with integral terms.
    Irrational number - a number that cannot be expressed as an integer or as a fraction with integral terms.
    $8, \frac{2}{9}, \sqrt[3]{8}, -7\frac{2}{3}, \sqrt{25}$

17. By using the product rules of radicals where one factor of the radicand is a perfect power.

$$\sqrt{40b^2c} = \sqrt{4b^2}\sqrt{10c} = 2b\sqrt{10c}$$
$$\sqrt{72mn^2} = \sqrt{36n^2}\sqrt{2m} = 6n\sqrt{2m}$$
$$\sqrt[3]{24} = \sqrt[3]{8}\sqrt[3]{3} = 2\sqrt[3]{3}$$

18. Radicals of the same order with the same radicand; by getting a common denominator for the exponents so they may be added.

Test A   Page 288

I 1. $10^0 = 1$ 2. $3^{-2} = \frac{1}{3^2} = \frac{1}{9}$ 3. $(a + b)^0 = 1$

4. $32^{\frac{2}{5}} = \sqrt[5]{32^2} = (\sqrt[5]{32})^2 = 2^2 = 4$ 5. $\frac{1}{2^{-3}} = 2^3 = 8$

6. $27^{\frac{4}{3}} = \sqrt[3]{27^4} = (\sqrt[3]{27})^4 = 3^4 = 81$

II 1. $\sqrt{24} = \sqrt{4}\,\sqrt{6} = 2\sqrt{6}$ 2. $\sqrt[3]{54} = \sqrt[3]{27}\,\sqrt[3]{2} = 3\sqrt[3]{2}$

3. $\sqrt{\frac{2}{3}} = \frac{\sqrt{2}}{\sqrt{3}} = \frac{\sqrt{2}}{\sqrt{3}}\frac{(\sqrt{3})}{(\sqrt{3})} = \frac{\sqrt{6}}{3}$ 4. $\sqrt[3]{\frac{3}{4}} = \frac{\sqrt[3]{3}}{\sqrt[3]{4}} = \frac{\sqrt[3]{3}}{\sqrt[3]{4}}\frac{(\sqrt[3]{2})}{(\sqrt[3]{2})} = \frac{\sqrt[3]{6}}{\sqrt[3]{8}} = \frac{\sqrt[3]{6}}{2}$

5. $\sqrt{5a^2b^5} = \sqrt{a^2b^4}\,\sqrt{5b} = ab^2\sqrt{5b}$ 6. $\sqrt[3]{5a^2b^5} = \sqrt[3]{b^3}\,\sqrt[3]{5a^2b^2} = b\sqrt[3]{5a^2b^2}$

III 1. $\sqrt{12} - \sqrt{27} + \sqrt{75} = \sqrt{4}\,\sqrt{3} - \sqrt{9}\,\sqrt{3} + \sqrt{25}\,\sqrt{3}$
$= 2\sqrt{3} - 3\sqrt{3} + 5\sqrt{3}$
$= 4\sqrt{3}$

2. $3\sqrt{50} - 5\sqrt{18} = 3\sqrt{25}\,\sqrt{2} - 5\sqrt{9}\,\sqrt{2}$
$= 3(5)\sqrt{2} - 5(3)\sqrt{2}$
$= 15\sqrt{2} - 15\sqrt{2}$
$= 0$

3. $5\sqrt[3]{16} - 2\sqrt[3]{54} = 5\sqrt[3]{8}\,\sqrt[3]{2} - 2\sqrt[3]{27}\,\sqrt[3]{2}$
$= 5(2)\sqrt[3]{2} - 2(3)\sqrt[3]{2}$
$= 10\sqrt[3]{2} - 6\sqrt[3]{2} = 4\sqrt[3]{2}$

4. $\sqrt{6}\,\sqrt{3} = \sqrt{18} = \sqrt{9}\,\sqrt{2} = 3\sqrt{2}$ 5. $(2\sqrt{3} + \sqrt{11})(2\sqrt{3} - \sqrt{11}) = 12 - 11 = 1$

6. $(3\sqrt{2} - 5)^2 = (3\sqrt{2})^2 + 2(3\sqrt{2})(-5) + (-5)^2$
$= 18 - 30\sqrt{2} + 25$
$= 43 - 30\sqrt{2}$

7. $\frac{9}{\sqrt{3}} = \frac{9}{\sqrt{3}}\frac{(\sqrt{3})}{(\sqrt{3})} = \frac{9\sqrt{3}}{3} = 3\sqrt{3}$

8. $\frac{5}{3 + \sqrt{2}} = \frac{5}{3 + \sqrt{2}}\frac{(3 - \sqrt{2})}{(3 - \sqrt{2})} = \frac{15 - 5\sqrt{2}}{9 - 2} = \frac{15 - 5\sqrt{2}}{7}$

Test B   Page 289

I 1. $5^0 = 1$ 2. $2^{-3} = \frac{1}{2^3} = \frac{1}{8}$ 3. $(3a - 5)^0 = 1$

4. $81^{\frac{3}{4}} = \sqrt[4]{81^3} = (\sqrt[4]{81})^3 = 3^3 = 27$ 5. $\frac{1}{5^{-2}} = 5^2 = 25$

6. $16^{\frac{5}{4}} = \sqrt[4]{16^5} = (\sqrt[4]{16})^5 = 2^5 = 32$

II 1. $\sqrt{54} = \sqrt{9}\sqrt{6} = 3\sqrt{6}$ 2. $\sqrt[3]{24} = \sqrt[3]{8}\,\sqrt[3]{3} = 2\,\sqrt[3]{3}$

3. $\sqrt{\frac{3}{5}} = \frac{\sqrt{3}}{\sqrt{5}} = \frac{\sqrt{3}}{\sqrt{5}}\frac{(\sqrt{5})}{(\sqrt{5})} = \frac{\sqrt{15}}{5}$ 4. $\sqrt[3]{\frac{5}{9}} = \frac{\sqrt[3]{5}}{\sqrt[3]{9}} = \frac{\sqrt[3]{5}}{\sqrt[3]{9}}\frac{(\sqrt[3]{3})}{(\sqrt[3]{3})} = \frac{\sqrt[3]{15}}{\sqrt[3]{27}} = \frac{\sqrt[3]{15}}{3}$

5. $\sqrt{6a^7b^2} = \sqrt{a^6b^2}\,\sqrt{6a} = a^3b\,\sqrt{6a}$ 6. $\sqrt[3]{6a^7b^2} = \sqrt[3]{a^6}\,\sqrt[3]{6ab^2} = a^2\,\sqrt[3]{6ab^2}$

III 1. $\sqrt{18} - \sqrt{8} + \sqrt{50} = \sqrt{9}\sqrt{2} - \sqrt{4}\sqrt{2} + \sqrt{25}\sqrt{2} = 3\sqrt{2} - 2\sqrt{2} + 5\sqrt{2} = 6\sqrt{2}$

2. $3\sqrt{12} - 2\sqrt{75} = 3\sqrt{4}\sqrt{3} - 2\sqrt{25}\sqrt{3} = 3(2)\sqrt{3} - 2(5)\sqrt{3} = 6\sqrt{3} - 10\sqrt{3}$
$= -4\sqrt{3}$

3. $6\,\sqrt[3]{375} - 5\,\sqrt[3]{24} = 6\,\sqrt[3]{125}\,\sqrt[3]{3} - 5\,\sqrt[3]{8}\,\sqrt[3]{3} = 6(5)\,\sqrt[3]{3} - 5(2)\,\sqrt[3]{3}$
$= 30\,\sqrt[3]{3} - 10\,\sqrt[3]{3} = 20\,\sqrt[3]{3}$

4. $\sqrt{10}\cdot\sqrt{5} = \sqrt{50} = \sqrt{25}\sqrt{2} = 5\sqrt{2}$

5. $(5\sqrt{3} - 4)^2 = (5\sqrt{3})^2 + 2(5\sqrt{3})(-4) + (-4)^2$
$= 75 - 40\sqrt{3} + 16 = 91 - 40\sqrt{3}$

6. $12 \div \sqrt{2} = \frac{12}{\sqrt{2}} = \frac{12}{\sqrt{2}}\frac{(\sqrt{2})}{(\sqrt{2})} = \frac{12\sqrt{2}}{2} = 6\sqrt{2}$

7. $\frac{6}{5 - \sqrt{7}} = \frac{6}{(5 - \sqrt{7})}\frac{(5 + \sqrt{7})}{(5 + \sqrt{7})} = \frac{30 + 6\sqrt{7}}{25 - 7} = \frac{30 + 6\sqrt{7}}{18} = \frac{6(5 + \sqrt{7})}{18} = \frac{5 + \sqrt{7}}{3}$

8. $\frac{\sqrt{5} - \sqrt{3}}{\sqrt{5} + \sqrt{3}} = \frac{\sqrt{5} - \sqrt{3}}{\sqrt{5} + \sqrt{3}}\frac{(\sqrt{5} - \sqrt{3})}{(\sqrt{5} - \sqrt{3})} = \frac{5 - 2\sqrt{15} + 3}{5 - 3} = \frac{8 - 2\sqrt{15}}{2} = \frac{2(4 - \sqrt{15})}{2}$
$= 4 - \sqrt{15}$

Test C   Page 289

1. a) $\sqrt{18} = \sqrt{9}\sqrt{2} = 3\sqrt{2}$ in.
   b) $4(3\sqrt{2}) = 12\sqrt{2}$ in.
   c) $\sqrt{(3\sqrt{2})^2 + (3\sqrt{2})^2} = \sqrt{18 + 18} = \sqrt{36} = 6$ in.

2.
$$8x^{\frac{3}{2}} = 1$$
$$x^{\frac{3}{2}} = \frac{1}{8}$$
$$(x^{\frac{3}{2}})^{\frac{2}{3}} = (\frac{1}{8})^{\frac{2}{3}}$$
$$x^3 = \frac{1}{64}$$
$$x = \sqrt[3]{\frac{1}{64}}$$
$$x = \frac{1}{4}$$

3.
$$y^{-\frac{2}{3}} = \frac{1}{49}$$
$$\frac{1}{y^{\frac{2}{3}}} = \frac{1}{49}$$
$$y^{\frac{2}{3}} = 49$$
$$(y^{\frac{2}{3}})^3 = 49^3$$
$$y^2 = (7^2)^3$$
$$y^2 = (7^3)^2$$
$$y = 7^3$$
$$y = 343$$

4.
$$\sqrt{5} = 5^{\frac{1}{2}} = 5^{\frac{3}{6}} = \sqrt[6]{5^3} = \sqrt[6]{125}$$
$$\sqrt[3]{11} = 11^{\frac{1}{3}} = 11^{\frac{2}{6}} = \sqrt[6]{11^2} = \sqrt[6]{121}$$

$\sqrt{5}$ is larger because its radicand is larger when both are expressed as similar radicals.

5. a)
$$\sqrt{2}\ \sqrt[3]{3} = (2^{\frac{1}{2}})(3^{\frac{1}{3}}) = (2^{\frac{3}{6}})(3^{\frac{2}{6}}) = \sqrt[6]{2^3}\ \sqrt[6]{3^2} = \sqrt[6]{8}\ \sqrt[6]{9} = \sqrt[6]{72}$$

b)
$$\begin{array}{rcccl} & 2\sqrt{2} & - 3\sqrt{3} & + \sqrt{5} & \\ & 2\sqrt{2} & + 3\sqrt{3} & - \sqrt{5} & \\ \hline 8 & - 6\sqrt{6} & + 2\sqrt{10} & & \\ -27 & + 6\sqrt{6} & & + 3\sqrt{15} & \\ -5 & & - 2\sqrt{10} & + 3\sqrt{15} & \\ \hline -24 & & & + 6\sqrt{15} & = 6\sqrt{15} - 24 \end{array}$$

6. What number used as a factor three times gives a particular value?
$\sqrt[3]{64} = 4$ because $4^3 = 64$; $\sqrt[3]{-64} = -4$ because $(-4)^3 = -64$

7. What number used as a factor twice gives a particular value?
$\sqrt{64} = \pm 8$ because $8(8) = 64$ and $(-8)(-8) = 64$.
$\sqrt{-64}$ cannot be found because there is no number when used as a factor twice yields a negative product.

8. No; no; $\sqrt{7}$ can be estimated as a decimal, but $\sqrt{-64}$ cannot.

9. $\frac{\sqrt{48}}{\sqrt{6}} = \sqrt{\frac{48}{6}} = \sqrt{8} = \sqrt{4}\ \sqrt{2} = 2\sqrt{2}$

10.
$$\begin{array}{rcl} 2\sqrt{5} & + \sqrt{6} & \\ 2\sqrt{5} & - \sqrt{6} & \\ \hline 20 & + 2\sqrt{30} & \\ & - 2\sqrt{30} & - 6 \\ \hline 20 & & - 6 = 14 \end{array}$$

11. $\sqrt{2}$ because $\sqrt{8}\ \sqrt{2} = \sqrt{16} = 4$.

Exercises 14.2   Page 296

1. $x^2 - 4x + 3 = 0$
   roots: $x = 1, 3$

x	y
2	-1
3	0
1	0
4	3
0	3

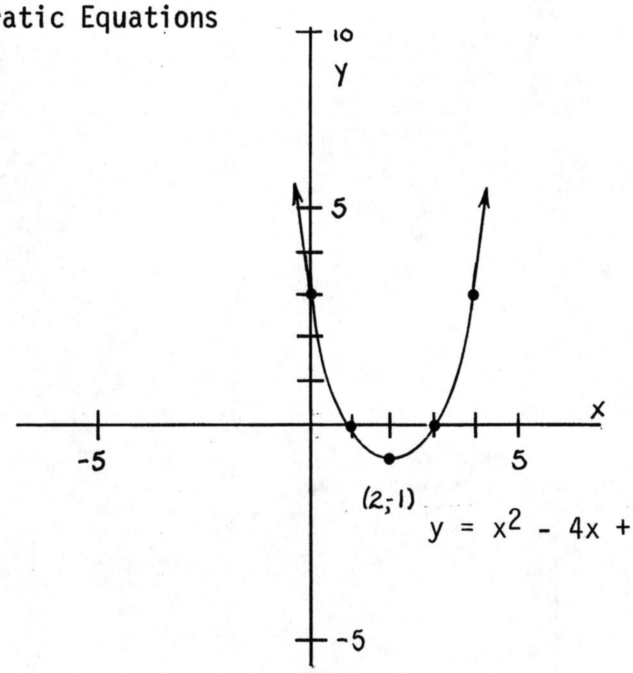

2. $x^2 - 6x + 7 = 0$
   roots: $x = 1.6, 4.4$

x	y
3	-2
4	-1
2	-1
5	2
1	2

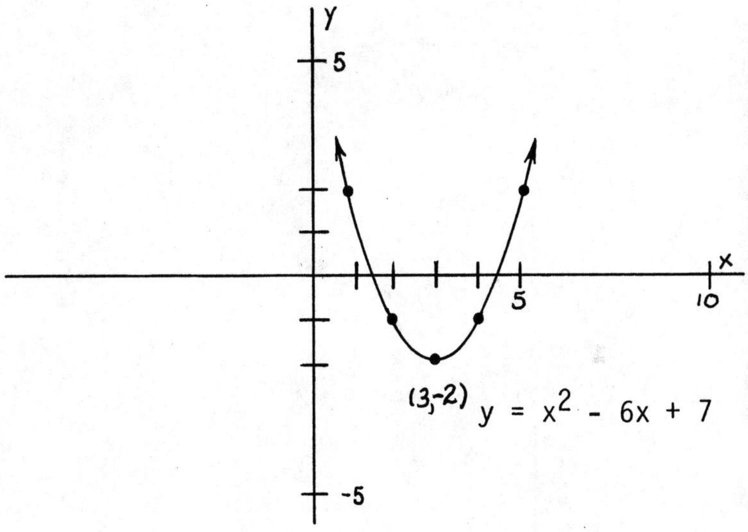

3. $x^2 - 4x = -2$
   $x^2 - 4x + 2 = 0$
   roots: $x = 0.6, 3.4$

x	y
2	-2
3	-1
1	-1
4	2
0	2

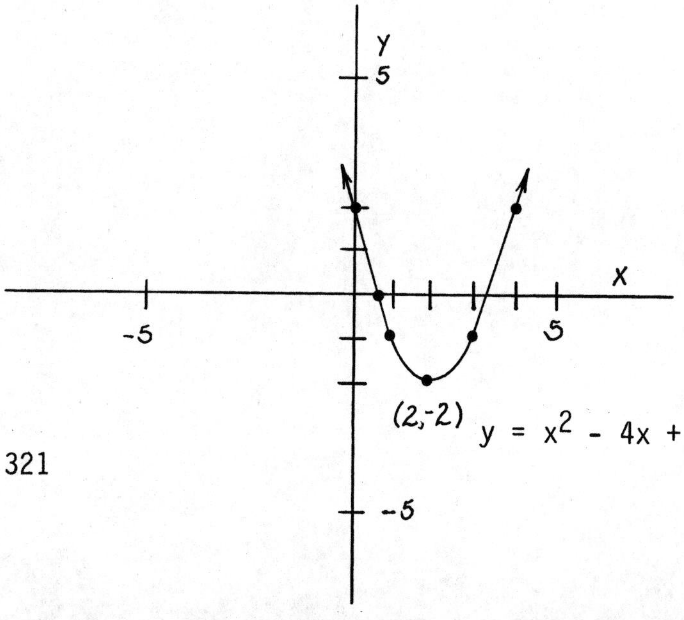

4. $x^2 + 2(x + 1) = 0$
$x^2 + 2x + 2 = 0$
roots: no real root

x	y
-1	1
0	2
-2	2
1	5
-3	5

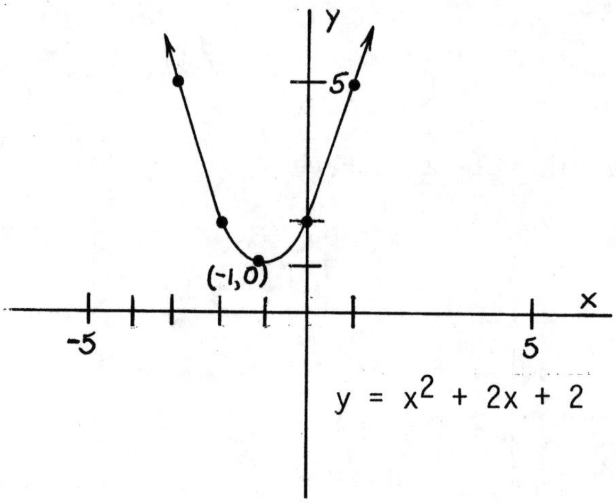

5. $x^2 - 4x + 6 = 0$
roots: no real root

x	y
2	2
3	3
1	3
4	6
0	6

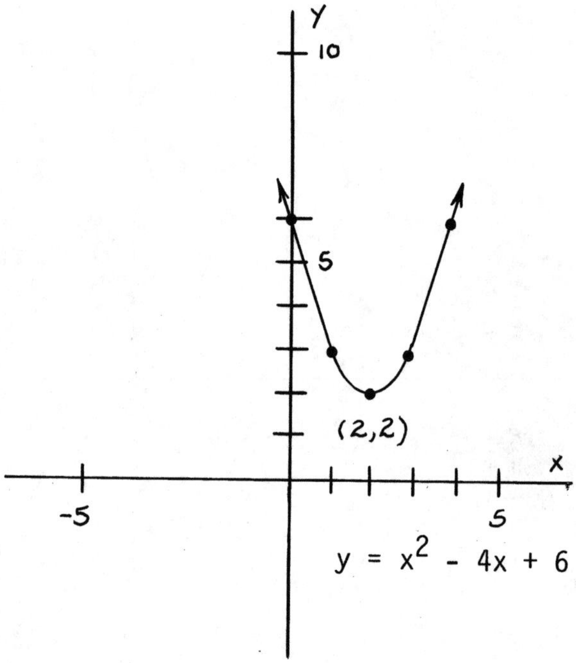

6. $x^2 - 2x - 2 = 0$
roots: $x = -0.7, 2.7$

x	y
1	-3
2	-2
0	-2
3	1
-1	1

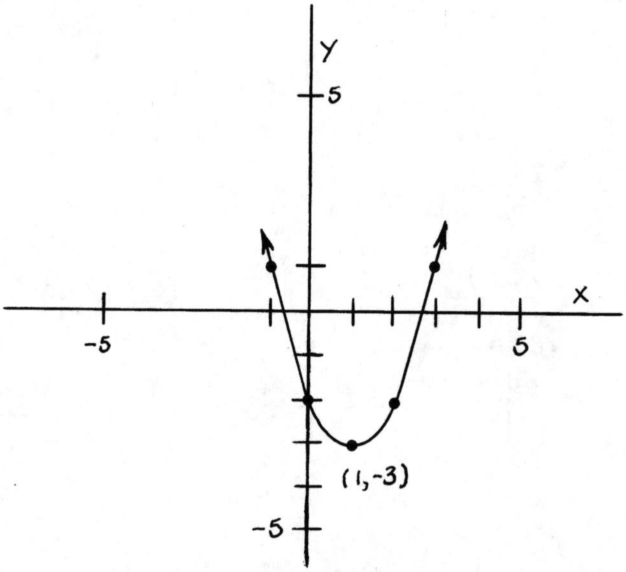

7. $x^2 = 6x - 9$

$x^2 - 6x + 9 = 0$

roots: $x = 3, 3$

x	y
3	0
4	1
2	1
5	4
1	4

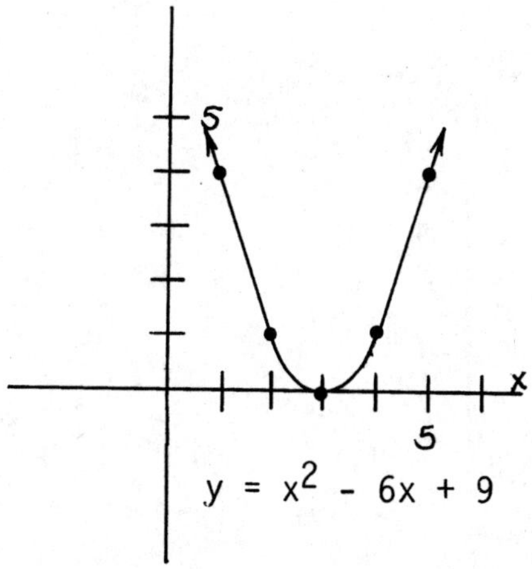

8. $x^2 + 4x + 2 = 0$

roots: $x = -0.6, -3.4$

x	y
-2	-2
-1	-1
-3	-1
0	2
-4	2

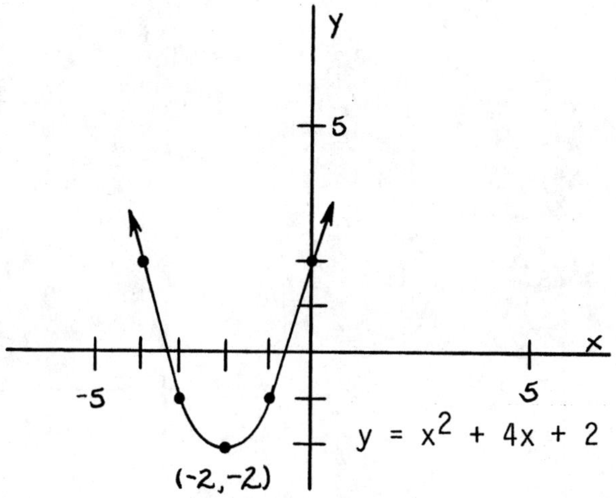

9. $x^2 - 2x + 6 = 0$

roots: no real root

x	y
1	5
2	6
0	6
3	9
-1	9

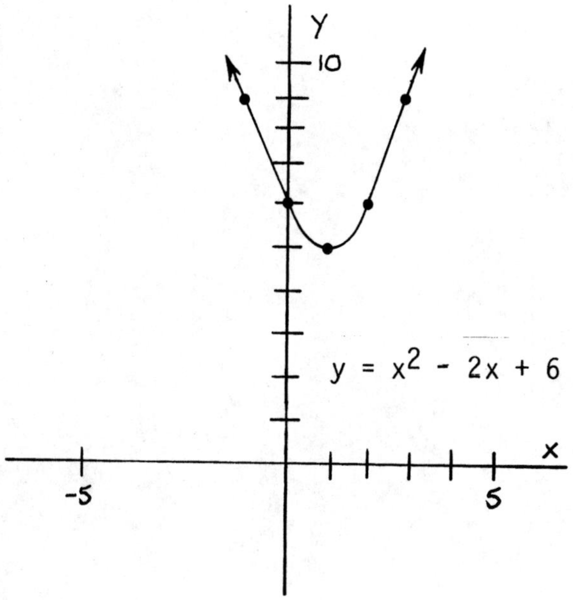

10. $x^2 - 4x - 1 = 0$
roots: $x = -0.2, 4.2$

x	y
2	-5
3	-4
1	-4
4	-1
0	-1
5	4
-1	4

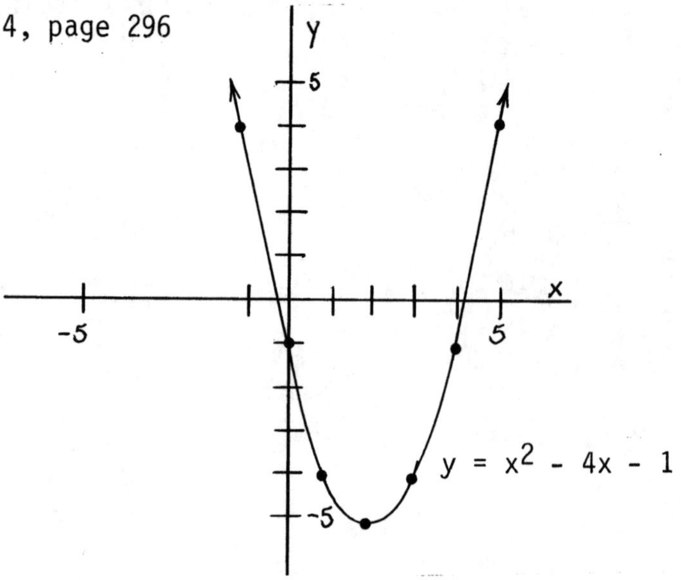

*11. $4x - 2x^2 + 1 = 0$
$-2x^2 + 4x + 1 = 0$
$2x^2 - 4x - 1 = 0$
$x^2 - 2x - \frac{1}{2} = 0$
roots: $x = -0.2, 2.2$

x	y
1	-3
2	-1
0	-1
3	5
-1	5

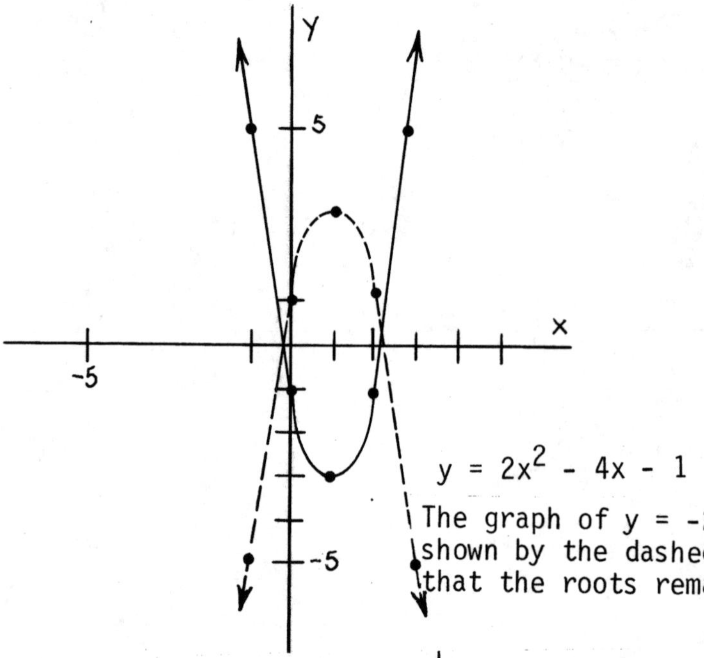

The graph of $y = -2x^2 + 4x + 1$ i shown by the dashed line. Note that the roots remain the same.

12. $2x^2 + 8x + 7 = 0$
$x^2 + 4x + \frac{7}{2} = 0$
roots: $x = -1.3, -2.7$

x	y
-2	-1
-1	1
-3	1
0	7
-4	7

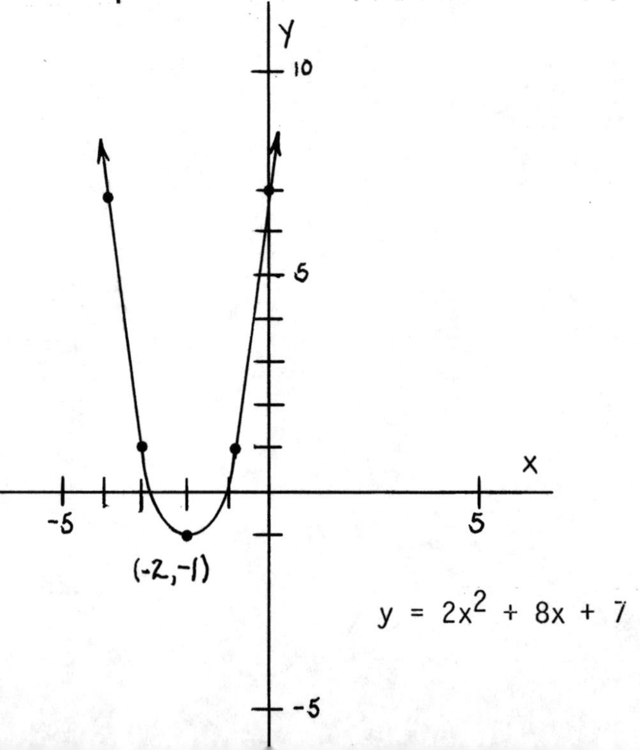

13. $2x^2 - 12x + 15 = 0$

$$x^2 - 6x + \frac{15}{2} = 0$$

roots: 1.8, 4.2

x	y
3	-3
4	-1
2	-1
5	5
1	5

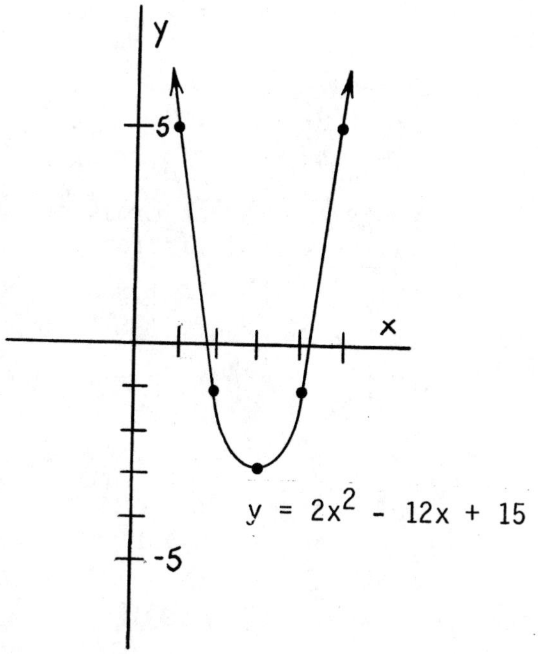

*14. $12x - 4x^2 - 1 = 0$

$$-4x^2 + 12x - 1 = 0$$

$$4x^2 - 12x + 1 = 0$$

$$x^2 - \frac{12}{4}x + \frac{1}{4} = 0$$

$$x^2 - 3x + \frac{1}{4} = 0$$

roots: 0.1, 2.9

x	y
$\frac{3}{2}$	8
3	-1
0	-1
4	-17
-1	-17

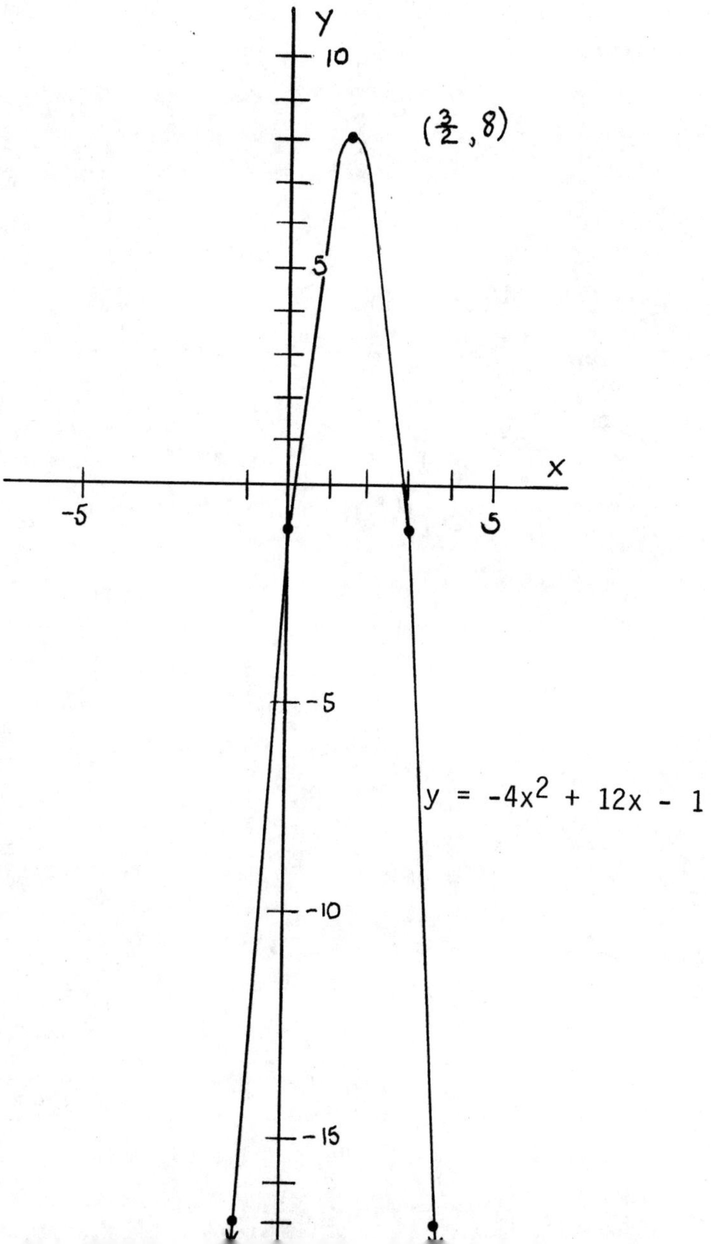

15. $11 + 8x + 2x^2 = 0$
$2x^2 + 8x + 11 = 0$
$x^2 + 4x + \frac{11}{2} = 0$

roots: does not cross or touch x-axis (no real root)

x	y
-2	3
-1	5
-3	5
0	11
-4	11

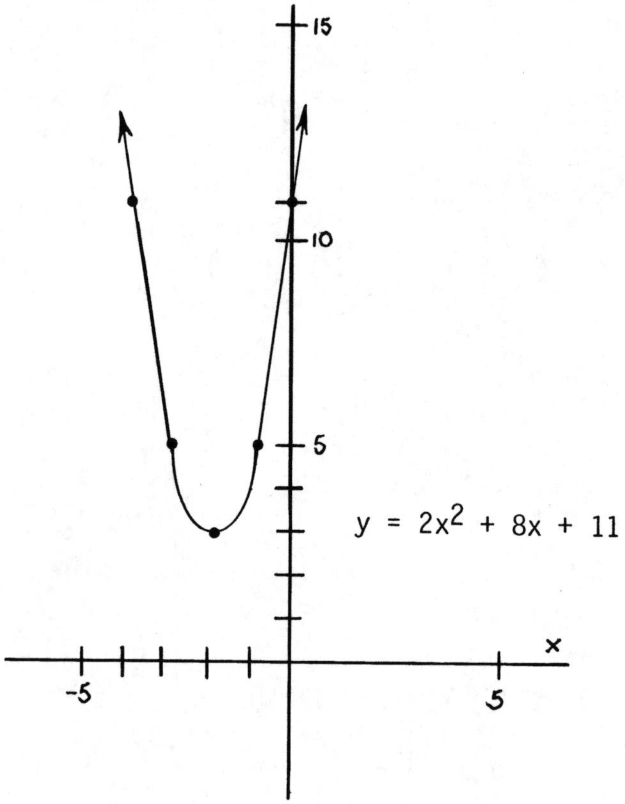

Exercises 14.3 Page 298

The check for exercises 1-6 is left for the teacher.

1. $3x^2 - 5 = 22$
$3x^2 = 27$
$x^2 = 9$
$x = \pm\sqrt{9}$
$x = \pm 3$

2. $2x^2 + 3x^2 = 80$
$5x^2 = 80$
$x^2 = 16$
$x = \pm\sqrt{16}$
$x = \pm 4$

3. $4x^2 = \frac{1}{9}$
$\frac{1}{4}(4x^2) = \frac{1}{4}(\frac{1}{9})$
$x^2 = \frac{1}{36}$
$x = \pm\sqrt{\frac{1}{36}}$
$x = \pm\frac{1}{6}$

4. $\frac{3}{4}x^2 - 5 = 22$
$\frac{3}{4}x^2 = 27$
$3x^2 = 108$
$x^2 = 36$
$x = \pm 6$

5. $5x^2 - 75 = 2x^2$
$3x^2 = 75$
$x^2 = 25$
$x = \pm\sqrt{25}$
$x = \pm 5$

6. $2x^2 - 25 = 73$
$2x^2 = 98$
$x^2 = 49$
$x = \pm\sqrt{49}$
$x = \pm 7$

7. $7x^2 = 4x^2 + 24$
$3x^2 = 24$
$x^2 = 8$
$x = \pm\sqrt{8}$
$x = \pm\sqrt{4}\sqrt{2}$
$x = \pm 2\sqrt{2}$

$7(2\sqrt{2})^2$	$4(2\sqrt{2})^2 + 24$
$7(8)$	$4(8) + 24$
56	$32 + 24$

$56 = 56$ ✓

$7(-2\sqrt{2})^2$	$4(-2\sqrt{2})^2 + 24$
$7(8)$	$4(8) + 24$

$56 = 56$ ✓

8. $4n^2 + 9 = 5n^2 - 7$
$-n^2 = -16$
$n^2 = 16$
$n = \pm\sqrt{16}$
$n = \pm 4$

$4(4)^2 + 9$	$5(4)^2 - 7$
$4(16) + 9$	$5(16) - 7$
$64 + 9$	$80 - 7$

$73 = 73$ ✓

$4(-4)^2 + 9$	$5(-4)^2 - 7$
$4(16) + 9$	$5(16) - 7$

$73 = 73$ ✓

9. $(x + 2)^2 - 4(x + 2) = 4$
$x^2 + 4x + 4 - 4x - 8 = 4$
$x^2 - 4 = 4$
$x^2 = 8$
$x = \pm\sqrt{8}$
$x = \pm\sqrt{4}\sqrt{2}$
$x = \pm 2\sqrt{2}$

$(2\sqrt{2} + 2)^2 - 4(2\sqrt{2} + 2)$	4
$8 + 8\sqrt{2} + 4 - 8\sqrt{2} - 8$	4

$4 = 4$ ✓

$(-2\sqrt{2} + 2)^2 - 4(-2\sqrt{2} + 2)$	4
$8 - 8\sqrt{2} + 4 + 8\sqrt{2} - 8$	4

$4 = 4$ ✓

10. $(3u - 8)(3u + 8) = 17$
$9u^2 - 64 = 17$
$9u^2 = 81$
$u^2 = 9$
$u = \pm\sqrt{9}$
$u = \pm 3$

$[3(3) - 8][3(3) + 8]$	17
$(9 - 8)(9 + 8)$	17
$1(17)$	17

$17 = 17$ ✓

$[3(-3) - 8][3(-3) + 8]$	17
$(-9 - 8)(-9 + 8)$	17
$-17(-1)$	17

$17 = 17$ ✓

11. $(x + 1)^3 - (x - 1)^3 = 38$
$(x + 1)^2(x + 1) - (x - 1)^2(x - 1) = 38$
$(x^2 + 2x + 1)(x + 1) - (x^2 - 2x + 1)(x - 1) = 38$
$x^3 + 3x^2 + 3x + 1 - (x^3 - 3x^2 + 3x - 1) = 38$
$\cancel{x^3} + 3x^2 + \cancel{3x} + 1 - \cancel{x^3} + 3x^2 - \cancel{3x} + 1 = 38$
$6x^2 + 2 = 38$
$6x^2 = 36$
$x^2 = 6$
$x = \pm\sqrt{6}$

$(\sqrt{6} + 1)^3 - (\sqrt{6} - 1)^3$	38
$(\sqrt{6} + 1)^2(\sqrt{6} + 1) - (\sqrt{6} - 1)^2(\sqrt{6} - 1)$	38
$(6 + 2\sqrt{6} + 1)(\sqrt{6} + 1) - (6 - 2\sqrt{6} + 1)(\sqrt{6} - 1)$	38
$19 + 9\sqrt{6} - (9\sqrt{6} - 19)$	38
$19 + 9\sqrt{6} - 9\sqrt{6} + 19$	38

$38 = 38$ ✓

(continued)

11. (Cont.)

$$\begin{array}{r|l}
(-\sqrt{6}+1)^3 - (-\sqrt{6}-1)^3 & 38 \\
(-\sqrt{6}+1)^2(-\sqrt{6}+1) - (-\sqrt{6}-1)^2(-\sqrt{6}-1) & 38 \\
(6-2\sqrt{6}+1)(-\sqrt{6}+1) - (6+2\sqrt{6}+1)(-\sqrt{6}-1) & 38 \\
-9\sqrt{6}+19-(-9\sqrt{6}-19) & 38 \\
-9\sqrt{6}+19+9\sqrt{6}+19 & 38 \\
38 = & 38 \checkmark
\end{array}$$

12.
$$\begin{aligned}
(x+1)^2 &= x(3x+2) - 3 \\
x^2+2x+1 &= 3x^2+2x-3 \\
-2x^2 &= -4 \\
x^2 &= 2 \\
x &= \pm\sqrt{2}
\end{aligned}$$

$$\begin{array}{r|l}
(-\sqrt{2}+1)^2 & \sqrt{2}(3\sqrt{2}+2) - 3 \\
2+2\sqrt{2}+1 & 6+2\sqrt{2}-3 \\
3+2\sqrt{2} = & 3+2\sqrt{2} \checkmark
\end{array}$$

$$\begin{array}{r|l}
(\sqrt{2}+1)^2 & -\sqrt{2}[3(-\sqrt{2})+2] - 3 \\
2-2\sqrt{2}+1 & 6-2\sqrt{2}-3 \\
3-2\sqrt{2} = & 3-2\sqrt{2} \checkmark
\end{array}$$

13.
$$\begin{aligned}
5(s+2) &= 3s^2 + s(5-s) \\
5s+10 &= 3s^2+5s-s^2 \\
5s+10 &= 2s^2+5s \\
-2s^2 &= -10 \\
s^2 &= 5 \\
s &= \pm\sqrt{5}
\end{aligned}$$

$$\begin{array}{r|l}
5(\sqrt{5}+2) & 3(\sqrt{5})^2 + \sqrt{5}(5-\sqrt{5}) \\
5\sqrt{5}+10 & 15+5\sqrt{5}-5 \\
10+5\sqrt{5} = & 10+5\sqrt{5} \checkmark
\end{array}$$

$$\begin{array}{r|l}
5(-\sqrt{5}+2) & 3(-\sqrt{5})^2 + (-\sqrt{5})[5-(-\sqrt{5})] \\
-5\sqrt{5}+10 & 15-\sqrt{5}(5+\sqrt{5}) \\
10-5\sqrt{5} & 15-5\sqrt{5}-5 \\
10-5\sqrt{5} = & 10-5\sqrt{5} \checkmark
\end{array}$$

14. $(2r + 1)(2r + 3) = 8(r + 3)$

$$4r^2 + 8r + 3 = 8r + 24$$
$$4r^2 = 21$$
$$r^2 = \frac{21}{4}$$
$$r = \pm \frac{\sqrt{21}}{2}$$

$$[2(\tfrac{1}{2}\sqrt{21}) + 1][2(\tfrac{1}{2}\sqrt{21}) + 3] \;\Big|\; 8(\tfrac{1}{2}\sqrt{21} + 3)$$
$$(\sqrt{21} + 1)(\sqrt{21} + 3) \;\Big|\; 4\sqrt{21} + 24$$
$$21 + 4\sqrt{21} + 3$$
$$24 + 4\sqrt{21} \doteq 24 + 4\sqrt{21} \checkmark$$

$$[2(-\tfrac{1}{2}\sqrt{21}) + 1][2(-\tfrac{1}{2}\sqrt{21}) + 3] \;\Big|\; 8(-\tfrac{1}{2}\sqrt{21}) + 24$$
$$(-\sqrt{21} + 1)(-\sqrt{21} + 3) \;\Big|\; -4\sqrt{21} + 24$$
$$21 - 4\sqrt{21} + 3 \;\Big|\; -4\sqrt{21} + 24$$
$$24 - 4\sqrt{21} \doteq 24 - 4\sqrt{21} \checkmark$$

Exercises 14.4 Page 299

1. let w = width 20 meters
4w = length 80 meters

$$4w(w) = 1600$$
$$4w^2 = 1600$$
$$w^2 = 400$$
$$w = \sqrt{400}$$
$$w = 20$$

80 is 4(20) ✓

$$80 \times 20 = 1600 \text{ sq. meters } \checkmark$$

2. let s = length of a side 20 meters
4s = perimeter 80 meters

$$s^2 = 400$$
$$s = \sqrt{400}$$
$$s = 20$$

$$20 \times 20 = 400 \text{ sq. meters}$$

$$\frac{460}{160} = 2.5 \checkmark$$

3. let x = thickness 4 in.
5x = width 20 in.

$$5x(x)(48) = 3840$$
$$240x^2 = 3840$$
$$x^2 = 16$$
$$x = \sqrt{16}$$
$$x = 4$$

(4)(20)(48) = 3840 cu. in. ✓

4. let ℓ = length of flag 50 ft.
$\frac{3}{5}\ell$ = width of flag 30 ft.

$$\frac{3}{5}\ell(\ell) = 1500$$
$$\frac{3}{5}\ell^2 = 1500$$
$$3\ell^2 = 7500$$
$$\ell^2 = 2500$$
$$\ell = \sqrt{2500}$$
$$\ell = 50$$

30 is $(\frac{3}{5})(50)$ ✓

(50)(30) = 1500 sq. ft. ✓

*5. let x = % of second discount 10%
5x = % of first discount 50%

$$.05x(20) + .01x(.05x \cdot 20) = 11$$
$$x + .01x^2 = 11$$
$$100x + x^2 = 1100$$
$$x^2 + 100x - 1100 = 0$$
$$(x + 110)(x - 10) = 0$$
~~x = -110~~ reject   x = 10

$20	$20	$10	$10
x.5	-10	x.1	-1
$10	$10	$ 1	$ 9

6. let x = number of pencils 12
$\frac{60}{x}$ = price of one pencil 5¢

$$(x + 3)\left(\frac{60}{x} - 1\right) = 60$$
$$60 - x + \frac{180}{x} - 3 = 60$$
$$-x + \frac{180}{x} = 3$$
$$x\left(-x + \frac{180}{x}\right) = 3x$$
$$-x^2 + 180 = 3x$$
$$x^2 + 3x - 180 = 0$$
$$(x + 15)(x - 12) = 0$$
~~x = -15~~ reject   x = 12

12	5¢
+3	-1
15	4¢

(15)(4¢) = 60¢ ✓

7. let x = number of board feet per tie 40
x = number of carloads
250x = total number of ties 10,000

$$250x(x) = 400{,}000$$
$$250x^2 = 400{,}000$$
$$x^2 = 1600$$
$$x = \sqrt{1600}$$
$$x = 40$$

10,000
x 40
400,000 ✓

8. let x = amount saved per week $12
$\frac{1}{2}x$ = number of weeks 6 wk.

$$\frac{1}{2}x(x) = 72$$
$$\frac{1}{2}x^2 = 72$$
$$x^2 = 144$$
$$x = \sqrt{144}$$
$$x = 12$$

$12
x 6
$72 ✓

Exercises 14.5   Pages 299-300

1.
$$d = \frac{1}{2}gt^2$$
$$2d = gt^2$$
$$\frac{2d}{g} = t^2$$
$$t = \sqrt{\frac{2d}{g}}$$

2.
$$E = \frac{1}{2}mv^2$$
$$2E = mv^2$$
$$\frac{2E}{m} = v^2$$
$$v = \sqrt{\frac{2E}{m}}$$

3.
$$t = 2\pi\sqrt{\frac{I}{g}}$$
$$t^2 = 4\pi^2\left(\frac{I}{g}\right)$$
$$t^2g = 4\pi^2 I$$
$$I = \frac{gt^2}{4\pi^2}$$

4.
$$F = \frac{mv^2}{R}$$
$$FR = mv^2$$
$$\frac{FR}{m} = v^2$$
$$v = \sqrt{\frac{FR}{m}}$$

5.
$$F = G\frac{mm'}{d^2}$$
$$Fd^2 = Gmm'$$
$$d^2 = \frac{Gmm'}{F}$$
$$d = \sqrt{\frac{Gmm'}{F}}$$

6.
$$t = \frac{\sqrt{2dg}}{g}$$
$$t = \frac{\sqrt{2(100.5)(32.16)}}{g}$$
$$t = \frac{80.4}{32.16}$$
$$t = 2.5 \text{ sec.}$$

7.
$$t = \frac{\sqrt{2dg}}{g}$$
$$t = \frac{\sqrt{2(2500)(32.16)}}{32.16}$$
$$t = \frac{\sqrt{160,800}}{32.16}$$
$$t = \frac{401}{32.16}$$
$$t \approx 12.5 \text{ sec.}$$
(This is an approximate answer.)

Note: Since numbers 8-18 are geometric formulas, only the positive root is given.

8.
$$c^2 = a^2 + b^2$$
$$b^2 = c^2 - a^2$$
$$b = \sqrt{c^2 - a^2}$$

9.
$$4m^2 = 2(a^2 + b^2) - c^2$$
$$4m^2 = 2a^2 + 2b^2 - c^2$$
$$m^2 = \frac{2a^2 + 2b^2 - c^2}{4}$$
$$m = \sqrt{\frac{2a^2 + 2b^2 - c^2}{4}}$$
$$m = \sqrt{\frac{2a^2 + 2b^2 - c^2}{2}}$$

10.
$$A = .7854d^2$$
$$\frac{A}{.7854} = d^2$$
$$d = \sqrt{\frac{A}{.7854}}$$
OR
$$d = \frac{\sqrt{.7854A}}{.7854}$$

11.
$$V = \frac{1}{3}\pi r^2 h$$
$$3V = \pi r^2 h$$
$$\frac{3V}{\pi h} = \frac{\pi r^2 h}{\pi h}$$
$$r^2 = \frac{3V}{\pi h}$$
$$r = \sqrt{\frac{3V}{\pi h}}$$
OR
$$r = \frac{\sqrt{3V\pi h}}{\pi h}$$

12.
$$c^2 = a^2 + b^2$$
$$c^2 = 8^2 + 6^2$$
$$c^2 = 64 + 36$$
$$c^2 = 100$$
$$c = \sqrt{100}$$
$$c = 10$$

13.
$$c^2 = a^2 + b^2$$
$$5^2 = a^2 + 3^2$$
$$25 = a^2 + 9$$
$$16 = a^2$$
$$a = \sqrt{16}$$
$$a = 4$$

14. $c^2 = a^2 + b^2$

substituting a for b

$$c^2 = a^2 + a^2$$
$$10^2 = 2a^2$$
$$100 = 2a^2$$
$$a^2 = 50$$
$$a = \sqrt{50}$$
$$a = \sqrt{25}\,\sqrt{2}$$
$$a = 5\,\sqrt{2}$$
$$a = 5(1.414)$$
$$a = 7.070 \approx 7.1$$

15.
$$a^2 + b^2 = c$$
$$(\tfrac{1}{2}c)^2 + b^2 = c^2$$
$$\tfrac{1}{4}c^2 + b^2 = c^2$$
$$b^2 = \tfrac{3}{4}c^2$$
$$b = \sqrt{\tfrac{3}{4}c^2}$$
$$b = \sqrt{\frac{c^2}{4}}\,\sqrt{3}$$
$$b = \frac{c}{2}\sqrt{3}$$

16.
$$m = \frac{1}{2}\sqrt{2a^2 + 2b^2 - c^2}$$
$$m = \frac{1}{2}\sqrt{2(11^2) + 2(8^2) - 9^2}$$
$$m = \frac{1}{2}\sqrt{2(121) + 2(64) - 81}$$
$$m = \frac{1}{2}\sqrt{242 + 128 - 81}$$
$$m = \frac{1}{2}\sqrt{289}$$
$$m = \frac{1}{2}(17)$$
$$m = 8.5$$

17.
$$d = \sqrt{\frac{A}{.7854}}$$
$$d = \sqrt{\frac{1000}{.7854}}$$
$$d = \sqrt{1273.24}$$
$$d \approx 35.7 \text{ ft.}$$

18.
$$r = \sqrt{\frac{3v}{\pi h}}$$
$$r = \sqrt{\frac{3(1000)}{3.1416(20)}}$$
$$r = \sqrt{\frac{3000}{62.832}}$$
$$r = \sqrt{47.746}$$
$$r = 6.9098$$
$$r \approx 7 \text{ cm}$$

Exercises 14.6 Page 301

The check is left for the teacher.

1.
$$x^2 - 5x + 6 = 0$$
$$(x - 3)(x - 2) = 0$$

$x - 3 = 0$ $\quad$ $x - 2 = 0$
$x = 3$ $\quad$ $x = 2$

$x = 2;\ 3$

2.
$$x^2 + 10x + 21 = 0$$
$$(x + 7)(x + 3) = 0$$

$x + 7 = 0$ $\quad$ $x + 3 = 0$
$x = -7$ $\quad$ $x = -3$

$x = -7;\ -3$

3.
$$x^2 + 12x - 28 = 0$$
$$(x + 14)(x - 2) = 0$$

$x + 14 = 0$ $\quad$ $x - 2 = 0$
$x = -14$ $\quad$ $x = 2$

$x = -14;\ 2$

4.
$$x^2 - 20x + 51 = 0$$
$$(x - 3)(x - 17) = 0$$

$x - 3 = 0$ $\quad$ $x - 17 = 0$
$x = 3$ $\quad$ $x = 17$

$x = 3;\ 17$

5.
$$x^2 - 5x = 24$$
$$x^2 - 5x - 24 = 0$$
$$(x - 8)(x + 3) = 0$$

$x - 8 = 0$ $\quad x + 3 = 0$
$x = 8$ $\quad x = -3$

$x = -3;\ 8$

6.
$$x^2 - 1 = 3(x + 1)$$
$$x^2 - 1 = 3x + 3$$
$$x^2 - 3x - 4 = 0$$
$$(x - 4)(x + 1) = 0$$

$x - 4 = 0$ $\quad x + 1 = 0$
$x = 4$ $\quad x = -1$

$x = -1;\ 4$

7.
$$x^2 + 10x = 39$$
$$x^2 + 10x - 39 = 0$$
$$(x + 13)(x - 3) = 0$$

$x + 13 = 0$ $\quad x - 3 = 0$
$x = -13$ $\quad x = 3$

$x = -13;\ 3$

8.
$$60 + x^2 = 17x$$
$$x^2 - 17x + 60 = 0$$
$$(x - 12)(x - 5) = 0$$

$x - 12 = 0$ $\quad x - 5 = 0$
$x = 12$ $\quad x = 5$

$x = 5;\ 12$

9.
$$x(x - 1) = 42$$
$$x^2 - x - 42 = 0$$
$$(x - 7)(x + 6) = 0$$

$x - 7 = 0$ $\quad x + 6 = 0$
$x = 7$ $\quad x = -6$

$x = -6;\ 7$

10.
$$x^2 - 3 = 2(x + 6)$$
$$x^2 - 3 = 2x + 12$$
$$x^2 - 2x - 15 = 0$$
$$(x - 5)(x + 3) = 0$$

$x - 5 = 0$ $\quad x + 3 = 0$
$x = 5$ $\quad x = -3$

$x = -3;\ 5$

11.
$$x^2 - 11(x + 3) = 9$$
$$x^2 - 11x - 33 = 9$$
$$x^2 - 11x - 42 = 0$$
$$(x - 14)(x + 3) = 0$$

$x - 14 = 0$ $\quad x + 3 = 0$
$x = 14$ $\quad x = -3$

$x = -3,\ 14$

12.
$$55 + x(x + 16) = 0$$
$$55 + x^2 + 16x = 0$$
$$x^2 + 16x + 55 = 0$$
$$(x + 11)(x + 5) = 0$$

$x + 11 = 0$ $\quad x + 5 = 0$
$x = -11$ $\quad x = -5$

$x = -11;\ -5$

13.
$$2x^2 - 7x + 3 = 0$$
$$(2x - 1)(x - 3) = 0$$

$2x - 1 = 0$ $\quad x - 3 = 0$
$2x = 1$ $\quad x = 3$
$x = \frac{1}{2}$

$x = \frac{1}{2};\ 3$

14.
$$2z^2 - z - 3 = 0$$
$$(2z - 3)(z + 1) = 0$$

$2z - 3 = 0$ $\quad z + 1 = 0$
$2z = 3$ $\quad z = -1$
$z = \frac{3}{2}$

$z = -1;\ \frac{3}{2}$

15. $3v^2 - 2v - 8 = 0$
$(3v + 4)(v - 2) = 0$

$3v + 4 = 0$ $\quad v - 2 = 0$
$3v = -4$ $\quad v = 2$
$v = -\frac{4}{3}$

$v = -\frac{4}{3};\ 2$

16. $10r^2 - 27r + 5 = 0$
$(5r - 1)(2r - 5) = 0$

$5r - 1 = 0$ $\quad 2r - 5 = 0$
$5r = 1$ $\quad 2r = 5$
$r = \frac{1}{5}$ $\quad r = \frac{5}{2}$

$r = \frac{1}{5};\ \frac{5}{2}$

17. $6(s^2 + 1) = 13s$
$6s^2 + 6 = 13s$
$6s^2 - 13s + 6 = 0$
$(3s - 2)(2s - 3) = 0$

$3s - 2 = 0$ $\quad 2s - 3 = 0$
$3s = 2$ $\quad 2s = 3$
$s = \frac{2}{3}$ $\quad s = \frac{3}{2}$

$s = \frac{2}{3};\ \frac{3}{2}$

18. $2t(t + 3) + 4 = 0$
$2t^2 + 6t + 4 = 0$
$t^2 + 3t + 2 = 0$
$(t + 2)(t + 1) = 0$

$t + 2 = 0$ $\quad t + 1 = 0$
$t = -2$ $\quad t = -1$

$t = -2;\ -1$

19. $3(x^2 - 2) - 7x = 0$
$3x^2 - 6 - 7x = 0$
$3x^2 - 7x - 6 = 0$
$(3x + 2)(x - 3) = 0$

$3x + 2 = 0$ $\quad x - 3 = 0$
$3x = -2$ $\quad x = 3$
$x = -\frac{2}{3}$

$x = -\frac{2}{3};\ 3$

20. $10(2 - 3x + x^2) = 0$
$2 - 3x + x^2 = 0$
$x^2 - 3x + 2 = 0$
$(x - 2)(x - 1) = 0$

$x - 2 = 0$ $\quad x - 1 = 0$
$x = 2$ $\quad x = 1$

$x = 1;\ 2$

Exercises 14.7 Page 304

The check for exercises 1-12 is left for the teacher.

1. $x^2 - 4x = 5$
$x^2 - 4x + 4 = 5 + 4$
$(x - 2)^2 = 9$
$x - 2 = \pm 3$
$x = 2 \pm 3$
$x = -1;\ 5$

2. $x^2 - 6x = 7$
$x^2 - 6x + 9 = 7 + 9$
$(x - 3)^2 = 16$
$x - 3 = \pm 4$
$x = 3 \pm 4$
$x = -1;\ 7$

3. $8x = x^2 - 9$
$-x^2 + 8x = -9$
$x^2 - 8x = 9$
$x^2 - 8x + 16 = 9 + 16$
$(x - 4)^2 = 25$
$x - 4 = \pm 5$
$x = 4 \pm 5$
$x = -1;\ 9$

4.
$$x^2 + 2x = 15$$
$$x^2 + 2x + 1 = 15 + 1$$
$$(x + 1)^2 = 16$$
$$x + 1 = \pm 4$$
$$x = -1 \pm 4$$
$$x = -5;\ 3$$

5.
$$x^2 - 2x = 24$$
$$x^2 - 2x + 1 = 24 + 1$$
$$(x - 1)^2 = 25$$
$$x - 1 = \pm 5$$
$$x = 1 \pm 5$$
$$x = -4;\ 6$$

6.
$$x^2 + 8x = -15$$
$$x2 + 8x + 16 = -15 + 16$$
$$(x + 4)^2 = 1$$
$$x + 4 = \pm 1$$
$$x = -4 \pm 1$$
$$x = -5;\ -3$$

7.
$$63 = x^2 + 2x$$
$$x^2 + 2x = 63$$
$$x^2 + 2x + 1 = 63 + 1$$
$$(x + 1)^2 = 64$$
$$x + 1 = \pm 8$$
$$x = -1 \pm 8$$
$$x = -9;\ 7$$

8.
$$x^2 - 12x = -11$$
$$x^2 - 12x + 36 = -11 + 36$$
$$(x - 6)^2 = 25$$
$$x - 6 = \pm 5$$
$$x = 6 \pm 5$$
$$x = 1;\ 11$$

9.
$$x^2 - 40 = 6x$$
$$x^2 - 6x = 40$$
$$x^2 - 6x + 9 = 40 + 9$$
$$(x - 3)^2 = 49$$
$$x - 3 = \pm 7$$
$$x = 3 \pm 7$$
$$x = -4;\ 10$$

10.
$$y^2 = 10 - 3y$$
$$y^2 + 3y = 10$$
$$y^2 + 3y + \left(\frac{3}{2}\right)^2 = 10 + \left(\frac{3}{2}\right)^2$$
$$y^2 + 3y + \frac{9}{4} = \frac{40}{4} + \frac{9}{4}$$
$$\left(y + \frac{3}{2}\right)^2 = \frac{49}{4}$$
$$y + \frac{3}{2} = \pm\frac{7}{2}$$
$$y = -\frac{3}{2} \pm \frac{7}{2}$$
$$y = -5;\ 2$$

11.
$$v^2 + 5v = 14$$
$$v^2 + 5v + \left(\frac{5}{2}\right)^2 = 14 + \left(\frac{5}{2}\right)^2$$
$$v^2 + 5v + \frac{25}{4} = \frac{56}{4} + \frac{25}{4}$$
$$\left(v + \frac{5}{2}\right)^2 = \frac{81}{4}$$
$$v + \frac{5}{2} = \pm\frac{9}{2}$$
$$v = -\frac{5}{2} \pm \frac{9}{2}$$
$$v = -7;\ 2$$

12.
$$n(n - 1) = 2$$
$$n^2 - n = 2$$
$$n^2 - n + \left(\frac{1}{2}\right)^2 = 2 + \left(\frac{1}{2}\right)^2$$
$$n^2 - n + \frac{1}{4} = \frac{8}{4} + \frac{1}{4}$$
$$\left(n - \frac{1}{2}\right)^2 = \frac{9}{4}$$
$$n - \frac{1}{2} = \pm\sqrt{\frac{9}{4}}$$
$$n = \frac{1}{2} \pm \frac{3}{2}$$
$$n = -1;\ 2$$

13.
$$\begin{aligned} v^2 + 3v &= 1 \\ v^2 + 3v + \left(\frac{3}{2}\right)^2 &= 1 + \left(\frac{3}{2}\right)^2 \\ v^2 + 3v + \frac{9}{4} &= \frac{4}{4} + \frac{9}{4} \\ \left(v + \frac{3}{2}\right)^2 &= \frac{13}{4} \\ v + \frac{3}{2} &= \pm\sqrt{\frac{13}{4}} \\ v &= -\frac{3}{2} \pm \frac{\sqrt{13}}{2} \\ v &= \frac{-3 \pm \sqrt{13}}{2} \end{aligned}$$

$$\begin{array}{r|l} \left(\frac{-3 + \sqrt{13}}{2}\right)^2 + 3\left(\frac{-3 + \sqrt{13}}{2}\right) & 1 \\ \frac{9 - 6\sqrt{13} + 13}{4} + \frac{-9 + 3\sqrt{13}}{2} & 1 \\ \frac{22 - 6\sqrt{13}}{4} + \frac{-18 + 6\sqrt{13}}{4} & 1 \\ \frac{4}{4} & 1 \\ 1 = & 1 \checkmark \end{array}$$

$$\begin{array}{r|l} \left(\frac{-3 - \sqrt{13}}{2}\right)^2 + 3\left(\frac{-3 - \sqrt{13}}{2}\right) & 1 \\ \frac{9 + 6\sqrt{13} + 13}{4} + \frac{-9 - 3\sqrt{13}}{2} & 1 \\ \frac{22 + 6\sqrt{13}}{4} + \frac{-18 - 6\sqrt{13}}{4} & 1 \\ \frac{4}{4} & 1 \\ 1 = & 1 \checkmark \end{array}$$

14.
$$\begin{aligned} 2x(x - 2) &= 8 \\ 2x^2 - 4x &= 8 \\ x^2 - 2x &= 4 \\ x^2 - 2x + 1 &= 4 + 1 \\ (x - 1)^2 &= 5 \\ x - 1 &= \pm\sqrt{5} \\ x &= 1 \pm \sqrt{5} \end{aligned}$$

$$\begin{array}{r|l} 2(1 + \sqrt{5})(1 + \sqrt{5} - 2) & 8 \\ (2 + 2\sqrt{5})(-1 + \sqrt{5}) & 8 \\ -2 + 10 & 8 \\ 8 = & 8 \checkmark \end{array}$$

$$\begin{array}{r|l} 2(1 - \sqrt{5})(1 - \sqrt{5} - 2) & 8 \\ (2 - 2\sqrt{5})(-1 - \sqrt{5}) & 8 \\ -2 + 10 & 8 \\ 8 = & 8 \checkmark \end{array}$$

15.
$$\begin{aligned} r^2 + 4r - 7 &= 0 \\ r^2 + 4r &= 7 \\ r^2 + 4r + 4 &= 7 + 4 \\ (r + 2)^2 &= 11 \\ r + 2 &= \pm\sqrt{11} \\ r &= -2 \pm \sqrt{11} \end{aligned}$$

$$\begin{array}{r|l} (-2 + \sqrt{11})^2 + 4(-2 + \sqrt{11}) - 7 & 0 \\ 4 - 4\sqrt{11} + 11 - 8 + 4\sqrt{11} - 7 & 0 \\ 0 = & 0 \checkmark \end{array}$$

$$\begin{array}{r|l} (-2 - \sqrt{11})^2 + 4(-2 - \sqrt{11}) - 7 & 0 \\ 4 + 4\sqrt{11} + 11 - 8 - 4\sqrt{11} - 7 & 0 \\ 0 = & 0 \checkmark \end{array}$$

16.
$$\begin{aligned} \ell^2 + 11\ell + 28 &= 0 \\ \ell^2 + 11\ell &= -28 \\ \ell^2 + 11\ell + \left(\frac{11}{2}\right)^2 &= -28 + \left(\frac{11}{2}\right)^2 \\ \ell^2 + 11\ell + \frac{121}{4} &= -\frac{112}{4} + \frac{121}{4} \\ \left(\ell + \frac{11}{2}\right)^2 &= \frac{9}{4} \\ \ell + \frac{11}{2} &= \pm\frac{3}{2} \\ \ell &= -\frac{11}{2} \pm \frac{3}{2} \\ \ell &= -4;\ -7 \end{aligned}$$

$$\begin{array}{r|l} (-7)^2 - 11(-7) + 28 & 0 \\ 49 - 77 + 28 & 0 \\ 0 = & 0 \checkmark \end{array}$$

$$\begin{array}{r|l} (-4)^2 + 11(-4) + 28 & 0 \\ 16 - 44 + 28 & 0 \\ 0 = & 0 \checkmark \end{array}$$

Exercises 14.8   Page 306

1. $2x^2 - 11x + 12 = 0$

$$x = \frac{11 \pm \sqrt{(-11)^2 - 4(2)(12)}}{2(2)}$$
$$x = \frac{11 \pm \sqrt{121 - 96}}{4}$$
$$x = \frac{11 \pm \sqrt{25}}{4}$$
$$x = \frac{11 \pm 5}{4}$$
$$x = \frac{3}{2};\ 4$$

2. $5x^2 - 14x = -8$

$$5x^2 - 14x + 8 = 0$$
$$x = \frac{14 \pm \sqrt{(-14)^2 - 4(5)(8)}}{2(5)}$$
$$x = \frac{14 \pm \sqrt{196 - 160}}{10}$$
$$x = \frac{14 \pm \sqrt{36}}{10}$$
$$x = \frac{14 \pm 6}{10}$$
$$x = \frac{4}{5};\ 2$$

3. $2x^2 + 5x = 7$

$$2x^2 + 5x - 7 = 0$$
$$x = \frac{-5 \pm \sqrt{5^2 - 4(2)(-7)}}{2(2)}$$
$$x = \frac{-5 \pm \sqrt{25 + 56}}{4}$$
$$x = \frac{-5 \pm \sqrt{81}}{4}$$
$$x = \frac{-5 \pm 9}{4}$$
$$x = -\frac{7}{2};\ 1$$

4. $2x^2 + 7x = -6$

$$2x^2 + 7x + 6 = 0$$
$$x = \frac{-7 \pm \sqrt{7^2 - 4(2)(6)}}{2(2)}$$
$$x = \frac{-7 \pm \sqrt{49 - 48}}{4}$$
$$x = \frac{-7 \pm 1}{4}$$
$$x = -2;\ -\frac{3}{2}$$

5. $3x^2 - 7x = -2$

$$3x^2 - 7x + 2 = 0$$
$$x = \frac{7 \pm \sqrt{(-7)^2 - 4(3)(2)}}{2(3)}$$
$$x = \frac{7 \pm \sqrt{49 - 24}}{6}$$
$$x = \frac{7 \pm \sqrt{25}}{6}$$
$$x = \frac{7 \pm 5}{6}$$
$$x = \frac{1}{3};\ 2$$

6. $4x^2 - x - 3 = 0$

$$x = \frac{1 \pm \sqrt{(-1)^2 - 4(4)(-3)}}{2(4)}$$
$$x = \frac{1 \pm \sqrt{1 + 48}}{8}$$
$$x = \frac{1 \pm \sqrt{49}}{8}$$
$$x = \frac{1 \pm 7}{8}$$
$$x = -\frac{3}{4};\ 1$$

7. $2a^2 - 5a = 63$

$2a^2 - 5a - 63 = 0$

$x = \frac{5 \pm \sqrt{(-5)^2 - 4(2)(-63)}}{2(2)}$

$x = \frac{5 \pm \sqrt{25 + 504}}{4}$

$x = \frac{5 \pm \sqrt{529}}{4}$

$x = \frac{5 \pm 23}{4}$

$x = -\frac{9}{2};\ 7$

8. $6a^2 + 26a + 24 = 0$

$3a^2 + 13a + 12 = 0$

$x = \frac{-13 \pm \sqrt{13^2 - 4(3)(12)}}{2(3)}$

$x = \frac{-13 \pm \sqrt{169 - 144}}{6}$

$x = \frac{-13 \pm \sqrt{25}}{6}$

$x = \frac{-13 \pm 5}{6}$

$x = -3;\ -\frac{4}{3}$

9. $2x^2 + x - 6 = 0$

$x = \frac{-1 \pm \sqrt{1^2 - 4(2)(-6)}}{2(2)}$

$x = \frac{-1 \pm \sqrt{1 + 48}}{4}$

$x = \frac{-1 \pm \sqrt{49}}{4}$

$x = \frac{-1 \pm 7}{4}$

$x = -2;\ \frac{3}{2}$

10. $2x^2 - 5x + 2 = 0$

$x = \frac{5 \pm \sqrt{(-5)^2 - 4(2)(2)}}{2(2)}$

$x = \frac{5 \pm \sqrt{25 - 16}}{4}$

$x = \frac{5 \pm \sqrt{9}}{4}$

$x = \frac{5 \pm 3}{4}$

$x = \frac{1}{2};\ 2$

11. $15x^2 - x - 2 = 0$

$x = \frac{1 \pm \sqrt{(-1)^2 - 4(15)(-2)}}{2(15)}$

$x = \frac{1 \pm \sqrt{1 + 120}}{30}$

$x = \frac{1 \pm \sqrt{121}}{30}$

$x = \frac{1 \pm 11}{30}$

$x = -\frac{1}{3};\ \frac{2}{5}$

12. $12x^2 - 5x - 2 = 0$

$x = \frac{5 \pm \sqrt{(-5)^2 - 4(12)(-2)}}{2(12)}$

$x = \frac{5 \pm \sqrt{25 + 96}}{24}$

$x = \frac{5 \pm \sqrt{121}}{24}$

$x = \frac{5 \pm 11}{24}$

$x = -\frac{1}{4};\ \frac{2}{3}$

13. $11x^2 - 10x - 1 = 0$

$x = \frac{10 \pm \sqrt{(-10)^2 - 4(11)(-1)}}{2(11)}$

$x = \frac{10 \pm \sqrt{100 + 44}}{22}$

$x = \frac{10 \pm \sqrt{144}}{22}$

$x = \frac{10 \pm 12}{22}$

$x = -\frac{1}{11};\ 1$

14. $5x^2 + 8x = -3$

$5x^2 + 8x + 3 = 0$

$x = \frac{-8 \pm \sqrt{8^2 - 4(5)(3)}}{2(5)}$

$x = \frac{-8 \pm \sqrt{64 - 60}}{10}$

$x = \frac{-8 \pm \sqrt{4}}{10}$

$x = \frac{-8 \pm 2}{10}$

$x = -1;\ -\frac{3}{5}$

15. $5x^2 - 7x = -2$

$5x^2 - 7x + 2 = 0$

$x = \frac{7 \pm \sqrt{(-7)^2 - 4(5)(2)}}{2(5)}$

$x = \frac{7 \pm \sqrt{49 - 40}}{10}$

$x = \frac{7 \pm \sqrt{9}}{10}$

$x = \frac{7 \pm 3}{10}$

$x = \frac{2}{5};\ 1$

16. $6x^2 + 5x = -1$

$6x^2 + 5x + 1 = 0$

$x = \frac{-5 \pm \sqrt{5^2 - 4(6)(1)}}{2(6)}$

$x = \frac{-5 \pm \sqrt{25 - 24}}{12}$

$x = \frac{-5 \pm 1}{12}$

$x = -\frac{1}{2};\ -\frac{1}{3}$

17. $2 + 5x + 2x^2 = 0$

$2x^2 + 5x + 2 = 0$

$x = \frac{-5 \pm \sqrt{5^2 - 4(2)(2)}}{2(2)}$

$x = \frac{-5 \pm \sqrt{25 - 16}}{4}$

$x = \frac{-5 \pm \sqrt{9}}{4}$

$x = \frac{-5 \pm 3}{4}$

$x = -2;\ -\frac{1}{2}$

18. $6x^2 + 2 = 7x$

$6x^2 - 7x + 2 = 0$

$x = \frac{7 \pm \sqrt{(-7)^2 - 4(6)(2)}}{2(6)}$

$x = \frac{7 \pm \sqrt{49 - 48}}{12}$

$x = \frac{7 \pm 1}{12}$

$x = \frac{1}{2};\ \frac{2}{3}$

19. $4x^2 + 4x = 3$

$4x^2 + 4x - 3 = 0$

$x = \frac{-4 \pm \sqrt{4^2 - 4(4)(-3)}}{2(4)}$

$x = \frac{-4 \pm \sqrt{16 + 48}}{8}$

$x = \frac{-4 \pm \sqrt{64}}{8}$

$x = \frac{-4 \pm 8}{8}$

$x = -\frac{3}{2};\ \frac{1}{2}$

20. $3x + 2x^2 = 9$

$2x^2 + 3x - 9 = 0$

$x = \frac{-3 \pm \sqrt{3^2 - 4(2)(-9)}}{2(2)}$

$x = \frac{-3 \pm \sqrt{9 + 72}}{4}$

$x = \frac{-3 \pm \sqrt{81}}{4}$

$x = \frac{-3 \pm 9}{4}$

$x = -3;\ \frac{3}{2}$

21. $6m^2 + 23m + 20 = 0$

$x = \frac{-23 \pm \sqrt{23^2 - 4(6)(20)}}{2(6)}$

$x = \frac{-23 \pm \sqrt{529 - 480}}{12}$

$x = \frac{-23 \pm \sqrt{49}}{12}$

$x = \frac{-23 \pm 7}{12}$

$x = -\frac{5}{2};\ -\frac{4}{3}$

22. $30p^2 + 59p + 15 = 0$

$x = \frac{-59 \pm \sqrt{59^2 - 4(30)(15)}}{2(30)}$

$x = \frac{-59 \pm \sqrt{3481 - 1800}}{60}$

$x = \frac{-59 \pm \sqrt{1681}}{60}$

$x = \frac{-59 \pm 41}{60}$

$x = -\frac{5}{3};\ -\frac{3}{10}$

23. (1)
$$x^2 - 4x = 5$$
$$x^2 - 4x - 5 = 0$$
$$x = \frac{4 \pm \sqrt{(-4)^2 - 4(1)(-5)}}{2(1)}$$
$$x = \frac{4 \pm \sqrt{16 + 20}}{2}$$
$$x = \frac{4 \pm \sqrt{36}}{2}$$
$$x = \frac{4 \pm 6}{2}$$
$$x = -1;\ 5$$

(2)
$$x^2 - 6x = 7$$
$$x^2 - 6x - 7 = 0$$
$$x = \frac{6 \pm \sqrt{(-6)^2 - 4(1)(-7)}}{2(1)}$$
$$x = \frac{6 \pm \sqrt{36 + 28}}{2}$$
$$x = \frac{6 \pm \sqrt{64}}{2}$$
$$x = \frac{6 \pm 8}{2}$$
$$x = -1;\ 7$$

(3)
$$8x = x^2 - 9$$
$$x^2 - 8x - 9 = 0$$
$$x = \frac{8 \pm \sqrt{(-8)^2 - 4(1)(-9)}}{2(1)}$$
$$x = \frac{8 \pm \sqrt{64 + 36}}{2}$$
$$x = \frac{8 \pm \sqrt{100}}{2}$$
$$x = \frac{8 \pm 10}{2}$$
$$x = -1;\ 9$$

(4)
$$x^2 + 2x = 15$$
$$x^2 + 2x - 15 = 0$$
$$x = \frac{-2 \pm \sqrt{2^2 - 4(1)(-15)}}{2(1)}$$
$$x = \frac{-2 \pm \sqrt{4 + 60}}{2}$$
$$x = \frac{-2 \pm \sqrt{64}}{2}$$
$$x = \frac{-2 \pm 8}{2}$$
$$x = -5;\ 3$$

(5)
$$x^2 - 2x = 24$$
$$x^2 - 2x - 24 = 0$$
$$x = \frac{2 \pm \sqrt{(-2)^2 - 4(1)(-24)}}{2(1)}$$
$$x = \frac{2 \pm \sqrt{4 + 96}}{2}$$
$$x = \frac{2 \pm \sqrt{100}}{2}$$
$$x = \frac{2 \pm 10}{2}$$
$$x = -4;\ 6$$

(6)
$$x^2 + 8x = -15$$
$$x^2 + 8x + 15 = 0$$
$$x = \frac{-8 \pm \sqrt{8^2 - 4(1)(15)}}{2(1)}$$
$$x = \frac{-8 \pm \sqrt{64 - 60}}{2}$$
$$x = \frac{-8 \pm \sqrt{4}}{2}$$
$$x = \frac{-8 \pm 2}{2}$$
$$x = -5;\ -3$$

(7)
$$63 = x^2 + 2x$$
$$x^2 + 2x - 63 = 0$$
$$x = \frac{-2 \pm \sqrt{2^2 - 4(1)(-63)}}{2(1)}$$
$$x = \frac{-2 \pm \sqrt{4 + 252}}{2}$$
$$x = \frac{-2 \pm \sqrt{256}}{2}$$
$$x = \frac{-2 \pm 16}{2}$$
$$x = -9;\ 7$$

(8)
$$x^2 - 12x = -11$$
$$x^2 - 12x + 11 = 0$$
$$x = \frac{12 \pm \sqrt{(-12)^2 - 4(1)(11)}}{2(1)}$$
$$x = \frac{12 \pm \sqrt{144 - 44}}{2}$$
$$x = \frac{12 \pm \sqrt{100}}{2}$$
$$x = \frac{12 \pm 10}{2}$$
$$x = 1;\ 11$$

23. (continued)

(9)
$$x^2 - 40 = 6x$$
$$x^2 - 6x - 40 = 0$$
$$x = \frac{6 \pm \sqrt{(-6)^2 - 4(1)(-40)}}{2(1)}$$
$$x = \frac{6 \pm \sqrt{36 + 160}}{2}$$
$$x = \frac{6 \pm \sqrt{196}}{2}$$
$$x = \frac{6 \pm 14}{2}$$
$$x = -4;\ 10$$

Exercises 14.9 Page 307

The check is left for the teacher.

1.
$$x^2 + 5 = 6x$$
$$x^2 - 6x + 5 = 0$$
$$(x - 5)(x - 1) = 0$$
$$x - 5 = 0 \qquad x - 1 = 0$$
$$x = 5 \qquad x = 1$$

2.
$$x^2 = 3x + 10$$
$$x^2 - 3x - 10 = 0$$
$$(x - 5)(x + 2) = 0$$
$$x - 5 = 0 \qquad x + 2 = 0$$
$$x = 5 \qquad x = -2$$

3.
$$5x + 3x^2 = 2$$
$$3x^2 + 5x - 2 = 0$$
$$(3x - 1)(x + 2) = 0$$
$$3x - 1 = 0 \qquad x + 2 = 0$$
$$3x = 1 \qquad x = -2$$
$$x = \frac{1}{3}$$

4.
$$2x^2 - 7x = 2$$
$$2x^2 - 7x - 2 = 0$$
$$x = \frac{7 \pm \sqrt{(-7)^2 - 4(2)(-2)}}{2(2)}$$
$$x = \frac{7 \pm \sqrt{49 + 16}}{4}$$
$$x = \frac{7 \pm \sqrt{65}}{4}$$

5.
$$x^2 - 12x = 28$$
$$x^2 - 12x - 28 = 0$$
$$(x - 14)(x + 2) = 0$$
$$x - 14 = 0 \qquad x + 2 = 0$$
$$x = 14 \qquad x = -2$$

6.
$$3x^2 - 10x = 8$$
$$3x^2 - 10x - 8 = 0$$
$$(3x + 2)(x - 4) = 0$$
$$3x + 2 = 0 \qquad x - 4 = 0$$
$$3x = -2 \qquad x = 4$$
$$x = -\frac{2}{3}$$

7.
$$x^2 - 13x - 30 = 0$$
$$(x - 15)(x + 2) = 0$$
$$x - 15 = 0 \qquad x + 2 = 0$$
$$x = 15 \qquad x = -2$$

8.
$$x^2 + 4(x - 3) = 0$$
$$x^2 + 4x - 12 = 0$$
$$(x + 6)(x - 2) = 0$$
$$x + 6 = 0 \qquad x - 2 = 0$$
$$x = -6 \qquad x = 2$$

9.
$$6 + 11x + 3x^2 = 0$$
$$3x^2 + 11x + 6 = 0$$
$$(3x + 2)(x + 3) = 0$$
$$3x + 2 = 0 \qquad x + 3 = 0$$
$$3x = -2 \qquad x = -3$$
$$x = -\frac{2}{3}$$

10.
$$(x + 5)^2 = 10x + 74$$
$$x^2 + 10x + 25 = 10x + 74$$
$$x^2 = 49$$
$$x = \pm 7$$

11.
$$4x^2 - 3x - 2 = 0$$
$$x = \frac{3 \pm \sqrt{(-3)^2 - 4(4)(-2)}}{2(4)}$$
$$x = \frac{3 \pm \sqrt{9 + 32}}{8}$$
$$x = \frac{3 \pm \sqrt{41}}{8}$$

12.
$$(x + 7)(x - 9) = 1 - 2x$$
$$x^2 - 2x - 63 = 1 - 2x$$
$$x^2 = 64$$
$$x = \pm 8$$

13.
$$x + \frac{1}{x} - \frac{5}{2} = 0$$
$$2x\left(x + \frac{1}{x} - \frac{5}{2}\right) = 2x(0)$$
$$2x^2 + 2 - 5x = 0$$
$$2x^2 - 5x + 2 = 0$$
$$(2x - 1)(x - 2) = 0$$
$$2x - 1 = 0 \qquad x - 2 = 0$$
$$2x = 1 \qquad x = 2$$
$$x = \frac{1}{2}$$

14.
$$\frac{x}{9(x - 1)} = \frac{x - 2}{6}$$
$$18(x - 1)\left[\frac{x}{9(x - 1)}\right] = 18(x - 1)\left(\frac{x - 2}{6}\right)$$
$$2x = (3x - 3)(x - 2)$$
$$2x = 3x^2 - 9x + 6$$
$$3x^2 - 11x + 6 = 0$$
$$(3x - 2)(x - 3) = 0$$
$$3x - 2 = 0 \qquad x - 3 = 0$$
$$3x = 2 \qquad x = 3$$
$$x = \frac{2}{3}$$

15.
$$\frac{x}{12} + \frac{x^2 - 15}{5x} = \frac{x}{5}$$
$$60x\left(\frac{x}{12} + \frac{x^2 - 15}{5x}\right) = 60x\left(\frac{x}{5}\right)$$
$$5x^2 + 12x^2 - 180 = 12x^2$$
$$5x^2 = 180$$
$$x^2 = 36$$
$$x = \pm 6$$

16.
$$\frac{x}{x - 5} - \frac{x - 5}{x} = \frac{3}{2}$$
$$2x(x - 5)\left[\frac{x}{x - 5} - \frac{x - 5}{x}\right] = 2x(x - 5)\left(\frac{3}{2}\right)$$
$$2x^2 - 2(x - 5)^2 = 3x(x - 5)$$
$$2x^2 - 2(x^2 - 10x + 25) = 3x^2 - 15x$$
$$2x^2 - 2x^2 + 20x - 50 = 3x^2 - 15x$$
$$3x^2 - 35x + 50 = 0$$
$$(3x - 5)(x - 10) = 0$$
$$3x - 5 = 0 \qquad x - 10 = 0$$
$$3x = 5 \qquad x = 10$$
$$x = \frac{5}{3}$$

17.
$$\frac{x + 4}{x - 2} + 3 = \frac{(x + 3)^2}{x^2 - 9}$$
$$\frac{x + 4 + 3x - 6}{x - 2} = \frac{\cancel{(x + 3)}(x + 3)}{\cancel{(x + 3)}(x - 3)}$$
$$\frac{4x - 2}{x - 2} = \frac{x + 3}{x - 3}$$
$$4x^2 - 14x + 6 = x^2 + x - 6$$
$$3x^2 - 15x + 12 = 0$$
$$3(x^2 - 5x + 4) = 0$$
$$3(x - 4)(x - 1) = 0$$
$$3 \neq 0 \qquad x - 4 = 0 \qquad x - 1 = 0$$
$$x = 4 \qquad x = 1$$

18.

$$\frac{x^2}{x - 2} = \frac{4}{x - 2} + 5$$
$$\frac{x^2}{x - 2} = \frac{4 + 5x - 10}{x - 2}$$
$$x^2 = 4 + 5x - 10$$
$$x^2 - 5x + 6 = 0$$
$$(x - 2)(x - 3) = 0$$

$x - 2 = 0$ $\quad x - 3 = 0$

$\cancel{x = 2}$ $\quad x = 3$

The check will reveal that 2 cannot be a root since it would make the denominator equal to zero; 3 is the only root.

19.

$$\frac{x}{x + 2} + \frac{1}{2} = \frac{x + 2}{2x}$$
$$\frac{x}{x + 2} + \frac{x}{2x} = \frac{x + 2}{2x}$$
$$\frac{x}{x + 2} = \frac{2}{2x}$$
$$\frac{x}{x + 2} = \frac{1}{x}$$
$$x^2 = x + 2$$
$$x^2 - x - 2 = 0$$
$$(x - 2)(x + 1) = 0$$

$x - 2 = 0$ $\quad x + 1 = 0$

$x = 2$ $\quad \cancel{x = -1}$

20.

$$\frac{5x}{x + 7} + \frac{x + 6}{x + 3} = 3$$
$$\frac{5x}{x + 7} = \frac{3x + 9 - x - 6}{x + 3}$$
$$\frac{5x}{x + 7} = \frac{2x + 3}{x + 3}$$
$$5x^2 + 15x = 2x^2 + 17x + 21$$
$$3x^2 - 2x - 21 = 0$$
$$(3x + 7)(x - 3) = 0$$

$3x + 7 = 0$ $\quad x - 3 = 0$

$3x = -7$ $\quad x = 3$

$x = -\frac{7}{3}$

21.

$$\frac{x + 2}{x - 7} - \frac{x + 5}{x - 5} = 1$$
$$\frac{x + 2}{x - 7} = \frac{x - 5 + x + 5}{x - 5}$$
$$\frac{x + 2}{x - 7} = \frac{2x}{x - 5}$$
$$x^2 - 3x - 10 = 2x^2 - 14x$$
$$0 = x^2 - 11x + 10$$
$$(x - 10)(x - 1) = 0$$

$x - 10 = 0$ $\quad x - 1 = 0$

$x = 10$ $\quad x = 1$

22.

$$\frac{2x - 3}{x^2 - 3x} = 2 - \frac{3}{x^2 - 3x}$$
$$\frac{2x}{x^2 - 3x} = 2$$
$$\frac{2x}{x(x - 3)} = 2$$
$$\frac{2}{x - 3} = 2$$
$$2 = 2x - 6$$
$$8 = 2x$$
$$x = 4$$

23.

$$\frac{x - 2}{x + 2} - \frac{x + 2}{2 - x} = \frac{40}{x^2 - 4}$$
$$\frac{x - 2}{x + 2} + \frac{x + 2}{x - 2} = \frac{40}{(x + 2)(x - 2)}$$
$$(x + 2)(x - 2)\left(\frac{x - 2}{x + 2} + \frac{x + 2}{x - 2}\right) = \cancel{(x + 2)}\cancel{(x - 2)}\left[\frac{40}{\cancel{(x + 2)}\cancel{(x - 2)}}\right]$$
$$(x - 2)^2 + (x + 2)^2 = 40$$
$$x^2 - 4x + 4 + x^2 + 4x + 4 = 40$$
$$2x^2 + 8 = 40$$
$$2x^2 = 32$$
$$x^2 = 16$$
$$x = \pm 4$$

24. $x^2 - 4x - 1 = 0$

$$x = \frac{4 \pm \sqrt{(-4)^2 - 4(1)(-1)}}{2(1)}$$
$$x = \frac{4 \pm \sqrt{16 + 4}}{2}$$
$$x = \frac{4 \pm \sqrt{20}}{2}$$
$$x = \frac{4 \pm 2\sqrt{5}}{2}$$
$$x = 2 \pm \sqrt{5}$$
$$x = 2 \pm 2.24$$
$$x = -.24;\ 4.24$$

25. $v^2 + 6v + 7 = 0$

$$v = \frac{-6 \pm \sqrt{6^2 - 4(1)(7)}}{2(1)}$$
$$v = \frac{-6 \pm \sqrt{36 - 28}}{2}$$
$$v = \frac{-6 \pm \sqrt{8}}{2}$$
$$v = \frac{-6 \pm 2\sqrt{2}}{2}$$
$$v = -3 \pm \sqrt{2}$$
$$v = -3 \pm 1.414$$
$$v = -4.41;\ -1.59$$

26. $u^2 + 5u + 5.5 = 0$

$$10u^2 + 50u + 55 = 0$$
$$u = \frac{-50 \pm \sqrt{50^2 - 4(10)(55)}}{2(10)}$$
$$u = \frac{-50 \pm \sqrt{2500 - 2200}}{20}$$
$$u = \frac{-50 \pm \sqrt{300}}{20}$$
$$u = \frac{-50 \pm 10\sqrt{3}}{20}$$
$$u = \frac{-5 \pm \sqrt{3}}{2}$$
$$u = \frac{-5 \pm 1.732}{2}$$
$$u = -3.37;\ -1.63$$

27. $t^2 - 12t + 16.5 = 0$

$$t = \frac{12 \pm \sqrt{144 - 66}}{2}$$
$$t = \frac{12 \pm \sqrt{78}}{2}$$
$$t = \frac{12 \pm 8.832}{2}$$
$$t = \frac{20.832}{2} \text{ and } \frac{3.168}{2}$$
$$t = 1.58;\ 10.42$$

Exercises 14.10 Pages 308-311

1. let x = the number <u>-1</u>

$$x = \frac{1}{x}$$
$$x^2 = 1$$
$$x = -\sqrt{1}$$
$$x = -1$$

-1 is the same as $\frac{1}{-1}$ ✓

2. let x = the number <u>±12</u>

$$x^2 + 25 = 13^2$$
$$x^2 + 25 = 169$$
$$x^2 = 144$$
$$x = \pm\sqrt{144}$$
$$x = \pm 12$$

$(\pm 12)^2 + 25 = 169$ ✓

3. let n = the number <u>±15</u>

$$n^2 = 25^2 - 20^2$$
$$n^2 = 625 - 400$$
$$n^2 = 225$$
$$n = \pm\sqrt{225}$$
$$n = \pm 15$$

$(25)^2 - (20)^2 = 625 - 400 = 225$ ✓

$(\pm 15)^2 = 225$ ✓

4. let u = the number $\underline{\pm 10}$

$$\begin{aligned}(n - 5)(n + 5) &= 75\\ n^2 - 25 &= 75\\ n^2 &= 100\\ n &= \pm\sqrt{100}\\ n &= \pm 10\end{aligned}$$

$$\begin{array}{r}10\\ -5\\ \hline 5\end{array} \quad \begin{array}{r}10\\ +5\\ \hline 15\end{array} \quad (5)(15) = 75 \checkmark$$

$$\begin{array}{r}-10\\ -\ 5\\ \hline -15\end{array} \quad \begin{array}{r}-10\\ +\ 5\\ \hline -5\end{array} \quad (-15)(-5) = 75 \checkmark$$

5. let s = length of a side $\underline{5 \text{ cm}}$

$$\begin{aligned}(s + 10)^2 &= s^2 + 200\\ \not{s}^2 + 20s + 100 &= \not{s}^2 + 200\\ 20s &= 100\\ s &= 5\end{aligned}$$

$$\begin{array}{r}5\\ +10\\ \hline 15\end{array} \quad \begin{array}{r}15\\ \times 15\\ \hline 225\end{array} \text{ cm}^2 \quad \begin{array}{r}5\\ \times 5\\ \hline 25\end{array} \text{ cm}^2 \quad \begin{array}{r}225\\ -25\\ \hline 200\end{array} \text{ cm}^2 \checkmark$$

6. let n = the number $\underline{\pm 8}$

$$\begin{aligned}(\tfrac{1}{4}n)n &= 16\\ \frac{n^2}{4} &= 16\\ n^2 &= 64\\ n &= \pm\sqrt{64}\\ n &= \pm 8\end{aligned}$$

$$(8)[(\tfrac{1}{4})(8)] = 16 \checkmark$$

$$(-8)[(\tfrac{1}{4})(-8)] = 16 \checkmark$$

7. let 5 + n = larger number $\underline{7}$
5 - n = smaller number $\underline{3}$

$$\begin{aligned}(5 + n)(5 - n) &= 21\\ 25 - n^2 &= 21\\ -n^2 &= -4\\ n^2 &= 4\\ n &= \pm 2\end{aligned}$$

5 + 2 = 7   5 - 2 = 3

$7 + 3 = 10 \checkmark$
$(7)(3) = 21 \checkmark$

8. let x = smaller number $\underline{5}$
16 - x = larger number $\underline{11}$

$$\begin{aligned}x(16 - x) &= 55\\ 16x - x^2 &= 55\\ x^2 - 16x + 55 &= 0\\ (x - 5)(x - 11) &= 0\end{aligned}$$

$x - 5 = 0 \quad x - 11 = 0$
$x = 5 \quad x = 11$

$$\begin{array}{r}5\\ +11\\ \hline 16\end{array} \checkmark$$

$(5)(11) = 55 \checkmark$

9. let n + 2 = one number $\underline{12}$ or $\underline{-8}$
n - 2 = other number $\underline{8}$ $\underline{-12}$

$$\begin{aligned}(n + 2)^2 + (n - 2)^2 &= 208\\ n^2 + 4n + 4 + n^2 - 4n + 4 &= 208\\ 2n^2 + 8 &= 208\\ 2n^2 &= 200\\ n^2 &= 100\\ n &= \pm 10\end{aligned}$$

$$\begin{array}{r}12\\ -8\\ \hline 4\end{array} \checkmark$$

$(12)^2 + (8)^2 = 144 + 64 = 208 \checkmark$

$$(-)\ \begin{array}{r}-8\\ -12\\ \hline 4\end{array} \checkmark$$

$(-8)^2 + (-12)^2 = 64 + 144 = 208 \checkmark$

10. let n = smaller integer $\underline{16}$ or $\underline{-17}$
$n + 1$ = larger integer $\underline{17}$ $\underline{-16}$

$$n(n + 1) = 272$$
$$n^2 + n = 272$$
$$n^2 + n - 272 = 0$$
$$(n + 17)(n - 16) = 0$$

$n + 17 = 0$ $\quad$ $n - 16 = 0$ $\quad$ $(16)(17) = 272$ ✓
$n = -17$ $\quad$ $n = 16$ $\quad$ $(-17)(-16) = 272$ ✓

11. let n = smaller integer $\underline{-8}$ or $\underline{7}$
$n + 1$ = larger integer $\underline{-7}$ $\underline{8}$

$$n^2 + (n + 1)^2 = 113$$
$$n^2 + n^2 + 2n + 1 = 113$$
$$2n^2 + 2n - 112 = 0$$
$$n^2 + n - 56 = 0$$
$$(n + 8)(n - 7) = 0$$

$n + 8 = 0$ $\quad$ $n - 7 = 0$ $\quad$ $(-8)^2 + (-7)^2 = 64 + 49 = 113$ ✓
$n = -8$ $\quad$ $n = 7$ $\quad$ $(7)^2 + (8)^2 = 49 + 64 = 113$ ✓

*12. let $2n - 1$ = the smaller odd integer $\underline{a - 1}$ or $\underline{-a - 1}$
$2n + 1$ = the larger odd integer $\underline{a + 1}$ $\underline{-a + 1}$

(No check provided)

$$(2n - 1)^2 + (2n + 1)^2 = 2(a^2 + 1)$$
$$4n^2 - 4n + 1 + 4n^2 + 4n + 1 = 2(a^2 + 1)$$
$$8n^2 + 2 = 2(a^2 + 1)$$
$$2(4n^2 + 1) = 2(a^2 + 1)$$
$$4n^2 + 1 = a^2 + 1$$
$$4n^2 = a^2$$
$$n^2 = \frac{a2}{4}$$
$$n = \pm\frac{a}{2}$$

$2n - 1 = 2(\frac{a}{2}) - 1 = a - 1$

$2n + 1 = 2(\frac{a}{2}) + 1 = a + 1$ ✓

$2n - 1 = 2(\frac{-a}{2}) - 1 = -a - 1$

$2n + 1 = 2(-\frac{a}{2}) + 1 = -a + 1$

Note: The numbers could also be represented by n and $n + 2$.

13. let w = width $\underline{6 \text{ ft.}}$
$3w + 12$ = length $\underline{30 \text{ ft.}}$

$$w(3w + 12) = 180$$
$$3w^2 + 12w - 180 = 0$$
$$w^2 + 4w - 60 = 0$$
$$(w + 10)(w - 6) = 0$$

$w + 10 = 0$ $\quad$ $w - 6 = 0$
~~$w = -10$~~ $\quad$ $w = 6$

$(6)(30) = 180$ ✓

14. let s = length of a side $\underline{16 \text{ ft.}}$

$$(s + 4)(s - 6) = 200$$
$$s^2 - 2s - 24 = 200$$
$$s^2 - 2s - 224 = 0$$
$$(s - 16)(s + 14) = 0$$

$s - 16 = 0$ $\quad$ $s + 14 = 0$
$x = 16$ $\quad$ ~~$s = -14$~~

$\begin{array}{r} 16 \\ +4 \\ \hline 20 \end{array}$ $\quad$ $\begin{array}{r} 16 \\ -6 \\ \hline 10 \end{array}$ $\quad$ $(20)(10) = 200$ ✓

15. let x = number of boxes $\underline{8}$
$x + 2$ = number of sheets per box $\underline{10}$

$$x(x + 2) = 80$$
$$x^2 + 2x - 80 = 0$$
$$(x + 10)(x - 8) = 0$$

$x + 10 = 0$ $\quad$ $x - 8 = 0$
~~$x = -10$~~ $\quad$ $x = 8$

$(10)(8) = 80$ ✓

16. let r = number of rows $\underline{12}$
$2r + 6$ = pins per row $\underline{30}$

$$r(2r + 6) = 360$$
$$2r^2 + 6r - 360 = 0$$
$$r^2 + 3r - 180 = 0$$
$$(r + 15)(r - 12) = 0$$

$r + 15 = 0$ $\quad$ $r - 12 = 0$
~~$r = -15$~~ $\quad$ $r = 12$

$(12)(30) = 360$ ✓

17. let ℓ = length $\underline{2.5 \text{ in.}}$
$5 - \ell$ = width $\underline{2.5 \text{ in.}}$
2ℓ = height $\underline{5 \text{ in.}}$

$$\ell(5 - \ell) = 6.25$$
$$5\ell - \ell^2 = 6.25$$
$$\ell^2 - 5\ell + 6.25 = 0$$
$$100\ell^2 - 500\ell + 625 = 0$$
$$4\ell^2 - 20\ell + 25 = 0$$
$$(2\ell - 5)(2\ell - 5) = 0$$
$$2\ell - 5 = 0$$
$$2\ell = 5$$
$$\ell = 2.5$$

Area of bottom =
$(2.5)(2.5) = 6.25$ ✓
Perimeter = $4(2.5) = 10$ ✓

18. let w = width $\underline{13 \text{ cm}}$
$\frac{208}{w}$ = length $\underline{16 \text{ cm}}$

$$2w(2w - 10) = 416$$
$$4w^2 - 20w = 416$$
$$4w^2 - 20w - 416 = 0$$
$$w^2 - 5w - 104 = 0$$
$$(w - 13)(w + 8) = 0$$

$w - 13 = 0$ $\quad$ $w + 8 = 0$
$w = 13$ $\quad$ ~~$w = -8$~~

$\frac{208}{w} = \frac{208}{13} = 16$

$(13)(16) = 208$ ✓

19. let n be the number $\underline{\frac{2}{3}}$ or $\underline{\frac{3}{2}}$

$$n + \frac{1}{n} = \frac{13}{6}$$
$$6n(n + \frac{1}{n}) = \frac{13}{6}(6n)$$
$$6n^2 + 6 = 13n$$
$$6n^2 - 13n + 6 = 0$$
$$(3n - 2)(2n - 3) = 0$$

$3n - 2 = 0$ $\quad$ $2n - 3 = 0$
$3n = 2$ $\quad$ $2n = 3$
$n = \frac{2}{3}$ $\quad$ $n = \frac{3}{2}$

$\frac{2}{3} + \frac{3}{2} = \frac{4}{6} + \frac{9}{6} = \frac{13}{6}$ ✓

20. let n = smaller integer $\underline{2}$
$n + 1$ = larger integer $\underline{3}$

$$\frac{1}{n} + \frac{1}{n + 1} = \frac{5}{6}$$
$$n(n + 1)(\frac{1}{n} + \frac{1}{n + 1}) = n(n + 1)(\frac{5}{6})$$
$$n + 1 + n = \frac{5n^2 + 5n}{6}$$
$$2n + 1 = \frac{5n^2 + 5n}{6}$$
$$12n + 6 = 5n^2 + 5n$$
$$5n^2 - 7n - 6 = 0$$
$$(5n + 3)(n - 2) = 0$$

$5n + 3 = 0$ $\quad$ $n - 2 = 0$
$5n = -3$ $\quad$ $n = 2$
~~$n = -\frac{3}{5}$~~
Not an integer $\quad$ $\frac{1}{2} + \frac{1}{3} = \frac{3}{6} + \frac{2}{6} = \frac{5}{6}$ ✓

*21. let n = the number
(No check provided)

$$n - c\left(\frac{1}{n}\right) = c - 1$$
$$n\left(n - \frac{c}{n}\right) = n(c - 1)$$
$$n^2 - c = nc - n$$
$$n^2 - c = n(c - 1)$$
$$n^2 - n(c - 1) - c = 0$$
$$n^2 + (1 - c)n - c = 0$$
$$n = \frac{c - 1 \pm \sqrt{(1 - c)^2 - 4(1)(-c)}}{2(1)}$$
$$n = \frac{c - 1 \pm \sqrt{1 - 2c + c2 + 4c}}{2}$$
$$n = \frac{c - 1 \pm \sqrt{c^2 + 2c + 1}}{2}$$
$$n = \frac{c - 1 \pm \sqrt{(c + 1)^2}}{2}$$
$$n = \frac{c - 1 \pm c + 1}{2}$$
$$n = \frac{c - 1 + c + 1}{2} \text{ and } \frac{c - 1 - c - 1}{2}$$
$$n = \frac{2c}{2} \text{ and } \frac{-2}{2}$$
$$n = c; -1$$

Alternate solution

$$n^2 + (1 - c)n - c = 0$$
$$(n - c)(n + 1) = 0$$

$n - c = 0$ $\quad$ $n + 1 = 0$
$n = c$ $\quad$ $n = -1$

22. let x = number of fowls per crate $\underline{60}$
$2x - 8$ = number of crates $\underline{112}$

$$x(2x - 8) = 6720$$
$$2x^2 - 8x - 6720 = 0$$
$$x^2 - 4x - 3360 = 0$$
$$(x - 60)(x + 56) = 0$$

$x - 60 = 0$ $\quad$ $x + 56 = 0$
$x = 60$ $\quad$ ~~$x = -56$~~
Reject

$(60)(112) = 6720$ ✓

23. let x = tons per minute $\underline{200}$
$\frac{10,000}{x}$ = minutes to lift 10,000 tons

$$\frac{10,000}{x + 50} + 10 = \frac{10,000}{x}$$
$$x(x + 50)\left(\frac{10,000}{x + 50} + 10\right) = x(x + 50)\left(\frac{10,000}{x}\right)$$
$$\cancel{10,000x} + 10x^2 + 500x = \cancel{10,000x} + 500,000$$
$$10x^2 + 500x - 500,000 = 0$$
$$x^2 + 50x - 50,000 = 0$$
$$(x + 250)(x - 200) = 0$$

$x + 250 = 0$ $\quad$ $x - 200 = 0$
~~$x = -250$~~ $\quad$ $x = 200$
Reject

$$\frac{10,000}{200} = 50 \text{ min.}$$
$$\frac{10,000}{250} = 40 \text{ min.}$$

$50 - 40 = 10$ min. ✓

24. let t = time <u>6 hr.</u>

$\frac{20}{t}$ = rate

$$\frac{20}{t+2} + \frac{5}{6} = \frac{20}{t}$$

$$6t(t+2)\left(\frac{20}{t+2} + \frac{5}{6}\right) = 6t(t+2)\left(\frac{20}{t}\right)$$

$$\cancel{120t} + 5t^2 + 10t = \cancel{120t} + 240$$

$$5t^2 + 10t - 240 = 0$$

$$t^2 + 2t - 48 = 0$$

$$(t+8)(t-6) = 0$$

$t + 8 = 0$ $\quad$ $t - 6 = 0$

~~$t = -8$~~ $\quad$ $t = 6$

Reject

$$\frac{20}{6} - \frac{20}{8} = \frac{80}{24} - \frac{60}{24} = \frac{20}{24} = \frac{5}{6} \checkmark$$

25. let w = width in inches 150

$\frac{w}{12}$ = width in feet 12.5

3w + 50 = length in feet <u>500 ft.</u>

$$\frac{w}{12}(3w + 50) = 6250$$

$$12\left[\frac{w}{12}(3w + 50)\right] = 12(6250)$$

$$3w^2 + 50w = 75{,}000$$

$$3w^2 + 50w - 75{,}000 = 0$$

$$(3w + 500)(w - 150) = 0$$

$3w + 500 = 0$ $\quad$ $w - 150 = 0$

$3w = -500$ $\quad$ $w = 150$

~~$w = -\frac{500}{3}$~~

Reject

$3w + 50 = 3(150) + 50 = 500 \checkmark$

$(12.5)(500) = 6250 \checkmark$

26. let b = number of boys <u>8</u>

$\frac{120}{b}$ = share per boy

$$\frac{120}{b-2} - 5 = \frac{120}{b}$$

$$b(b-2)\left(\frac{120}{b-2} - 5\right) = b(b-2)\left(\frac{120}{b}\right)$$

$$\cancel{120b} - (5b^2 - 10b) = \cancel{120b} - 240$$

$$-5b^2 + 10b + 240 = 0$$

$$b^2 - 2b - 48 = 0$$

$$(b-8)(b+6) = 0$$

$b - 8 = 0$ $\quad$ $b + 6 = 0$

$b = 8$ $\quad$ ~~$b = -6$~~

Reject

8 - 2 = 6

$\frac{\$120}{8} = \$15$ $\quad$ $\frac{\$120}{6} = \$20$ $\quad$ \$20 − 15 = \$ 5 more

27. let ℓ = length <u>53 ft.</u>

$\ell - 3$ = width <u>50 ft.</u>

$$\ell(\ell - 3) = 2650$$

$$\ell^2 - 3\ell - 2650 = 0$$

$$(\ell - 53)(\ell + 50) = 0$$

$\ell - 53 = 0$ $\quad$ $\ell + 50 = 0$

$\ell = 53$ $\quad$ ~~$\ell = -50$~~

Reject

$(53)(50) = 2650 \checkmark$

28.

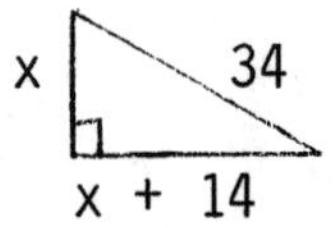

$$x^2 + (x + 14)^2 = 34^2$$
$$x^2 + x^2 + 28x + 196 = 1156$$
$$2x^2 + 28x - 960 = 0$$
$$x^2 + 14x - 480 = 0$$
$$(x + 30)(x - 16) = 0$$

$x + 30 = 0$ ~~$x = -30$~~ Reject

$x - 16 = 0$, $x = 16$

The legs are 16 ft. and 30 ft.

30 is 14 more than 16 ✓
$(34)^2 = (16)^2 + (30)^2$ is a right triangle?
$1156 \stackrel{?}{=} 256 + 900$
$1156 = 1156$ ✓

29. let c = cost of one orange <u>24¢</u>
$\frac{360}{c}$ = number of oranges

$$\frac{360}{c - 4} - 3 = \frac{360}{c}$$
$$c(c - 4)\left(\frac{360}{c - 4} - 3\right) = c(c - 4)\left(\frac{360}{c}\right)$$
$$\cancel{360c} - 3c^2 + 12c = \cancel{360c} - 1440$$
$$3c^2 - 12c - 1440 = 0$$
$$c^2 - 4c - 480 = 0$$
$$(c - 24)(c + 20) = 0$$

$c - 24 = 0$, $c = 24$

$c + 20 = 0$ ~~$c = -20$~~ Reject

$\frac{\$3.60}{\$.24} = 15$ $\frac{\$3.60}{\$.20} = 18$

18 is 3 more than 15 ✓

30. let d = distance between poles <u>132 ft.</u>
$\frac{5280}{d}$ = number of poles 40

$$\frac{5280}{d - 22} - 8 = \frac{5280}{d}$$
$$d(d - 22)\left(\frac{5280}{d - 22} - 8\right) = d(d - 22)\left(\frac{5280}{d}\right)$$
$$\cancel{5280d} - 8d^2 + 176d = \cancel{5280d} - 116{,}160$$
$$8d^2 - 176d - 116{,}160 = 0$$
$$d^2 - 22d - 14{,}520 = 0$$
$$(d - 132)(d + 110) = 0$$

$d - 132 = 0$, $d = 132$

$d + 110 = 0$ ~~$d = -110$~~ Reject

$\frac{5280}{48} = 110$

$132 - 110 = 22$ ft. less ✓

31. let x = width of strip <u>10 ft.</u>
$60 - 2x$ = width of remaining part
$80 - 2x$ = length of remaining part

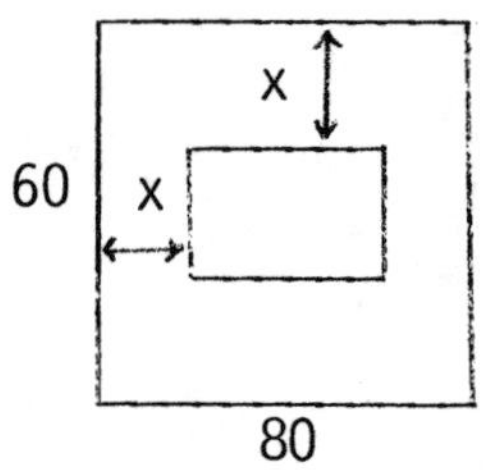

$$(80 - 2x)(60 - 2x) = \frac{1}{2}(80)(60)$$
$$4800 - 280x + 4x^2 = 2400$$
$$4x^2 - 280x + 2400 = 0$$
$$x^2 - 70x + 600 = 0$$
$$(x - 60)(x - 10) = 0$$

$x - 60 = 0$, $x = 60$ Reject

$x - 10 = 0$, $x = 10$

$80 \times 60 = 4800$ $60 \times 40 = 2400$

2400 is $\frac{1}{2}(4800)$ ✓

32. let w = width $\underline{10\text{ yd.}}$
w + 5 = length $\underline{15\text{ yd.}}$

$$10[2w + 2(w + 5)] = \frac{10}{3}[w(w + 5)]$$
$$10(4w + 10) = \frac{10}{3}(w^2 + 5w)$$
$$30(4w + 10) = 10(w^2 + 5w)$$
$$120w + 300 = 10w^2 + 50w$$
$$10w^2 - 70w - 300 = 0$$
$$w^2 - 7w - 30 = 0$$
$$(w - 10)(w + 3) = 0$$

$w - 10 = 0$ $w + 3 = 0$
$w = 10$ ~~$w = -3$~~ Reject

$2(10) + 2(15) = 20 + 30 = 50$

$(10)(15)(3.33\frac{1}{3}) = 500$ ✓

$ 50
x 10
$500 ✓

33. let r = rate for trip $\underline{32\text{ mph}}$
r + 8 = return rate $\underline{40\text{ mph}}$

$\frac{80}{r}$ = time for trip

$\frac{80}{r + 8}$ = time to return

$$\frac{80}{r} + \frac{80}{r + 8} = \frac{9}{2}$$
$$2r(r + 8)\left(\frac{80}{r} + \frac{80}{r + 8}\right) = 2r(r + 8)\left(\frac{9}{2}\right)$$
$$160r + 1280 + 160r = 9r^2 + 72r$$
$$320r + 1280 = 9r^2 + 72r$$
$$9r^2 - 248r - 1280 = 0$$
$$(9r + 40)(r - 32) = 0$$

$9r + 40 = 0$ $r - 32 = 0$
~~$r = \frac{-40}{9}$~~ Reject $r = 32$

Alternate solution

$$9r^2 - 248r - 1280 = 0$$
$$r = \frac{248 \pm \sqrt{(-248)^2 - 4(9)(-1280)}}{2(9)}$$
$$r = \frac{248 \pm \sqrt{61{,}504 + 46{,}080}}{18}$$
$$r = \frac{248 \pm \sqrt{107{,}584}}{18}$$
$$r = \frac{248 \pm 328}{18}$$
$r = \frac{576}{18}$ and ~~$\frac{-80}{18}$~~

$r = 32$

$\frac{80}{32} = 2\frac{1}{2}$ $\frac{80}{40} = 2$ $2\frac{1}{2} + 2 = 4\frac{1}{2}$ ✓

34. let x = time for Craig $\underline{24\text{ da.}}$
x - 12 = time for Micah $\underline{12\text{ da.}}$

$\frac{1}{x}$ = part of job done in one day by Craig

$\frac{1}{x - 12}$ = part of job done in one day by Micah

$$8\left(\frac{1}{x}\right) + 8\left(\frac{1}{x - 12}\right) = 1$$
$$\frac{8}{x} + \frac{8}{x - 12} = 1$$
$$x(x - 12)\left(\frac{8}{x} + \frac{8}{x - 12}\right) = x(x - 12)$$
$$8x - 96 + 8x = x^2 - 12x$$
$$16x - 96 = x^2 - 12x$$
$$x^2 - 28x + 96 = 0$$
$$(x - 4)(x - 24) = 0$$

$x - 4 = 0$ $x - 24 = 0$
~~$x = 4$~~ $x = 24$
Reject since Micah's time would be negative.

$8\left(\frac{1}{24}\right) = \frac{1}{3}$ $8\left(\frac{1}{12}\right) = \frac{2}{3}$ $\frac{1}{3} + \frac{2}{3} = 1$ ✓

35. let x = number bought <u>65</u>

$\frac{78}{x}$ = cost per melon

$x - 5$ = number sold

$\frac{78}{x} + .25$ = selling price per melon

$$(x - 5)\left(\frac{78}{x} + .25\right) = 78 + 9$$
$$\frac{78x - 390}{x} + .25x - 1.25 = 87$$
$$78x - 390 + .25x^2 - 1.25x = 87x$$
$$.25x^2 - 10.25x - 390 = 0$$
$$25x^2 - 1025x - 39,000 = 0$$
$$x^2 - 41x - 1560 = 0$$
$$(x - 65)(x + 24) = 0$$

$x - 65 = 0$ $\quad x + 24 = 0$
$x = 65$ $\quad$ ~~$x = -24$~~

$\frac{78}{65} = 1.20$ $\quad (60)(1.45) = \$87$
-78
$\$ 9$ ✓

36. let s = length of side of square <u>6 ft.</u>

$s + 10$ = length of rectangular bed 16 ft.

$s + 3$ = width of rectangular bed 9 ft.

$$4s^2 = (s + 10)(s + 3)$$
$$4s^2 = s^2 + 13s + 30$$
$$3s^2 - 13s - 30 = 0$$
$$(3s + 5)(s - 6) = 0$$

$3s + 5 = 0$ $\quad s - 6 = 0$
$3s = -5$ $\quad s = 6$
~~$s = -\frac{5}{3}$~~
Reject

$(4)(6^2) = 144$ sq. ft.
$(16)(9) = 144$ sq. ft. ✓

37. let c = rate of current <u>2 mph</u>

$8 + c$ = rate downstream 10

$8 - c$ = rate upstream 6

$\frac{10}{8 + c}$ = time downstream

$\frac{10}{8 - c}$ = time upstream

$$\frac{10}{8 + c} + \frac{10}{8 - c} = 2\frac{2}{3}$$
$$3(8 + c)(8 - c)\left(\frac{10}{8 + c} + \frac{10}{8 - c}\right) = 3(8 + c)(8 - c)\left(\frac{8}{3}\right)$$
$$240 - 30c + 240 + 30c = (64 - c^2)8$$
$$480 = 512 - 8c^2$$
$$8c^2 = 32$$
$$c^2 = 4$$
$c = 2$; ~~-2~~ Reject

$\frac{10}{10} = 1$

$\frac{10}{6} = \frac{5}{3} = 1\frac{2}{3}$

$1 + 1\frac{2}{3} = 2\frac{2}{3}$ or
2hr. 40 min. ✓

38. let x = width of paths <u>4 ft.</u>

$24x$ = area of one path <u>96 ft.^{2}</u>

$30x$ = area of other path 120 ft.^{2}

x^2 = area of square where paths intersect 16 ft.^{2}

$(24)(30) =$ 720 ft.^{2}

$$24x + 30x - x^2 = \frac{5}{18}(30)(24)$$
$$-x^2 + 54x = 200$$
$$x^2 - 54x + 200 = 0$$
$$(x - 50)(x - 4) = 0$$

$x - 50 = 0$ $\quad x - 4 = 0$
~~$x = 50$~~ $\quad x = 4$
Reject as this is wider than entire plot.

$96 + 120 = 216$ $\quad 216 - 16 = 200$ ft.^{2}

$\frac{200}{720} = \frac{20}{72} = \frac{5}{18}$ ✓

Test A   Page 311

I
1. Factoring, completing the square, by the quadratic formula, and by graphing
2. Factoring (Answers will vary.)
3. Not all quadratics will factor because their roots are not all integers or rational.

II

1.
$$x^2 - 6x - 3 = 0$$
$$x^2 - 6x = 3$$
$$x^2 - 6x + 9 = 3 + 9$$
$$(x - 3)^2 = 12$$
$$x - 3 = \pm\sqrt{12}$$
$$x - 3 = \pm 2\sqrt{3}$$
$$x = 3 \pm 2\sqrt{3}$$

2.
$$2x^2 - 7x + 5 = 0$$
$$(2x - 5)(x - 1) = 0$$
$$2x - 5 = 0$$
$$2x = 5$$
$$x = \frac{5}{2}$$
$$x - 1 = 0$$
$$x = 1$$

3.
$$5x^2 + 4x = 2$$
$$5x^2 + 4x - 2 = 0$$
$$x = \frac{-4 \pm \sqrt{4^2 - 4(5)(-2)}}{2(5)}$$
$$x = \frac{-4 \pm \sqrt{16 + 40}}{10}$$
$$x = \frac{-4 \pm \sqrt{56}}{10}$$
$$x = \frac{-4 \pm 2\sqrt{14}}{10}$$
$$x = \frac{-2 \pm \sqrt{14}}{5}$$

III $x^2 - 2x - 8 = 0$ $y = x^2 - 2x - 8$

Solutions are x = -2 and x = 4.

x	y
1	-9
2	-8
0	-8
3	-5
-1	-5
4	0
-2	0

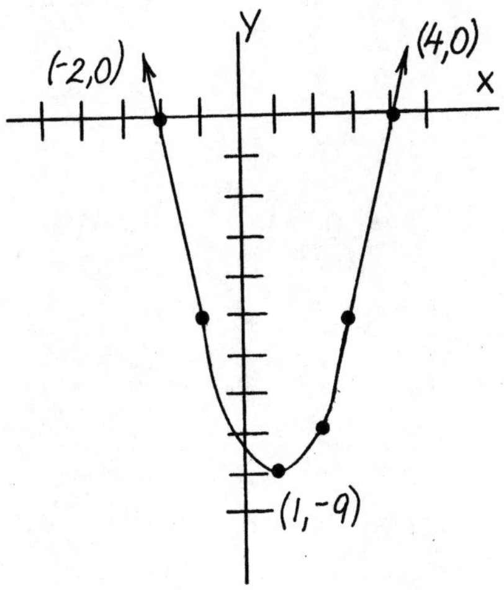

IV 1. let x = the divisor -14 or 6

$$\frac{84}{x} - 8 = x$$
$$84 - 8x = x^2$$
$$x^2 + 8x - 84 = 0$$
$$(x + 14)(x - 6) = 0$$

$x + 14 = 0$ $x = -14$ $x - 6 = 0$ $x = 6$

$\frac{84}{-14} = -6$; -6 is 8 more than -14 ✓

$\frac{84}{6} = 14$; 14 is 8 more than 6 ✓

2. let x = number of boys 24

$\frac{18}{x}$ = original share $.75

x - 4 = number of boys left

$\frac{16}{x-4}$ = new share

$\frac{18}{x} = \frac{18}{24} = \$.75$

(24)(.75) = $18 ✓
(20)(.80) = $16 ✓

$$\frac{16}{x-4} - .05 = \frac{18}{x}$$

$$x(x-4)\left(\frac{16}{x-4} - .05\right) = x(x-4)\left(\frac{18}{x}\right)$$

$$16x - .05x^2 + .2x = 18x - 72$$

$$-.05x^2 + 16.2x = 18x - 72$$

$$-5x^2 + 1620x = 1800x - 7200$$

$$5x^2 + 180x - 7200 = 0$$

$$x^2 + 36x - 1440 = 0$$

$$(x - 24)(x + 60) = 0$$

x - 24 = 0 x + 60 = 0
x = 24 ~~x = -60~~
Reject

Test B Pages 311-312

I 1. $x = \frac{-b \pm \sqrt{b^2 - 4ac}}{2a}$

2. Completing the square

3. The quadratic formula because it can be used for all quadratic equations

II 1. $3x^2 - 2x - 8 = 0$
$(3x + 4)(x - 2) = 0$

$3x + 4 = 0$ $x - 2 = 0$
$3x = -4$ $x = 2$
$x = -\frac{4}{3}$

2. $x^2 - 8x + 5 = 0$
$x^2 - 8x = -5$
$x^2 - 8x + 16 = -5 + 16$
$(x - 4)^2 = 11$
$x - 4 = \pm\sqrt{11}$
$x = 4 \pm \sqrt{11}$

3. $4x^2 - x = 6$
$4x^2 - x - 6 = 0$
$x = \frac{1 \pm \sqrt{(-1)^2 - 4(4)(-6)}}{2(4)}$
$x = \frac{1 \pm \sqrt{97}}{8}$

III $x^2 - 6x - 16 = 0$ $y = x^2 - 6x - 16$

The solutions are x = 8 and x = -2.

x	y
3	-25
5	-21
1	-21
7	-9
-1	-9
8	0
-2	0

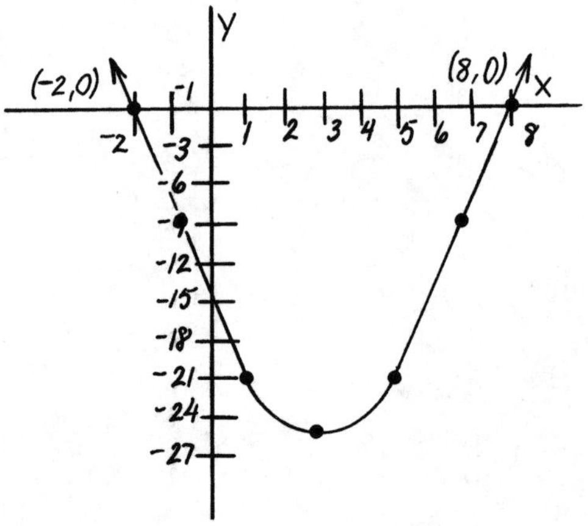

IV 1. let x = one number

2x + 8 = other number

$\underline{5}$ or $\underline{-15\frac{2}{3}}$

$\underline{18}$ $\underline{-23\frac{1}{3}}$

$$(2x + 8)^2 - x^2 = 299$$
$$4x^2 + 32x + 64 - x^2 = 299$$
$$3x^2 + 32x - 235 = 0$$
$$(3x + 47)(x - 5) = 0$$

$$3x + 47 = 0 \qquad x - 5 = 0$$
$$3x = -47 \qquad x = 5$$
$$x = -\frac{47}{3}$$
$$x = -15\frac{2}{3}$$

$$2x + 8 = 2(-\frac{47}{3}) + \frac{24}{3}$$
$$= -\frac{94 + 24}{3}$$
$$= -\frac{70}{3}$$
$$= -23\frac{1}{3}$$

$$(18)^2 - (5)^2 = 324 - 25 = 299$$
$$(-23\frac{1}{3})^2 - (-15\frac{2}{3})^2 = \frac{4900}{9} - \frac{2209}{9}$$
$$= \frac{2691}{9} = 299 \checkmark$$

2. let x = number bought $\underline{72}$

$\frac{18}{x}$ = cost per piece

$\frac{18}{x} + .10$ = selling price per piece

x - 10 = number sold

$$(x - 10)(\frac{18}{x} + .10) = 21.70$$
$$18 + .10x - \frac{180}{x} - 1 = 21.70$$
$$.10x - \frac{180}{x} = 4.70$$
$$10x(.1x - \frac{180}{x}) = 10x(4.7)$$
$$x^2 - 1800 = 47x$$
$$x^2 - 47x - 1800 = 0$$
$$(x - 72)(x + 25) = 0$$

$$x - 72 = 0 \qquad x + 25 = 0$$
$$x = 72 \qquad \text{~~x = -25~~}$$

Reject

$\frac{18}{72} = \frac{1}{4}$ or \$.25

$$\begin{array}{r} 72 \\ -10 \\ \hline 62 \end{array} \qquad \frac{21.70}{62} = \$.35$$

\$.35 is \$.10 more than \$.25 ✓

<u>Test C</u> Pages 312-313

I 1. $x = \frac{-b \pm \sqrt{b^2 - 4ac}}{2a}$

2. $\frac{-b + \sqrt{b^2 - 4ac}}{2a} + \frac{-b - \sqrt{b^2 - 4ac}}{2a}$

$$= \frac{-2b}{2a} = -\frac{b}{a}$$

3. $6x^2 - 7x - 5 = 0$

$$\frac{-b}{a} = \frac{-(-7)}{6} = \frac{7}{6}$$

4. $6x^2 - 7x - 5 = 0$

$$x = \frac{7 \pm \sqrt{(-7)^2 - 4(6)(-5)}}{2(6)}$$
$$x = \frac{7 \pm \sqrt{49 + 120}}{12}$$
$$x = \frac{7 \pm \sqrt{169}}{12}$$
$$x = \frac{7 \pm 13}{12}$$
$$x = \frac{20}{12} \text{ and } -\frac{6}{12}$$
$$x = \frac{10}{6} \text{ and } -\frac{3}{6} \text{ or } \frac{5}{3}, -\frac{1}{2}$$

$\frac{10}{6} + (-\frac{3}{6}) = \frac{7}{6}$ as shown in no. 3

II 1. $\frac{9 + 27}{2} = \frac{36}{2} = 18$

$\frac{7 + 19}{2} = \frac{26}{2} = 13$

$\frac{14 + 34}{2} = \frac{48}{2} = 24$

$\frac{5 + 12}{2} = \frac{17}{2} = 8.5$

2. Add them and divide by two.

3. $\frac{a + b}{2}$

4. $\frac{1}{2}(-\frac{b}{a}) = \frac{-b}{2a}$

5. $x^2 - 4x - 12 = 0$
$(x - 6)(x + 2) = 0$

$x - 6 = 0$ $x + 2 = 0$
$x = 6$ $x = -2$
2 is 4 units from each root.

$-\frac{b}{2a} = \frac{-(-4)}{2(1)} = \frac{4}{2} = 2$

2 is midway between the roots.

6. This value is the x-coordinate of the vertex of the parabola.

III 1. $x^2 - 2x - 3 = y$

x	y
1	-4
2	-3
0	-3
3	0
-1	0
4	5
-2	5
5	12
-3	12

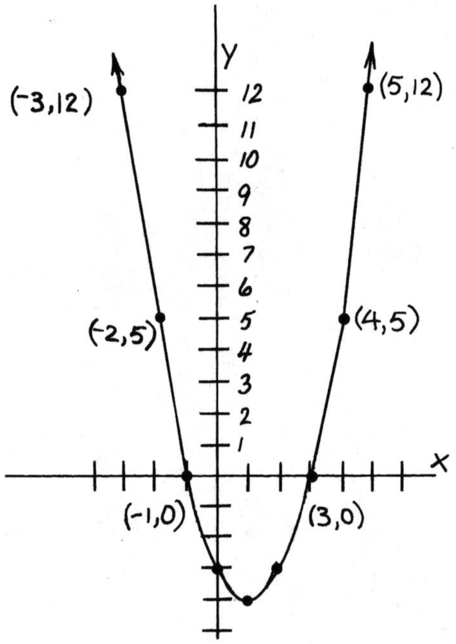

2. x = 3 and -1

The roots are the x-coordinates of the points where the graph intersects the x-axis.

3. Find y = 5 on the vertical axis and go horizontally to the curve when y = 5, x = -2 and 4. These are the solutions for $x^2 - 2x - 3 = 5$.

4. $x^2 - 2x - 15 = 0$
$x^2 - 2x - 3 - 12 = 0$
$x^2 - 2x - 3 = 12$

Find 12 on the y-axis, determine the x-coordinate corresponding to y = 12.

5. $x^2 - 2x + 1 = 0$
$x^2 - 2x + 1 - 4 = 0 - 4$
$x^2 - 2x - 3 = -4$

Find -4 on the y-axis and locate the x-coordinates of the curve when y = -4. When y = -4, x = 1 is the only solution.

6. $x^2 - 2x + 4 = 0$
$x^2 - 2x + 4 - 7 = 0 - 7$
$x^2 - 2x - 3 = -7$

The graph's minimum point is at y = -4; therefore there are no real roots.

IV 1.

Number of seconds (t)	1	2	3	4	5	6
Number of feet above ground (h)	80	128	144	128	80	0

$h = 96t - 16t^2$

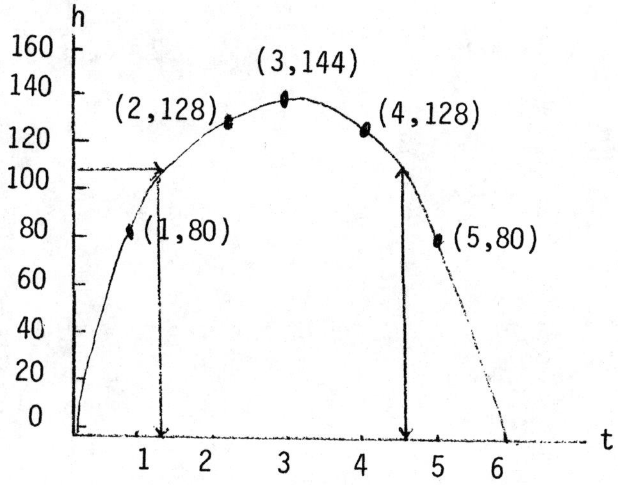

2. (a) at 1.5 sec. and at 4.5 sec.
(b) in 3 sec. at 144 ft.
(c) 6 sec.

UNIT 15 — Numerical Trigonometry

Exercises 15.1 Page 316

1. $\angle AOB = 60^\circ$ or $\angle BOA = 60^\circ$
   $\angle COD = 30^\circ$ or $\angle DOC = 30^\circ$
   $\angle XOY = 180^\circ$ or $\angle YOX = 180^\circ$
   $\angle MON = 90^\circ$ or $\angle NOM = 90^\circ$
   $\angle EOF = 120^\circ$ or $\angle FOE = 120^\circ$
2. a right angle
3. 90°
4. 180°

Exercises 15.2a Page 316

1. Answers will vary.
2. Teacher, check angles.

Exercises 15.2b Page 317

1. Right triangle
   $\angle \quad = 40^\circ$
   $\angle B = 50^\circ$

   Equilateral triangle

   Isosceles triangle
   $\angle M = 40^\circ$
2. 90°
3. 60°
4. $180 - (65 + 35)$
   $= 180 - 100$
   $= 80^\circ$
5. (1) $\angle C = \underline{90^\circ}$
   (2) $\angle C = \underline{90^\circ}$
   (3) $\angle B = \underline{60^\circ}$
   (4) $\angle C = \underline{60^\circ}$
   (5) $\angle C = \underline{80^\circ}$
   (6) $\angle B = \underline{70^\circ}$
   (7) $\angle A = \underline{90^\circ}$
   (8) $\angle A = \underline{45^\circ}$
   (9) $\angle B = \underline{30^\circ}$
6. $c = \sqrt{a^2 + b^2}$
   $c = \sqrt{5^2 + 12^2}$
   $c = \sqrt{25 + 144}$
   $c = \sqrt{169}$
   $c = 13$
7. $a = \sqrt{c^2 - b^2}$
   $a = \sqrt{5^2 - 4^2}$
   $a = \sqrt{25 - 16}$
   $a = \sqrt{9}$
   $a = 3$
8. $b = \sqrt{c^2 - a^2}$
   $b = \sqrt{17^2 - 15^2}$
   $b = \sqrt{289 - 225}$
   $b = \sqrt{64}$
   $b = 8$

Exercises 15.4a Page 319

1. The size of triangles and therefore the values of a and b vary, but the ratio of the side opposite to the side adjacent for this angle is always approximately .839. (Student answers may vary due to unavoidable measurement error.)
2. $\tan 20^\circ = .364$
3. $\tan 50^\circ = 1.192$
4. $\tan 10^\circ = .176$
5. $\tan 70^\circ = 2.748$
6. $\tan 80^\circ = 5.671$

Exercises 15.4b   Pages 320-321

1.

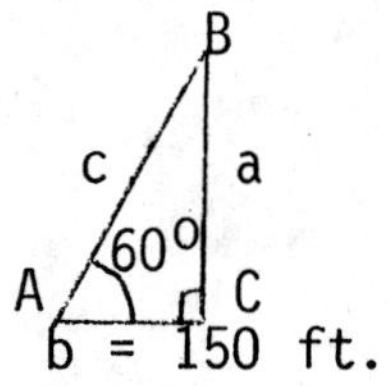

$\tan 60^\circ = \frac{a}{150}$

$1.732 = \frac{a}{150}$

$a = 150(1.732)$

$a = 260$ ft.

2.

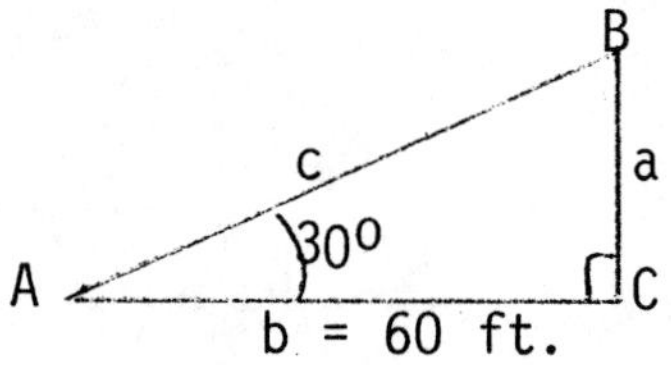

$\tan 30^\circ = \frac{a}{60}$

$a = 60 \tan 30^\circ$

$a = 60(.577)$

$a = 34.6$ ft.

3.

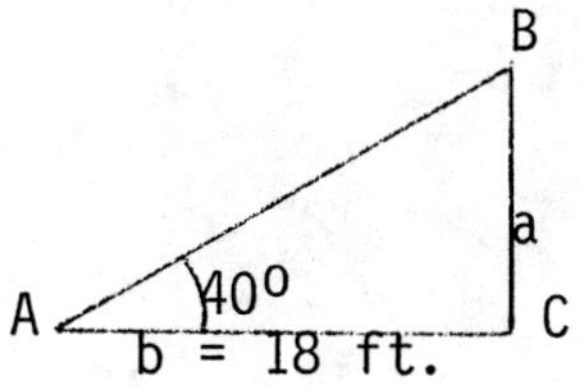

$\tan 40^\circ = \frac{a}{18}$

$a = 18 \tan 40^\circ$

$a = 18(.839)$

$a = 15.1$

4.

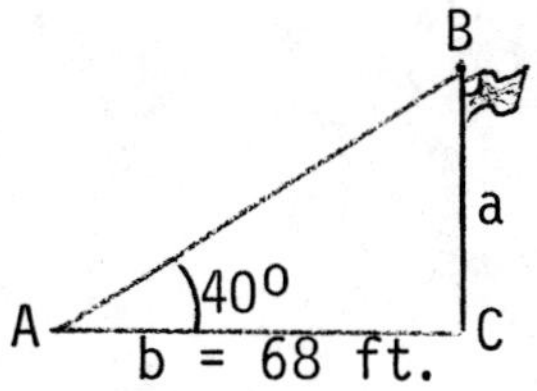

$\tan 40^\circ = \frac{a}{68}$

$a = 68 \tan 40^\circ$

$a = 68(.839)$

$a = 57.1$ ft.

5.

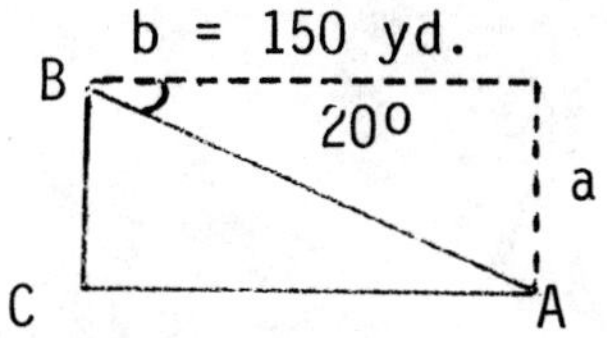

$\tan 20^\circ = \frac{a}{150}$

$a = 150 \tan 20^\circ$

$a = 150(.364)$

$a = 54.6$ yd.

Exercises 15.5a   Page 322

1. The size of triangles will vary and therefore the values of a and c, but the ratio of the side opposite this angle to the hypotenuse will always be .174 to the nearest thousandth. (Actual answers will vary somewhat due to unavoidable measurement error.)

2. $\sin 20^\circ = .342$ 3. $\sin 80^\circ = .985$ 4. $\sin 50^\circ = .766$

5. $\sin 70^\circ = .940$ 6. $\sin 40^\circ = .643$ 7. $\sin 90^\circ = 1.000$

Exercises 15.5b   Page 323

1.

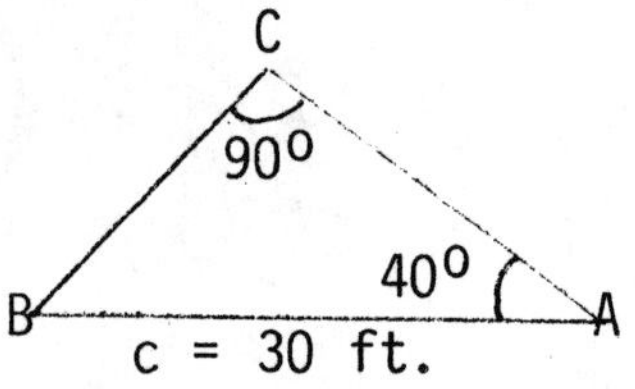

$\sin 40^\circ = \frac{BC}{30}$

$BC = 30 \sin 40^\circ$

$BC = 30(.6428)$

$BC = 19.3$ ft.

2.

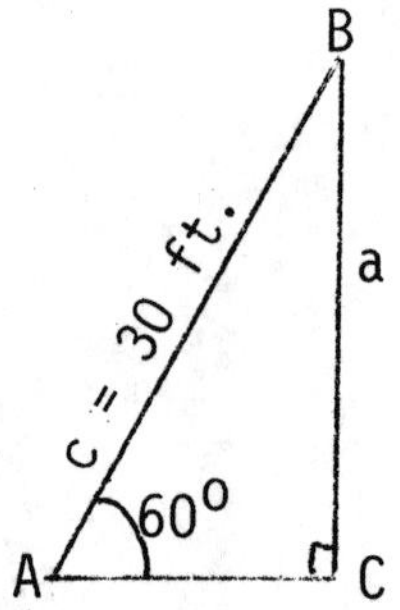

$\sin 60^\circ = \frac{a}{30}$

$a = 30 \sin 60^\circ$

$a = 30(.8660)$

$a = 26.0$ ft.

3. Given

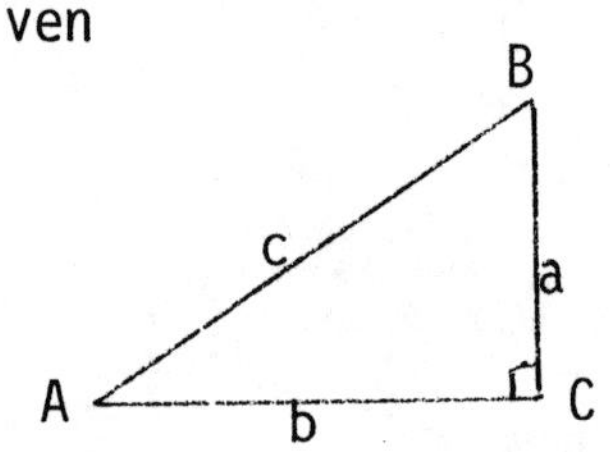

(a) $\angle A = 20^\circ$
$c = 120$ ft.

$\sin 20^\circ = \frac{a}{120}$

$a = 120 \sin 20^\circ$

$a = 120(.3420)$

$a = 41.0$ ft.

(b) $\angle A = 40^\circ$
$c = 60$ ft.

$\sin 40^\circ = \frac{a}{60}$

$a = 60 \sin 40^\circ$

$a = 60(.6428)$

$a = 38.6$ ft.

(c) $\angle A = 70^\circ$
$c = 76.5$ ft.

$\sin 70^\circ = \frac{a}{76.5}$

$a = 76.5 \sin 70^\circ$

$a = 76.5(.9397)$

$a - 71.9$ ft.

(d) $\angle A = 60^\circ$
$a = 48.5$ ft.

$\sin 60^\circ = \frac{48.5}{c}$

$c \sin 60^\circ = 48.5$

$c = \frac{48.5}{\sin 60^\circ}$

$c = \frac{48.5}{.8660}$

$c = 56.0$ ft.

(e) $\angle B = 50^0$
$c = 84.6$ ft.

$$\sin 50^0 = \frac{b}{84.6}$$
$$b = 84.6 \sin 50^0$$
$$b = 84.6(.7660)$$
$$b = 64.8 \text{ ft.}$$

(f) $\angle B = 80^0$
$b = 68.5$ ft.

$$\sin 80^0 = \frac{68.5}{c}$$
$$c \sin 80^0 = 68.5$$
$$c = \frac{68.5}{\sin 80}$$
$$c = \frac{68.5}{.9848}$$
$$c = 69.6 \text{ ft.}$$

Exercises 15.6a   Page 324

1. The size of triangles and therefore of b and c will vary, but the ratio of the side adjacent to the given angle to the hypotenuse of the right triangle will always be approximately .766.

2. $\cos 10^0 = .985$
3. $\cos 20^0 = .940$
4. $\cos 70^0 = .342$
5. $\cos 80^0 = .174$
6. $\cos 50^0 = .643$
7. $\cos 90^0 = 0$

Exercises 15.6b   Page 325

1.

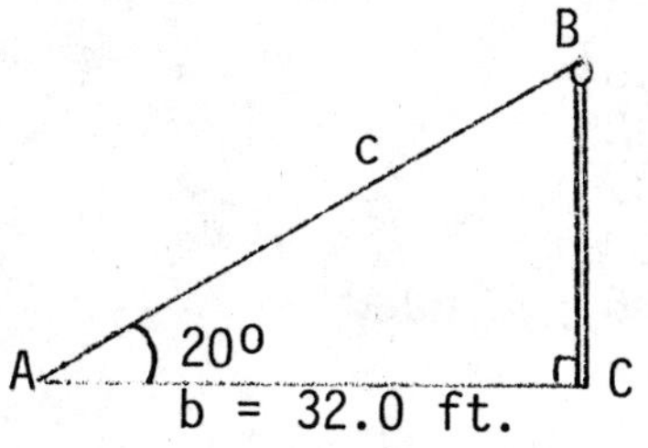

$$\cos 20^0 = \frac{32}{c}$$
$$c \cos 20^0 = 32$$
$$c = \frac{32}{\cos 20^0}$$
$$c = \frac{32}{.9397}$$
$$c = 34.1 \text{ ft.}$$

2.

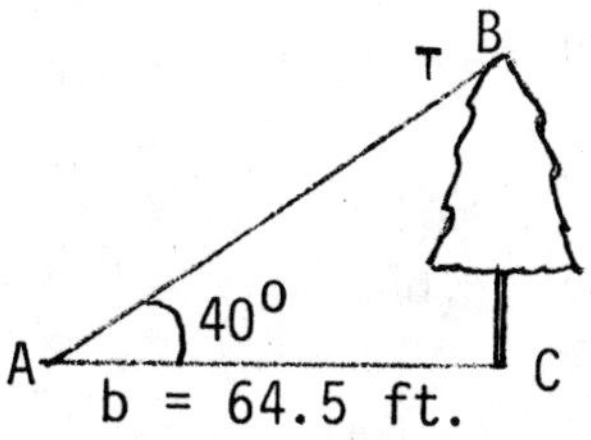

$$\cos 40^0 = \frac{64.5}{AT}$$
$$AT \cos 40^0 = 64.5$$
$$AT = \frac{64.5}{\cos 40^0}$$
$$AT = \frac{64.5}{.7660}$$
$$AT = 84.2 \text{ ft.}$$

3.

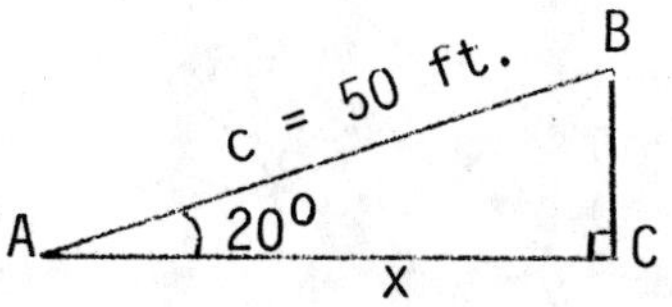

$$\cos 20^0 = \frac{x}{50}$$
$$x = 50 \cos 20^0$$
$$x = 50(.9397)$$
$$x = 47.0 \text{ ft.}$$

4.

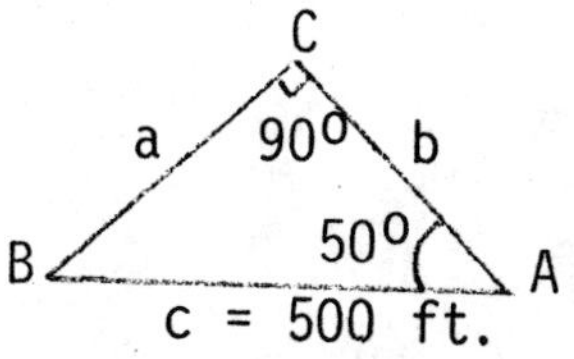

$$\cos 50^0 = \frac{CA}{500}$$
$$CA = 500 \cos 50^0$$
$$CA = 500(.6428)$$
$$CA = 321.4 \text{ ft.}$$

Exercises 15.7a   Page 328

For these exercises, the precise answer found using a calculator, rounded to four decimal places, is shown in the first line (underlined). The rest of the solution demonstrates finding the value by interpolation. Note that some interpolated values do not match the precise value; make allowance for this discrepancy if any of your students are using interpolation.

1. $\sin 36.5^{\circ} = \underline{.5948}$

$$\begin{aligned} \sin 37^{\circ} &= .6018 \\ \sin 36^{\circ} &= \underline{.5878} \\ d &= .0140 \\ .5d &= .0070 \\ \sin 36.5^{\circ} &= .5878 + .0070 \\ \sin 36.5^{\circ} &= .5948 \end{aligned}$$

2. $\sin 62.6^{\circ} = \underline{.8878}$

$$\begin{aligned} \sin 63^{\circ} &= .8910 \\ \sin 62^{\circ} &= \underline{.8829} \\ d &= .0081 \\ .6d &= .0049 \\ \sin 62.6^{\circ} &= .8829 + .0049 \\ \sin 62.6^{\circ} &= .8878 \end{aligned}$$

3. $\sin 19.2^{\circ} = \underline{.3289}$

$$\begin{aligned} \sin 20^{\circ} &= .3420 \\ \sin 19^{\circ} &= \underline{.3256} \\ d &= .0164 \\ .2d &= .0033 \\ \sin 19.2^{\circ} &= .3256 + .0033 \\ \sin 19.2^{\circ} &= .3289 \end{aligned}$$

4. $\cos 25.5^{\circ} = \underline{.9026}$

$$\begin{aligned} \cos 25^{\circ} &= .9063 \\ \cos 26^{\circ} &= \underline{.8988} \\ d &= .0075 \\ .5d &= .0038 \\ \cos 25.5^{\circ} &= .9063 - .0038 \\ \cos 25.5^{\circ} &= .9025 \end{aligned}$$

5. $\cos 27.8^{\circ} = \underline{.8846}$

$$\begin{aligned} \cos 27^{\circ} &= .8910 \\ \cos 28^{\circ} &= \underline{.8829} \\ d &= .0081 \\ .8d &= .0065 \\ \cos 27.8^{\circ} &= .8910 - .0065 \\ \cos 27.8^{\circ} &= .8845 \end{aligned}$$

6. $\cos 41.7^{\circ} = \underline{.7466}$

$$\begin{aligned} \cos 41^{\circ} &= .7547 \\ \cos 42^{\circ} &= \underline{.7431} \\ d &= .0116 \\ .7d &= .0081 \\ \cos 41.7^{\circ} &= .7547 - .0081 \\ \cos 41.7^{\circ} &= .7466 \end{aligned}$$

7. $\tan 72.1^{\circ} = \underline{3.0961}$

$$\begin{aligned} \tan 73^{\circ} &= 3.2709 \\ \tan 72^{\circ} &= \underline{3.0777} \\ d &= .1932 \\ .1d &= .0193 \\ \tan 72.1^{\circ} &= 3.0777 + .0193 \\ \tan 72.1^{\circ} &= 3.0970 \end{aligned}$$

8. $\tan 31.4^{\circ} = \underline{.6104}$

$$\begin{aligned} \tan 32^{\circ} &= .6249 \\ \tan 31^{\circ} &= \underline{.6009} \\ d &= .0240 \\ .4d &= .0096 \\ \tan 31.4^{\circ} &= .6009 + .0096 \\ \tan 31.4^{\circ} &= .6105 \end{aligned}$$

9. $\tan 18.3^0 = \underline{.3307}$

$\tan 19^0 = .3443$
$\tan 18^0 = .3249$
$d = .0194$
$.3d = .0058$
$\tan 18.3^0 = .3249 + .0058$
$\tan 18.3^0 = .3307$

10. $\cos 80.9^0 = \underline{.1582}$

$\cos 80^0 = .1736$
$\cos 81^0 = .1564$
$d = .0172$
$.9d = .0155$
$\cos 80.9^0 = .1736 - .0155$
$\cos 80.9^0 = .1581$

11. $\sin 20^0\ 30'$ $(\sin 20.5^0) = \underline{.3502}$

$\sin 21^0 = .3584$
$\sin 20^0 = .3420$
$d = .0164$
$.5d = .0082$
$\sin 20^0 30' = .3420 + .0082$
$\sin 20^0 30' = .3502$

12. $\sin 31^0 20'$ $(31.\bar{3}^0) = \underline{.5200}$

$\sin 32^0 = .5299$
$\sin 31^0 = .5150$
$d = .0149$
$.33d = .0049$
$\sin 31^0 20' = .5150 + .0049$
$\sin 31^0 20' = .5199$

13. $\cos 24^0 12'$ $(\cos 24.2^0) = \underline{.9121}$

$\cos 24^0 = .9135$
$\cos 25^0 = .9063$
$d = .0072$
$.2d = .0014$
$\cos 24^0 12' = .9135 - .0014$
$\cos 24^0 12' = .9121$

14. $\cos 48^0 2'$ $(\cos 48.0\bar{3}^0) = \underline{.6687}$

$\cos 48^0 = .6691$
$\cos 49^0 = .6561$
$d = .0130$
$.03d = .0004$
$\cos 48^0 2' = .6691 - .0004$
$\cos 48^0 2' = .6687$

15. $\tan 84^0 40'$ $(\tan 84.\bar{6}^0) = \underline{10.7119}$

$\tan 85^0 = 11.4301$
$\tan 84^0 = 9.5144$
$d = 1.9157$
$67d = 1.2835$
$\tan 84^0 40' = 9.5144 + 1.2835$
$\tan 84^0 40' = 10.7979$

16. $\tan 86^0 45'$ $(\tan 86.75^0) = \underline{17.6106}$

$\tan 87^0 = 19.0811$
$\tan 86^0 = 14.3007$
$d = 4.7804$
$.75d = 3.5853$
$\tan 86^0 45' = 14.3007 + 3.5853$
$\tan 86^0 45' = 17.8860$

<u>Exercises 15.7b</u> Page 330

1. $.2672 = \sin \underline{15.5^0}$

.2672 is between $\sin 15^0$ and $\sin 16^0$

$\sin 16^0 = .2756$
$\sin 15^0 = .2588$
$d = .0168$

$\sin x^0 = .2672$
$\sin 15^0 = .2588$
$d' = .0084$

$$\frac{d'}{d} = \frac{.0084}{.0168} = .5$$

$x = 15.5^0$

2. $.7697 = \sin \underline{50.3^0}$

.7697 is between $\sin 50^0$ and $\sin 51^0$

$\sin 51^0 = .7771$
$\sin 50^0 = .7660$
$d = .0111$

$\sin x^0 = .7697$
$\sin 50^0 = .7660$
$d' = .0037$

$$\frac{d'}{d} = \frac{.0037}{.0111} = .3$$

$x = 50.3^0$

3. $.8704 = \cos \underline{29.5^\circ}$

$.8704$ is between $\cos 29^\circ$ and $\cos 30^\circ$

$$\begin{aligned} \cos 29^\circ &= .8746 \\ \cos 30^\circ &= \underline{.8660} \\ d &= .0086 \end{aligned}$$

$$\begin{aligned} \cos 29^\circ &= .8746 \\ \cos x^\circ &= \underline{.8704} \\ d' &= .0042 \end{aligned}$$

$$\frac{d'}{d} = \frac{.0042}{.0086} = .5$$

$$x = 29.5^\circ$$

4. $.8100 = \cos \underline{35.9^\circ}$

$.8100$ is between $\cos 35^\circ$ and $\cos 36^\circ$

$$\begin{aligned} \cos 35^\circ &= .8192 \\ \cos 36^\circ &= \underline{.8090} \\ d &= .0102 \end{aligned}$$

$$\begin{aligned} \cos 35^\circ &= .8192 \\ \cos x^\circ &= \underline{.8100} \\ d' &= .0092 \end{aligned}$$

$$\frac{d'}{d} = \frac{.0092}{.0102} = .9$$

$$x = 35.9^\circ$$

5. $.4552 = \tan \underline{24.5^\circ}$

$.4552$ is between $\tan 24^\circ$ and $\tan 25^\circ$

$$\begin{aligned} \tan 25^\circ &= .4663 \\ \tan 24^\circ &= \underline{.4452} \\ d &= .0211 \end{aligned}$$

$$\begin{aligned} \tan x^\circ &= .4552 \\ \tan 24^\circ &= \underline{.4452} \\ d' &= .0100 \end{aligned}$$

$$\frac{d'}{d} = \frac{.0100}{.0211} = .5$$

$$x = 24.5^\circ$$

6. $1.772 = \tan \underline{60.6^\circ}$

1.772 is between $\tan 60^\circ$ and $\tan 61^\circ$

$$\begin{aligned} \tan 61^\circ &= 1.8040 \\ \tan 60^\circ &= \underline{1.7321} \\ d &= .0719 \end{aligned}$$

$$\begin{aligned} \tan x^\circ &= 1.7720 \\ \tan 60^\circ &= \underline{1.7321} \\ d' &= .0399 \end{aligned}$$

$$\frac{d'}{d} = \frac{.0399}{.0719} = .6$$

$$x = 60.6^\circ$$

<u>Review Exercises</u> Pages 330-332

1.

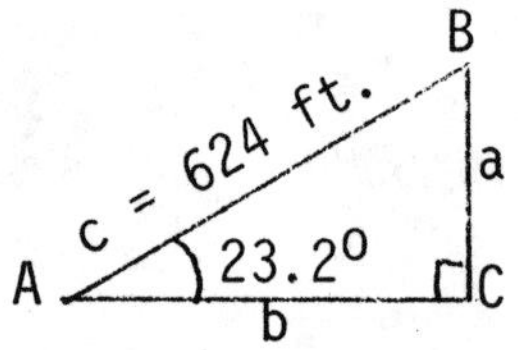

$$\sin 23.2^\circ = \frac{a}{624}$$
$$a = 624 \sin 23.2^\circ$$
$$\sin 23.2^\circ = .3939$$
$$a = 624(.3939)$$
$$a = 245.8 \text{ ft.}$$

$$\cos A = \frac{b}{624}$$
$$b = 624 \cos 23.2^\circ$$
$$\cos 23.2^\circ = .9191$$
$$b = 624(.9191)$$
$$b = 573.5 \text{ ft.}$$

$$\angle C = 90^\circ$$
$$\angle B = 90^\circ - 23.2^\circ$$
$$\angle B = 66.8^\circ$$

<u>Alternate solution:</u>

$\sin 66.8^\circ = \frac{b}{624}$. Using pythagorean theorem, $(245.8)^2 + b^2 = 624^2$

2.

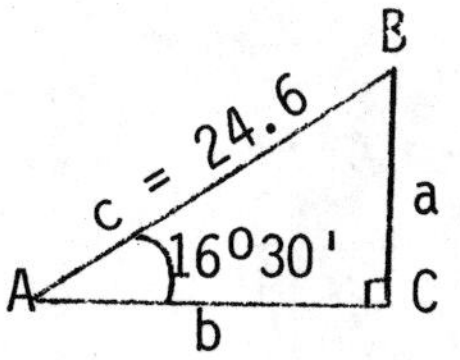

$\sin 16^\circ 30' = \frac{a}{24.6}$

$a = 24.6 \sin 16.5^\circ$

$a = 24.6(.2840)$

$a = 7.0$

$\sin 17^\circ = .2924$

$\sin 16^\circ = .2756$

$d = .0168$

$.5d = .0084$

$\sin 16.5^\circ = .2756 + .0084$

$\sin 16.5^\circ = .2840$

3.

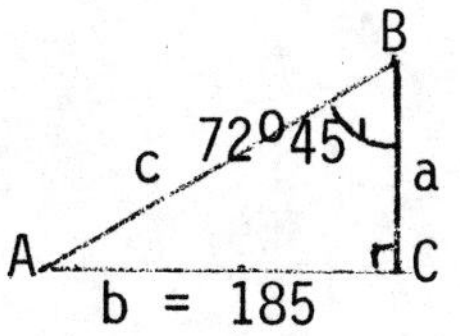

$\tan 72^\circ 45' = \frac{185}{a}$

$\tan 72.75^\circ = \frac{185}{a}$

$a \tan 72.75^\circ = 185$

$a = \frac{185}{\tan 72.75^\circ}$

$a = \frac{185}{3.2205}$

$a = 57.4$

$\tan 73^\circ = 3.2709$

$\tan 72^\circ = 3.0777$

$d = .1932$

$.8d = .1546$

$\tan 72.8^\circ = 3.0777 + .1546$

$\tan 72.8^\circ = 3.2323$

<u>Alternate solution:</u> $\angle A = 90 - 72^\circ 45' = 17^\circ 15' = 17.3^\circ$

$\tan 17.3^\circ = \frac{a}{185}$ $\quad a = 185 \tan 17.3^\circ$

Notice multiplication is used rather than division as in previous solution.

4. Left column uses actual ratios (rounded); right column shows interpolation. If interpolation used, allow for discrepancy between interpolated and actual values.

(a)

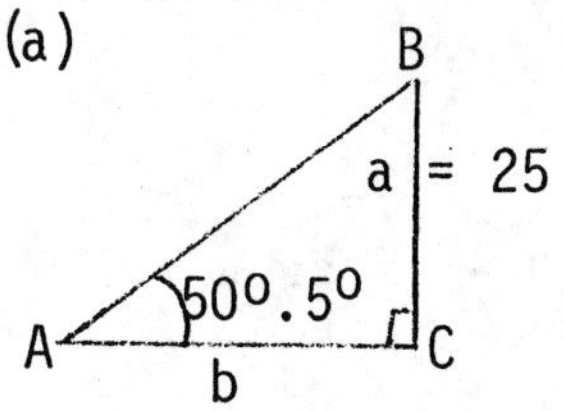

$\tan 50.5^\circ = \frac{25}{b}$

$b \tan 50.5^\circ = 25$

$b = \frac{25}{\tan 50.5^\circ}$

$b = \frac{25}{1.2131}$

$b = 20.6$

$\tan 51^\circ = 1.2349$

$\tan 50^\circ = 1.1918$

$d = .0431$

$.5d = .0216$

$\tan 50.5^\circ = 1.1918 + .0216$

$\tan 50.5^\circ = 1.2134$

(b)

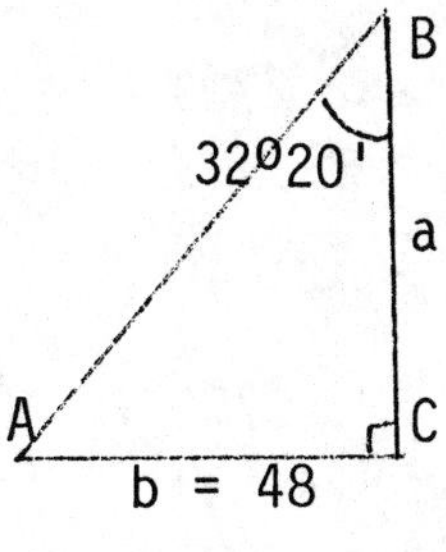

$\tan 35^\circ 20' = \frac{48}{a}$

$a \tan 35.\bar{3}^\circ = 48$

$a = \frac{48}{\tan 35.\bar{3}^\circ}$

$a = \frac{48}{.7089}$

$a = 67.7$

$\tan 36^\circ = .7265$

$\tan 35^\circ = .7002$

$d = .0263$

$.33d = .0087$

$\tan 35.3^\circ = .7002 + .0087$

$\tan 35.3^\circ = .7089$

(c)

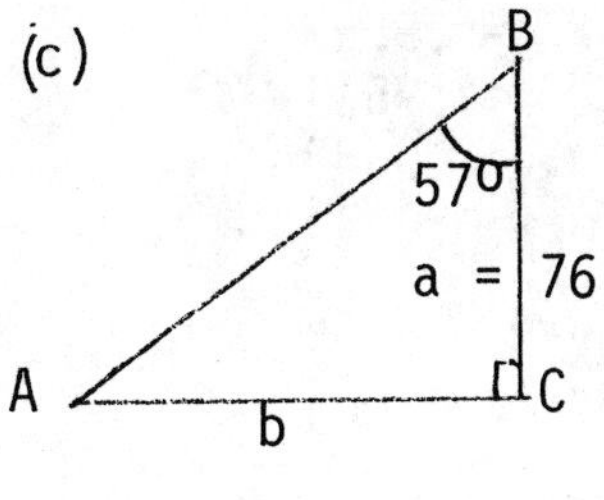

$\tan 57^\circ = \frac{b}{76}$

$b = 76 \tan 57^\circ$

$b = 76(1.5399)$

$b = 117$

4. (continued)

(d)

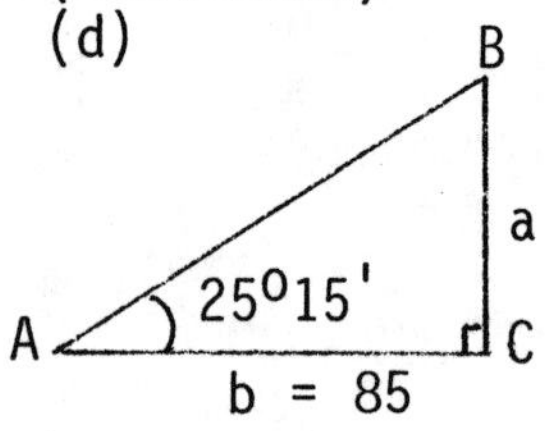

$\tan 25^{\circ}15' = \frac{a}{85}$

$a = 85 \tan 25.25^{\circ}$

$a = 85(.4716)$

$a = 40.1$

$\tan 26^{\circ} = .4877$

$\tan 25^{\circ} = .4663$

$d = .0214$

$.25d = .0054$

$\tan 25.3^{\circ} = .4663 + .0064$

$\tan 25.3^{\circ} = .4717$

(e)

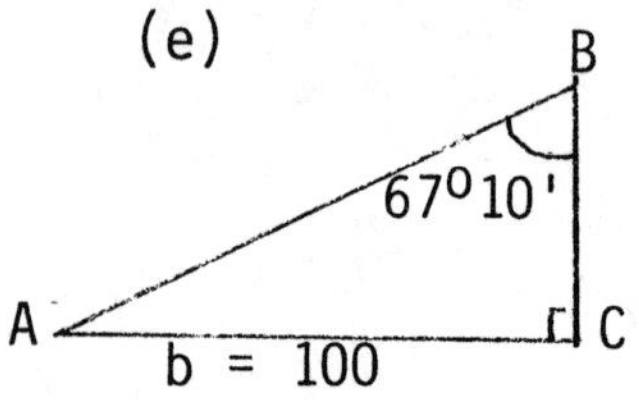

$\tan 67^{\circ}10' = \frac{100}{a}$

$a \tan 67.1\bar{6}^{\circ} = 100$

$a = \frac{100}{\tan 67.1\bar{6}^{\circ}}$

$a = \frac{100}{2.3750}$

$a = 42.1$

$\tan 68^{\circ} = 2.4751$

$\tan 67^{\circ} = 2.3559$

$d = .1192$

$.167d = .0199$

$\tan 67.2^{\circ} = 2.3559 + .0199$

$\tan 67.2^{\circ} = 2.3758$

(f)

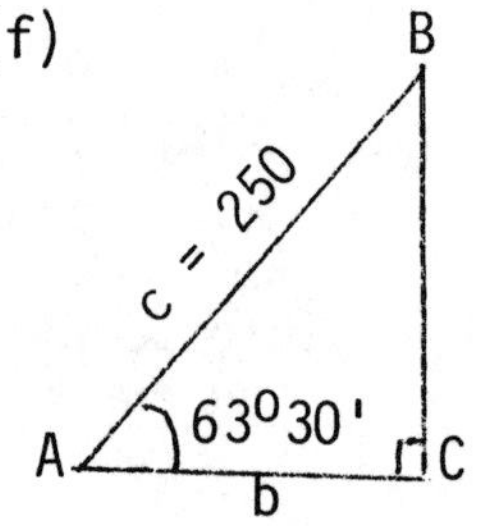

$\cos 63^{\circ}30' = \frac{b}{250}$

$b = 250 \cos 63.5^{\circ}$

$b = 250(.4462)$

$b = 111.6$

($b = 111.5$ if full cosine used)

$\cos 63^{\circ} = .4540$

$\cos 64^{\circ} = .4384$

$d = .0156$

$.5d = .0078$

$\cos 63.5^{\circ} = .4540 - .0078$

$\cos 63.5^{\circ} = .4462$

(g)

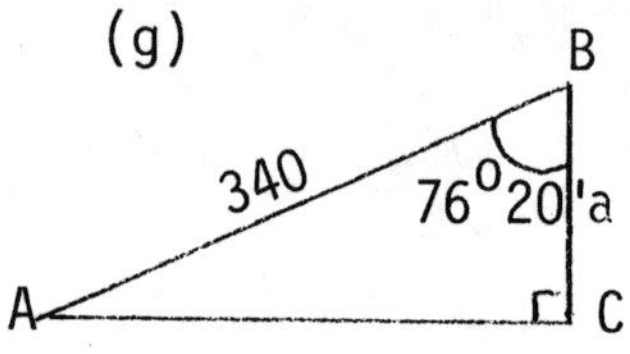

$\cos 76^{\circ}20' = \frac{a}{340}$

$a = 340 \cos 76.\bar{3}^{\circ}$

$a = 340(.2363)$

$a = 80.3$

$\cos 76^{\circ} = .2419$

$\cos 77^{\circ} = .2250$

$d = .0169$

$.33d = .0056$

$\cos 76.3^{\circ} = .2419 - .0056$

$\cos 76.3^{\circ} = .2363$

(h)

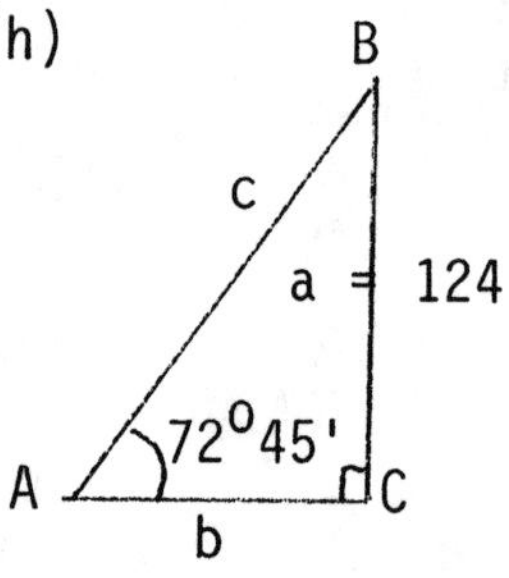

$\tan 72^{\circ}45' = \frac{124}{b}$

$b \tan 72.75^{\circ} = 124$

$b = \frac{124}{\tan 72.75^{\circ}}$

$b = \frac{124}{3.2205}$

$b = 38.50$

$\tan 73^{\circ} = 3.2709$

$\tan 72^{\circ} = 3.0777$

$d = .1932$

$.75d = .1449$

$\tan 72.8^{\circ} = 3.0777 + .1449$

$\tan 72.8^{\circ} = 3.2226$

$\sin 72^{\circ}45' = \frac{124}{c}$

$c \sin 72.75^{\circ} = 124$

$c = \frac{124}{\sin 72.75^{\circ}}$

$c = \frac{124}{.9550}$

$c = 129.8$

$\sin 73^{\circ} = .9563$

$\sin 72^{\circ} = .9511$

$d = .0052$

$.75d = .0039$

$\sin 72.8^{\circ} = .9511 + .0039$

$\sin 72.8^{\circ} = .9550$

4. (continued)

(i)

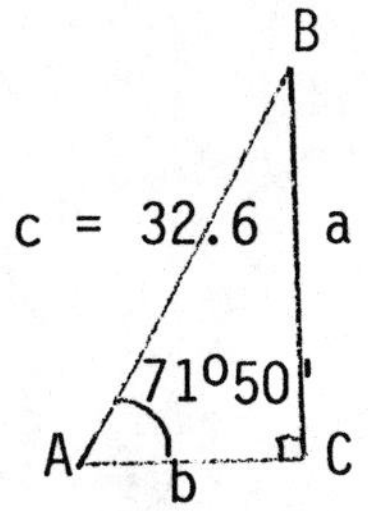

$\sin 71^{\circ}50' = \dfrac{a}{32.6}$

$a = 32.6 \sin 71.8\bar{3}^{\circ}$

$a = 32.6(.9502)$

$a = 30.98 \approx 31.0$

$\cos 71^{\circ}50' = \dfrac{b}{32.6}$

$b = 32.6 \cos 71.8\bar{3}^{\circ}$

$b = 32.6(.3118)$

$b = 10.2$

$\sin 72^{\circ} = .9511$
$\sin 71^{\circ} = .9455$
$d = .0056$
$.83d = .0046$

$\sin 71.83^{\circ} = .9455 + .0046$
$\sin 71.83^{c} = .9501$

$\cos 71^{\circ} = .3256$
$\cos 72^{\circ} = .3090$
$d = .0166$
$.83d = .0138$

$\cos 71.8^{\circ} = .3256 - .0138$
$\cos 71.8^{\circ} = .3118$

(j)

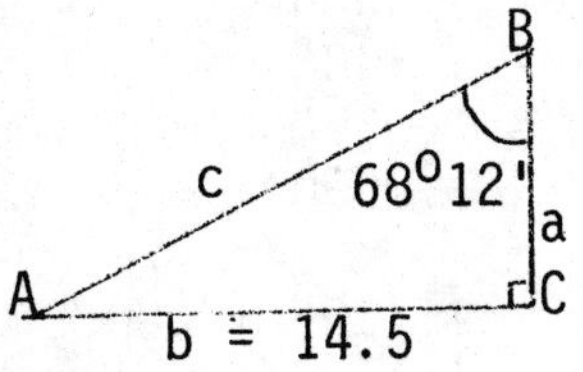

$\tan 68^{\circ}12' = \dfrac{14.5}{a}$

$a \tan 68.2^{\circ} = 14.5$

$a = \dfrac{14.5}{\tan 68.2}$

$a = \dfrac{14.5}{2.5002}$

$a = 5.80$

$\sin 68^{\circ}12' = \dfrac{14.5}{c}$

$c \sin 68.2^{\circ} = 14.5$

$c = \dfrac{14.5}{\sin 68.2^{\circ}}$

$c = \dfrac{14.5}{.9285}$

$c = 15.6$

$\tan 69^{\circ} = 2.6051$
$\tan 68^{\circ} = 2.4751$
$d = .1300$
$.2d = .0260$

$\tan 68.2^{\circ} = 2.4751 + .0260$
$\tan 68.2^{\circ} = 2.5011$

$\sin 69^{\circ} = .9336$
$\sin 68^{\circ} = .9272$
$d = .0064$
$.2d = .0013$

$\sin 68.2^{\circ} = .9272 + .0013$
$\sin 68.2^{\circ} = .9285$

5.

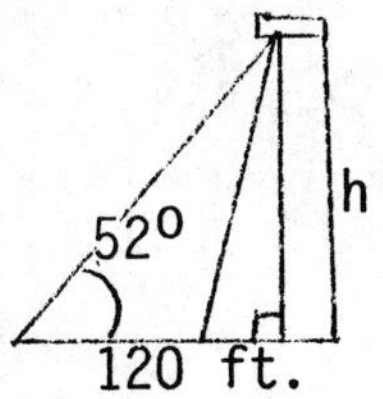

$\tan 52^{\circ} = \dfrac{h}{120}$

$h = 120 \tan 52^{\circ}$

$h = 120(1.2799)$

$h = 153.6$ ft.

6.

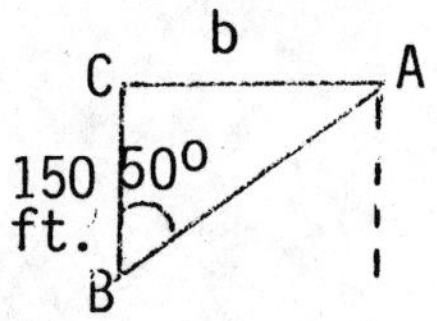

$\tan 50^{\circ} = \dfrac{b}{150}$

$h = 150 \tan 50^{\circ}$

$h = 150(1.1918)$

$h = 178.8$ ft.

7.

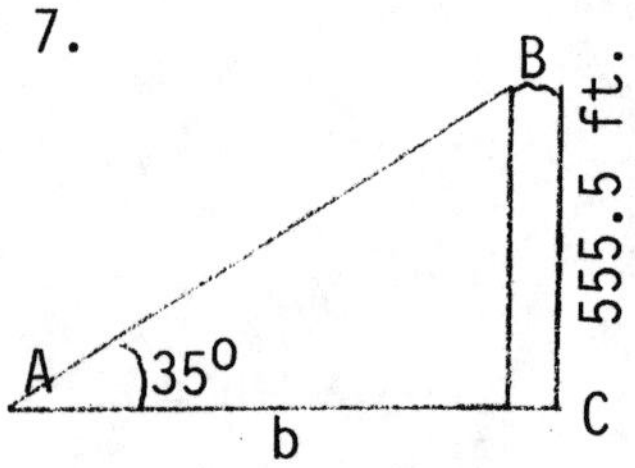

$\tan 35^\circ = \dfrac{555.5}{b}$

$b \tan 35^\circ = 555.5$

$b = \dfrac{555.5}{\tan 35^\circ}$

$b = \dfrac{555.5}{.7002}$

$b = 793.3$ ft.

8.

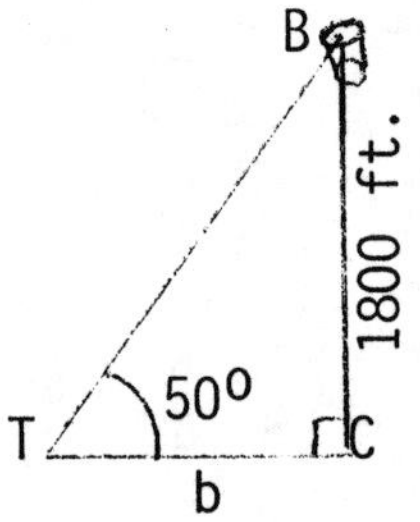

$\tan 50^\circ = \dfrac{1800}{b}$

$b \tan 50^\circ = 1800$

$b = \dfrac{1800}{\tan 50^\circ}$

$b = \dfrac{1800}{1.1918}$

$b = 1510$ ft.

9.

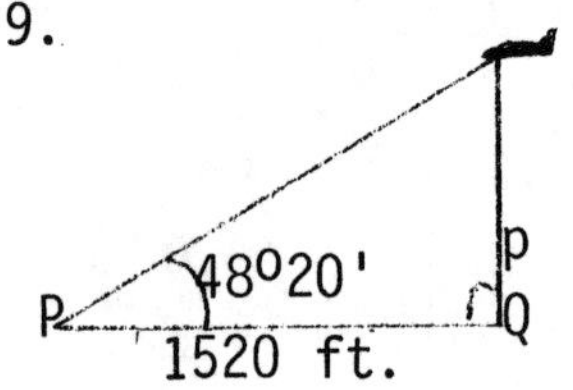

$\tan 48.20^\circ = \dfrac{p}{1520}$

$p = 1520 \tan 48.20^\circ$

$p = 1520\ (1.1184)$

$p = 1700$ ft.

$\tan 49^\circ = 1.1504$
$\tan 48^\circ = \underline{1.1106}$
$d = .0398$
$.20d = .0080$

$\tan 48.3^\circ = 1.1106 + .0080$
$\tan 48.3^\circ = 1.1186$

10.

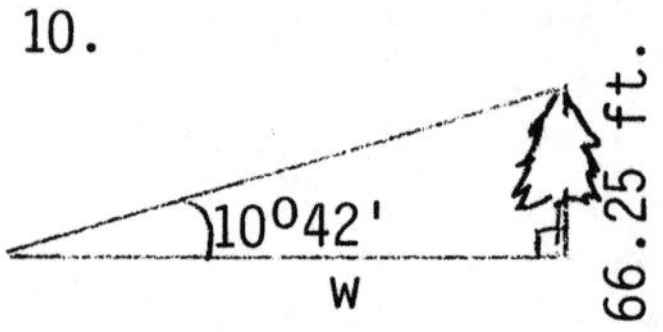

$\tan 10^\circ 42' = \dfrac{66.25}{w}$

$w \tan 10.7^\circ = 66.25$

$w = \dfrac{66.25}{\tan 10.7^\circ}$

$w = \dfrac{66.25}{.1890}$

$w = 350.5$ ft.

($w = 350.6$ if full tangent used)

$\tan 11^\circ = .1944$
$\tan 10^\circ = \underline{.1763}$
$d = .0181$
$.7d = .0127$

$\tan 10.7^\circ = .1763 + .0127$
$\tan 10.7^\circ = .1890$

11.

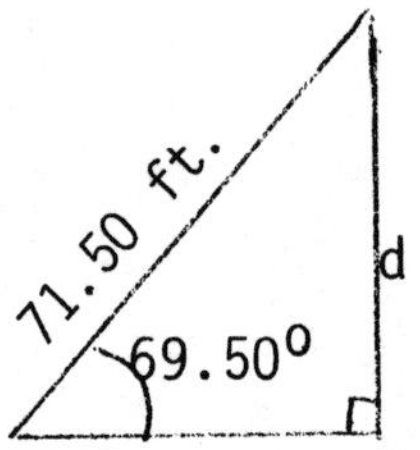

$\sin 69.50^\circ = \dfrac{d}{71.50}$

$d = 71.50 \sin 69.50^\circ$

$d = 71.50\ (.9367)$

$d = 66.97$ ft.

$\sin 70^\circ = .9397$
$\sin 69^\circ = \underline{.9336}$
$d = .0061$
$.50d = .0031$

$\sin 69.50^\circ = .9336 + .0031$
$\sin 69.50^\circ = .9367$

12. let x = vertical portion
y = leaning portion
x + y = original height

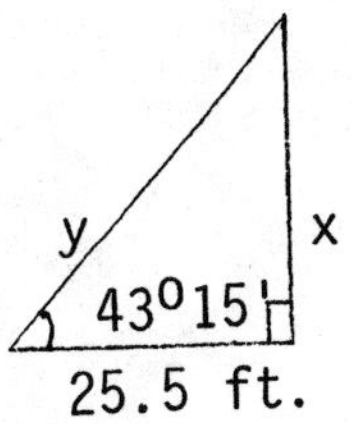

$\tan 43^\circ 15' = \frac{x}{25.5}$

$x = 25.5 \tan 43.25^\circ$

$x = 25.5(.9407)$

$x = 24.0$

$\cos 43^\circ 15' = \frac{25.5}{y}$

$y \cos 43.25^\circ = 25.5$

$y = \frac{25.5}{\cos 43.25^\circ}$

$y = \frac{25.5}{.7284}$

$y = 35.0$

$x + y = 24.0 + 35.0 = 59.0$ ft.

$\tan 44^\circ = .9657$
$\tan 43^\circ = \underline{.9325}$
$d = .0332$
$.25d = .0083$

$\tan 43.25^\circ = .9325 + .0083$
$\tan 43.25^\circ = .9408$

$\cos 43^\circ = .7314$
$\cos 44^\circ = \underline{.7193}$
$d = .0121$
$.25d = .0036$
$\cos 43.25^\circ = .7314 - .0030$
$\cos 43.25^\circ = .7284$

13.

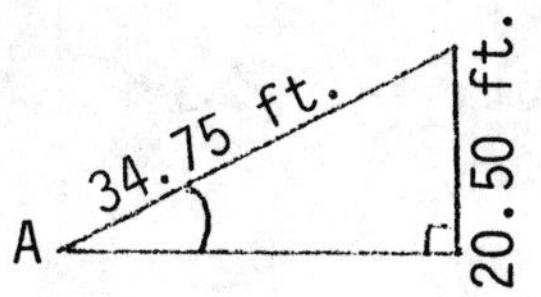

$\sin A = \frac{20.50}{34.75}$

$\sin A = .5899$

$A = 36.15^\circ$ or $36^\circ 9'$

Note: Since both 20.50 and 34.75 have 4 significant digits, 4 have been retained in $\frac{d'}{d}$ and therefore in A. However, rounding to 36.2° is also acceptable.

.5899 is between $\sin 36^\circ$ and $\sin 37^\circ$

$\sin 37^\circ = .6018$
$\sin 36^\circ = \underline{.5878}$
$d = .0140$

$\sin x^\circ = .5899$
$\sin 36^\circ = \underline{.5878}$
$d' = .0021$
$\frac{d'}{d} = \frac{.0021}{.0140} = .15$

14.

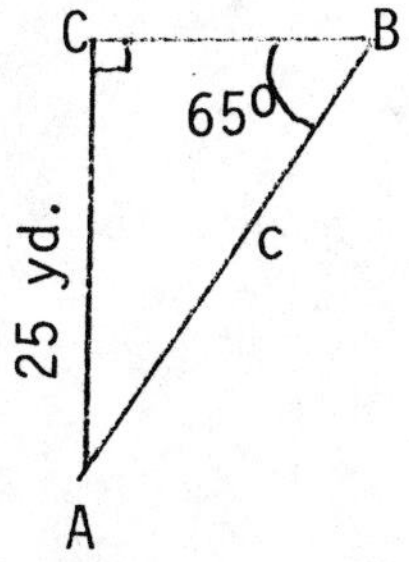

$\sin 65^\circ = \frac{25}{c}$

$c \sin 65^\circ = 25$

$c = \frac{25}{\sin 65^\circ}$

$c = \frac{25}{.9063}$

$c = 27.6$ yd.

15.

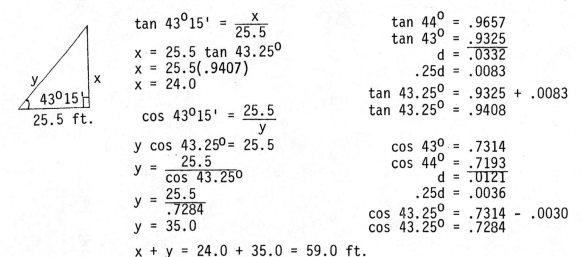

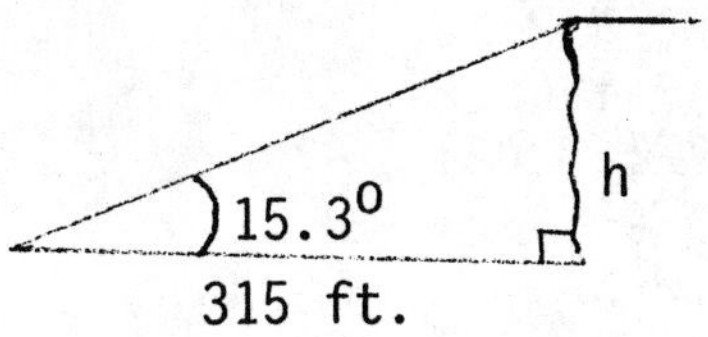

$\tan 15.3^\circ = \frac{h}{315}$

$h = 315 \tan 15.3^\circ$

$h = 315(.2736)$

$h = 86.2$ ft.

$\tan 16^\circ = .2867$
$\tan 15^\circ = \underline{.2679}$
$d = .0188$
$.3d = .0056$

$\tan 15.3^\circ = .2679 + .0056$
$\tan 15.3^\circ = .2735$

16.

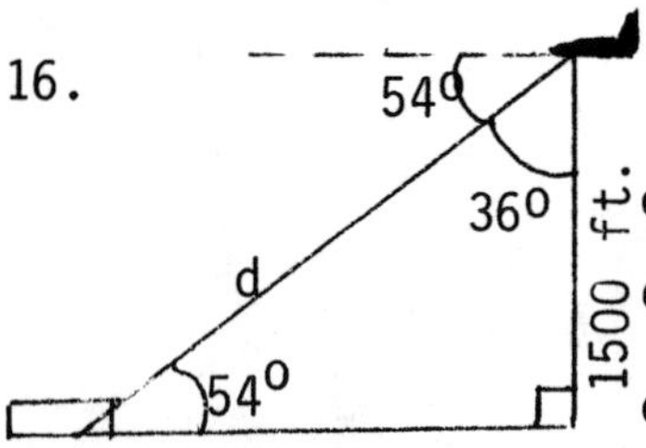

$\cos 36^\circ = \frac{1500}{d}$

$d \cos 36^\circ = 1500$

$d = \frac{1500}{\cos 36^\circ}$

$d = \frac{1500}{.8090}$

$d = 1854$ ft.

Alternate solution

$\sin 54^\circ = \frac{1500}{d}$

$d \sin 54^\circ = 1500$

$d = \frac{1500}{\sin 54^\circ}$

$d = \frac{1500}{.8090}$

$d = 1854$ ft.

17.

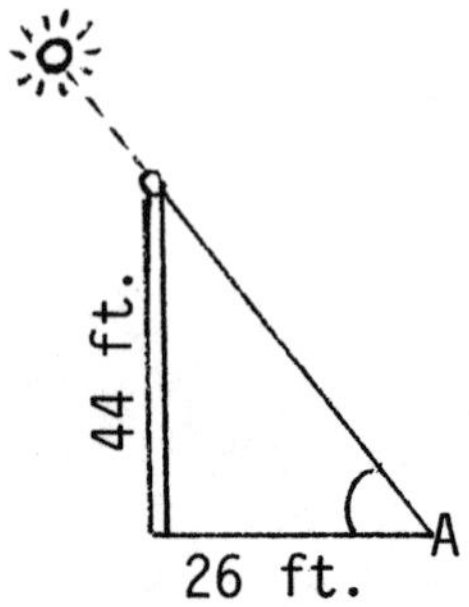

$\tan A = \frac{44}{26}$

$\tan A = 1.6923$

$A = 59.4^\circ$ or $59^\circ 25'$

1.6923 is between $\tan 59^\circ$ and $\tan 60^\circ$

$$\begin{aligned} \tan 60^\circ &= 1.7321 \\ \tan 59^\circ &= \underline{1.6643} \\ d &= .0678 \end{aligned}$$

$$\begin{aligned} \tan x^\circ &= 1.6923 \\ \tan 59^\circ &= \underline{1.6643} \\ d' &= .0280 \\ \frac{d'}{d} &= \frac{.0280}{.0678} = .4 \end{aligned}$$

18.

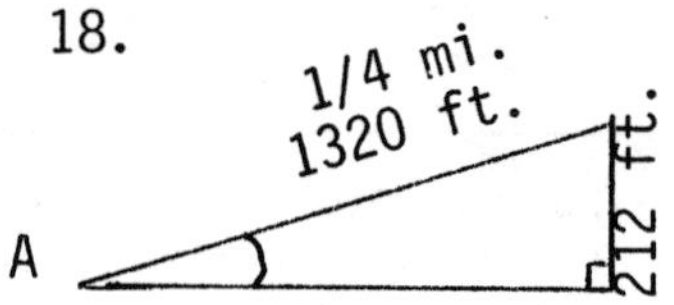

$\frac{1}{4}$ mi. $= \frac{1}{4}(5280) = 1320$ ft.

$\tan A = \frac{212}{1320}$

$\tan A = .1606$

$A = 9.24^\circ$ or $9^\circ 15'$

.1606 is between $\tan 9^\circ$ and $\tan 10^\circ$

$$\begin{aligned} \tan 10^\circ &= .1763 \\ \tan 9^\circ &= \underline{.1584} \\ d &= .0179 \end{aligned}$$

$$\begin{aligned} \tan x^\circ &= .1606 \\ \tan 9^\circ &= \underline{.1584} \\ d' &= .0022 \\ \frac{d'}{d} &= \frac{.0022}{.0179} = .1 \end{aligned}$$

19.

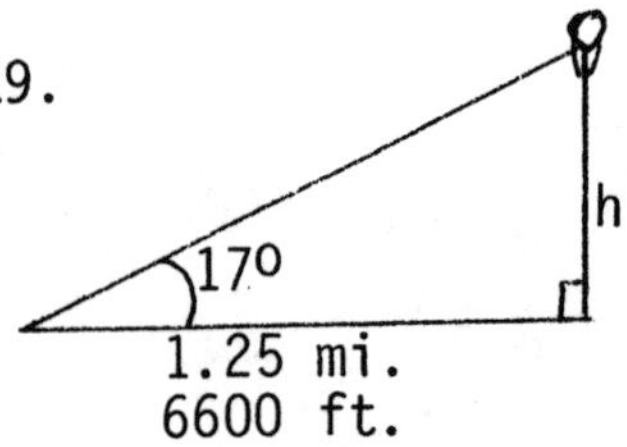

1.25 mi. = 5280(1.25) = 6600 ft.

$\tan 17^\circ = \frac{h}{6600}$

$h = 6600 \tan 17^\circ$

$h = 6600(.3057)$

$h = 2018$ ft.

*20. let x = combined height of building and flagpole
y = height of building
$x - y$ = height of flagpole

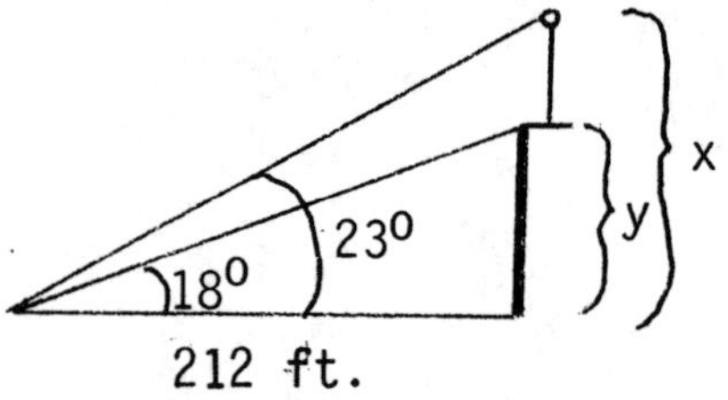

$\tan 23^\circ = \frac{x}{212}$ $\qquad$ $\tan 18^\circ = \frac{y}{212}$

$x = 212 \tan 23^\circ$ $\qquad$ $y = 212 \tan 18^\circ$

$x = 212(.4245)$ $\qquad$ $y = 212(.3249)$

$x = 90.0$ $\qquad$ $y = 68.9$

$x - y = 90.0 - 68.9$

$x - y = 21.1$ ft.

21.

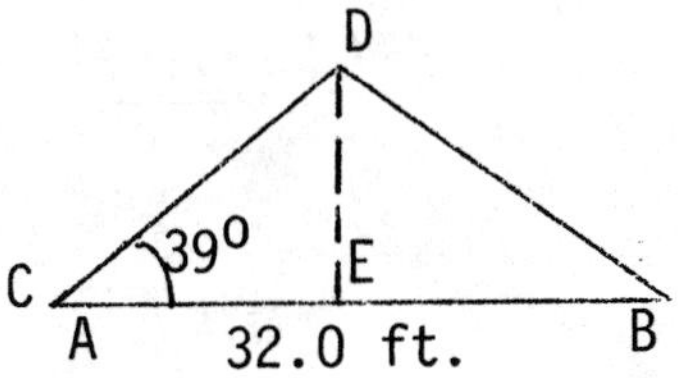

$\cos 39^o = \frac{AE}{AD}$

$AE = \frac{1}{2}(AB) = 16.0$ ft.

$\cos 39^o = \frac{16}{AD}$

$AD \cos 39^o = 16$

$AD = \frac{16}{\cos 39^o}$

$AD = \frac{16}{.7771}$

$AD = 20.6$

$CD = AD + 1$
$CD = 20.6 + 1$
$CD = 21.6$ ft.

22.

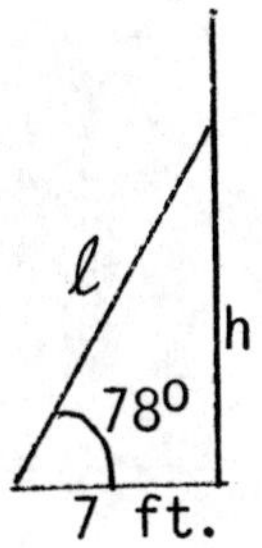

$\tan 78^o = \frac{h}{7}$

$h = 7 \tan 78^o$
$h = 7(4.7046)$
$h = 32.9$ ft.

$\cos 78^o = \frac{7}{\ell}$

$\ell \cos 78^o = 7$

$\ell = \frac{7}{\cos 78^o}$

$\ell = \frac{7}{.2079}$

$\ell = 33.7$ ft.

23.

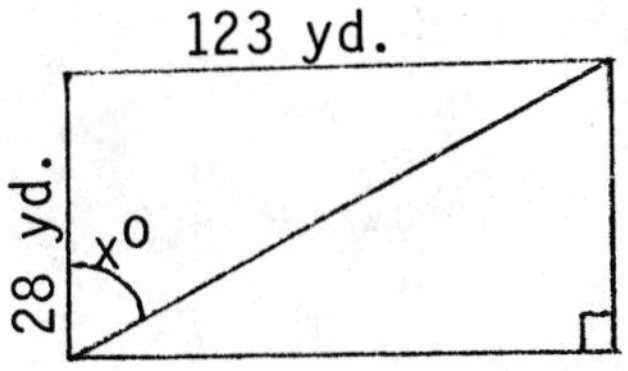

$\tan x^o = \frac{123}{28}$

$\tan x^o = 4.3929$
$x = 77^o$

Note: Since only two significant digits are found in the measurement 28 yd., only two are given in the answer. It is only necessary to determine whether x is closer to 77° or 78°.

4.3929 is between $\tan 77^o$ and $\tan 78^o$

$\tan 78^o = 4.7046$
$\tan 77^o = 4.3315$
$d = .3731$

$\tan x^o = 4.3929$
$\tan 77^o = 4.3315$
$d' = .0614$

$\frac{d'}{d} = \frac{.0614}{.3731} < .5$

*24. let x = distance from foot of cliff to farther boat
y = distance from foot of cliff to nearer boat
x - y = distance between boats

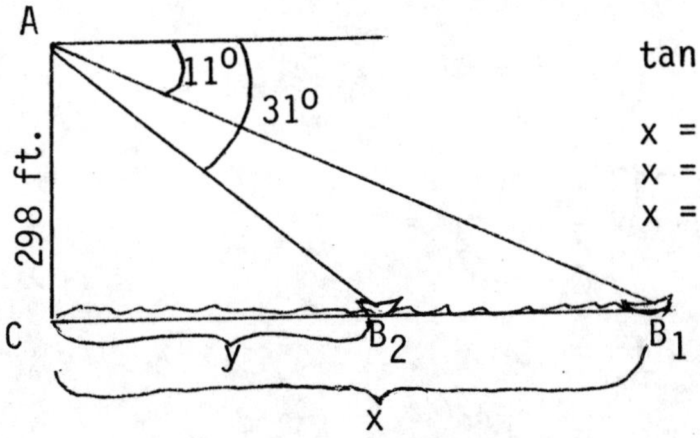

$\tan 79^o = \frac{x}{298}$

$x = 298 \tan 79^o$
$x = 298(5.1446)$
$x = 1533$

$\tan 59^o = \frac{y}{298}$

$y = 298 \tan 59^o$
$y = 298(1.6643)$
$y = 496.0$

$x - y = 1037$ ft.

$\angle CAB_1 = 90^o - 11^o = 79^o$
$\angle CAB_2 = 90^o - 31^o = 59^o$

Test A Pages 332-333 Underlined ratios are accurate; workthroughs demonstrate interpolation (allow for discrepancy).

I

1. $\sin 36^\circ = \underline{.5878}$
2. $\tan 52^\circ = \underline{1.2799}$
3. $\cos 67^\circ = \underline{.3907}$

4. $\cos 42.3^\circ = \underline{.7396}$

$$\begin{aligned} \cos 42^\circ &= .7431 \\ \cos 43^\circ &= \underline{.7314} \\ d &= .0117 \\ .3d &= .0035 \end{aligned}$$

$$\begin{aligned} \cos 42.3^\circ &= .7431 - .0035 \\ \cos 42.3^\circ &= .7396 \end{aligned}$$

5. $\sin 63.6^\circ = \underline{.8957}$

$$\begin{aligned} \sin 64^\circ &= .8988 \\ \sin 63^\circ &= \underline{.8910} \\ d &= .0078 \\ .6d &= .0047 \end{aligned}$$

$$\begin{aligned} \sin 63.6^\circ &= .8910 + .0047 \\ \sin 63.6^\circ &= .8957 \end{aligned}$$

6. $\tan 13.4^\circ = \underline{.2382}$

$$\begin{aligned} \tan 14^\circ &= .2493 \\ \tan 13^\circ &= \underline{.2309} \\ d &= .0184 \\ .4d &= .0074 \end{aligned}$$

$$\begin{aligned} \tan 13.4^\circ &= .2309 + .0074 \\ \tan 13.4^\circ &= .2383 \end{aligned}$$

7. $\tan 55^\circ 30' = \tan 55.5^\circ = \underline{1.4550}$

$$\begin{aligned} \tan 56^\circ &= 1.4826 \\ \tan 55^\circ &= \underline{1.4281} \\ d &= .0545 \\ .5d &= .0273 \end{aligned}$$

$$\begin{aligned} \tan 55.5^\circ &= 1.4281 + .0273 \\ \tan 55.5^\circ &= 1.4554 \end{aligned}$$

8. $\cos 27^\circ 18' = \cos 27.3 = \underline{.8886}$

$$\begin{aligned} \cos 27^\circ &= .8910 \\ \cos 28^\circ &= \underline{.8829} \\ d &= .0081 \\ .3d &= .0024 \end{aligned}$$

$$\begin{aligned} \cos 27^\circ 18' &= .8910 - .0024 \\ \cos 27^\circ 18' &= .8886 \end{aligned}$$

9. $\sin 75^\circ 48' = \sin 75.8^\circ = \underline{.9694}$

$$\begin{aligned} \sin 76^\circ &= .9703 \\ \sin 75^\circ &= \underline{.9659} \\ d &= .0044 \\ .8d &= .0035 \end{aligned}$$

$$\begin{aligned} \sin 75^\circ 48' &= .9659 + .0035 \\ \sin 75^\circ 48' &= .9694 \end{aligned}$$

II

1. $\sin A = .9205$, $A = 67.0^\circ$
2. $\tan A = .9325$, $A = 43.0^\circ$
3. $\cos A = .5000$, $A = 60.0^\circ$

4. $\tan A = 2.2054$

2.2054 is between $\tan 65^\circ$ and $\tan 66^\circ$

$$\begin{aligned} \tan 66^\circ &= 2.2460 \\ \tan 65^\circ &= \underline{2.1445} \\ d &= .1015 \end{aligned}$$

$$\begin{aligned} \tan A &= 2.2054 \\ \tan 65^\circ &= \underline{2.1445} \\ d' &= .0609 \\ \frac{d'}{d} &= \frac{.0609}{.1015} = .6 \\ A &= 65.6^\circ \text{ or } 65^\circ 37' \end{aligned}$$

5. $\cos A = .9802$

.9802 is between $\cos 11^\circ$ and $\cos 12^\circ$

$$\begin{aligned} \cos 11^\circ &= .9816 \\ \cos 12^\circ &= \underline{.9781} \\ d &= .0035 \end{aligned}$$

$$\begin{aligned} \cos 11^\circ &= .9816 \\ \cos A &= \underline{.9802} \\ d' &= .0014 \\ \frac{d'}{d} &= \frac{.0014}{.0035} = .4 \\ A &= 11.4^\circ \text{ or } 11^\circ 25' \end{aligned}$$

6. $\sin A = .9941$

$.9941$ is between $\sin 83^\circ$ and $\sin 24^\circ$

$$\begin{aligned} \sin 84^\circ &= .9945 \\ \sin 83^\circ &= \underline{.9925} \\ d &= .0020 \end{aligned}$$

$$\begin{aligned} \sin A &= .9941 \\ \sin 83^\circ &= \underline{.9925} \\ d' &= .0016 \\ \frac{d'}{d} &= \frac{.0016}{.0020} = .8 \\ A &= 83.8^\circ \text{ or } 83^\circ 46' \end{aligned}$$

III 1.

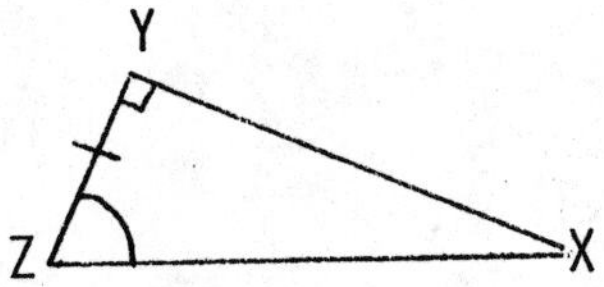

$\cos Z = \frac{ZY}{ZX}$

2.

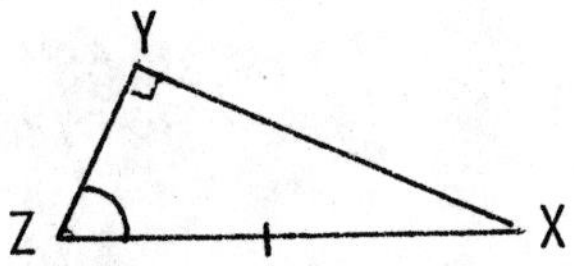

$\sin Z = \frac{XY}{ZX}$

3.

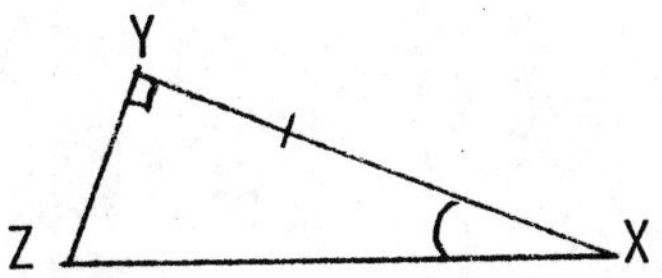

$\tan X = \frac{ZY}{XY}$

4.

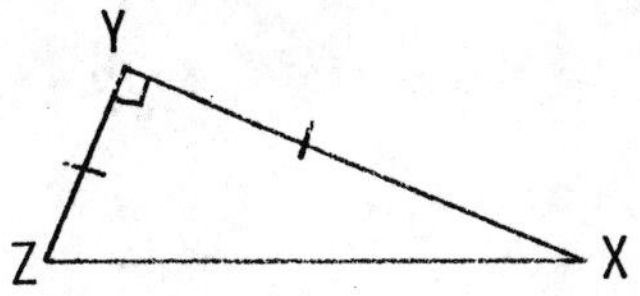

$\tan Z = \frac{XY}{ZY}$

5.

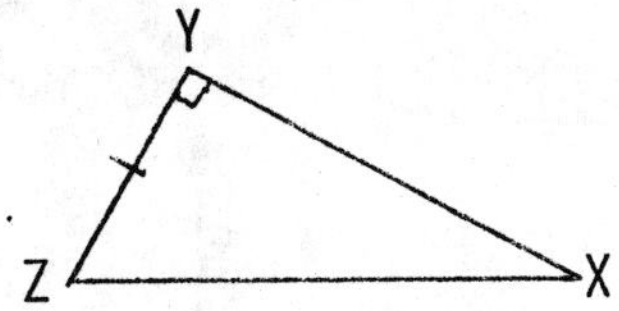

$\sin X = \frac{ZY}{ZX}$

IV 1.

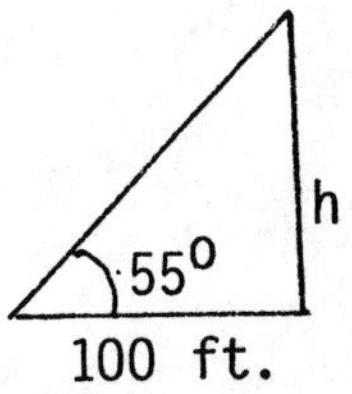

$$\begin{aligned} \tan 55^\circ &= \frac{h}{100} \\ h &= 100 \tan 55^\circ \\ h &= 100(1.4281) \\ h &= 143 \text{ ft.} \end{aligned}$$

2.

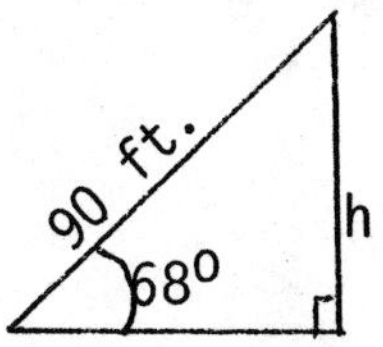

$$\begin{aligned} \sin 68^\circ &= \frac{h}{90} \\ h &= 90 \sin 68^\circ \\ h &= 90(.9272) \\ h &= 83.4 \text{ ft.} \end{aligned}$$

3.

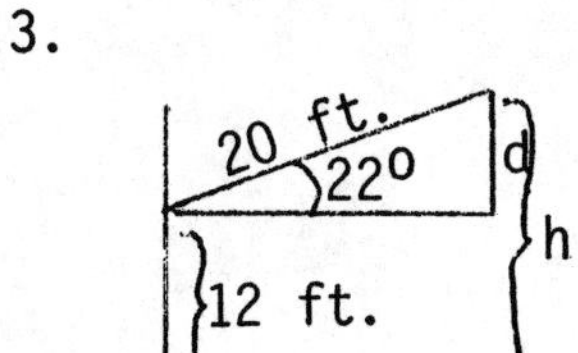

$$\begin{aligned} \sin 22^\circ &= \frac{d}{20} \\ d &= 20 \sin 22^\circ \\ d &= 20(.3746) \\ d &= 7.5 \text{ ft.} \end{aligned}$$

$$\begin{aligned} h &= 7.5 + 12 \\ h &= 19.5 \text{ ft.} \end{aligned}$$

4.

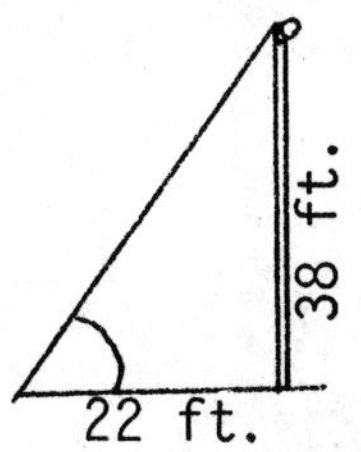

$$\begin{aligned} \tan A &= \frac{38}{22} \\ \tan A &= 1.7273 \end{aligned}$$

1.7273 is between $\tan 59^\circ$ and $\tan 60^\circ$ but closer to 60°

$A = 60^\circ$

Test B   Pages 333-334   Underlined ratios are accurate; workthroughs show interpolation (allow for discrepancy).

I 1. $\sin 27^{\circ} = .4540$ 2. $\tan 76^{\circ} = 4.0108$ 3. $\cos 58^{\circ} = .5299$

4. $\cos 38.2^{\circ} = \underline{.7859}$

$\cos 38^{\circ} = .7880$
$\cos 39^{\circ} = \underline{.7771}$
$d = .0109$
$.2d = .0022$

$\cos 38.2^{\circ} = .7880 - .0022$
$\cos 38.2^{\circ} = .7858$

5. $\sin 72.4^{\circ} = \underline{.9532}$

$\sin 73^{\circ} = .9563$
$\sin 72^{\circ} = \underline{.9511}$
$d = .0052$
$.4d = .0021$

$\sin 72.4^{\circ} = .9511 + .0021$
$\sin 72.4^{\circ} = .9532$

6. $\tan 21.6^{\circ} = \underline{.3959}$
$\tan 22^{\circ} = .4040$
$\tan 21^{\circ} = \underline{.3839}$
$d = .0201$
$.6d = .0121$

$\tan 21.6^{\circ} = .3839 + .0121$
$\tan 21.6^{\circ} = .3960$

7. $\tan 67^{\circ}42' = \tan 67.7^{\circ} = \underline{2.4383}$

$\tan 68^{\circ} = 2.4751$
$\tan 67^{\circ} = \underline{2.3559}$
$d = .1192$
$.7d = .0834$

$\tan 67.7^{\circ} = 2.3559 + .0834$
$\tan 67.7^{\circ} = 2.4393$

8. $\cos 18^{\circ}24' = \cos 18.4^{\circ} = \underline{.9489}$

$\cos 18^{\circ} = .9511$
$\cos 19^{\circ} = \underline{.9455}$
$d = .0056$
$.4d = .0022$

$\cos 18.4^{\circ} = .9511 - .0022$
$\cos 18.4^{\circ} = .9489$

9. $\sin 58^{\circ}36' = \sin 58.6^{\circ} = \underline{.8536}$

$\sin 59^{\circ} = .8572$
$\sin 58^{\circ} = \underline{.8480}$
$d = .0092$
$.6d = .0055$

$\sin 58.6^{\circ} = .8480 + .0055$
$\sin 58.6^{\circ} = .8535$

II 1. $A = 24^{\circ}$ 2. $A = 18^{\circ}$ 3. $A = 52^{\circ}$

4. $\tan A = 1.3568$

$\tan 54^{\circ} = 1.3764$
$\tan 53^{\circ} = \underline{1.3270}$
$d = .0494$

$\tan A = 1.3568$
$\tan 53^{\circ} = \underline{1.3270}$
$d' = .0298$
$\frac{d'}{d} = \frac{.0298}{.0494} = .6$
$A = 53.6^{\circ}$ or $53^{\circ}36.5'$

5. $\cos A = .9347$

$\cos 20^{\circ} = .9397$
$\cos 21^{\circ} = \underline{.9336}$
$d = .0061$

$\cos 20^{\circ} = .9397$
$\cos A = \underline{.9347}$
$d' = .0050$
$\frac{d'}{d} = \frac{.0050}{.0061} = .8$
$A = 20.8^{\circ}$ or $20^{\circ}49'$

6. $\sin A = .8520$

$$\begin{aligned}\sin 59^\circ &= .8572\\ \sin 58^\circ &= \underline{.8480}\\ d &= .0092\end{aligned}$$

$$\begin{aligned}\sin A &= .8520\\ \sin 58^\circ &= \underline{.8480}\\ d' &= .0040\end{aligned}$$

$$\frac{d'}{d} = \frac{.0040}{.0092} = .4$$

$$A = 58.4^\circ \text{ or } 58^\circ 26'$$

III 1.

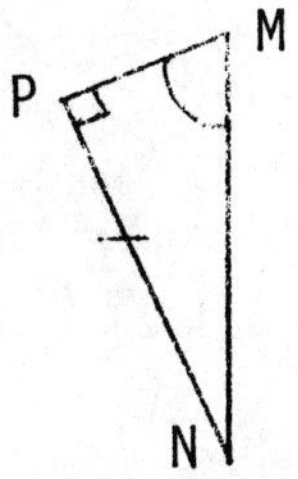

$\sin M = \frac{NP}{MN}$

2.

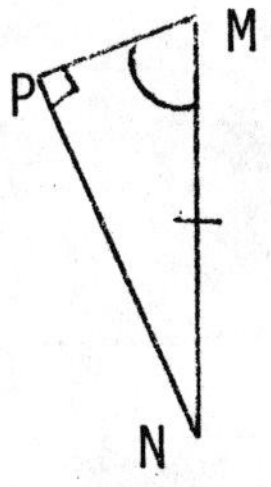

$\cos M = \frac{MP}{MN}$

3.

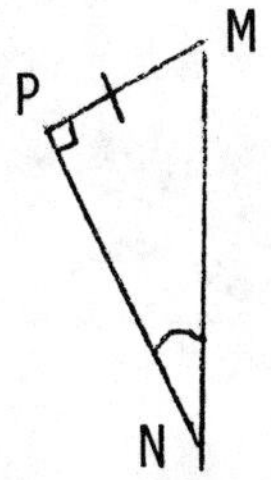

$\tan N = \frac{PM}{NP}$

4.

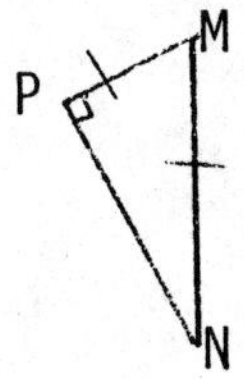

$\sin N = \frac{MP}{MN}$

5.

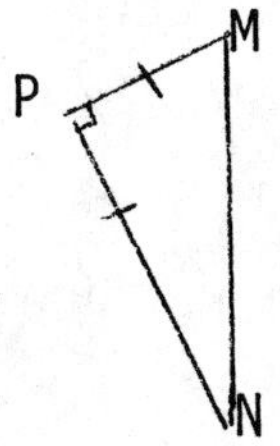

$\tan M = \frac{NP}{MP}$

IV 1.

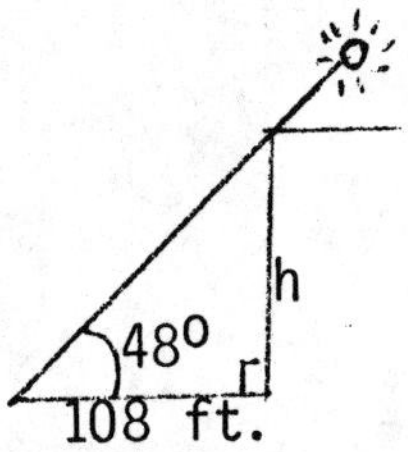

$$\begin{aligned}\tan 48^\circ &= \frac{h}{108}\\ h &= 108 \tan 48^\circ\\ h &= 108(1.1106)\\ h &= 120 \text{ ft.}\end{aligned}$$

2.

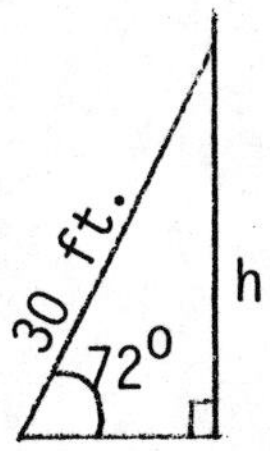

$$\begin{aligned}\sin 72^\circ &= \frac{h}{30}\\ h &= 30 \sin 72^\circ\\ h &= 30(.9511)\\ h &= 28.5 \text{ ft.}\end{aligned}$$

3.

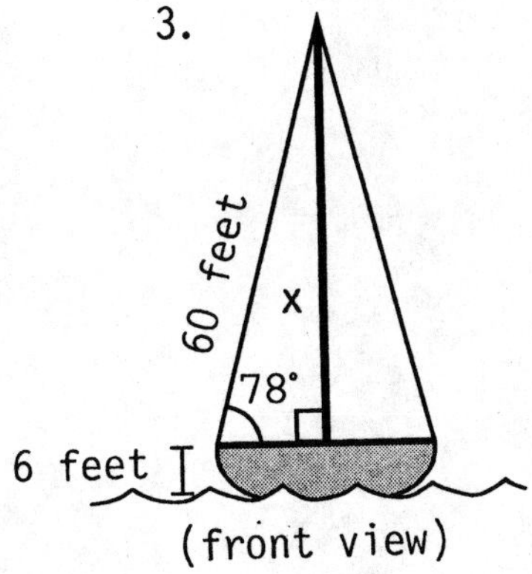

$$\begin{aligned}\sin 78^\circ &= \frac{x}{60}\\ x &= 60 \sin 78^\circ\\ x &= 60(.9781)\\ x &= 58.7 \text{ ft.}\end{aligned}$$

$$\begin{aligned}x + 6 &= 58.7 + 6\\ x + 6 &= 64.7 \text{ ft.}\end{aligned}$$

4.

$$\begin{aligned}\sin A &= \frac{300}{3960}\\ \sin A &= .0758\end{aligned}$$

.0758 is between $\sin 4^\circ$ and $\sin 5^\circ$

$$\begin{aligned}\sin 5^\circ &= .0872\\ \sin A &= \underline{.0758}\\ & .0114\end{aligned} \qquad \begin{aligned}\sin A &= .0758\\ \sin 4^\circ &= \underline{.0698}\\ & .0060\end{aligned}$$

A is closer to 4°

Test C   Page 334

1.

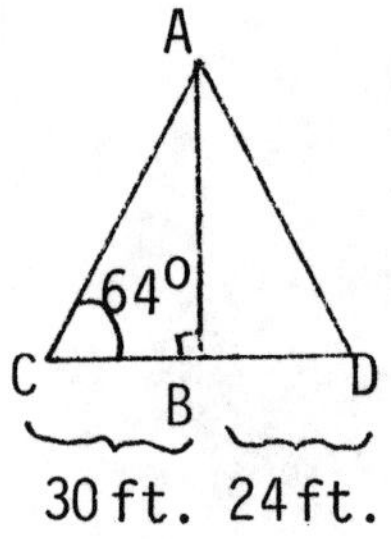

$\tan 64^\circ = \frac{AB}{30}$

$AB = 30 \tan 64^\circ$

$AB = 30(2.0503)$

$AB = 61.5$ ft.

$\tan D = \frac{61.5}{24}$

$\tan D = 2.5625$

$\tan 69^\circ = 2.6051$

$\tan 68^\circ = 2.4751$

$d = .1300$

$\tan D = 2.5625$

$\tan 68^\circ = 2.4751$

$d' = .0874$

$\frac{d'}{d} = \frac{.0874}{.1300} = .7$

$\angle D = 68.7^\circ$

2.

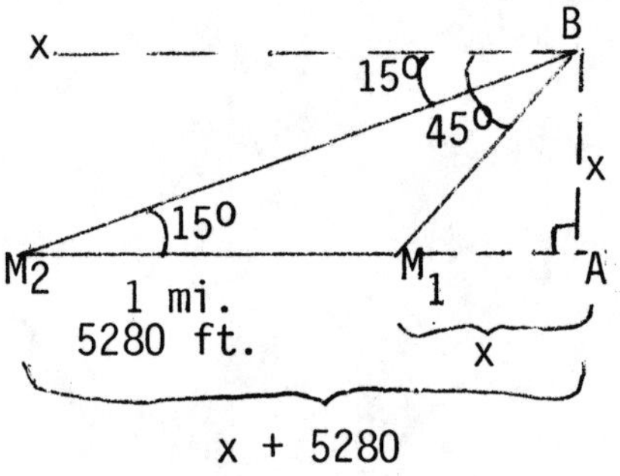

$\angle M_2BM_1 = 45^\circ - 15^\circ = 30^\circ$

$\angle ABM_1 = 90^\circ - 45^\circ = 45^\circ$

$\angle ABM_2 = 30^\circ + 45^\circ = 75^\circ$

$\angle M_2 = 90 - \angle ABM_2 = 90 - 75 = 15^\circ$

$\tan M_2 = \frac{x}{x + 5280}$

$\tan 15^\circ = \frac{x}{x + 5280}$

$.2679(x + 5280) = x$

$.2679x + 1415 = x$

$.7321x = 1415$

$x = 1933$ ft.

3.

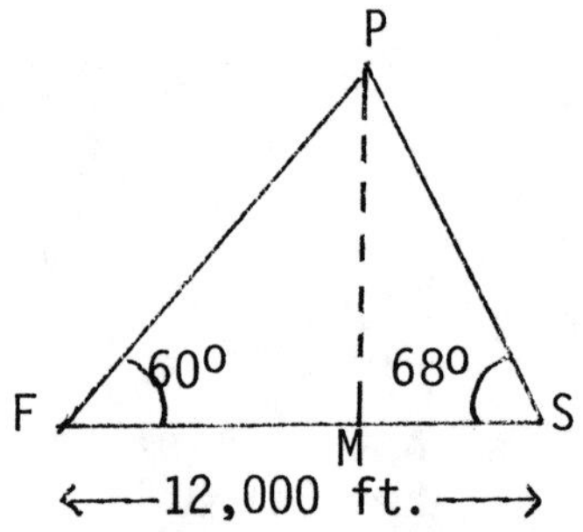

let FM = x, then SM = 12,000 - x

$\tan 68^\circ = \frac{PM}{12{,}000 - x}$

$2.4751(12{,}000 - x) = PM$

$PM = 29{,}701 - 2.4751x$

$\tan 60^\circ = \frac{PM}{X}$

$\tan 60^\circ = \frac{29{,}701 - 2.4751x}{x}$

$1.7321x = 29{,}701 - 2.4751x$

$4.2072x = 29{,}701$

$x \approx 7060$ ft. from F to M

$\tan 60^\circ = \frac{PM}{X}$

$1.7321 = \frac{PM}{7060}$

$PM \approx 12{,}230$ ft.

4.

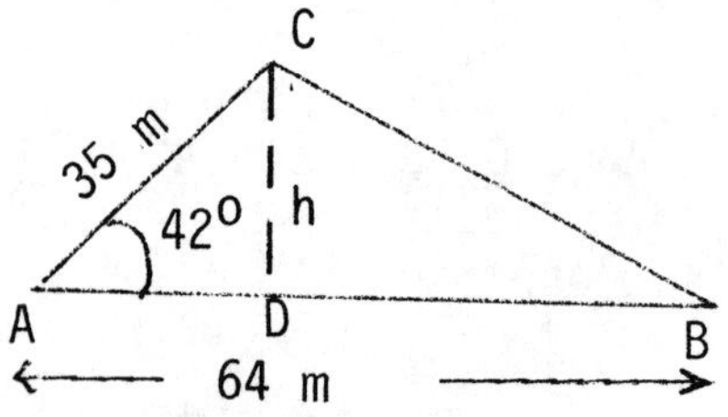

$\sin 42^\circ = \frac{h}{35}$

$h = .6691(35)$

$h = 23.4$ m

$A = \frac{1}{2} bh$

$A = \frac{1}{2}(64)(23.4)$

$A = 749$ sq. meters

Evaluation Exercises Page 336

1. $4r^2s + 7rs^2 \qquad r = 3,\ s = 4$

$= 4(3^2)(4) + 7(3)(4^2)$
$= 4(9)(4) + 7(3)(16)$
$= 144 + 336$
$= 480$

2. $5x^2y + 7xy + y^2 \qquad x = 7,\ y = 5$

$= 5(7^2)(5) + 7(7)(5) + 5^2$
$= 5(49)(5) + 245 + 25$
$= 1225 + 245 + 25$
$= 1495$

3. $\frac{m^2}{4} + mn + \frac{n^2}{2} \qquad m = 8,\ n = 4$

$= \frac{8^2}{4} + 8(4) + \frac{4^2}{2}$
$= \frac{64}{4} + 32 + \frac{16}{2}$
$= 16 + 32 + 8$
$= 56$

4. $\frac{3a^2b}{2} + ab + 2ab^2 \qquad a = 6,\ b = 3$

$= \frac{3(6^2)(3)}{2} + 6(3) + 2(6)(3^2)$
$= \frac{3(36)(3)}{2} + 18 + 2(6)(9)$
$= 162 + 18 + 108$
$= 288$

5. $4rs + 6r + 7s$
$r = 3.2,\ s = 4.5$
$= 4(3.2)(4.5) + 6(3.2) + 7(4.5)$
$= 57.6 + 19.2 + 31.5$
$= 108.3$

6. $9x + 7y + 3.25$
$x = 7.25,\ y = 4.75$
$= 9(7.25) + 7(4.75) + 3.25$
$= 65.25 + 33.25 + 3.25$
$= 101.75$

7. $\frac{3m}{2} + \frac{6m}{n} + 2n \qquad m = 8.2,\ n = 6.4$

$= \frac{3(8.2)}{2} + \frac{6(8.2)}{6.4} + 2(6.4)$

$= 3(4.1) + \frac{49.2}{6.4} + 12.8$

$= 12.3 + 7.6875 + 12.8$

$= 32.7875$

8. $\frac{6a}{2b} + \frac{3a^2b}{2b} + ab \qquad a = 4.8,\ b = 3.2$

$= \frac{6(4.8)}{2(3.2)} + \frac{3(4.8)^2(\cancel{3.2})}{2(\cancel{3.2})} + 4.8(3.2)$

$= 3(1.5) + \frac{3(23.04)}{2} + 15.36$

$= 4.5 + 34.56 + 15.36$

$= 54.42$

9. $d = vt$
$d = (220)(30)$
$d = 6600$ ft.

10. $d = vt$
$d = (8.2)(11)$
$d = 90.2$ mi.

11. $d = vt$
$d = 110(75)$
$d = 8250$ ft.

12. $d = \frac{1}{2}gt^2$
$d = \frac{1}{2}(32.16)(5^2)$
$d = 16.08(25)$
$d = 402$ ft.

13. $d = \frac{1}{2}gt^2$
$d = \frac{1}{2}(32.16)(4^2)$
$d = (16.08)(16)$
$d = 257.28$ ft.

$d = \frac{1}{2}(9.8)(4^2)$
$d = 4.9(16)$
$d = 78.4$ meters

14. $d = \frac{1}{2}gt^2$
$d = \frac{1}{2}(9.8)(3^2)$
$d = 4.9(9)$
$d = 44.1$ meters

Graphic Representation Exercises Pages 337-338

1.

High School Senior Class

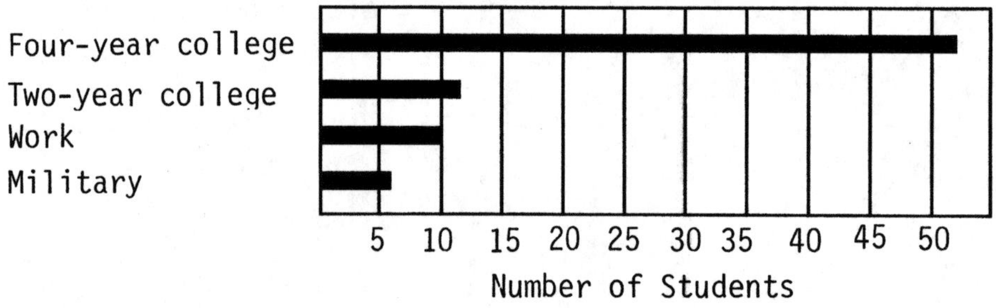

2.

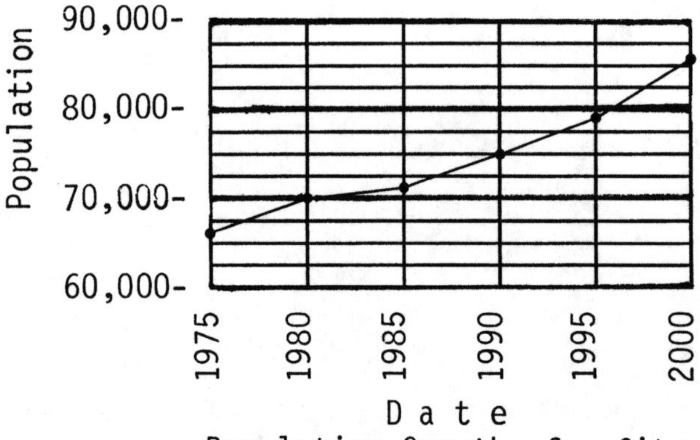

Population Growth of a City

Estimated Population
1978 - 68,000
1989 - 74,000
1997 - 83,000
2001 - 87,000
2004 - 92,000

3. Answers will vary.

4.

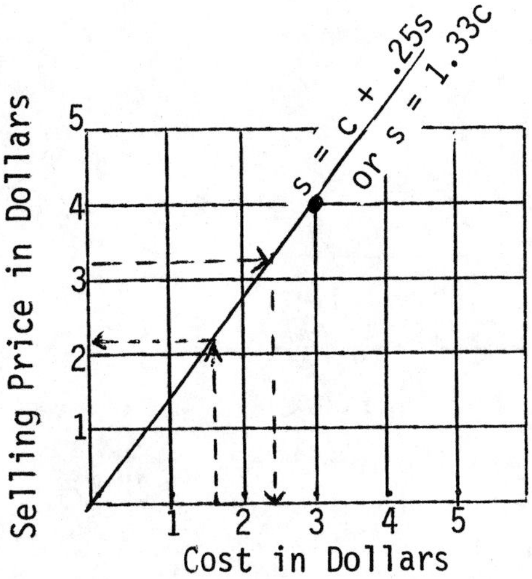

\$2.40; \$2.13

c	s
0	0
3	4
1.5	2

5.

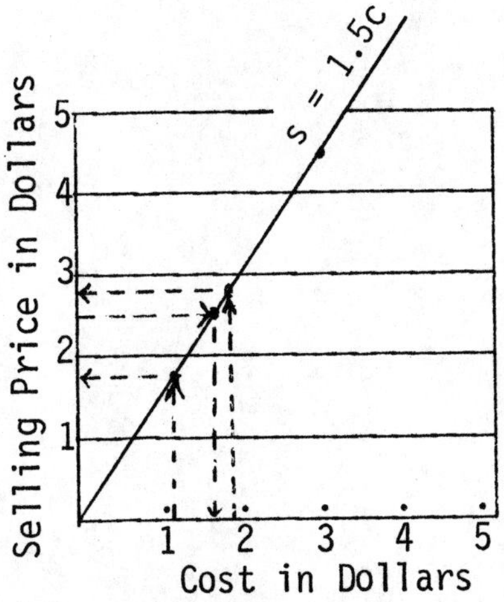

\$1.88, \$2.85, \$1.67

6.

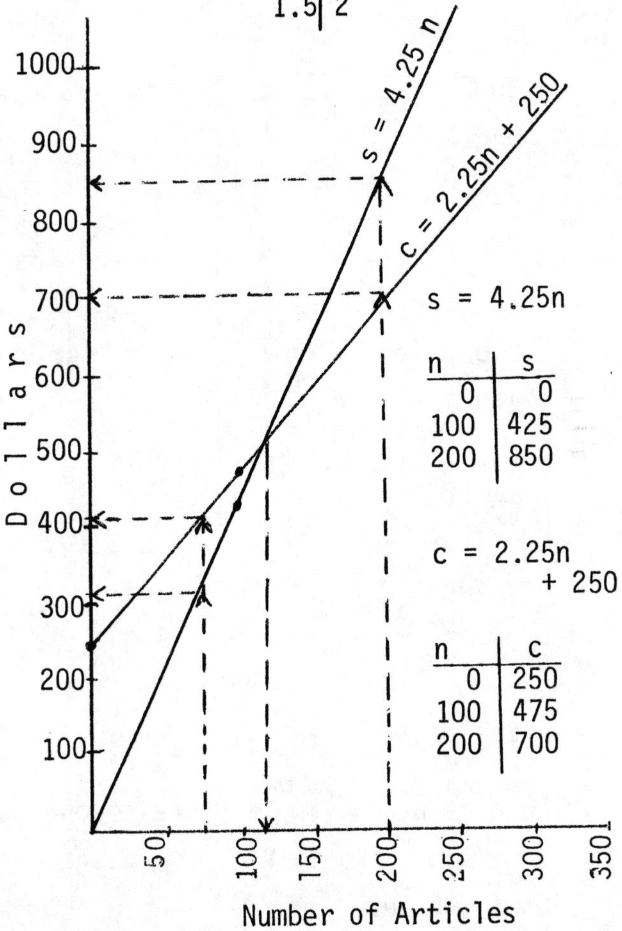

s = 4.25n

n	s
0	0
100	425
200	850

c = 2.25n + 250

n	c
0	250
100	475
200	700

For 75 articles \$318.75 - \$418.75 = -\$100 loss of \$100
For 200 articles \$850 - \$700 = \$150 gain
n = 125 articles when cost = sales
\$250 is the preparation cost

7.

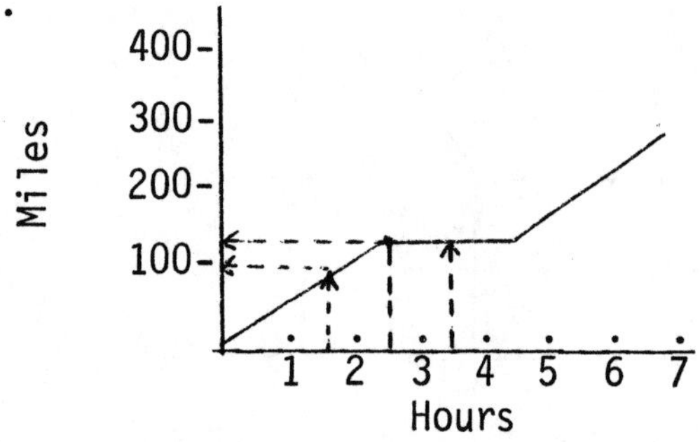

$d = 54t$

t	d
0	0
2.5	135

94.5 mi., 135 mi.

8.

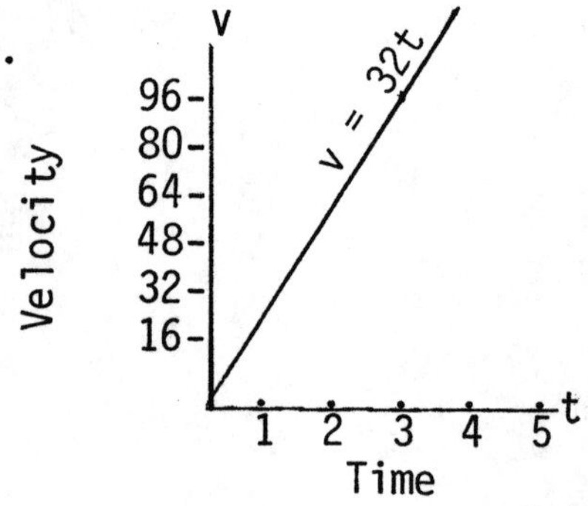

$v = 32t$

t	v
0	0
1	32
2	64
3	96

v increases by 32 for every increase of 1 in t.

9.

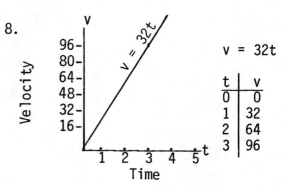

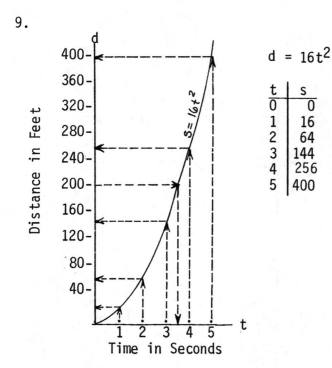

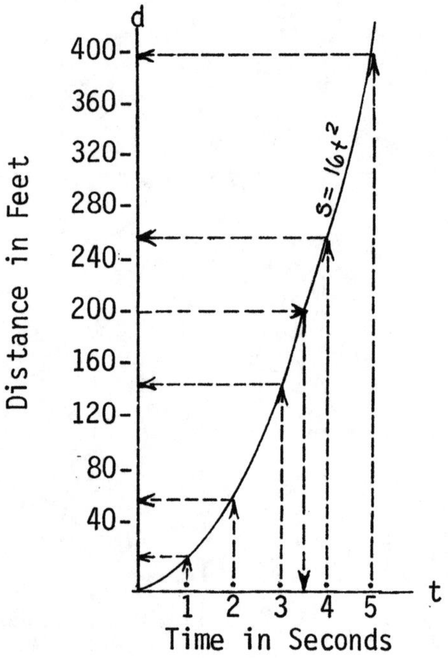

$d = 16t^2$

t	s
0	0
1	16
2	64
3	144
4	256
5	400

16 ft., 64 ft., 144 ft., 256 ft.

The distance during any one second increases by 32 ft. for each second the object has fallen.

About 3.5 sec.

Addition and Subtraction Exercises   Pages 338-339

1. $a^2 - c^2 + b^2 + a^2 + c^2$
   $= 2a^2 + b^2$

2. $5r - 6s + t - r + 5s$
   $= 4r - s + t$

3. $x^2z - 5y^2 + 3x^2z + y^2$
   $= 4x^2z - 4y^2$

4. $x^3 - 2y^3 - z^3 + 2y^3 - 4z^3$
   $= x^3 - 5z^3$

5. $ab + bc - bc - ab$
   $= 0$

6. $c^2d^2 + a^2b^2 - 2a^2b^2 - c^2d^2$
   $= -a^2b^2$

7. $x + 3y - z - 4y - 5x + 3z + 4x + y - 5z$
   $= -3z$

8. $b^2 + a^2c^2 - 5d^2 - 3a^2c^2 + 4b^2 + 3d^2 + 2a^2c^2 - b^2$
   $= 4b^2 - 2d^2$

9.
$$\begin{array}{rrrr} 2a & +\ b & & \\ & 3b & -\ c & \\ -2a & & & +\ d \\ & & c & +\ d \\ & b & & -\ d \\ \hline & 5b & & +\ d \end{array}$$

10.
$$\begin{array}{rrr} \frac{1}{4}x & +\ \frac{1}{2}y & -\ z \\ \frac{1}{2}x & -\ y & +\ \frac{1}{4}z \\ x & +\ \frac{1}{4}y & +\ \frac{1}{2}z \\ \hline \frac{7}{4}x & -\ \frac{1}{4}y & -\ \frac{1}{4}z \end{array}$$

11. $9x - 8y - (5x + y)$
    $= 9x - 8y - 5x - y$
    $= 4x - 9y$

12. $7c + 6d - (3c - 4d)$
    $= 7c + 6d - 3c + 4d$
    $= 4c + 10d$

13. $-5p + q - (4p - 4q)$
    $= -5p + q - 4p + 4q$
    $= -9p + 5q$

14. $2x - 9y - (-3x + y)$
    $= 2x - 9y + 3x - y$
    $= 5x - 10y$

15. $5m + n - (-m + 6n)$
    $= 5m + n + m - 6n$
    $= 6m - 5n$

16. $10x + 3y - (18x - 7y)$
    $= 10x + 3y - 18x + 7y$
    $= -8x + 10y$

17. $-12a - 5b - (7a + 2b)$
    $= -12a - 5b - 7a - 2b$
    $= -19a - 7b$

18. $16c + 9d - (-10c - 5d)$
    $= 16c + 9d + 10c + 5d$
    $= 26c + 14d$

19. $15p - 8q - (18p - 4q)$
    $= 15p - 8q - 18p + 4q$
    $= -3p - 4q$

20. $14x - 10y - (25y + 6x)$
    $= 14x - 10y - 25y - 6x$
    $= 8x - 35y$

21. $10m - 5n - (5n - 10m)$
    $= 10m - 5n - 5n + 10m$
    $= 20m - 10n$

22. $r + s - v - (r - s + v)$
    $= r + s - v - r + s - v$
    $= 2s - 2v$

23. $x + y - z - (3x - y + z)$
    $= x + y - z - 3x + y - z$
    $= -2x + 2y - 2z$

24. $2a + b + c - (a + 2b + c)$
    $= 2a + b + c - a - 2b - c$
    $= a - b$

25. $x - 2y + z - (x + 2y + z)$
    $= x - 2y + z - x - 2y - z$
    $= -4y$

26. $x^m - 2x^my^n + y^n - (x^my^n + y^n)$
    $= x^m - 2x^my^n + y^n - x^my^n - y^n$
    $= x^m - 3x^my^n$

Parentheses Exercises   Pages 339-340

1. $a + [b - (c - d)]$
$= a + [b - c + d]$
$= a + b - c + d$

2. $x - [x + (a + b)]$
$= x - [x + a + b]$
$= x - x - a - b$
$= -a - b$

3. $2a - (a - b) + (a + b)$
$= 2a - a + b + a + b$
$= 2a + 2b$

4. $4x - (x - y) - (y - z)$
$= 4x - x + y - y + z$
$= 3x + z$

5. $3ab + a^2 - (a^2 + 2ab + b^2)$
$= 3ab + a^2 - a^2 - 2ab - b^2$
$= ab - b^2$

6. $m + n - [(m + n) - (m - n)]$
$= m + n - [m + n - m + n]$
$= m + n - 2n$
$= m - n$

7. $3a - [-2a + (3a + 2) - (4a - 4) + 6a]$
$= 3a - [-2a + 3a + 2 - 4a + 4 + 6a]$
$= 3a - [3a + 6]$
$= 3a - 3a - 6$
$= -6$

8. $2.2x - [1.2x + 4.1y - (2.0x - 7.1y) + 3.5x]$
$= 2.2x - [1.2x + 4.1y - 2.0x + 7.1y + 3.5x]$
$= 2.2x - [2.7x + 11.2y]$
$= 2.2x - 2.7x - 11.2y$
$= -.5x - 11.2y$

9. $5.6m - 3.5n - (2.4m - 3.2n) + [6.7m - (2.4m + 1.5n)]$
$= 5.6m - 3.5n - 2.4m + 3.2n + 6.7m - 2.4m - 1.5n$
$= 7.5m - 1.8n$

10. $x^2 - y^2 - 2yz - z^2$
$= x^2 - (y^2 + 2yz + z^2)$

11. $m^2 + a^2 + 2ab + b^2$
$= m^2 + (a^2 + 2ab + b^2)$

12. $r^2 - 2rs + s^2 - m^2 - 2mn - n^2$
$= r^2 - 2rs + s^2 - (m^2 + 2mn + n^2)$

13. $a^2 - 2ab + b^2 - c^2 + 2cd - d^2$
$= a^2 - 2ab + b^2 - (c^2 - 2cd + d^2)$

14. $4s - 10s^2 - 3st + t$
$= 4s - (10s^2 + 3st - t)$

15. $ay^3 + by^2 + cy - dy^3 - dy^2 + dy$
$= ay^3 - dy^3 + by^2 - dy^2 + cy + dy$
$= (ay^3 - dy^3) + (by^2 - dy^2) + (cy + dy)$

16. $ay^4 + by^2 - cy^4 - cy^2$
$= ay^4 - cy^4 + by^2 - cy^2$
$= (ay^4 - cy^4) + (by^2 - cy^2)$

17. $4.2y^2 - 3.7y + ay^2 - by$
$= 4.2y^2 + ay^2 - 3.7y - by$
$= (4.2y^2 + ay^2) - (3.7y + by)$

18. $my^4 - my^3 - my^2 + ny^4 - ny^3 + ny^2$
$= my^4 + ny^4 - my^3 - ny^3 - my^2 + ny^2$
$= (my^4 + ny^4) - (my^3 + ny^3) - (my^2 - ny^2)$

19. $ry^3 + sy - sy^3 + ry$
$= ry^3 - sy^3 + ry + sy$
$= (ry^3 - sy^3) + (ry + sy)$

20. $a^2 + b^2 - x^2 - y^2 - 2ab + 2xy$
$= a^2 - 2ab + b^2 - x^2 + 2xy - y^2$
$= (a^2 - 2ab + b^2) - (x^2 - 2xy + y^2)$

21. $a^2 - 2b^2 - x^2 + y^2 + ab$
$= a^2 + ab - 2b^2 - x^2 + y^2$
$= (a^2 + ab - 2b^2) - (x^2 - y^2)$

Multiplication Exercises Pages 340-341

1. $$\begin{array}{r} -4a^2by^3 \\ -3ab^4y^5 \\ \hline 12a^3b^5y^8 \end{array}$$

2. $$\begin{array}{r} 6x^ny^b \\ -x^my^a \\ \hline -6x^{m+n}y^{a+b} \end{array}$$

3. $$\begin{array}{r} 9a^3b^2y^2 \\ 2a^{-1}b^{-1}y \\ \hline 18a^2by^3 \end{array}$$

4. $$\begin{array}{l} 3x^{-1}y^2 \\ 2x^2y^{-3} \\ \hline 6xy^{-1} = \dfrac{6x}{y} \end{array}$$

5. $$\begin{array}{r} 2y^{2n}x \\ -xy^n \\ \hline -2x^2y^{3n} \end{array}$$

6. $$\begin{array}{l} x^{r-1} \\ x \\ \hline x^r \end{array}$$

7. $$\begin{array}{r} 4a^2b \\ -.5ab \\ \hline -2a^3b^2 \end{array}$$

8. $$\begin{array}{r} 8b^{m+1} \\ -4b^{n-1} \\ \hline -32b^{m+n} \end{array}$$

9. $$\begin{array}{r} y^{b+c} \\ -y^{b-c} \\ \hline -y^{2b} \end{array}$$

10. $$\begin{array}{r} 4x^{n+3} \\ 7x^{n-4} \\ \hline 28x^{2n-1} \end{array}$$

11. $$\begin{array}{r} -a^2b^mc^n \\ -a^3b^nc^m \\ \hline a^5b^{m+n}c^{m+n} \end{array}$$

12. $$\begin{array}{r} x^ay^{b+1}z \\ x^by^{a-1}z \\ \hline x^{a+b}y^{a+b}z^2 \end{array}$$

13. $(-4)(-5ax)(4ax^2) = 80a^2x^3$

14. $(-6b)(-a^2b^2)(-ab^2) = -6a^3b^5$

15. $(-2xy)(-4x^3y)(4x^2)(8y^3) = 256x^6y^5$

16. $(-3^2)(-2^3)(2^2\cdot 3)(2\cdot 3^2)$
$= (-9)(-8)(12)(18)$
$= 15{,}552$

17. $$\begin{array}{r} 5bc^2 + b^3 \\ 2b^2 \\ \hline 10b^3c^2 + 2b^5 \end{array}$$

18. $$\begin{array}{r} 4a^2 - 3ab \\ 4ab \\ \hline 16a^3b - 12a^2b^2 \end{array}$$

19. $$\begin{array}{r} x^2y^3 - z^3 \\ -xyz \\ \hline -x^3y^4z + xyz^4 \end{array}$$

20. $$\begin{array}{r} 2rs - t^3 \\ 4r^2s^2 \\ \hline 8r^3s^3 - 4r^2s^2t^3 \end{array}$$

21. $$\begin{array}{r} 6b^2d^3 - cd \\ 3cd \\ \hline 18b^2cd^4 - 3c^2d^2 \end{array}$$

22. $$\begin{array}{r} x + 7 \\ x - 5 \\ \hline x^2 + 7x \quad\quad \\ -5x - 35 \\ \hline x^2 + 2x - 35 \end{array}$$

23. $$\begin{array}{r} 5x + 8 \\ 3x + 6 \\ \hline 15x^2 + 24x \quad\quad \\ 30x + 48 \\ \hline 15x^2 + 54x + 48 \end{array}$$

24. $$\begin{array}{r} 4y - 9z \\ 8y - 5z \\ \hline 32y^2 - 72yz \quad\quad \\ -20yz + 45z^2 \\ \hline 32y^2 - 92yz + 45z^2 \end{array}$$

25. $$\begin{array}{r} x^2 + xy + y^2 \\ x - y \\ \hline x^3 + x^2y + xy^2 \quad\quad \\ -x^2y - xy^2 - y^3 \\ \hline x^3 \quad\quad\quad\quad - y^3 \end{array}$$

26. $$\begin{array}{r} 3c^2 - 2cd + 5d^2 \\ c^2 - cd - d^2 \\ \hline 3c^4 - 2c^3d + 5c^2d^2 \quad\quad\quad\quad \\ -3c^3d + 2c^2d^2 - 5cd^3 \quad\quad \\ -3c^2d^2 + 2cd^3 - 5d^4 \\ \hline 3c^4 - 5c^3d + 4c^2d^2 - 3cd^3 - 5d^4 \end{array}$$

27. $$\begin{array}{r} x^4y^4 + x^2y^2z^2 + z^4 \\ x^2y^2 - z^2 \\ \hline x^6y^6 + x^4y^4z^2 + x^2y^2z^4 \quad\quad \\ -x^4y^4z^2 - x^2y^2z^4 - z^6 \\ \hline x^6y^6 \quad\quad\quad\quad\quad\quad - z^6 \end{array}$$

28. $$\begin{array}{r} a^{-2} + b^{-2} \\ a^{-2} - b^{-2} \\ \hline a^{-4} + a^{-2}b^{-2} \quad\quad \\ -a^{-2}b^{-2} - b^{-4} \\ \hline a^{-4} \quad\quad\quad - b^{-4} \end{array} \text{ or } \frac{1}{a^4} - \frac{1}{b^4}$$

29. $$\begin{array}{r} a^4 + 3a^2 - 2 \\ a^4 - 4a^2 + 1 \\ \hline a^8 + 3a^6 - 2a^4 \quad\quad\quad\quad \\ -4a^6 - 12a^4 + 8a^2 \quad\quad \\ a^4 + 3a^2 - 2 \\ \hline a^8 - a^6 - 13a^4 + 11a^2 - 2 \end{array}$$

30. $$\begin{array}{l} x^2 + 4y^2 + 3z^2 \\ \underline{x^2 - 2y^2 - 3z^2} \\ x^4 + 4x^2y^2 + 3x^2z^2 \\ \qquad - 2x^2y^2 \qquad\qquad - 8y^4 - 6y^2z^2 \\ \qquad\qquad - 3x^2z^2 \qquad\qquad - 12y^2z^2 - 9z^4 \\ \hline x^4 + 2x^2y^2 \qquad\qquad - 8y^4 - 18y^2z^2 - 9z^4 \end{array}$$

31. $$\begin{array}{l} x^2 - 1 + x^{-2} \\ \underline{x^2 + 1 + x^{-2}} \\ x^4 - x^2 + 1 \\ \qquad x^2 - 1 + x^{-2} \\ \qquad\qquad 1 - x^{-2} + x^{-4} \\ \hline x^4 \qquad + 1 \qquad + x^{-4} \end{array}$$

or $x^4 + 1 + \frac{1}{x^4}$

<u>Division Exercises</u> Pages 341-342

1. $4^5 \div 4 = 4^{5-1} = 4^4 = 256$

2. $2^7 \div 2^0 = 2^{7-0} = 2^7 = 128$

3. $5^8 \div 5^3 = 5^{8-3} = 5^5 = 3125$

4. $-21 \div 7 = -3$

5. $x^5 \div x^3 = x^{5-3} = x^2$

6. $-c^5 \div c = -c^{5-1} = -c^4$

7. $-a^6 \div (-a) = a^{6-1} = a^5$

8. $-8b^4 \div \frac{1}{2}b^2 = -16b^{4-2} = -16b^2$

9. $.6a^{2n} \div .2a^n = 3a^{2n-n} = 3a^n$

10. $12c^4d^4 \div 2cd^5 = 6c^{4-1}d^{4-5} = \frac{6c^3}{d}$

11. $\frac{1}{2}x^3z^3 \div \frac{1}{4}xz = 2x^{3-1}z^{3-1} = 2x^2z^2$

12. $-x^my^m \div x^ny^n = -x^{m-n}y^{m-n}$

13. $\frac{1}{3}x^4y^6z^5 \div 4y^3z = \frac{1}{12}x^4y^{6-3}z^{5-1} = \frac{1}{12}x^4y^3z^4$

14. $9(a + b)^3 \div 3(a + b) = 3(a + b)^{3-1} = 3(a + b)^2$

15. $\frac{8xz^3 + 4x^3z}{4xz} = \frac{8xz^3}{4xz} + \frac{4x^3z}{4xz} = 2z^2 + x^2$

16. $\frac{-x + y - z + u}{-1} = x - y + z - u$

17. $\frac{.6x^2 - .8xy + .4}{.2} = \frac{.6x^2}{.2} - \frac{.8xy}{.2} + \frac{.4}{.2} = 3x^2 - 4xy + 2$

18. $\frac{ab^2 + a^2b - a^2b^2}{\frac{1}{2}ab} = \frac{ab^2}{\frac{1}{2}ab} + \frac{a^2b}{\frac{1}{2}ab} - \frac{a^2b^2}{\frac{1}{2}ab} = 2a + 2b - 2ab$

19. $\frac{a^{2n} - 5a^n + 6a^{3n} + 3a^{4n} + 4a^{5n}}{a^n} = a^{2n-n} - 5a^{n-n} + 6a^{3n-n} + 3a^{4n-n} + 4a^{5n-n}$

$= a^n - 5 + 6a^{2n} + 3a^{3n} + 4a^{4n}$

20. $\frac{3(a + b) - 9(a + b)^2 - 6(a + b)^3}{a + b} = 3(a + b)^{1-1} - 9(a + b)^{2-1} - 6(a + b)^{3-1}$

$= 3 - 9(a + b) - 6(a + b)^2$

The check is left for the teacher.

21.

$$\begin{array}{r|l} & 3x - 5 \\ \cline{2-2} 2x - 7 & 6x^2 - 31x + 35 \\ & 6x^2 - 21x \\ \cline{2-2} & \quad - 10x + 35 \\ & \quad - 10x + 35 \\ \cline{2-2} \end{array}$$

22.

$$\begin{array}{r|l} & a^n + 4b \\ \cline{2-2} a^n + b & a^{2n} + 5a^nb + 4b^2 \\ & a^{2n} + a^nb \\ \cline{2-2} & \quad 4a^nb + 4b^2 \\ & \quad 4a^nb + 4b^2 \\ \cline{2-2} \end{array}$$

23.

$$\begin{array}{r|l} & 1.6x^2 + x - .3 \\ \cline{2-2} 2.5x - 2 & 4x^3 - .7x^2 - 2.75x + .6 \\ & 4x^3 - 3.2x^2 \\ \cline{2-2} & \quad 2.5x^2 - 2.75x + .6 \\ & \quad 2.5x^2 - 2x \\ \cline{2-2} & \qquad - .75x + .6 \\ & \qquad - .75x + .6 \\ \cline{2-2} \end{array}$$

24.

$$\begin{array}{r|l} & a^2 - 5a - 1 + \frac{-1}{2a^2 + 5a - 1} \\ \cline{2-2} 2a^2 + 5a - 1 & 2a^4 - 5a^3 - 28a^2 \\ & 2a^4 + 5a^3 - a^2 \\ \cline{2-2} & \quad -10a^3 - 27a^2 \\ & \quad -10a^3 - 25a^2 + 5a \\ \cline{2-2} & \qquad - 2a^2 - 5a \\ & \qquad - 2a^2 - 5a + 1 \\ \cline{2-2} & \qquad\qquad - 1 \end{array}$$

25.

$$\begin{array}{r|l} & 3x - 2 + \frac{15x - 9}{x^2 + x - 1} \\ \cline{2-2} x^2 + x - 1 & 3x^3 + x^2 + 10x - 7 \\ & 3x^3 + 3x^2 - 3x \\ \cline{2-2} & \quad - 2x^2 + 13x - 7 \\ & \quad - 2x^2 - 2x + 2 \\ \cline{2-2} & \qquad 15x - 9 \end{array}$$

*26.

$$\begin{array}{r|l} & x^{a+1} + x^a + x^{a-1} \\ \cline{2-2} x^2 - x + 1 & x^{a+3} + 0x^{a+2} + x^{a+1} + 0x^a + x^{a-1} \\ & x^{a+3} - x^{a+2} + x^{a+1} \\ \cline{2-2} & \quad x^{a+2} + 0 + 0x^a + x^{a-1} \\ & \quad x^{a+2} - x^{a+1} + x^a \\ \cline{2-2} & \qquad x^{a+1} - x^a + x^{a-1} \\ & \qquad x^{a+1} - x^a + x^{a-1} \\ \cline{2-2} \end{array}$$

Key to Supplementary Exercises, page 342

27.

$$
\begin{array}{r|l}
 & a^5 - a^4b + a^3b^2 - a^2b^3 + ab^4 \\ \hline
a + b & a^6 + 0a^5b + 0a^4b^2 + 0a^3b^3 + 0a^2b^4 + 0ab^5 + b^6 \\
 & \underline{a^6 + a^5b} \\
 & \quad - a^5b + 0a^4b^2 \\
 & \quad \underline{- a^5b - a^4b^2} \\
 & \qquad a^4b^2 + 0a^3b^3 \\
 & \qquad \underline{a^4b^2 + a^3b^3} \\
 & \qquad\quad - a^3b^3 + 0a^2b^4 \\
 & \qquad\quad \underline{- a^3b^3 - a^2b^4} \\
 & \qquad\qquad a^2b^4 + 0ab^5 \\
 & \qquad\qquad \underline{a^2b^4 + ab^5} \\
 & \qquad\qquad\quad - ab^5
\end{array}
$$

Special Cases in Multiplication   Pages 342-343

1. $(3a + b)^2 = (3a)^2 + 2(3a)(b) + b^2$
   $= 9a^2 + 6ab + b^2$

2. $(4x + 7)^2 = (4x)^2 + 2(4x)(7) + 7^2$
   $= 16x^2 + 56x + 49$

3. $(5y + 3z)^2 = (5y)^2 + 2(5y)(3z) + (3z)^2$
   $= 25y^2 + 30yz + 9z^2$

4. $(2x^2 + y^2)^2 = (2x^2)^2 + 2(2x^2)(y^2) + (y^2)^2$
   $= 4x^4 + 4x^2y^2 + y^4$

5. $(3a^3 + 3b^3)^2 = (3a^3)^2 + 2(3a^3)(3b^3) + (3b^3)^2$
   $= 9a^6 + 18a^3b^3 + 9b^6$

6. $21^2 = (20 + 1)^2$
   $= 20^2 + 2(20)(1) + 1^2$
   $= 400 + 40 + 1$
   $= 441$

7. $32^2 = (30 + 2)^2$
   $= 30^2 + 2(30)(2) + 2^2$
   $= 900 + 120 + 4$
   $= 1024$

8. $41^2 = (40 + 1)^2$
   $= 40^2 + 2(40)(1) + 1^2$
   $= 1600 + 80 + 1$
   $= 1681$

9. $201^2 = (200 + 1)^2$
   $= 200^2 + 2(200)(1) + 1^2$
   $= 40{,}000 + 400 + 1$
   $= 40{,}401$

10. $102^2 = (100 + 2)^2$
    $= 100^2 + 2(100)(2) + 2^2$
    $= 10{,}000 + 400 + 4$
    $= 10{,}404$

11. $(3\frac{1}{2})^2 = (3 + \frac{1}{2})^2 = 3^2 + 2(3)(\frac{1}{2}) + (\frac{1}{2})^2$
    $= 9 + 3 + \frac{1}{4} = 12\frac{1}{4}$ or 12.25

12. $11.5^2 = (11 + .5)^2$
    $= 11^2 + 2(11)(.5) + (.5)^2$
    $= 121 + 11 + .25$
    $= 132.25$

13. $6.5^2 = (6 + .5)^2$
    $= 6^2 + 2(6)(.5) + (.5)^2$
    $= 36 + 6 + .25$
    $= 42.25$

14. $55^2 = (50 + 5)^2$
$= 50^2 + 2(50)(5) + 5^2$
$= 2500 + 500 + 25$
$= 3025$

15. $125^2 = (100 + 25)^2$
$= 100^2 + 2(100)(25) + 25^2$
$= 10{,}000 + 5000 + 625$
$= 15{,}625$

16. $(y^a + z^a)^2 = (y^a)^2 + 2(y^a)(z^a) + (z^a)^2$
$= y^{2a} + 2y^a z^a + z^{2a}$

17. $(\frac{1}{2}x + \frac{1}{3}y)^2 = (\frac{1}{2}x)^2 + 2(\frac{1}{2}x)(\frac{1}{3}y) + (\frac{1}{3}y)^2$
$= \frac{1}{4}x^2 + \frac{1}{3}xy + \frac{1}{9}y^2$

18. $(.3x + .5y)^2 = (.3x)^2 + 2(.3x)(.5y) + (.5y)^2$
$= .09x^2 + .3xy + .25y^2$

19. $(2c^a + 3d^a) = (2c^a)^2 + 2(2c^a)(3d^a) + (3d^a)^2$
$= 4c^{2a} + 12c^a d^a + 9d^{2a}$

20. $(1 + .03)^2 = 1^2 + 2(1)(.03) + (.03)^2$
$= 1 + .06 + .0009$
$= 1.0609$

21. $(x^2 - y^2)^2 = (x^2)^2 + 2(x^2)(-y^2) + (-y^2)^2$
$= x^4 - 2x^2y^2 + y^4$

22. $(2x - 4y)^2 = (2x)^2 + 2(2x)(-4y) + (-4y)^2$
$= 4x^2 - 16xy + 16y^2$

23. $(5y^2 - z^2)^2 = (5y^2)^2 + 2(5y^2)(-z^2) + (-z^2)^2$
$= 25y^4 - 10y^2z^2 + z^4$

24. $(x^3 - y^3)^2 = (x^3)^2 + 2(x^3)(-y^3) + (-y^3)^2$
$= x^6 - 2x^3y^3 + y^6$

25. $(\frac{1}{2}x - 2y)^2 = (\frac{1}{2}x)^2 + 2(\frac{1}{2}x)(-2y) + (-2y)^2$
$= \frac{1}{4}x^2 - 2xy + 4y^2$

26. $(5 - 3ab)^2 = 5^2 + 2(5)(-3ab) + (-3ab)^2$
$= 25 - 30ab + 9a^2b^2$

27. $(xy^a - z^a)^2 = (xy^a)^2 + 2(xy^a)(-z^a) + (-z^a)^2$
$= x^2y^{2a} - 2xy^a z^a + z^{2a}$

28. $(2b^m - c^n d)^2 = (2b^m)^2 + 2(2b^m)(-c^n d) + (-c^n d)^2$
$= 4b^{2m} - 4b^m c^n d + c^{2n} d^2$

29. $(.3x - 2.5y)^2 = (.3x)^2 + 2(.3x)(-2.5y) + (-2.5y)^2$
$= .09x^2 - 1.5xy + 6.25y^2$

30. $(x^{\frac{1}{2}} - 2b^{\frac{1}{2}})^2 = (x^{\frac{1}{2}})^2 + 2(x^{\frac{1}{2}})(-2b^{\frac{1}{2}}) + (-2b^{\frac{1}{2}})^2$
$= x - 4x^{\frac{1}{2}}b^{\frac{1}{2}} + 4b$

31. $19^2 = (20 - 1)^2$
$= 20^2 + 2(20)(-1) + (-1)^2$
$= 400 - 40 + 1$
$= 361$

32. $(1.05)^2 = (1 + .05)^2$
$= 1^2 + 2(1)(.05) + (.05)^2$
$= 1 + .10 + .0025$
$= 1.1025$

33. $1.045^2 = (1.05 - .005)^2$
$= (1.05)^2 + 2(1.05)(-.005) + (.005)^2$
$= 1.1025 - .0105 + .000025$
$= 1.092025$

34. $(a^2 - 5)(a^2 + 5) = (a^2)^2 - 5^2$
$= a^4 - 25$

35. $(b^2 + 7)(b^2 - 7) = (b^2)^2 - 7^2$
$= b^4 - 49$

36. $(x^3 - 8)(x^3 + 8) = (x^3)^2 - 8^2$
$= x^6 - 64$

37. $(d + b^2)(d - b^2) = d^2 - (b^2)^2$
$= d^2 - b^4$

38. $22 \times 18 = (20 + 2)(20 - 2)$
$= 20^2 - 2^2$
$= 400 - 4$
$= 396$

39. $37 \times 23 = (30 + 7)(30 - 7)$
$= 30^2 - 7^2$
$= 900 - 49$
$= 851$

40. $41 \times 59 = (50 - 9)(50 + 9)$
$= 50^2 - 9^2$
$= 2500 - 81$
$= 2419$

41. $68 \times 52 = (60 + 8)(60 - 8)$
$= 60^2 - 8^2$
$= 3600 - 64$
$= 3536$

42. $74 \times 66 = (70 + 4)(70 - 4)$
$= 70^2 - 4^2$
$= 4900 - 16$
$= 4884$

43. $(3y - z^3)(3y + z^3) = (3y)^2 - (z^3)^2$
$= 9y^2 - z^6$

44. $(\frac{1}{2}a - \frac{2}{3}b)(\frac{1}{2}a + \frac{2}{3}b) = (\frac{1}{2}a)^2 - (\frac{2}{3}b)^2$
$= \frac{1}{4}a^2 - \frac{4}{9}b^2$

45. $(2x^2b - y)(2x^2b + y) = (2x^2b)^2 - y^2$
$= 4x^4b^2 - y^2$

46. $(4x^a - y^2)(4x^a + y^2) = (4x^a)^2 - (y^2)^2$
$= 16x^{2a} - y^4$

47. $(2c^m - d^n)(2c^m + d^n) = (2c^m)^2 - (d^n)^2$
$= 4c^{2m} - d^{2n}$

48. $(2x - 3y)(2x - 5y) = 4x^2 - 16xy + 15y^2$

49. $(m^2n^2 - 9)(m^2n^2 + 10) = m^4n^4 + m^2n^2 - 90$

50. $(x^a + c)(x^a - d) = x^{2a} - dx^a + cx^a - cd$
$= x^{2a} + (c - d)x^a - cd$

51. $(xy - 2a)(xy - 3b) = x^2y^2 - 3bxy - 2axy + 6ab$
$= x^2y^2 - (2a + 3b)xy + 6ab$

52. $[(a + b) - 3][(a + b) + 4]$
$= (a + b)^2 + (a + b) - 12$
$= a^2 + 2ab + b^2 + a + b - 12$

53. $2(\frac{1}{2}a + b)^2 - (4a - b)^2$
$= 2(\frac{1}{4}a^2 + ab + b^2) - (16a^2 - 8ab + b^2)$
$= \frac{1}{2}a^2 + 2ab + 2b^2 - \frac{32}{2}a^2 + 8ab - b^2$
$= -\frac{31}{2}a^2 + 10ab + b^2$

54. $5(7x + 3y)^2 - 3(2x - 5y)^2$
$= 5(49x^2 + 42xy + 9y^2) - 3(4x^2 - 20xy + 25y^2)$
$= 245x^2 + 210xy + 45y^2 - 12x^2 + 60xy - 75y^2$
$= 233x^2 + 270xy - 30y^2$

55. $(a - 3b)(a + 6b) - 2(a - 4b)^2$
$= a^2 + 3ab - 18b^2 - 2(a^2 - 8ab + 16b^2)$
$= a^2 + 3ab - 18b^2 - 2a^2 + 16ab - 32b^2$
$= -a^2 + 19ab - 50b^2$

56. $(3a + 5b)(2a - 3b) + (a - 7b)(2a - 5b)$
$= 6a^2 + ab - 15b^2 + 2a^2 - 19ab + 35b^2$
$= 8a^2 - 18ab + 20b^2$

57. $(.2x - 1.3y)^2 - (.3x + 2.5y)^2$
$= .04x^2 - .52xy + 1.69y^2 - (.09x^2 + 1.5xy + 6.25y^2)$
$= .04x^2 - .52xy + 1.69y^2 - .09x^2 - 1.5xy - 6.25y^2$
$= -.05x^2 - 2.02xy - 4.56y^2$

Factoring Exercises   Pages 343-344

1. $m^2 + 2mn = m(m + 2n)$

2. $4r^3 - 8r = 4r(r^2 - 2)$

3. $16a^2 - 8ab + b^2 = (4a - b)^2$

4. $9 - 12xy + 4x^2y^2 = (3 - 2xy)^2$

5. $4a^{2m} + 16a^mb^m + 16b^{2m} = 4(a^{2m} + 4a^mb^m + 4b^{2m})$
$= 4(a^m + 2b^m)^2$

6. $49 - c^2 = (7 + c)(7 - c)$

7. $ax^4 - 4ay^2 = a(x^4 - 4y^2)$
$= a(x^2 + 2y)(x^2 - 2y)$

8. $45ac^2 - 20a = 5a(9c^2 - 4)$
$= 5a(3c + 2)(3c - 2)$

9. $rs^2 - 4r^3 = r(s^2 - 4r^2)$
$= r(s + 2r)(s - 2r)$

10. $27a^2b^2 - 3 = 3(9a^2b^2 - 1)$
$= 3(3ab + 1)(3ab - 1)$

11. $8 - 98c^2d^2 = 2(4 - 49c^2d^2)$
$= 2(2 + 7cd)(2 - 7cd)$

12. $24b^2 - 6a^2d^2 = 6(4b^2 - a^2d^2)$
$= 6(2b + ad)(2b - ad)$

13. $x^2y - 3xy + 2y = y(x^2 - 3x + 2)$
$= y(x - 2)(x - 1)$

14. $5a^2 + 45a + 70 = 5(a^2 + 9a + 14)$
$= 5(a + 7)(a + 2)$

15. $xy^2 - 5xy + 6x = x(y^2 - 5y + 6)$
$= x(y - 3)(y - 2)$

16. $12ax^2 - 33ax - 9a = 3a(4x^2 - 11x - 3)$
$= 3a(4x + 1)(x - 3)$

17. $42 + 35r - 42r^2 = 7(6 + 5r - 6r^2)$
$= 7(3 - 2r)(2 + 3r)$

18. $24ay^2 + 22ay + 4a = 2a(12y^2 + 11y + 2)$
$= 2a(4y + 1)(3y + 2)$

19. $6x^{2n} + 38x^n - 28 = 2(3x^{2n} + 19x^n - 14)$
$= 2(3x^n - 2)(x^n + 7)$

20. $a^2b^2 - 3abc - 4c^2 = (ab - 4c)(ab + c)$

21. $10d^2 + 21dx + 9x^2 = (5d + 3x)(2d + 3x)$

22. $4c^2d^2 + 9abcd + 5a^2b^2$
$= (4cd + 5ab)(cd + ab)$

23. $2m^2 - 3mn - 2n^2 = (2m + n)(m - 2n)$

24. $ab(x - 2y) - 4(x - 2y)$
$= (x - 2y)(ab - 4)$

25. $am^2 + 6amy^2 + 9ay^4 = a(m^2 + 6my^2 + 9y^4)$
$= a(m + 3y^2)^2$

26. $49a^{2n} - 36 = (7a^n + 6)(7a^n - 6)$

27. $2p^2 - 18p - 180 = 2(p^2 - 9p - 90)$
$= 2(p - 15)(p + 6)$

28. $5x^2 + 15axy - 20a^2y^2$
$= 5(x^2 + 3axy - 4a^2y^2)$
$= 5(x + 4ay)(x - ay)$

29. $7z^2 - 21abz - 126a^2b^2$
$= 7(z^2 - 3abz - 18a^2b^2)$
$= 7(z - 6ab)(z + 3ab)$

30. $-5x^2 + 5x + 60 = -5(x^2 - x - 12)$
$= -5(x - 4)(x + 3)$

31. $3y^2 - 3ay - 6a^2 = 3(y^2 - ay - 2a^2)$
$= 3(y - 2a)(y + a)$

32. $18a^2 - 21ac - 60c^2 = 3(6a^2 - 7ac - 20c^2)$
$= 3(3a + 4c)(2a - 5c)$

33. $21ab + 42a^2c + 21a^2b^2 = 21a(b + 2ac + ab^2)$

34. $12x^4 - 16x^2 = 4x^2(3x^2 - 4)$

35. $180a^4 - 405b^4 = 45(4a^4 - 9b^4)$
$= 45(2a^2 + 3b^2)(2a^2 - 3b^2)$

36. $.04a^2 - .25b^2 = (.2a + .5b)(.2a - .5b)$

37. $1.08b^2 - 1.47c^2 = 3(.36b^2 - .49c^2)$
$= 3(.6b + .7c)(.6b - .7c)$

38. $.01a^2 + .06ab + .09b^2$
$= (.1a + .3b)^2$ or $.01(a + 3b)^2$

39. $r(t + 3) - s(t + 3) = (t + 3)(r - s)$

40. $a(x - y) + b(x - y) = (x - y)(a + b)$

41. $ax - ay + bx - by = a(x - y) + b(x - y)$
$= (x - y)(a + b)$

42. $c(a + b) + d(a + b) = (a + b)(c + d)$

43. $ac + bc + ad + bd = c(a + b) + d(a + b)$
$= (a + b)(c + d)$

44. $ac + bd - bc - ad$
$= ac - bc - ad + bd$
$= c(a - b) - d(a - b)$
$= (a - b)(c - d)$

45. $mn - nk + mk - k^2$
$= n(m - k) + k(m - k)$
$= (m - k)(n + k)$

46. $ab + 2c - 2b - ac$
$= ab - ac - 2b + 2c$
$= a(b - c) - 2(b - c)$
$= (b - c)(a - 2)$

Fraction Exercises   Pages 344-346

1. $\dfrac{2c}{(x+y)^2}\left(\dfrac{3a}{3a}\right) = \dfrac{6ac}{3a(x+y)^2}$

$\dfrac{4}{3a(x+y)}\left(\dfrac{x+y}{x+y}\right) = \dfrac{4x+4y}{3a(x+y)^2}$

2. $\dfrac{2}{r^3 - s^3} = \dfrac{2}{(r-s)(r^2+rs+s^2)}$

$\dfrac{2}{r^2+rs+s^2} = \dfrac{2}{r^2+rs+s^2}\left(\dfrac{r-s}{r-s}\right) = \dfrac{2r-2s}{(r-s)(r^2+rs+s^2)}$

3. $\dfrac{x-1}{x^2-5x+6} = \dfrac{x-1}{(x-3)(x-2)}\left(\dfrac{x-1}{x-1}\right) = \dfrac{x^2-2x+1}{(x-1)(x-2)(x-3)}$

$\dfrac{x-2}{x^2-4x+3} = \dfrac{x-2}{(x-3)(x-1)}\left(\dfrac{x-2}{x-2}\right) = \dfrac{x^2-4x+4}{(x-1)(x-2)(x-3)}$

4. $a = \dfrac{a}{1}\left[\dfrac{b(a+b)(a-b)}{b(a+b)(a-b)}\right] = \dfrac{ab(a+b)(a-b)}{b(a+b)(a-b)}$

$\dfrac{ab^2}{a^2-b^2} = \dfrac{ab^2}{(a+b)(a-b)}\left(\dfrac{b}{b}\right) = \dfrac{ab^3}{b(a+b)(a-b)}$

$\dfrac{a^3}{ab-b^2} = \dfrac{a^3}{b(a-b)}\left(\dfrac{a+b}{a+b}\right) = \dfrac{a^3(a+b)}{b(a+b)(a-b)}$

5. $\dfrac{1}{1-z^2} = \dfrac{1}{(1+z)(1-z)}\left(\dfrac{1+z+z^2}{1+z+z^2}\right) = \dfrac{1+z+z^2}{(1+z)(1-z)(1+z+z^2)}$

$\dfrac{3}{1-z^3} = \dfrac{3}{(1-z)(1+z+z^2)}\left(\dfrac{1+z}{1+z}\right) = \dfrac{3+3z}{(1+z)(1-z)(1+z+z^2)}$

$\dfrac{4a}{z-1} = \dfrac{-4a}{1-z}\left[\dfrac{(1+z)(1+z+z^2)}{(1+z)(1+z+z^2)}\right] = \dfrac{-4a(1+z)(1+z+z^2)}{(1+z)(1-z)(1+z+z^2)}$

6. $\dfrac{5a}{x^2+x-2} = \dfrac{5a}{(x+2)(x-1)}\left(\dfrac{x-2}{x-2}\right) = \dfrac{5ax-10a}{(x-1)(x+2)(x-2)}$

$\dfrac{3a}{x^2-4} = \dfrac{3a}{(x+2)(x-2)}\left(\dfrac{x-1}{x-1}\right) = \dfrac{3ax-3a}{(x-1)(x+2)(x-2)}$

$\dfrac{ab}{x-1} = \dfrac{ab}{x-1}\left[\dfrac{(x+2)(x-2)}{(x+2)(x-2)}\right] = \dfrac{ab(x+2)(x-2)}{(x-1)(x+2)(x-2)}$

7. $\dfrac{8c}{ab} - \dfrac{3a}{bc} = \dfrac{8c^2}{abc} - \dfrac{3a^2}{abc} = \dfrac{8c^2-3a^2}{abc}$

8. $\frac{5}{x} + \frac{3}{2x} + \frac{27}{8x^2} = \frac{40x}{8x^2} + \frac{12x}{8x^2} + \frac{27}{8x^2} = \frac{52x + 27}{8x^2}$

9. $\frac{x + 7a}{2b} - \frac{2x + a}{5b} = \frac{5(x + 7a)}{10b} - \frac{2(2x + a)}{10b} = \frac{5x + 35a - 4x - 2a}{10b}$

$= \frac{x + 33a}{10b}$

10. $\frac{2x + 5}{3x} - \frac{13}{8x^2} - \frac{1}{2x} = \frac{8x(2x + 5)}{24x^2} - \frac{39}{24x^2} - \frac{12x}{24x^2}$

$= \frac{16x^2 + 40x - 39 - 12x}{24x^2}$

$= \frac{16x^2 + 28x - 39}{24x^2}$

11. $\frac{a - x}{x} + \frac{a + x}{a} + \frac{a^2 - x^2}{2ax}$

$= \frac{2a(a - x)}{2ax} + \frac{2x(a + x)}{2ax} + \frac{a^2 - x^2}{2ax} = \frac{2a^2 - 2ax + 2ax + 2x^2 + a^2 - x^2}{2ax} = \frac{3a^2 + x^2}{2ax}$

12. $\frac{5(x - 3)}{x^2 - x - 2} - \frac{2(x + 2)}{x^2 + 4x + 3} - \frac{x - 1}{6 - x - x^2}$

$= \frac{5(x - 3)}{(x - 2)(x + 1)} - \frac{2(x + 2)}{(x + 3)(x + 1)} + \frac{x - 1}{(x + 3)(x - 2)}$

$= \frac{5x - 15}{(x - 2)(x + 1)}\left(\frac{x + 3}{x + 3}\right) - \frac{2x + 4}{(x + 3)(x + 1)}\left(\frac{x - 2}{x - 2}\right) + \frac{x - 1}{(x + 3)(x - 2)}\left(\frac{x + 1}{x + 1}\right)$

$= \frac{5x^2 - 45 - 2x^2 + 8 + x^2 - 1}{(x + 1)(x - 2)(x + 3)} = \frac{4x^2 - 38}{(x + 1)(x - 2)(x + 3)}$

13. $\frac{a^2 + 2ab + b^2}{a^2 + b^2} + \frac{2ab}{a^2 - b^2} - 1$

$= \frac{a^2 + 2ab + b^2}{a^2 + b^2}\left(\frac{a^2 - b^2}{a^2 - b^2}\right) + \frac{2ab}{a^2 - b^2}\left(\frac{a^2 + b^2}{a^2 + b^2}\right) - \frac{(a^2 + b^2)(a^2 - b^2)}{(a^2 + b^2)(a^2 - b^2)}$

$= \frac{a^4 - a^2b^2 + 2a^3b - 2ab^3 + a^2b^2 - b^4 + 2a^3b + 2ab^3 - a^4 + b^4}{(a^2 + b^2)(a^2 - b^2)} = \frac{4a^3b}{(a^2 + b^2)(a^2 - b^2)}$

14. $\dfrac{x - 5}{2x^2 + x - 21} - \dfrac{x - 3}{2x^2 - 3x - 35}$

$= \dfrac{x - 5}{(2x + 7)(x - 3)} - \dfrac{x - 3}{(2x + 7)(x - 5)}$

$= \dfrac{x - 5}{(2x + 7)(x - 3)}\left(\dfrac{x - 5}{x - 5}\right) - \dfrac{x - 3}{(2x + 7)(x - 5)}\left(\dfrac{x - 3}{x - 3}\right)$

$= \dfrac{x^2 - 10x + 25 - x^2 + 6x - 9}{(2x + 7)(x - 3)(x - 5)} = \dfrac{-4x + 16}{(2x + 7)(x - 3)(x - 5)}$

15. $\dfrac{x + 1}{x - 1} + \dfrac{x - 1}{x + 1} - \dfrac{x + 2}{x - 2} - \dfrac{x - 2}{x + 2}$

$= \dfrac{x + 1}{x - 1}\left(\dfrac{x + 1}{x + 1}\right) + \dfrac{x - 1}{x + 1}\left(\dfrac{x - 1}{x - 1}\right) - \dfrac{x + 2}{x - 2}\left(\dfrac{x + 2}{x + 2}\right) - \dfrac{x - 2}{x + 2}\left(\dfrac{x - 2}{x - 2}\right)$

$= \dfrac{x^2 + 2x + 1 + x^2 - 2x + 1}{x^2 - 1} - \dfrac{x^2 + 4x + 4 + x^2 - 4x + 4}{x^2 - 4}$

$= \dfrac{2x^2 + 2}{x^2 - 1} - \dfrac{2x^2 + 8}{x^2 - 4}$

$= \dfrac{2x^2 + 2}{x^2 - 1}\left(\dfrac{x^2 - 4}{x^2 - 4}\right) - \left(\dfrac{2x^2 + 8}{x^2 - 4}\right)\left(\dfrac{x^2 - 1}{x^2 - 1}\right)$

$= \dfrac{2x^4 - 6x^2 - 8 - 2x^4 - 6x^2 + 8}{(x^2 - 1)(x^2 - 4)} = \dfrac{-12x^2}{(x^2 - 1)(x^2 - 4)}$

16. $\dfrac{x}{x - 1} - \dfrac{x}{x + 2} - \dfrac{x}{x + 1} + \dfrac{x}{x - 2}$

$= \dfrac{x}{x - 1}\left(\dfrac{x + 1}{x + 1}\right) - \dfrac{x}{x + 1}\left(\dfrac{x - 1}{x - 1}\right) + \dfrac{x}{x - 2}\left(\dfrac{x + 2}{x + 2}\right) - \dfrac{x}{x + 2}\left(\dfrac{x - 2}{x - 2}\right)$

$= \dfrac{x^2 + x - x^2 + x}{x^2 - 1} + \dfrac{x^2 + 2x - x^2 + 2x}{x^2 - 4}$

$= \dfrac{2x}{x^2 - 1}\left(\dfrac{x^2 - 4}{x^2 - 4}\right) + \dfrac{4x}{x^2 - 4}\left(\dfrac{x^2 - 1}{x^2 - 1}\right)$

$= \dfrac{2x^3 - 8x + 4x^3 - 4x}{(x^2 - 1)(x^2 - 4)}$

$= \dfrac{6x^3 - 12x}{(x^2 - 1)(x^2 - 4)}$

17. $\dfrac{a + 5}{a^2 + a - 20} + \dfrac{a - 5}{a^2 - 9a + 20} - \dfrac{a + 4}{a^2 - 25}$

$= \dfrac{a + 5}{(a + 5)(a - 4)} + \dfrac{a - 5}{(a - 5)(a - 4)} - \dfrac{a + 4}{(a + 5)(a - 5)}$

$= \dfrac{a + 5}{(a + 5)(a - 4)}\left(\dfrac{a - 5}{a - 5}\right) + \dfrac{a - 5}{(a - 5)(a - 4)}\left(\dfrac{a + 5}{a + 5}\right) - \dfrac{a + 4}{(a + 5)(a - 5)}\left(\dfrac{a - 4}{a - 4}\right)$

$= \dfrac{a^2 - 25 + a^2 - 25 - a^2 + 16}{(a + 5)(a - 5)(a - 4)} = \dfrac{a^2 - 34}{(a + 5)(a - 5)(a - 4)}$

18. $\dfrac{5x + 4}{x - 2} + \dfrac{3x - 2}{3 - x} - \dfrac{x^2 - 2x - 17}{x^2 - 5x + 6}$

$= \dfrac{5x + 4}{x - 2} - \dfrac{3x - 2}{x - 3} - \dfrac{x^2 - 2x - 17}{(x - 2)(x - 3)}$

$= \dfrac{5x + 4}{x - 2}\left(\dfrac{x - 3}{x - 3}\right) - \dfrac{3x - 2}{x - 3}\left(\dfrac{x - 2}{x - 2}\right) - \dfrac{x^2 - 2x - 17}{(x - 2)(x - 3)}$

$= \dfrac{5x^2 - 11x - 12 - 3x^2 + 8x - 4 - x^2 + 2x + 17}{(x - 2)(x - 3)}$

$= \dfrac{x^2 - x + 1}{(x - 2)(x - 3)}$

19. $3y - \dfrac{a}{4} = \dfrac{12y}{4} - \dfrac{a}{4} = \dfrac{12y - a}{4}$

20. $ab + \dfrac{1}{x} = \dfrac{abx}{x} + \dfrac{1}{x} = \dfrac{abx + 1}{x}$

21. $\dfrac{a^2}{z^2} - 4n = \dfrac{a^2}{z^2} - \dfrac{4nz^2}{z^2} = \dfrac{a^2 - 4nz^2}{z^2}$

22. $3r - \dfrac{r + s}{2} = \dfrac{6r}{2} - \dfrac{r + s}{2} = \dfrac{6r - r - s}{2} = \dfrac{5r - s}{2}$

23. $\dfrac{2}{x + 1} + 3 = \dfrac{2}{x + 1} + \dfrac{3(x + 1)}{x + 1} = \dfrac{2 + 3x + 3}{x + 1} = \dfrac{3x + 5}{x + 1}$

24. $\dfrac{a + b}{a - b} - 1 = \dfrac{a + b}{a - b} - \dfrac{a - b}{a - b} = \dfrac{a + b - a + b}{a - b} = \dfrac{2b}{a - b}$

25. $4x - \dfrac{2xy}{x - y} = \dfrac{4x(x - y)}{x - y} - \dfrac{2xy}{x - y} = \dfrac{4x^2 - 4xy - 2xy}{x - y} = \dfrac{4x^2 - 6xy}{x - y}$

26. $a - b + \frac{a^2}{a+b} = \frac{(a-b)(a+b)}{a+b} + \frac{a^2}{a+b} = \frac{a^2 - b^2 + a^2}{a+b} = \frac{2a^2 - b^2}{a+b}$

27. $x + y - \frac{x^2+y^2}{x+y} = \frac{(x+y)(x+y)}{x+y} - \frac{x^2+y^2}{x+y} = \frac{x^2+2xy+y^2-x^2-y^2}{x+y} = \frac{2xy}{x+y}$

28. $\frac{a^2-b^2}{a^2+ab}\cdot\frac{4a}{a-b} = \frac{\cancel{(a+b)}\cancel{(a-b)}}{\cancel{a}\cancel{(a+b)}}\cdot\frac{\overset{4}{\cancel{4a}}}{\cancel{a-b}} = \frac{4}{1} = 4$

29. $\frac{3a^2}{5a-10}\cdot\frac{3a-6}{4a^3} = \frac{\overset{3}{\cancel{3a^2}}}{5\cancel{(a-2)}}\cdot\frac{3\cancel{(a-2)}}{\underset{4a}{\cancel{4a^3}}} = \frac{9}{20a}$

30. $\frac{x^2+2x+1}{y}\cdot\frac{4y^2}{x^2-1} = \frac{(x+1)\cancel{(x+1)}}{\cancel{y}}\cdot\frac{\overset{4y}{\cancel{4y^2}}}{\cancel{(x+1)}(x-1)} = \frac{4y(x+1)}{x-1}$

31. $\frac{x^4-y^4}{8x^3+8xy^2}\cdot\frac{4}{x^2-y^2} = \frac{\cancel{(x^2+y^2)}\cancel{(x+y)}\cancel{(x-y)}}{\underset{2x}{\cancel{8x}}\cancel{(x^2+y^2)}}\cdot\frac{\cancel{4}}{\cancel{(x+y)}\cancel{(x-y)}} = \frac{1}{2x}$

32. $\frac{c+d}{5x}\cdot\frac{10x^2}{c^2-cd-2d^2}\cdot\frac{ac-2ad}{2x} = \frac{\cancel{c+d}}{\cancel{5x}}\cdot\frac{\overset{2x}{\cancel{10x^2}}}{\cancel{(c-2d)}\cancel{(c+d)}}\cdot\frac{a\cancel{(c-2d)}}{\cancel{2x}} = a$

33. $\frac{7c^3d}{3} \div 21c^3d = \frac{\cancel{7c^3d}}{3}\cdot\frac{1}{\underset{3}{\cancel{21c^3d}}} = \frac{1}{9}$

34. $\frac{x^2y+yz}{9}\div\frac{ay+by}{18} = \frac{\cancel{y}(x^2+z)}{\cancel{9}}\cdot\frac{\overset{2}{\cancel{18}}}{\cancel{y}(a+b)} = \frac{2(x^2+z)}{a+b}$

35. $\frac{8}{ab^2-a^2b}\div\frac{2x+2y}{ab} = \frac{\overset{4}{\cancel{8}}}{\cancel{ab}(b-a)}\cdot\frac{\cancel{ab}}{\cancel{2}(x+y)} = \frac{4}{(b-a)(x+y)}$

36. $\frac{x^2-y^2}{4}\div\frac{x+y}{12a} = \frac{\cancel{(x+y)}(x-y)}{\cancel{4}}\cdot\frac{\overset{3a}{\cancel{12a}}}{\cancel{x+y}} = 3a(x-y)$

37. $\frac{4-x^2}{2-3x+x} \div (2+x) = \frac{\cancel{(2+x)}\cancel{(2-x)}}{\cancel{(2-x)}(1-x)}\cdot\frac{1}{\cancel{2+x}} = \frac{1}{1-x}$

38. $\frac{xy-x^2y^2}{axy}\div\frac{a-axy}{a^2x+a^2y} = \frac{\cancel{xy(1-xy)}}{\underset{\cancel{a}}{\cancel{axy}}}\cdot\frac{\overset{\cancel{a}}{\cancel{a^2}}(x+y)}{\cancel{a(1-xy)}} = x+y$

39. $(1 + \frac{a}{y}) \div (1 - \frac{y^2}{a^2}) = (\frac{y + a}{y}) + (\frac{a^2 - y^2}{a^2}) = \frac{\cancel{a + y}}{y} \cdot \frac{a^2}{(\cancel{a + y})(a - y)} = \frac{a^2}{y(a - y)}$

40. $\frac{ab - b^2}{3xy^3} \div \frac{a^2 - 2ab + b^2}{27x^3y^3} = \frac{b(\cancel{a - b})}{\cancel{3xy^3}} \cdot \frac{\overset{9x^2}{\cancel{27x^3y^3}}}{(\cancel{a - b})(a - b)} = \frac{9bx^2}{a - b}$

41. $\frac{1 - 9x^2}{a - 2ax} \div 1 + 3x = \frac{(\cancel{1 + 3x})(1 - 3x)}{a(1 - 2x)} \cdot \frac{1}{\cancel{1 + 3x}} = \frac{1 - 3x}{a(1 - 2x)}$

42. $(x^2 - 4y^2z^2) \div \frac{3x + 6yz}{9a} = (\cancel{x + 2yz})(x - 2yz) \cdot \frac{\overset{3a}{\cancel{9a}}}{\cancel{3(x + 2yz)}} = 3a(x - 2yz)$

43. $\frac{4a - 8b}{(a - b)^2} \div \frac{a^2 - ab - 2b^2}{a^2 - b^2} = \frac{4(\cancel{a - 2b})}{(a - b)(\cancel{a - b})} \cdot \frac{(\cancel{a + b})(\cancel{a - b})}{(\cancel{a + b})(\cancel{a - 2b})} = \frac{4}{a - b}$

*44. $\frac{(r - 2s)^2}{s - r} \div \frac{r^2 - rs - 2s^2}{r^2 - s^2} = \frac{(\cancel{r - 2s})(r - 2s)}{s - r} \cdot \frac{(\cancel{r + s})\overset{-1}{(r - s)}}{(\cancel{r - 2s})(\cancel{r + s})} = -1(r - 2s) = 2s - r$

45. $(\frac{10}{x - x^3}) \div (\frac{1}{1 - x} - \frac{1}{1 + x})$

$= \left[\frac{10}{x(1 - x^2)}\right] \div \left[\frac{1 + x - (1 - x)}{(1 - x)(1 + x)}\right] = \frac{\overset{5}{\cancel{10}}}{x(\cancel{1 + x})(\cancel{1 - x})} \cdot \frac{(\cancel{1 - x})(\cancel{1 + x})}{\underset{x}{\cancel{2x}}} = \frac{5}{x^2}$

46. $(a - \frac{1}{a})^2 \div (1 - \frac{1}{a})^2$

$= (\frac{a^2 - 1}{a})^2 \div (\frac{a - 1}{a})^2$

$= \frac{(a + 1)(\cancel{a - 1})(a + 1)(\cancel{a - 1})}{\cancel{a^2}} \cdot \frac{\cancel{a^2}}{\underset{1}{(\cancel{a - 1})(\cancel{a - 1})}} = (a + 1)^2$

47. $(x + \frac{xy}{x - y})(x - \frac{xy}{x + y}) \div \frac{x^2 + y^2}{x^2 - y^2}$

$= (\frac{x^2 - xy}{x - y} + \frac{xy}{x - y})(\frac{x^2 + xy}{x + y} - \frac{xy}{x + y})[\frac{(x + y)(x - y)}{x^2 + y^2}]$

$= \frac{x^2}{\cancel{x - y}} \cdot \frac{x^2}{\cancel{x + y}} \cdot \frac{(\cancel{x + y})(\cancel{x - y})}{x^2 + y^2} = \frac{x^4}{x^2 + y^2}$

48. $$\left(\frac{x}{1 + x} + \frac{1 - x}{x}\right) \div \left(\frac{x}{1 + x} - \frac{1 - x}{x}\right)$$

$$= \left[\frac{x^2}{(1 + x)x} + \frac{1 - x^2}{(1 + x)x}\right] \div \left[\frac{x^2}{(1 + x)x} - \frac{1 - x^2}{(1 + x)x}\right]$$

$$= \frac{1}{(1 + x)x} \div \frac{2x^2 - 1}{(1 + x)x}$$

$$= \frac{1}{\cancel{(1 + x)x}} \cdot \frac{\cancel{(1 + x)x}}{2x^2 - 1} = \frac{1}{2x^2 - 1}$$

49. $$\left[\frac{5}{2(x - 3)} - \frac{3}{2(x - 1)}\right] \cdot \left[\frac{5}{x + 2} - \frac{4}{x + 1}\right]$$

$$= \left[\frac{5(x - 1) - 3(x - 3)}{2(x - 3)(x - 1)}\right] \cdot \left[\frac{5(x + 1) - 4(x + 2)}{(x + 2)(x + 1)}\right]$$

$$= \frac{2x + 4}{2(x - 3)(x - 1)} \cdot \frac{x - 3}{(x + 2)(x + 1)}$$

$$= \frac{\cancel{2(x + 2)}}{\cancel{2(x - 3)}(x - 1)} \cdot \frac{\cancel{x - 3}}{\cancel{(x + 2)}(x + 1)} = \frac{1}{(x + 1)(x - 1)}$$

50. $$\left(a + \frac{1}{a + 1}\right) \div \left(1 + \frac{a}{1 + a}\right)$$

$$= \frac{a^2 + a + 1}{a + 1} \div \frac{2a + 1}{a + 1}$$

$$= \frac{a^2 + a + 1}{\cancel{a + 1}} \cdot \frac{\cancel{a + 1}}{2a + 1} = \frac{a^2 + a + 1}{2a + 1}$$

51. $$\left(x + y + \frac{y^2}{x}\right) \div \left(x - y + \frac{y^2}{x}\right)$$

$$= \frac{x^2 + xy + y^2}{x} \div \frac{x^2 - xy + y^2}{x}$$

$$= \frac{x^2 + xy + y^2}{\cancel{x}} \cdot \frac{\cancel{x}}{x^2 - xy + y^2} = \frac{x^2 + xy + y^2}{x^2 - xy + y^2}$$

Equations Involving Fractions   Pages 346-347

The check is left for the teacher.

1. $$\frac{3 - r}{2} = \frac{r - 2}{3}$$
$$3(3 - r) = 2(r - 2)$$
$$9 - 3r = 2r - 4$$
$$-5r = -13$$
$$r = \frac{13}{5} = 2.6$$

2. $$\frac{24}{n - 3} = 4$$
$$4n - 12 = 24$$
$$4n = 36$$
$$n = 9$$

3. $$\frac{x + 2}{x - 2} = 3$$
$$x + 2 = 3x - 6$$
$$-2x = -8$$
$$x = 4$$

4. $$\frac{24}{x - 2} = 12$$
$$24 = 12x - 24$$
$$-12x = -48$$
$$x = 4$$

5. $$\frac{12 - s}{4} - \frac{s}{2} = \frac{13 - s}{3}$$
$$12\left(\frac{12 - s}{4} - \frac{s}{2}\right) = 12\left(\frac{13 - s}{3}\right)$$
$$3(12 - s) - 6s = 4(13 - s)$$
$$36 - 3s - 6s = 52 - 4s$$
$$36 - 9s = 52 - 4s$$
$$-5s = 16$$
$$s = \frac{-16}{5} = -3.2$$

6. $$\frac{41 - y}{3} - y = \frac{19 - y}{2}$$
$$6\left(\frac{41 - y}{3} - y\right) = 6\left(\frac{19 - y}{2}\right)$$
$$2(41 - y) - 6y = 3(19 - y)$$
$$82 - 2y - 6y = 57 - 3y$$
$$82 - 8y = 57 - 3y$$
$$-5y = -25$$
$$y = 5$$

7. $$\frac{5p - 4}{3} = p + 4$$
$$5p - 4 = 3p + 12$$
$$2p = 16$$
$$p = 8$$

8. $$\frac{36}{x} + 2 = 14$$
$$x\left(\frac{36}{x} + 2\right) = 14x$$
$$36 + 2x = 14x$$
$$-12x = -36$$
$$x = 3$$

9. $$\frac{12}{3n + 2} = 4$$
$$12 = 12n + 8$$
$$-12n = -4$$
$$n = \frac{4}{12} = \frac{1}{3}$$

10. $$\frac{20}{2x - 1} - 2 = 18$$
$$\frac{20}{2x - 1} = 20$$
$$20 = 40x - 20$$
$$-40x = -40$$
$$x = 1$$

11. $$\frac{2}{y} + \frac{3}{y} + \frac{4}{y} = 1$$
$$\frac{9}{y} = 1$$
$$y = 9$$

12. $$\frac{m - 2}{m + 3} = \frac{3}{4}$$
$$4m - 8 = 3m + 9$$
$$m = 17$$

13.
$$\frac{2m - 12}{15 - m} = \frac{40 - 2m}{m - 8}$$
$$(m - 8)(2m - 12) = (15 - m)(40 - 2m)$$
$$2m^2 - 28m + 96 = 600 - 70m + 2m^2$$
$$42m = 504$$
$$m = 12$$

14.
$$\frac{3p}{p - 3} = \frac{3p + 3}{p - 4}$$
$$3p(p - 4) = (p - 3)(3p + 3)$$
$$3p^2 - 12p = 3p^2 - 6p - 9$$
$$-6p = -9$$
$$p = \frac{9}{6} = \frac{3}{2} = 1.5$$

15.
$$\frac{10m + 20}{3m - 5} = \frac{25}{2}$$
$$20m + 40 = 75m - 125$$
$$-55m = -165$$
$$m = 3$$

16.
$$\frac{5}{3x + 2} = 1$$
$$5 = 3x + 2$$
$$-3x = -3$$
$$x = 1$$

17.
$$\frac{3}{x - 2} - \frac{6x}{2 - x} = 9$$
$$\frac{3}{x - 2} + \frac{6x}{x - 2} = 9$$
$$\frac{3 + 6x}{x - 2} = 9$$
$$3 + 6x = 9x - 18$$
$$-3x = -21$$
$$x = 7$$

18.
$$\frac{6}{2r + 1} - \frac{2 + 4r}{2r - 1} = \frac{8r^2}{1 - 4r^2}$$
$$\frac{6}{2r + 1} - \frac{2 + 4r}{2r - 1} = \frac{8r^2}{(1 + 2r)(1 - 2r)}$$
$$(2r + 1)(2r - 1)\left(\frac{6}{2r + 1} - \frac{4r + 2}{2r - 1}\right) = (2r + 1)(2r - 1)\left[\frac{-8r^2}{(2r + 1)(2r - 1)}\right]$$
$$6(2r - 1) - (2r + 1)(4r + 2) = -8r^2$$
$$12r - 6 - (8r^2 + 8r + 2) = -8r^2$$
$$12r - 6 - 8r^2 - 8r - 2 = -8r^2$$
$$4r - 8 = 0$$
$$4r = 8$$
$$r = 2$$

19.
$$\frac{6m - 3}{2m + 7} = \frac{3m - 2}{m + 5}$$
$$(m + 5)(6m - 3) = (2m + 7)(3m - 2)$$
$$6m^2 + 27m - 15 = 6m^2 + 17m - 14$$
$$10m = 1$$
$$m = .1$$

20.
$$\frac{3r - 1}{r - 5} = \frac{5r + 4}{r + 8} - 2$$
$$(r - 5)(r + 8)\left(\frac{3r - 1}{r - 5}\right) = (r - 5)(r + 8)\left(\frac{5r + 4}{r + 8} - 2\right)$$
$$(r + 8)(3r - 1) = (r - 5)(5r + 4) - 2(r - 5)(r + 8)$$
$$3r^2 + 23r - 8 = 5r^2 - 21r - 20 - 2r^2 - 6r + 80$$
$$3r^2 + 23r - 8 = 3r^2 - 27r + 60$$
$$50r = 68$$
$$r = \frac{34}{25} \text{ or } 1.36$$

21. $\frac{t^2 + 5}{t + 3} - (t - 7) = 3$

$$\frac{t^2 + 5}{t + 3} = 3 + t - 7$$
$$\frac{t^2 + 5}{t + 3} = t - 4$$
$$t^2 + 5 = t^2 - t - 12$$
$$t = -17$$

22. $\frac{\frac{1}{4} - p}{\frac{1}{4} + p} + \frac{1}{4} = \frac{p}{\frac{1}{4} + p} - \frac{1}{4}$

$$\frac{\frac{1}{4} - p}{\frac{1}{4} + p} - \frac{p}{\frac{1}{4} + p} = -\frac{1}{2}$$
$$\frac{\frac{1}{4} - p - p}{\frac{1}{4} + p} = -\frac{1}{2}$$
$$\frac{\frac{1}{4} - 2p}{\frac{1}{4} + p} = -\frac{1}{2}$$
$$\frac{1}{2} - 4p = -\frac{1}{4} - p$$
$$\frac{3}{4} = 3p$$
$$12p = 3$$
$$p = \frac{1}{4}$$

23. let x = the number <u>3</u>

$$\frac{5 - x}{8 - x} = \frac{2}{5}$$
$$5(5 - x) = 2(8 - x)$$
$$25 - 5x = 16 - 2x$$
$$-3x = -9$$
$$x = 3$$

$$\frac{5 - 3}{8 - 3} \;\Big|\; \frac{2}{5}$$
$$\frac{2}{5} = \frac{2}{5} \checkmark$$

24. let x = the number <u>1</u>

$$\frac{2 + x}{3 + x} = \frac{3}{4}$$
$$4(2 + x) = (3 + x)3$$
$$8 + 4x = 9 + 3x$$
$$x = 1$$

$$\frac{2 + 1}{3 + 1} \;\Big|\; \frac{3}{4}$$
$$\frac{3}{4} = \frac{3}{4} \checkmark$$

25. let x = number of days for assistant to finish <u>2.8</u>

$$2(\tfrac{1}{5}) + 2(\tfrac{1}{8}) + x(\tfrac{1}{8}) = 1$$
$$\frac{2}{5} + \frac{2}{8} + \frac{x}{8} = 1$$
$$40(\tfrac{2}{5} + \tfrac{2}{8} + \tfrac{x}{8}) = 40$$
$$16 + 10 + 5x = 40$$
$$5x = 14$$
$$x = 2.8 \text{ da.}$$

$$\frac{2}{5} + \frac{2}{8} + \frac{2.8}{8} = .4 + .25 + .35 = 1 \checkmark$$

26. let x = days for second contractor to finish <u>6</u>

$$8\left(\frac{1}{20}\right) + x\left(\frac{1}{10}\right) = 1$$
$$\frac{8}{20} + \frac{x}{10} = 1$$
$$20\left(\frac{8}{20} + \frac{x}{10}\right) = 20$$
$$8 + 2x = 20$$
$$2x = 12$$
$$x = 6 \qquad \frac{8}{20} + \frac{6}{10} = \frac{8}{20} + \frac{12}{20} = \frac{20}{20} = 1 \checkmark$$

27. let x = minutes until filled <u>36</u>

$$x\left(\frac{1}{18}\right) + x\left(\frac{1}{12}\right) - x\left(\frac{1}{9}\right) = 1$$
$$36\left(\frac{x}{18} + \frac{x}{12} - \frac{x}{9}\right) = 36$$
$$2x + 3x - 4x = 36$$
$$x = 36 \qquad 36\left(\frac{1}{18}\right) + 36\left(\frac{1}{12}\right) - 36\left(\frac{1}{9}\right) = 2 + 3 - 4 = 1 \checkmark$$

28. .2(4.5) = .9

<u>.9</u> gallons of antifreeze

let x = quarts of antifreeze <u>1.5 qt.</u> or <u>.375 gal.</u>

$$4(4.5)(.2) - .2(3) + x = (4.5)(4)(.25)$$
$$3.6 - .6 + x = 4.5$$
$$3 + x = 4.5$$
$$x = 1.5$$

$$\frac{.9 \text{ gal.}}{4.5 \text{ gal.}} = \frac{9}{45} = \frac{1}{5} = 20\% \checkmark$$

$$4(.9) - .2(3) + 1.5 = 3.6 - .6 + 1.5 = 4.5 \text{ qt.}$$

$$\frac{4.5 \text{ qt.}}{4(4.5) \text{ qt.}} = \frac{4.5}{18} = \frac{45}{180} = \frac{1}{4} = 25\% \checkmark$$

29. let x = pounds of green tea to add <u>2</u>

$$.4(10) + x = .5(10 + x)$$
$$4 + x = 5 + .5x$$
$$.5x = 1$$
$$5x = 10$$
$$x = 2$$

$$\frac{4}{10} = 40\% \checkmark \qquad \frac{4 + 2}{10 + 2} = \frac{6}{12} = 50\% \checkmark$$

30. let d = number of dimes <u>6</u>
    2d = number of nickels <u>12</u>
    number of quarters = 5

$$.05(2d) + .10d + .25(5) = 2.45$$
$$.1d + .1d + 1.25 = 2.45$$
$$.2d = 1.20$$
$$2d = 12$$
$$d = 6$$

$$.05(12) + .10(6) + .25(5)$$
$$= .05(12) + .60 + 1.25$$
$$= .6 + .60 + 1.25$$
$$= 2.45 \checkmark$$

31. let d = one-way distance <u>18 mi.</u>

$$\frac{d}{4} + \frac{d}{12} = 6$$
$$12\left(\frac{d}{4} + \frac{d}{12}\right) = 72$$
$$3d + d = 72$$
$$4d = 72$$
$$d = 18$$

$$\frac{18}{4} + \frac{18}{12} = 4.5 + 1.5 = 6 \checkmark$$

<u>Ratio and Proportion Exercises</u> Page 348

1. let x = 1st person's share <u>$150</u>
   350 - x = 2nd person's share <u>$200</u>

$$\frac{x}{350 - x} = \frac{3}{4}$$
$$4x = 1050 - 3x$$
$$7x = 1050$$
$$x = 150$$

$$\frac{150}{350 - 150} = \frac{150}{200} = \frac{3}{4} \checkmark$$

2. let 3x = first number <u>12</u>
   2x = second number <u>8</u>

$$\frac{3x + 4}{2x + 4} = \frac{4}{3}$$
$$9x + 12 = 8x + 16$$
$$x = 4$$

$$\frac{12 + 4}{8 + 4} = \frac{16}{12} = \frac{4}{3} \checkmark$$

3. let 3x = number on first shelf <u>18</u>
   5x = number on second shelf <u>30</u>

$$3x + 5x = 48$$
$$8x = 48$$
$$x = 6$$

$$\frac{18}{30} = \frac{3}{5} \checkmark$$

<u>alternate solution</u>
let x = number on first shelf <u>18</u>
48 - x = number on second shelf <u>30</u>

$$\frac{x}{48 - x} = \frac{3}{5}$$
$$5x = 3(48 - x)$$
$$5x = 144 - 3x$$
$$8x = 144$$
$$x = 18$$

$$\frac{18}{48 - 18} = \frac{18}{30} = \frac{3}{5} \checkmark$$

4. let x = greater part $15\frac{2}{3}$

$25 - x$ = smaller part $9\frac{1}{3}$

$$\frac{x+1}{25-x-1} = \frac{2}{1}$$
$$\frac{x+1}{24-x} = \frac{2}{1}$$
$$x + 1 = 48 - 2x$$
$$3x = 47$$
$$x = \frac{47}{3} = 15\frac{2}{3}$$

$$\frac{\frac{47}{3}+1}{9\frac{1}{3}-1} = \frac{\frac{47}{3}+\frac{3}{3}}{\frac{28}{3}-\frac{3}{3}} = \frac{\frac{50}{3}}{\frac{25}{3}} = 2 \checkmark$$

5. let x = first number 9
$12 - x$ = second number 3

$$\frac{x+3}{12-x+3} = \frac{2}{1}$$
$$\frac{x+3}{15-x} = \frac{2}{1}$$
$$30 - 2x = x + 3$$
$$-3x = -27$$
$$x = 9$$

$$\frac{9+3}{3+3} = \frac{12}{6} = \frac{2}{1} \checkmark$$

6. let x = the number $\frac{1}{2}$

$$\frac{1+x}{2+x} = \frac{4+x}{7+x}$$
$$(1+x)(7+x) = (2+x)(4+x)$$
$$7 + 8x + x^2 = 8 + 6x + x^2$$
$$2x = 1$$
$$x = .5$$

$$\frac{1+.5}{2+.5} \;\Big|\; \frac{4+.5}{7+.5}$$
$$\frac{1.5}{2.5} \;\Big|\; \frac{4.5}{7.5}$$
$$\frac{15}{25} \;\Big|\; \frac{45}{75}$$
$$\frac{3}{5} = \frac{3}{5} \checkmark$$

7. let the angles = $2x$ 40^0
$3x$ 60^0
$4x$ 80^0

$$2x + 3x + 4x = 180$$
$$9x = 180$$
$$x = 20$$

$$40^0 + 60^0 + 80^0 = 180^0 \checkmark$$

8. let x = investment of first partner $8000
$18,000 - x$ = investment of second partner $10,000

$$\frac{x}{18,000 - x} = \frac{4}{5}$$
$$5x = 4(18,000 - x)$$
$$5x = 72,000 - 4x$$
$$9x = 72,000$$
$$x = 8000$$

$$\frac{8000}{10,000} = \frac{4}{5} \checkmark$$

9. let x = the number $\underline{7}$

$$\frac{11 + x}{17 + x} = \frac{2 + x}{5 + x}$$
$$(11 + x)(5 + x) = (17 + x)(2 + x)$$
$$55 + 16x + x^2 = 34 + 19x + x^2$$
$$-3x = -21$$
$$x = 7$$

$$\frac{11 + 7}{17 + 7} \,\Big|\, \frac{2 + 7}{5 + 7}$$
$$\frac{18}{24} \,\Big|\, \frac{9}{12}$$
$$\frac{3}{4} = \frac{3}{4} \checkmark$$

*10.
$x + 2\frac{2}{3}$ = first number $\underline{4}$

$6\frac{1}{3} - x$ = second number $\underline{5}$

let x = third number $\underline{\frac{4}{3}}$

fourth number $\underline{\frac{5}{3}}$

"Numbers in proportion" implies first and second numbers are in the same ratio as the third and fourth numbers.

$$\frac{x + 2\frac{2}{3}}{6\frac{1}{3} - x} = \frac{4}{5}$$

$$\left(\frac{3}{3}\right)\left(\frac{x + \frac{8}{3}}{\frac{19}{3} - x}\right) = \frac{4}{5}$$

$$\frac{3x + 8}{19 - 3x} = \frac{4}{5}$$
$$15x + 40 = 76 - 12x$$
$$27x = 36$$
$$3x = 4$$
$$x = \frac{4}{3}$$

$$x + 2\frac{2}{3} = \frac{4}{3} + \frac{8}{3} = \frac{12}{3} = 4 \checkmark$$
$$6\frac{1}{3} - x = \frac{19}{3} - \frac{4}{3} - \frac{15}{3} = 5 \checkmark$$

$$\frac{4}{5} = \frac{\frac{4}{3}}{x}$$
$$4x = \frac{20}{3}$$
$$12x = 20$$
$$x = \frac{20}{12} = \frac{5}{3}$$

$$\frac{4}{5} \,\Big|\, \frac{\frac{4}{3}}{\frac{5}{3}}$$
$$\Big|\, \frac{4}{3} \cdot \frac{3}{5}$$
$$\frac{4}{5} = \frac{4}{5} \checkmark$$

11.
$$\frac{1^2}{t^2} = \frac{39.1}{156.4}$$
$$\frac{1}{t^2} = \frac{39.1}{156.4}$$
$$39.1t^2 = 156.4$$
$$t^2 = 4$$
$$t = \sqrt{4}$$
t = 2 sec. per oscillation

$$\frac{1^2}{2^2} \,\Big|\, \frac{39.1}{156.4}$$
$$\frac{1}{4} \,\Big|\, \frac{391}{1564}$$
$$\frac{1}{4} = \frac{1}{4} \checkmark$$

Formula Exercises   Page 349

1.(a) $\frac{A}{A'} = (\frac{166}{664})^2$

$\frac{A}{A'} = (\frac{1}{4})^2$

$\frac{A}{A'} = \frac{1}{16}$

(b) $\frac{P}{P'} = \frac{166}{664}$

$\frac{P}{P'} = \frac{1}{4}$

2. let w = width

$\frac{A}{A'} = \frac{100w}{125w}$

$\frac{A}{A'} = \frac{4}{5}$

3. let s = side of second polygon 31.5 in.

$\frac{96}{144} = \frac{21}{s}$

$\frac{2}{3} = \frac{21}{s}$

$2s = 63$

$s = 31.5$

4. $\frac{A}{A'} = (\frac{24}{36})^2$ $\frac{C}{C'} = \frac{24}{36}$

$\frac{A}{A'} = (\frac{2}{3})^2$ $\frac{C}{C'} = \frac{2}{3}$

$\frac{A}{A'} = \frac{4}{9}$

5. $\frac{2\frac{7}{9}A}{A} = (\frac{12}{d})^2$

$\frac{\frac{25}{9}A}{A} = \frac{144}{d^2}$

$\frac{25A}{9A} = \frac{144}{d^2}$

$\frac{25}{9} = \frac{144}{d^2}$

$25d^2 = 1296$

$d^2 = \frac{1296}{25}$

$d = \sqrt{\frac{1296}{25}} = \frac{\sqrt{1296}}{\sqrt{25}}$

$d = \frac{36}{5} = 7.2$ in.

6. $\frac{54}{128} = (\frac{3}{h})^3$

$\frac{27}{64} = \frac{27}{h^3}$

$h^3 = 64$

$h = \sqrt[3]{64} = 4$ ft.

7. $\frac{1000}{1728} = \frac{5^3}{\ell}$

$\frac{1000}{1728} = \frac{125}{\ell^3}$

$1000\ell^3 = 125(1728)$

$\ell^3 = \frac{216,000}{1000} = 216$

$\ell = \sqrt[3]{216} = 6$ ft.

8. $\frac{250}{w} = (\frac{5}{6})^3$

$\frac{250}{w} = \frac{125}{216}$

$\frac{250}{w} = \frac{125(2)}{216(2)}$

$\frac{250}{w} = \frac{250}{432}$

$w = 432$ g

9. $(\frac{7}{8})^3 = \frac{686}{w}$

$\frac{343}{512} = \frac{686}{w}$

$343w = 351,232$

$w = 1024$ g

Exponent and Radical Exercises Pages 349-350

1. $c^2 = a^2 + b^2$
$c^2 - b^2 = a^2$
$a = \sqrt{c^2 - b^2}$
$a = \sqrt{32^2 - 24^2}$
$a = \sqrt{1024 - 576}$
$a = \sqrt{448}$
$a = \sqrt{64}\,\sqrt{7}$
$a = 8\sqrt{7}$
$a = 8(2.645)$
$a \approx 21.2$

2. $h = \frac{1}{2}a\sqrt{3}$
$h = \frac{1}{2}(21.5)(1.732)$
$h \approx 18.6$ in.

3. $h = \frac{1}{2}a\sqrt{3}$
$16.45 = \frac{1}{2}a(1.732)$
$32.90 = 1.732a$
$a \approx 19.0$ in.

4. $A = \frac{1}{2}bh$
$A = \frac{1}{2}(21.5)(18.6)$
$A = 21.5(9.3)$
A 200 sq. in.

$A = \frac{1}{2}bh$
$A = \frac{1}{2}(19.0)(16.45)$
$A = 9.5(16.45)$
$A \approx 156$ sq. in.

alternate solution

$A = \frac{a^2\sqrt{3}}{4}$
$A = \frac{(21.5)^2\sqrt{3}}{4}$

$A = \frac{a^2\ \ 3}{4}$
$A = \frac{(19.0)^2\sqrt{3}}{4}$

5. $5a\sqrt{7x^2 - ay}$
$= 5(7.2)\sqrt{7(3)^2 - 7.2(4.8)}$
$= 36\sqrt{63 - 34.56}$
$= 36\sqrt{28.44}$
$= 36(5.33)$
≈ 191.9

$a = 7.2$
$x = 3$
$y = 4.8$

*6. $\frac{1}{2}\sqrt{72a^2b} + 4a\sqrt{\frac{9b}{8}} - \sqrt{2b(6a - 1)^2}$
$= \frac{6a\sqrt{2b}}{2} + \frac{12a\sqrt{b}}{2\sqrt{2}} - (6a - 1)\sqrt{2b}$
$= 3a\sqrt{2b} + \frac{6a\sqrt{b}}{\sqrt{2}} - (6a - 1)\sqrt{2b}$
$= 3a\sqrt{2b} + \frac{6a\sqrt{2b}}{2} - (6a - 1)\sqrt{2b}$
$= 3a\sqrt{2b} + 3a\sqrt{2b} - (6a - 1)\ \ 2b$
$= (3a + 3a - 6a + 1)\sqrt{2b}$
$= \sqrt{2b}$

*7. $(a^2 - b^2)^{\frac{1}{2}}(a^2 + 4ab + 3b^2)^{\frac{1}{2}}$
$= [(a+b)(a-b)]^{\frac{1}{2}}[(a + 3b)(a + b)]^{\frac{1}{2}}$
$= [(a + b)^2(a - b)(a + 3b)]^{\frac{1}{2}}$
$= [(a+b)^2]^{\frac{1}{2}}[(a-b)(a+3b)]^{\frac{1}{2}}$
$= (a + b)(a^2 + 2ab - 3b^2)^{\frac{1}{2}}$
or $(a + b)\sqrt{a^2 + 2ab - 3b^2}$

8. $(\sqrt{6} - \sqrt{10})(\sqrt{3} - \sqrt{5})$

$= \sqrt{18} - 2\sqrt{30} + \sqrt{50}$

$= 3\sqrt{2} - 2\sqrt{30} + 5\sqrt{2}$

$= 8\sqrt{2} - 2\sqrt{30}$

9.

$$r = \sqrt{\frac{\pi V^3}{2.5}}$$

$$r^2 = \frac{\pi V^3}{2.5}$$

$$2.5r^2 = \pi V^3$$

$$\frac{2.5r^2}{\pi} = V^3$$

$$V = \sqrt[3]{\frac{2.5r^2}{\pi}} = \frac{\sqrt[3]{2.5r^2}}{\sqrt[3]{\pi}} \cdot \frac{\sqrt[3]{\pi^2}}{\sqrt[3]{\pi^2}} = \frac{\sqrt[3]{2.5\pi^2 r^2}}{\pi}$$

10. $(\sqrt{8} - \sqrt{12})(\sqrt{2} - \sqrt{6})$

$= \sqrt{16} - \sqrt{48} - \sqrt{24} + \sqrt{72}$

$= 4 - \sqrt{16}\sqrt{3} - \sqrt{4}\sqrt{6} + \sqrt{36}\sqrt{2}$

$= 4 - 4\sqrt{3} - 2\sqrt{6} + 6\sqrt{2}$

11. $T = \frac{2}{b + c}\sqrt{bcs(s - a)}$

$a = 17$
$b = 10$
$c = 15$

$s = \frac{a + b + c}{2}$

$s = \frac{17 + 10 + 15}{2}$

$s = 21$

$T = \frac{2}{10 + 15}\sqrt{10(15)(21)(21 - 17)}$

$T = \frac{2}{25}\sqrt{150(21)(4)}$

$T = \frac{2}{25}\sqrt{25 \cdot 6 \cdot 21 \cdot 4}$

$T = \frac{2}{\cancel{25}_{\,5}} \cdot \overset{2}{\cancel{10}}\sqrt{126}$

$T = \frac{4}{5}\sqrt{9 \cdot 14}$

$T = \frac{12}{5}\sqrt{14}$ or $2.4\sqrt{14}$

$T = 2.4\sqrt{14}$

$T = 2.4(3.74)$

$T \approx 9.0$

12. $x + y = 5\sqrt{5}$

$2\sqrt{5} + 3\sqrt{5} = 5\sqrt{5}$; yes

$3x^2 - 4xy + y^2 = 65$

$3(2\sqrt{5})^2 - 4(2\sqrt{5})(3\sqrt{5}) + (3\sqrt{5})^2$

$= 3(4)(5) - 4(6)(5) + 9(5)$

$= 60 - 120 + 45$

$= -15 \neq 65$

no

<u>Quadratic Equation Exercises</u> Page 350

Some checks are left for the teacher.

1. $y^2 + 3.9y + 1.4 = 0$
$10y^2 + 39y + 14 = 0$
$(5y + 2)(2y + 7) = 0$

$5y + 2 = 0 \qquad 2y + 7 = 0$
$5y = -2 \qquad 2y = -7$
$y = -.4 \qquad y = -3.5$

2. $.2x^2 - x = 2.8$
$2x^2 - 10x = 28$
$2x^2 - 10x - 28 = 0$
$x^2 - 5x - 14 = 0$
$(x - 7)(x + 2) = 0$

$x - 7 = 0 \qquad x + 2 = 0$
$x = 7 \qquad x = -2$

3. $2x^2 - .1x - .08 - .002$
$2000x^2 - 100x - 80 = 2$
$2000x^2 - 100x - 82 = 0$
$1000x^2 - 50x - 41 = 0$

$$x = \frac{50 \pm \sqrt{(-50)^2 - 4(1000)(-41)}}{2(1000)}$$

$$x = \frac{50 \pm \sqrt{166{,}500}}{2000}$$

$$x = \frac{50 \pm 30\sqrt{185}}{2000}$$

$$x = \frac{5 \pm 3(13.60)}{200}$$

$$x = \frac{5 \pm 40.80}{200}$$

$$x = \frac{45.8}{200} \approx .23$$

and

$$x = \frac{-35.8}{200} \approx -.18$$

$2(.23)^2 - .1(.23) - .08 = .1058 - .023 - .08 = .0028$
$2(-.18)^2 - .1(-.18) - .08 = .0648 + .018 - .08 = .0028$

.0028 differs from original value of .002 due to rounding of solution to the equation.

*4. $5x - 3 = 7x^2$
$7x^2 - 5x + 3 = 0$

$$x = \frac{5 \pm \sqrt{(-5)^2 - 4(7)(3)}}{2(7)}$$

$$x = \frac{5 \pm \sqrt{25 - 84}}{14}$$

$$x = \frac{5 \pm \sqrt{-59}}{14}$$

No real solution.

5. $3x^2 - .4x = 0$
$30x^2 - 4x = 0$
$2x(15x - 2) = 0$

$2x = 0 \qquad 15x - 2 = 0$
$x = 0 \qquad 15x = 2$

$$x = \frac{2}{15}$$

6.

$$\frac{x - 2}{x - 3} + \frac{x + 3}{x + 2} = 6$$

$$(x - 3)(x + 2)\left(\frac{x - 2}{x - 3} + \frac{x + 3}{x + 2}\right) = 6(x - 3)(x + 2)$$

$$(x + 2)(x - 2) + (x - 3)(x + 3) = 6(x^2 - x - 6)$$

$$x^2 - 4 + x^2 - 9 = 6x^2 - 6x - 36$$

$$4x^2 - 6x - 23 = 0$$

$$x = \frac{6 \pm \sqrt{36 - 4(4)(-23)}}{2(4)}$$

$$x = \frac{6 \pm \sqrt{404}}{8}$$

$$x = \frac{6 \pm 2\sqrt{101}}{8}$$

$$x = \frac{3 \pm \sqrt{101}}{4}$$

* $$\frac{\frac{3 + \sqrt{101}}{4} - 2}{\frac{3 + \sqrt{101}}{4} - 3} + \frac{\frac{3 + \sqrt{101}}{4} + 3}{\frac{3 + \sqrt{101}}{4} + 2} = \frac{\frac{-5 + \sqrt{101}}{4}}{\frac{-9 + \sqrt{101}}{4}} + \frac{\frac{15 + \sqrt{101}}{4}}{\frac{11 + \sqrt{101}}{4}}$$

$$= \frac{-5 + \sqrt{101}}{-9 + \sqrt{101}} + \frac{15 + \sqrt{101}}{11 + \sqrt{101}}$$

$$= \frac{-55 + 6\sqrt{101} + 101}{-99 + 2\sqrt{101} + 101} + \frac{-135 + 6\sqrt{101} + 101}{-99 + 2\sqrt{101} + 101}$$

$$= \frac{12 + 12\sqrt{101}}{2 + 2\sqrt{101}}$$

$$= \frac{12(1 + \sqrt{101})}{2(1 + \sqrt{101})}$$

$$= 6 \checkmark$$

$$\frac{\frac{3 - \sqrt{101}}{4} - 2}{\frac{3 - \sqrt{101}}{4} - 3} + \frac{\frac{3 - \sqrt{101}}{4} + 3}{\frac{3 - \sqrt{101}}{4} + 2} = \frac{\frac{-5 - \sqrt{101}}{4}}{\frac{-9 - \sqrt{101}}{4}} + \frac{\frac{15 - \sqrt{101}}{4}}{\frac{11 - \sqrt{101}}{4}}$$

$$= \frac{-5 - \sqrt{101}}{-9 - \sqrt{101}} + \frac{15 - \sqrt{101}}{11 - \sqrt{101}}$$

$$= \frac{-55 - 6\sqrt{101} + 101}{-99 - 2\sqrt{101} + 101} + \frac{-135 - 6\sqrt{101} + 101}{-99 - 2\sqrt{101} + 101}$$

$$= \frac{12 - 12\sqrt{101}}{2 - 2\sqrt{101}}$$

$$= \frac{12(1 - \sqrt{101})}{2(1 - \sqrt{101})}$$

$$= 6 \checkmark$$

7.

$$\frac{6x + 3}{2x + 3} = \frac{3x + 3}{3x + 2}$$

$$(6x + 3)(3x + 2) = (2x + 3)(3x + 3)$$

$$18x^2 + 21x + 6 = 6x^2 + 15x + 9$$

$$12x^2 + 6x - 3 = 0$$

$$4x^2 + 2x - 1 = 0$$

$$x = \frac{-2 \pm \sqrt{2^2 - 4(4)(-1)}}{2(4)}$$

$$x = \frac{-2 \pm \sqrt{20}}{8}$$

$$x = \frac{-2 \pm 2\sqrt{5}}{8}$$

$$x = \frac{-2(1 \pm \sqrt{5}}{8}$$

$$x = \frac{-1 \pm \sqrt{5}}{4}$$

8.

$$\frac{y + 2}{3y - 2} = \frac{15}{3y + 2}$$

$$(y + 2)(3y + 2) = 15(3y - 2)$$

$$3y^2 + 8y + 4 = 45y - 30$$

$$3y^2 - 37y + 34 = 0$$

$$(3y - 34)(y - 1) = 0$$

$$3y - 34 = 0 \qquad y - 1 = 0$$

$$3y = 34 \qquad y = 1$$

$$y = \frac{34}{3}$$

*

$\dfrac{6(\frac{-1 + \sqrt{5}}{4}) + 3}{2(\frac{-1 + \sqrt{5}}{4}) + 3}$	$\dfrac{3(\frac{-1 + \sqrt{5}}{4}) + 3}{3(\frac{-1 + \sqrt{5}}{4}) + 2}$
$\dfrac{\frac{6 + 6\sqrt{5}}{4}}{\frac{10 + 2\sqrt{5}}{4}}$	$\dfrac{\frac{9 + 3\sqrt{5}}{4}}{\frac{5 + 3\sqrt{5}}{4}}$
$\dfrac{6 + 6\sqrt{5}}{10 + 2\sqrt{5}}$	$\dfrac{9 + 3\sqrt{5}}{5 + 3\sqrt{5}}$
$\dfrac{3 + 3\sqrt{5}}{5 + \sqrt{5}} \cdot \dfrac{5 - \sqrt{5}}{5 - \sqrt{5}}$	$\dfrac{9 + 3\sqrt{5}}{5 + 3\sqrt{5}} \cdot \dfrac{5 - 3\sqrt{5}}{5 - 3\sqrt{5}}$
$\dfrac{15 + 12\sqrt{5} - 15}{25 - 5}$	$\dfrac{45 - 12\sqrt{5} - 45}{25 - 45}$
$\dfrac{12\sqrt{5}}{20}$	$\dfrac{-12\sqrt{5}}{-20}$
$\dfrac{3\sqrt{5}}{5}$ =	$\dfrac{3\sqrt{5}}{5}$

(Use a similar approach for the other root.)

9. let x = first consecutive integer $\underline{-9}$ or $\underline{8}$

   x + 1 = second consecutive integer $\underline{-8}$ or $\underline{9}$

$$\begin{aligned} x^2 + (x + 1)^2 &= 145 \\ x^2 + x^2 + 2x + 1 &= 145 \\ 2x^2 + 2x - 144 &= 0 \\ x^2 + x - 72 &= 0 \\ (x + 9)(x - 8) &= 0 \end{aligned}$$

$x + 9 = 0$ $x - 8 = 0$ $(-9)^2 + (-8)^2 = 81 + 64 = 145$ ✓

$x = -9$ $x = 8$ $8^2 + 9^2 = 64 + 81 = 145$ ✓

10. s = length of side of square $\underline{5}$

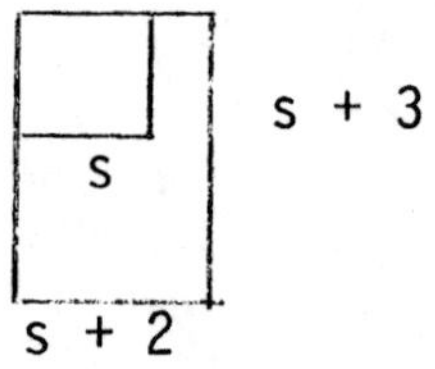

$$\begin{aligned} (s + 3)(s + 2) - s^2 &= 31 \\ s^2 + 5s + 6 - s^2 &= 31 \\ 5s + 6 &= 31 \\ 5s &= 25 \\ s &= 5 \end{aligned}$$

$(5 + 3)(5 + 2) - 5^2 = 8(7) - 25 = 56 - 25 = 31$ ✓

11. let 3x = the smaller number $\underline{6}$ or $\underline{-6}$

    4x = the larger number $\underline{8}$ or $\underline{-8}$

$$\begin{aligned} (3x)^2 + (4x)^2 &= 100 \\ 9x^2 + 16x &= 100 \\ 25x^2 &= 100 \\ x^2 &= 4 \\ x &= \pm 2 \end{aligned}$$

$[3(2)]^2 + [4(2)]^2 = 6^2 + 8^2 = 36 + 64 = 100$ ✓

$[3(-2)]^2 + [4(-2)]^2 = (-6)^2 + (-8)^2 = 36 + 64 = 100$ ✓

12. let x = one part $\underline{15.5}$ or $\underline{4.5}$

    20 - x = other part $\underline{4.5}$ or $\underline{15.5}$

$$\begin{aligned} x(20 - x) &= 69.75 \\ 20x - x^2 &= 69.75 \\ x^2 - 20x + 69.75 &= 0 \\ x &= \frac{20 \pm \sqrt{400 - 4(1)(69.75)}}{2(1)} \\ x &= \frac{20 \pm \sqrt{121}}{2} \\ x &= \frac{20 \pm 11}{2} \\ x &= 15.5; \quad 4.5 \end{aligned}$$

$$\begin{array}{r} 15.5 \\ \times 4.5 \\ \hline 775 \\ 620 \\ \hline 69.75 \end{array}$$ ✓

13. let r = number of rows <u>16</u>
$r + 9$ = hills per row

$$r(r + 9) = 400$$
$$r^2 + 9r - 400 = 0$$
$$(r + 25)(r - 16) = 0$$

~~$r + 25 = 0$~~ ~~$r = -25$~~ $\quad r - 16 = 0$, $\ r = 16$

$16(16 + 9) = 16(25) = 400$ ✓

14. let x = short side <u>10 ft.</u>
$2x + 4$ = other side <u>24 ft.</u>
$2x + 6$ = hypotenuse <u>26 ft.</u>

$$x^2 + (2x + 4)^2 = (2x + 6)^2$$
$$x^2 + 4x^2 + 16x + 16 = 4x^2 + 24x + 36$$
$$x^2 - 8x - 20 = 0$$
$$(x - 10)(x + 2) = 0$$

$x - 10 = 0$, $\ x = 10$ $\quad$ ~~$x + 2 = 0$~~ ~~$x = -2$~~

$10^2 + 24^2$	26^2
$100 + 576$	676

$676 = 676$ ✓

15. let s = initial speed <u>30 mph</u>
$s + 8$ = final speed

$$\frac{60}{s} + \frac{57}{s + 8} = 3.5$$
$$s(s + 8)\left(\frac{60}{s} + \frac{57}{s + 8}\right) = 3.5s(s + 8)$$
$$60(s + 8) + 57s = 3.5s^2 + 28s$$
$$60s + 480 + 57s = 3.5s^2 + 28s$$
$$3.5s^2 - 89s - 480 = 0$$
$$35s^2 - 890s - 4800 = 0$$
$$7s^2 - 178s - 960 = 0$$
$$(7s + 32)(s - 30) = 0$$

$7s + 32 = 0$, $\ 7s = -32$, ~~$s = \frac{-32}{7}$~~ $\quad s - 30 = 0$, $\ s = 30$

$$\frac{60}{30} + \frac{57}{30 + 8} = 2 + 1.5 = 3.5 \checkmark$$

16. let x = number of bushels <u>45.3</u>

$$\frac{320}{x} = \frac{320}{x - 10} - 2$$
$$x(x - 10)\left(\frac{320}{x}\right) = x(x - 10)\left(\frac{320}{x - 10} - 2\right)$$
$$320(x - 10) = 320x - 2x(x - 10)$$
$$320x - 3200 = 320x - 2x^2 + 20x$$
$$2x^2 - 20x - 3200 = 0$$
$$x^2 - 10x - 1600 = 0$$
$$x = \frac{10 \pm \sqrt{100 - 4(1)(1600)}}{2(1)}$$
$$x = \frac{10 \pm \sqrt{6500}}{2}$$
$$x = \frac{10 \pm 10\ \ 65}{2}$$
$$x = 5 \pm 5\sqrt{65}$$
$$x = 5 \pm 5\ (8.062)$$
$$x = 5 \pm 40.31$$
$x = 45.3$; ~~-35.3~~

45.3 bu. - 10 bu. = 35.3 bu.

$\frac{\$320}{35.3 \text{ bu.}} \approx \$9.065$ per bu.

$\frac{\$320}{45.3 \text{ bu.}} \approx \$7.064$ per bu.

\$9.065 - \$7.064 $\quad$ \$2 per bu. ✓

Key to General Review, page 351

General Review   Pages 351-355

1. Unknown numbers such as x may have different values in different equations. Known numbers such as 5 and π always have the same value.

2. a) Multiply and divide left to right and then add and subtract left to right.
   b) $7 - 3 \cdot 2 + 6 \div 2 = 7 - 6 + 6 \div 2 = 7 - 6 + 3 = 1 + 3 = 4$

3.

with an x	3×2	using the symbol $\div$	$3 \div 7$
with a dot	$3 \cdot 2$	as a fraction	$\frac{3}{7}$
using parentheses	$3(2)$		

4. An algebraic expression with three terms; a number or expression generated by multiplying a quantity by itself; when the only number that will divide into both numerator and denominator is one; fractions with like denominators.

5. Dividing both numerator and denominator of a fraction by the same number does not change the value of the fraction.

6. power - a number consisting of two or more factors of the same number
   root - one of the equal factors of a number
   like terms - terms that differ only in their numerical coefficients
   systems of equations - two or more equations that must be satisfied by the same set of values
   surd - an indicated root of a rational number that cannot be obtained exactly

7. $(a^2x^m)^n = a^{2n}x^{mn}$ $-[-(a^2)^2]^2 = -[-a^4]^2 = -[a^8] = -a^8$
   $(a^3)^4 = a^{12}$ $(a^4)^3 = a^{12}$ $(-a^2)^5 = -a^{10}$

8. positive, positive, negative

9. similar surds - surds having the same indicated root

10. 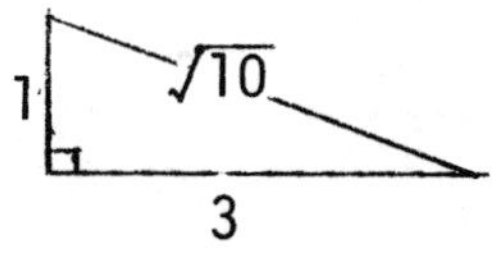

11. coordinate axes - perpendicular lines with positive and negative coordinates used to locate points in a plane and to graph lines
    axiom - a statement so evident that it is accepted without proof
    coefficient - any factor or factors in a product
    elimination - deriving from a system of equations another system involving fewer unknown numbers

12. By the highest power of any term where the degree of a term is the sum of powers of its variables; one, two, two

13. linear, quadratic

14. An equation with no first degree term, $x^2 - 5 = 0$; an equation with first and second degree terms, $3x^2 - 5x = 4$

15.(a) The value or values of the unknown number that makes the equation a true statement; Put the variable on one side of the equation, the constant on the other, and take the square roots of both sides.

(b)
$$7x^2 - 5 = 23$$
$$7x^2 = 28$$
$$x^2 = 4$$
$$x = \pm\sqrt{4}$$
$$x = \pm 2$$

16.(a) (1) Put the equation in the form $ax^2 + bx = c$.
(2) Divide each term by a, the coefficient of the squared term.
(3) Take the new coefficient of the first degree term, $\frac{b}{a}$, and find half of it.
(4) Take this result, $\frac{b}{2a}$, and square it.
(5) Add this amount, $\frac{b^2}{4a^2}$, to each side of the equation.
(6) Rewrite the left member of the equation as a binomial squared.
(7) Take the square root of each member of the equation.
(8) Solve for x.

(b) $3x^2 + 5x = 22$

(1) $3x^2 + 5x = 22$

(2) $x^2 + \frac{5}{3}x = \frac{22}{3}$

(3) $\frac{1}{2}(\frac{5}{3}) = \frac{5}{6}$

(4) $(\frac{5}{6})^2 = \frac{25}{36}$

(5) $x^2 + \frac{5}{3}x + \frac{25}{36} = \frac{22}{3} + \frac{25}{36}$

(6) $(x + \frac{5}{6})^2 = \frac{289}{36}$

(7) $x + \frac{5}{6} = \pm \frac{\sqrt{289}}{6}$

(8) $x = \frac{-5 \pm 17}{6} = 2, \frac{-11}{3}$

17.(a) (1) Put the equation in the form $ax^2 + bx + c = 0$.
(2) Determine the possible factors of a.
(3) Determine the possible factors of c.
(4) By trial and error using the FOIL method, determine the combination of factors for a and for c that result in a coefficient of b for the first degree term.
(5) Write the product as a product of binomial factors.
(6) Set each factor equal to zero and solve.

(b) $2x^2 - 5x = 12$

(1) $2x^2 - 5x - 12 = 0$
(2) The factors of 2 are 2 and 1.
(3) The factors of 12 are 3, 4; 6, 2; 12, 1.
(4) $(2x + 3)(x - 4) = 0$
(5) $2x + 3 = 0$

$2x = -3$ $\quad$ $x - 4 = 0$

$x = \frac{-3}{2}$ $\quad$ $x = 4$

18. $x = \dfrac{-b \pm \sqrt{b^2 - 4ac}}{2a}$

Begin with the general form and subtract c from each member.	$ax^2 + bx + c = 0$ $ax^2 + bx = -c$
Divide each term by a.	$x^2 + \frac{b}{a}x = \frac{-c}{a}$
Take one half the coefficient of the first degree term.	$\frac{1}{2}(\frac{b}{a}) = \frac{b}{2a}$
Square the result.	$(\frac{b}{2a})^2 = \frac{b^2}{4a^2}$
Add this amount to both sides of the equation.	$x^2 + \frac{bx}{a} + \frac{b^2}{4a^2} = \frac{b^2}{4a^2} - \frac{c}{a}$
Rewrite the left term as a perfect square.	$(x + \frac{b}{2a})^2 = \frac{b^2}{4a^2} - \frac{c}{a}$
Get a common denominator and combine terms on the right side.	$(x + \frac{b}{2a})^2 = \frac{b^2 - 4ac}{4a^2}$
Take the square root of each member.	$x + \frac{b}{2a} = \pm\frac{\sqrt{b^2 - 4ac}}{2a}$
Subtract the constant on the left from each member.	$x = \frac{-b \pm \sqrt{b^2 - 4ac}}{2a}$

19. $2x^2 - 3x = 9$

$2x^2 - 3x - 9 = 0$

$a = 2,\ b = -3,\ c = -9$

$x = \dfrac{3 \pm \sqrt{(-3)^2 - 4(2)(-9)}}{2(2)}$

$x = \dfrac{3 \pm \sqrt{9 + 72}}{4}$

$x = \dfrac{3 \pm \sqrt{81}}{4}$

$x = \dfrac{3 \pm 9}{4}$

$x = \dfrac{12}{4};\ \dfrac{-6}{4}$

$x = 3;\ \dfrac{-3}{2}$

20. Negative roots are often excluded by the context. For example, problems involving area result in roots representing lengths. Such values cannot be negative.

21. The graph intersects the x-axis in only one point. The graph intersects the x-axis in two points.

22. a straight line; two parallel lines

23. It graphs as a parabola.

24. (a) The point on the graph having the smallest value for y.

(b) $x^2 + 6x + 5 = 0$

$-[\frac{1}{2}(6)] = -3$

Begin with x = -3

x	y
-3	-4
-2	-3
-4	-3
-1	0
-5	0
0	5
-6	5

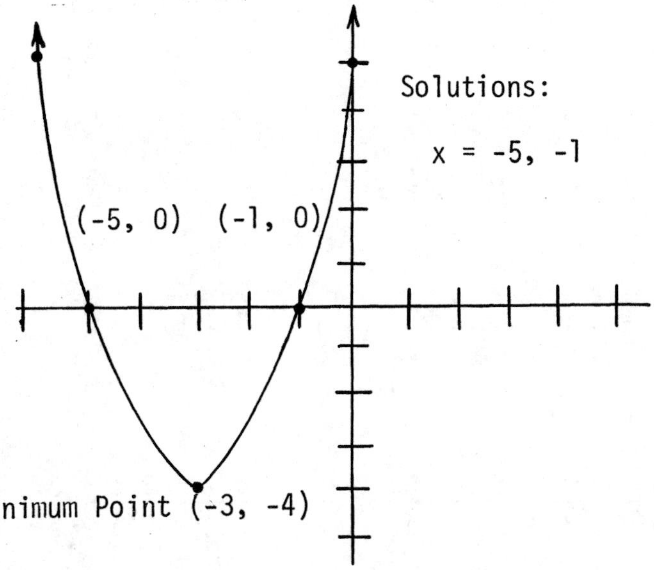

Solutions:

x = -5, -1

25. One; zero, one, or two

26. ratio - the relation of two numbers of the same kind expressed as a quotient of the first divided by the second
proportion - an equality of ratios
variation - the resulting change of the value of a quantity when the value of a second quantity changes

27. Any two of the following three are required.

a. In any proportion, the product of the means is equal to the product of the extremes. $\frac{2}{3} = \frac{4}{6}$ $2 \cdot 6 = 3 \cdot 4 = 12$

b. A mean proportional between two numbers is equal to the square root of their product. $\frac{4}{6} = \frac{6}{9}$ $\sqrt{4 \cdot 9} = \sqrt{36} = 6$

c. If the product of two numbers is equal to the product of two other numbers, one pair of them may be made the extremes and the other pair the means in a proportion. $8 \cdot 12 = 6 \cdot 16$ $\frac{8}{6} = \frac{16}{12}$

All of these principles depend upon the fact that the changes that can be made to a proportion without destroying equality correspond to those that can be made to an equation without destroying equality.

28. The means are y and y; the extremes are x and z; y is the mean proportional between x and z.

29. $\frac{8a}{x} = \frac{x}{2a}$

$x^2 = 16a^2$

$x = \pm\sqrt{16a^2}$

$x = \pm 4a$

30. $x\sqrt{y} + y\sqrt{x} + \sqrt{xy} \quad = x\sqrt{y} + y\sqrt{x} + \sqrt{xy} \quad = y\sqrt{x} + x\sqrt{y} + \sqrt{xy}$

$x^{\frac{1}{2}}y^{\frac{1}{2}} - \sqrt{x^2y} - \sqrt{xy^2} \quad = \sqrt{xy} - x\sqrt{y} - y\sqrt{x} \quad = -y\sqrt{x} - x\sqrt{y} + \sqrt{xy}$

$\sqrt{x^2y} - \sqrt{xy^2} - \sqrt{xy} \quad = x\sqrt{y} - y\sqrt{x} - \sqrt{xy} \quad = -y\sqrt{x} + x\sqrt{y} - \sqrt{xy}$

$y\sqrt{x} - x\sqrt{4y} - \sqrt{9xy} = y\sqrt{x} - 2x\sqrt{y} - 3\sqrt{xy} = \underline{y\sqrt{x} - 2x\sqrt{y} - 3\sqrt{xy}}$

$-x\sqrt{y} - 2\sqrt{xy}$

31. $a - b - [a - b - (2a + b + 2a - b) - a] - b$
$= a - b - [a - b - (4a) - a] - b$
$= a - b - [-b - 4a] - b$
$= a - b + b + 4a - b$
$= 5a - b$

32. $$\frac{a^2 - b^2 - c^2 - 2bc}{a^2 - b^2 + c^2 + 2ac} = \frac{a^2 - (b^2 + 2bc + c^2)}{(a^2 + 2ac + c^2) - b^2} = \frac{a^2 - (b + c)^2}{(a + c)^2 - b^2}$$
$$= \frac{[a - (b + c)][a + (b + c)]}{[(a + c) - b][(a + c) + b]}$$
$$= \frac{(a - b - c)\cancel{(a + b + c)}}{(a - b + c)\cancel{(a + b + c)}}$$
$$= \frac{a - b - c}{a - b + c}$$

33. $$\frac{x}{x + 1} - \frac{x}{1 - x} + \frac{x^2}{x^2 - 1} = \frac{x}{x + 1} + \frac{x}{x - 1} + \frac{x^2}{(x + 1)(x - 1)}$$
$$= \frac{x(x - 1)}{(x + 1)(x - 1)} + \frac{x(x + 1)}{(x + 1)(x - 1)} + \frac{x^2}{(x + 1)(x - 1)}$$
$$= \frac{x^2 - x + x^2 + x + x^2}{(x + 1)(x - 1)}$$
$$= \frac{3x^2}{(x + 1)(x - 1)}$$

34. $$\frac{1}{(a - b)(b - c)} - \frac{1}{(c - b)(c - a)} + \frac{1}{(c - a)(a - b)}$$
$$= \frac{1}{(a - b)(b - c)} + \frac{1}{(c - a)(b - c)} + \frac{1}{(c - a)(a - b)}$$
$$= \frac{c - a}{(a - b)(b - c)(c - a)} + \frac{a - b}{(a - b)(b - c)(c - a)} + \frac{b - c}{(a - b)(b - c)(c - a)}$$
$$= \frac{c - a + a - b + b - c}{(a - b)(b - c)(c - a)} = 0$$

35.(a) $\sqrt{\frac{2}{3}} = \frac{\sqrt{2}}{\sqrt{3}} = \frac{\sqrt{2}\cdot\sqrt{3}}{\sqrt{3}\,\sqrt{3}} = \frac{\sqrt{6}}{3}$

(b) $\sqrt[4]{25a^4} = \sqrt[4]{a^4}\,\sqrt[4]{5^2} = a(5^{\frac{2}{4}}) = a(5^{\frac{1}{2}})$
$= a\sqrt{5}$

$$(c)\ \sqrt[3]{4^2} \cdot \sqrt[9]{8} \cdot 3\sqrt[3]{4} = (4^2)^{\frac{1}{3}}(2^3)^{\frac{1}{9}}(3)(4^{\frac{1}{3}})$$
$$= 4^{\frac{2}{3}}(2^{\frac{3}{9}})(3)(4^{\frac{1}{3}})$$
$$= 4(3)(2^{\frac{1}{3}})$$
$$= 12\sqrt[3]{2}$$

36.
$$3x^2 - 2x = 65$$
$$3x^2 - 2x - 65 = 0$$
$$(3x + 13)(x - 5) = 0$$
$$3x + 13 = 0 \qquad x - 5 = 0$$
$$3x = -13 \qquad x = 5$$
$$x = \frac{-13}{3}$$

37.
$$x^2 + \frac{1}{2} = \frac{3x}{2}$$
$$2x^2 + 1 = 3x$$
$$2x^2 - 3x + 1 = 0$$
$$(2x - 1)(x - 1) = 0$$
$$2x - 1 = 0 \qquad x - 1 = 0$$
$$2x = 1 \qquad x = 1$$
$$x = \frac{1}{2}$$

38.
$$\begin{cases} \frac{1}{x} + \frac{1}{y} = 10 \\ \frac{3}{x} + \frac{2}{y} = 10 \end{cases}$$
$$\frac{2}{x} + \frac{2}{y} = 20$$
$$(-)\ \frac{3}{x} + \frac{2}{y} = 10$$
$$-\frac{1}{x} = 10$$
$$-1 = 10x$$
$$x = -\frac{1}{10}$$
$$\frac{1}{-\frac{1}{10}} + \frac{1}{y} = 10$$
$$-10 + \frac{1}{y} = 10$$
$$\frac{1}{y} = 20$$
$$y = \frac{1}{20}$$

Solution $(-\frac{1}{10}, \frac{1}{20})$

39. $x^2 + 9x + 4 = 0$
$$x = \frac{-9 \pm \sqrt{9^2 - 4(1)(4)}}{2(1)}$$
$$x = \frac{-9 \pm \sqrt{81 - 16}}{2}$$
$$x = \frac{-9 \pm \sqrt{65}}{2}$$

40.
$$x^2 + a^2 = 2ax + 3b$$
$$x^2 - 2ax + a^2 = 3b$$
$$(x - a)^2 = 3b$$
$$x - a = \pm\sqrt{3b}$$
$$x = a \pm \sqrt{3b}$$

41.
$$\sqrt{n + 5} = 4$$
$$(\sqrt{n + 5})^2 = 4^2$$
$$n + 5 = 16$$
$$n = 11$$
$$\sqrt{11 + 5} = \sqrt{16} = 4 \checkmark$$

42.
$$\begin{cases} y - x = 11 \\ x + 3y = 1 \end{cases}$$
$$-x + y = 11$$
$$(+)\ x + 3y = 1$$
$$4y = 12$$
$$y = 3$$
$$3 - x = 11$$
$$-x = 8$$
$$x = -8$$

Solution (-8; 3)

43.
$$\frac{7\frac{2}{3}}{6} = \frac{x}{4\frac{1}{2}}$$
$$\frac{\frac{23}{3}}{6} = \frac{x}{\frac{9}{2}}$$
$$6x = \frac{207}{6}$$
$$36x = 207$$
$$x = 5.75$$

44. let x = his income $\underline{\$26,000}$

$$
\begin{aligned}
(11,000)(.14) + (x - 11,000 - 5000)(.18) &= 3340 \\
1540 + (x - 16,000)(.18) &= 3340 \\
.18x - 2880 &= 1800 \\
.18x &= 4680 \\
18x &= 468,000 \\
x &= 26,000
\end{aligned}
$$

$\begin{array}{r} \$11,000 \\ \times\ .14 \\ \hline \$\ \ 1540 \end{array}$ $\quad \$26,000 - 11,000 - 5000 = \$10,000 \quad$ $\begin{array}{r} \$10,000 \\ \times\ \ .18 \\ \hline \$\ \ 1800 \end{array}$ $\quad \begin{array}{r} \$1540 \\ +1800 \\ \hline \$3340 \end{array}$ ✓

45.

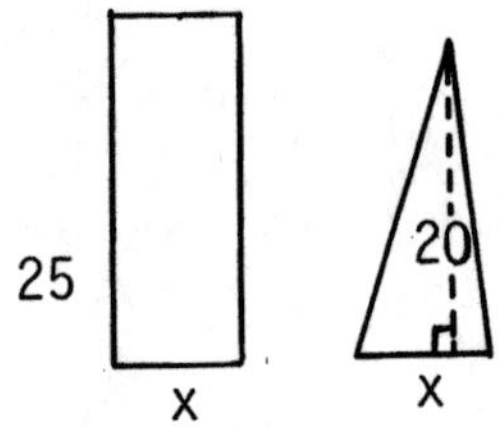

$$
\begin{aligned}
25x + \tfrac{1}{2}(20)x &= 280 \\
25x + 10x &= 280 \\
35x &= 280 \\
x &= 8 \text{ ft.}
\end{aligned}
$$

$$
\begin{aligned}
(8)(25) &= 200 \\
\tfrac{1}{2}(8)(20) &= \underline{\ 80\ } \\
& \quad 280 \text{ sq. ft.} ✓
\end{aligned}
$$

46. let t = time downstream 3
8 - t = time upstream 5

12 + 3 = 15 mph = rate downstream
12 - 3 = 9 mph = rate upstream

15t = one-way distance $\underline{45 \text{ mi.}}$

$$
\begin{aligned}
15t &= 9(8 - t) \\
15t &= 72 - 9t \\
24t &= 72 \\
t &= 3
\end{aligned}
$$

15t = 45

$\begin{array}{r} 15 \\ \times 3 \\ \hline 45 \end{array} \quad \begin{array}{r} 9 \\ \times 5 \\ \hline 45 \end{array}$ ✓

*47. let d = one-way distance $\underline{\dfrac{amn}{m + n}}$

$$
\begin{aligned}
\frac{d}{m} + \frac{d}{n} &= a \\
mn\left(\frac{d}{m} + \frac{d}{n}\right) &= amn \\
nd + md &= amn \\
d(n + m) &= amn \\
d &= \frac{amn}{m + n}
\end{aligned}
$$

48. let w = width **11.5 in.**
$w + 5.5$ = length **17 in.**

$$w + 5.5 + 6 = 2w$$
$$w + 11.5 = 2w$$
$$-w = -11.5$$
$$w = 11.5$$

$$\begin{array}{r} 17.0 \\ -11.5 \\ \hline 5.5 \end{array} ✓ \qquad \begin{array}{r} 11.5 \\ \times 2 \\ \hline 23 \end{array} \qquad \begin{array}{r} 23.0 \\ -17.0 \\ \hline 6.0 \end{array} ✓$$

*49. let s = number of shipments **65**
$\frac{16{,}250{,}000}{s}$ = number of matches per shipment

$$\left(\frac{16{,}250{,}000}{s} + 75{,}000\right)(s - 15) = 16{,}250{,}000$$
$$s\left(\frac{16{,}250{,}000}{s} + 75{,}000\right)(s - 15) = 16{,}250{,}000s$$
$$(16{,}250{,}000 + 75{,}000s)(s - 15) = 16{,}250{,}000s$$
$$75{,}000s^2 + 15{,}125{,}000s - 243{,}750{,}000 = 16{,}250{,}000s$$
$$75{,}000s^2 - 1{,}125{,}000s - 243{,}750{,}000 = 0$$
$$75s^2 - 1125s - 243{,}750 = 0$$
$$s^2 - 15s - 3250 = 0$$
$$(s - 65)(s + 50) = 0$$

$s - 65 = 0$, $s = 65$ $\qquad$ $s + 50 = 0$, ~~$s = -50$~~

$$\frac{16{,}250{,}000}{65} = 250{,}000 \qquad \frac{16{,}250{,}000}{50} = 325{,}000 \qquad \begin{array}{r} 325{,}000 \\ -250{,}000 \\ \hline 75{,}000 \end{array} ✓$$

*50. let x = lb. of baggage for one passenger **83 lb.**
$170 - x$ = lb. of baggage for second passenger **87 lb.**
y = limit in pounds **75 lb.**
$\frac{475}{170 - y}$ = cost per pound of excess baggage **\$5.00**

$$\begin{cases} (x - y)\dfrac{475}{170 - y} = 40 \\ \left[(170 - x) - y\right]\dfrac{475}{170 - y} = 60 \end{cases}$$

$$(x - y)\frac{475}{170 - y} = 40$$
$$(x - y)475 = 40(170 - y)$$
$$475x - 475y = 6800 - 40y$$
$$475x - 435y = 6800$$

$$\left[(170 - x) - y\right]\frac{475}{170 - y} = 60$$
$$475(170 - x) - 475y = 10{,}200 - 60y$$
$$80{,}750 - 475x - 475y = 10{,}200 - 60y$$
$$-475x - 475y = -70{,}550 - 60y$$
$$-475x - 415y = -70{,}550$$

$$\begin{array}{rrcl} & 475x - 435y & = & 6800 \\ (+) & -475x - 415y & = & -70{,}550 \\ \hline & -850y & = & -63{,}750 \\ & y & = & 75 \end{array}$$

limit is 75 lb.

lb. for first passenger:
$$475x - 435y = 6800$$
$$475x - 435(75) = 6800$$
$$475x - 32{,}625 = 6800$$
$$475x = 39{,}425$$
$$x = 83 \text{ lb.}$$
(8 lb. over)

lb. for second passenger:
$= 170 - x$
$= 87$ lb.
(12 lb. over)

Check:
Cost / lb. excess $\left(\frac{475}{170 - y}\right)$: \$5.00
$8 \times \$5.00 = \$40.00$ ✓
$12 \times \$5.00 = \$60.00$ ✓

General Review Tests   Pages 354-355

1. $(3x^2 + 4xy - 5y^2) + (6x^2 - 8xy + 6y^2) - (2x^2 + 6xy + 9y^2) = 7x^2 - 10xy - 8y^2$

2. $(4a^2 - 7a + 12)(a^2 + 2a - 3) =$

$$\begin{array}{rrrrr} 4a^4 & + 8a^2 & - 12a^2 & & \\ & - 7a^3 & - 14a^2 & + 21a & \\ & & 12a^2 & + 24a & - 36 \\ \hline 4a^4 & + a^3 & - 14a^2 & + 45a & - 36 \end{array}$$

3.

$$\begin{array}{r|l} & x^2 - x + 1 \\ \hline x^2 + 2x - 3 & x^4 + x^3 - 4x^2 + 5x - 3 \\ & \underline{x^4 + 2x^3 - 3x^2} \\ & \quad - x^3 - x^2 + 5x \\ & \quad \underline{- x^3 - 2x^2 + 3x} \\ & \qquad\quad x^2 + 2x - 3 \\ & \qquad\quad \underline{x^2 + 2x - 3} \end{array}$$

4. $\dfrac{a^2 + 9ab + 18b^2}{a^2 - 9ab + 20b^2} \cdot \dfrac{ab^2 - 4b^3}{a^2 + 6ab + 9b^2} = \dfrac{(a + 6b)\cancel{(a + 3b)}}{(a - 5b)\cancel{(a - 4b)}} \cdot \dfrac{b^2\cancel{(a - 4b)}}{\cancel{(a + 3b)}(a + 3b)}$

$= \dfrac{b^2(a + 6b)}{(a - 5b)(a + 3b)}$

5. $\dfrac{x^2 - 16}{x^2 - 9} \div \dfrac{x^2 - x - 20}{x^2 - 6x + 9} = \dfrac{x^2 - 16}{x^2 - 9} \cdot \dfrac{x^2 - 6x + 9}{x^2 - x - 20}$

$= \dfrac{\cancel{(x + 4)}(x - 4)}{(x + 3)\cancel{(x - 3)}} \cdot \dfrac{\cancel{(x - 3)}(x - 3)}{(x - 5)\cancel{(x + 4)}} = \dfrac{(x - 4)(x - 3)}{(x + 3)(x - 5)}$

6. $\dfrac{x + 1}{9} - \dfrac{x - 1}{15} = \dfrac{5(x + 1)}{45} - \dfrac{3(x - 1)}{45} = \dfrac{5x + 5 - 3x + 3}{45} = \dfrac{2x + 8}{45}$

7. $\dfrac{x + 7}{x^2 - 3x - 10} - \dfrac{x + 2}{x^2 + 2x - 35} = \dfrac{x + 7}{(x - 5)(x + 2)} - \dfrac{x + 2}{(x + 7)(x - 5)}$

$= \dfrac{(x + 7)(x + 7)}{(x + 2)(x - 5)(x + 7)} - \dfrac{(x + 2)(x + 2)}{(x + 2)(x - 5)(x + 7)}$

$= \dfrac{x^2 + 14x + 49 - x^2 - 4x - 4}{(x + 2)(x - 5)(x + 7)}$

$= \dfrac{10x + 45}{(x + 2)(x - 5)(x + 7)}$

8. $\dfrac{1}{a^2 - 4} + \dfrac{2}{a + 2} + \dfrac{3}{2 - a} = \dfrac{1}{(a + 2)(a - 2)} + \dfrac{2(a - 2)}{(a + 2)(a - 2)} - \dfrac{3(a + 2)}{(a - 2)(a + 2)}$

$= \dfrac{1 + 2a - 4 - 3a - 6}{(a + 2)(a - 2)} = \dfrac{-a - 9}{(a + 2)(a - 2)}$

or $- \dfrac{a + 9}{(a + 2)(a - 2)}$

9. $\sqrt{45} + \sqrt{20} = \sqrt{9}\sqrt{5} + \sqrt{4}\sqrt{5} = 3\sqrt{5} + 2\sqrt{5} = 5\sqrt{5}$

10. $(3 - 2\sqrt{3})(2 + \sqrt{3}) = 6 - \sqrt{3} - 2\sqrt{9} = 6 - \sqrt{3} - 6 = -\sqrt{3}$

Equations

The check is left for the teacher.

1. $$\begin{aligned} 5z + 12 &= 8 - 3z \\ 8z &= -4 \\ z &= -\frac{4}{8} = -\frac{1}{2} \end{aligned}$$

2. $$\begin{aligned} 2x - 3(x - 6) &= 17 \\ 2x - 3x + 18 &= 17 \\ -x &= -1 \\ x &= 1 \end{aligned}$$

3. $$\begin{aligned} (4x - 1)(3x + 5) &= (6x - 2)(2x + 3) \\ 12x^2 + 17x - 5 &= 12x^2 + 14x - 6 \\ 3x &= -1 \\ x &= -\frac{1}{3} \end{aligned}$$

4. $$\begin{aligned} \frac{3x}{4} - 5 &= \frac{7x}{8} - 6 \\ 8\left(\frac{3x}{4} - 5\right) &= 8\left(\frac{7x}{8} - 6\right) \\ 6x - 40 &= 7x - 48 \\ -x &= -8 \\ x &= 8 \end{aligned}$$

5. $$\begin{aligned} \frac{6}{2r + 3} &= \frac{2}{r - 4} \\ 6(r - 4) &= 2(2r + 3) \\ 6r - 24 &= 4r + 6 \\ 2r &= 30 \\ r &= 15 \end{aligned}$$

6. $$\begin{aligned} \frac{2m + 1}{2m - 1} + \frac{8}{1 - 4m^2} &= \frac{2m - 1}{2m + 1} \\ \frac{2m + 1}{2m - 1} - \frac{2m - 1}{2m + 1} &= \frac{8}{4m^2 - 1} \\ \frac{4m^2 + 4m + 1 - 4m^2 + 4m - 1}{4m^2 - 1} &= \frac{8}{4m^2 - 1} \\ \frac{8m}{4m^2 - 1} &= \frac{8}{4m^2 - 1} \\ 8m &= 8 \\ m &= 1 \end{aligned}$$

7. $$\begin{aligned} 3s - 4t &= 45 \\ 2s + 6t &= 4 \quad (\div 2) \end{aligned}$$

$$\begin{aligned} s + 3t &= 2 \\ s &= 2 - 3t \end{aligned}$$

$$\begin{aligned} 3(2 - 3t) - 4t &= 45 \\ 6 - 9t - 4t &= 45 \\ -13t &= 39 \\ t &= -3 \end{aligned}$$

$$\begin{aligned} s &= 2 - 3(-3) \\ s &= 11 \end{aligned}$$

8. $$\begin{aligned} 5x^2 - 6x - 8 &= 0 \\ (5x + 4)(x - 2) &= 0 \end{aligned}$$

$$\begin{aligned} 5x + 4 &= 0 \\ 5x &= -4 \\ x &= -\frac{4}{5} \end{aligned} \qquad \begin{aligned} x - 2 &= 0 \\ x &= 2 \end{aligned}$$

9. $x^2 - 6x + 4 = 0$

$$x = \frac{6 \pm \sqrt{(-6)^2 - 4(1)(4)}}{2(1)}$$

$$x = \frac{6 \pm \sqrt{36 - 16}}{2}$$

$$x = \frac{6 \pm \sqrt{20}}{2}$$

$$x = \frac{6 \pm 2\sqrt{5}}{2}$$

$$x = 3 \pm \sqrt{5}$$

10. $\ell = a + d(n - 1)$

$$\ell - a = d(n - 1)$$

$$\frac{\ell - a}{d} = n - 1$$

$$n = \frac{\ell - a}{d} + 1$$

$$n = \frac{\ell - a}{d} + \frac{d}{d}$$

$$n = \frac{\ell - a + d}{d}$$

Word Problems

1. let w = width
   3w - 8 = length

   $2(3w - 8) + 2w = 24$

2. let s = length of side of square
   s + 4 = length of rectangle
   s - 3 = width of rectangle

   $(s + 4)(s - 3) = s^2$

3. let x = Lindsey's age now
   x + 8 = Miranda's age now
   x - 4 = Lindsey's age 4 years ago
   x + 4 = Miranda's age 4 years ago

   $x + 4 = 2(x - 4)$

4. let x = time together

   $\frac{x}{3} + \frac{x}{2.5} = 1$

5. let n = number of nickels
   46 n = number of quarters

   $.05n + .25(46 - n) = 6.70$

6. let x = smaller number
   x + 4 = larger number

   $\frac{1}{2}(x + 4) - \frac{1}{6}x = 8$

7. let x = number of "Fancy"
   768 - x = number of "Fine"

   $\frac{x}{768 - x} = \frac{5}{7}$

8. let s = usual speed
   s - 60 = slower speed
   $\frac{360}{s}$ = time at usual speed
   $\frac{360}{s - 60}$ = time at slower speed

   $\frac{360}{s - 60} - 1 = \frac{360}{s}$

9. let x = pints of water to be added
   9 + x = pints of solution after addition

   $.18(9) = .12(9 + x)$

   alternate equation
   $.82(9) + x = .88(9 + x)$

10. let t = tens digit
    u = units digit
    10t + u = number

$$\begin{cases} t + u = 11 \\ 10t + u + 27 = 10u + t \end{cases}$$

Final Review   Pages 356-359

1. Any four required

a) $a^3b^2 - 81a^3 = a^3(b^2 - 81) = a^3(b + 9)(b - 9)$

$x^{2a} - 18x^a + 81 = (x^a - 9)^2$

$x^2 + 2x - 24 = (x + 6)(x - 4)$

$4a^2 - 15ab - 4b^2 = (4a + b)(a - 4b)$

$$\begin{aligned} a^2 - x^2 - 9y^2 + 6xy = a^2 - (x^2 - 6xy + 9y^2) &= a^2 - (x - 3y)^2 \\ &= [a + (x - 3y)][a - (x - 3y)] \\ &= (a + x - 3y)(a - x + 3y) \end{aligned}$$

b)

$$\begin{array}{r|l} & 2m^2 - 3m + 1 \\ \hline 2m^2 + 3m - 1 & 4m^4 + 0m^3 - 9m^2 + 6m - 1 \\ & \underline{4m^4 + 6m^3 - 2m^2} \\ & \quad -6m^3 - 7m^2 + 6m \\ & \quad \underline{-6m^3 - 9m^2 + 3m} \\ & \qquad 2m^2 + 3m - 1 \\ & \qquad \underline{2m^2 + 3m - 1} \end{array}$$

c) $$\frac{3c^2 - 6c}{6c^2 - 24} = \frac{3c(c - 2)}{6(c^2 - 4)} = \frac{\cancel{3}c\cancel{(c - 2)}}{\cancel{6}_{2}(c + 2)\cancel{(c - 2)}} = \frac{c}{2(c + 2)}$$

d) $$\begin{aligned} 30\sqrt{\frac{1}{2}} - \frac{9}{2}\sqrt{8} + 9\sqrt{\frac{169}{2}} &= 30\left(\frac{1}{\sqrt{2}}\right) - \frac{9}{2}(2\sqrt{2}) + 9\left(\frac{13}{\sqrt{2}}\right) \\ &= \frac{30}{\sqrt{2}}\left(\frac{\sqrt{2}}{\sqrt{2}}\right) - 9\sqrt{2} + \frac{117}{\sqrt{2}}\left(\frac{\sqrt{2}}{\sqrt{2}}\right) \\ &= \frac{30\sqrt{2}}{2} - \frac{18}{2}\sqrt{2} + \frac{117\sqrt{2}}{2} \\ &= \frac{129}{2}\sqrt{2} \end{aligned}$$

e) $$\begin{aligned} (3\sqrt{5} - 2\sqrt{10})(4\sqrt{5} + \sqrt{10}) &= 60 - 5\sqrt{50} - 20 \\ &= 40 - 5(5\sqrt{2}) \\ &= 40 - 25\sqrt{2} \end{aligned}$$

f) $$\begin{cases} ax + by = 2 & (a) \\ abx + aby = a + b \end{cases}$$

$$\begin{aligned} a^2x + aby &= 2a \\ (-)\quad abx + aby &= a + b \\ \hline a^2x - abx &= 2a - (a + b) \\ ax(a - b) &= a - b \\ x &= \frac{\cancel{a - b}}{a\cancel{(a - b)}} \\ x &= \frac{1}{a} \end{aligned}$$

$$\begin{aligned} a\left(\frac{1}{a}\right) + by &= 2 \\ 1 + by &= 2 \\ by &= 1 \\ y &= \frac{1}{b} \end{aligned}$$

g)
$$\frac{7k}{5} - \frac{1}{14}(k - 11) = \frac{3}{7}(k - 25) + 34$$
$$70\left[\frac{7k}{5} - \frac{1}{14}(k - 11)\right] = 70\left[\frac{3}{7}(k - 25) + 34\right]$$
$$98k - 5(k - 11) = 30(k - 25) + 2380$$
$$98k - 5k + 55 = 30k - 750 + 2380$$
$$93k + 55 = 30k + 1630$$
$$63k = 1575$$
$$k = 25$$

h)
$$\frac{x}{3(x - 1)} = \frac{x - 2}{2}$$
$$3(x - 1)(x - 2) = 2x$$
$$3(x^2 - 3x + 2) = 2x$$
$$3x^2 - 9x + 6 = 2x$$
$$3x^2 - 11x + 6 = 0$$
$$(3x - 2)(x - 3) = 0$$

$3x - 2 = 0$ $\quad$ $x - 3 = 0$

$3x = 2$ $\quad$ $x = 3$

$x = \frac{2}{3}$

$$\frac{\frac{2}{3}}{3(\frac{2}{3} - 1)} \;\Big|\; \frac{\frac{2}{3} - 2}{2}$$
$$\frac{\frac{2}{3}}{3(-\frac{1}{3})} \;\Big|\; \frac{\frac{2}{3} - \frac{6}{3}}{2}$$
$$\frac{\frac{2}{3}}{-1} \;\Big|\; \frac{-\frac{4}{3}}{2}$$
$$-\frac{2}{3} = -\frac{2}{3} \checkmark$$

one check required

$$\frac{3}{3(3 - 1)} \;\Big|\; \frac{3 - 2}{2}$$
$$\frac{3}{6}$$
$$\frac{1}{2} = \frac{1}{2} \checkmark$$

2. let x = smaller number $\quad$ 7

x + 12 = larger number $\quad$ 19

$$7x - (x + 12) = 30$$
$$7x - x - 12 = 30$$
$$6x = 42$$
$$x = 7$$

$$\begin{array}{r} 7 \\ \times\ 7 \\ \hline 49 \\ -19 \\ \hline 30 \checkmark \end{array}$$

3. a)
$$T = 2\pi R(R + H)$$
$$T = 2\pi R^2 + 2\pi RH$$
$$T - 2\pi R^2 = 2\pi RH$$
$$H = \frac{T - 2\pi R^2}{2\pi R} \text{ or } \frac{T}{2\pi R} - R$$

b)
$$H = \frac{794.42 - 2(3.14)(10^2)}{2(3.14)(10)}$$
$$H = \frac{794.42 - 628}{62.8}$$
$$H = \frac{166.42}{62.8} = 2.65$$

H = 2.7 to nearest tenth
(2.6 if more precise value used for π)

4.
$$\begin{cases} x - 2y = a \\ 2x - y = b \quad (2) \end{cases}$$

$$\begin{array}{rl} x - 2y &= a \\ (-)\ 4x - 2y &= 2b \\ \hline -3x &= a - 2b \\ x &= \frac{a - 2b}{-3} \\ x &= \frac{2b - a}{3} \end{array}$$

$$\frac{2b - a}{3} - 2y = a$$
$$2b - a - 6y = 3a$$
$$-6y = 4a - 2b$$
$$y = \frac{4a - 2b}{-6}$$
$$y = \frac{2b - 4a}{6}$$
$$y = \frac{b - 2a}{3}$$

5.
$$x^2 + 11 = 7x$$
$$x^2 - 7x + 11 = 0$$
$$x = \frac{7 \pm \sqrt{(-7)^2 - 4(1)(11)}}{2(1)}$$
$$x = \frac{7 \pm \sqrt{5}}{2}$$
$$x = \frac{7 \pm 2.236}{2}$$
$$x = \frac{9.236}{2}; \frac{4.764}{2}$$
$$x = 4.62; 2.38$$

6. let t = time for second man $1\frac{3}{4}$ hr.

$t + \frac{5}{2}$ = time for first man $4\frac{1}{4}$ hr.

$$\frac{17}{2}t = \frac{7}{2}(t + \frac{5}{2})$$
$$\frac{17}{2}t = \frac{7}{2}t + \frac{35}{4}$$
$$5t = \frac{35}{4}$$
$$t = \frac{1}{5}(\frac{35}{4}) = \frac{7}{4} \qquad (\frac{17}{4})(\frac{7}{2}) = \frac{119}{8} \checkmark$$
$$t = 1\frac{3}{4} \qquad (\frac{7}{4})(\frac{17}{2}) = \frac{119}{8}$$

7. a) $100a + 10b + c$; $100c + 10b + a$
b) $36(c - s)$ dollars
c) $4(y - 3) = 2(y + 5)$

8. a)

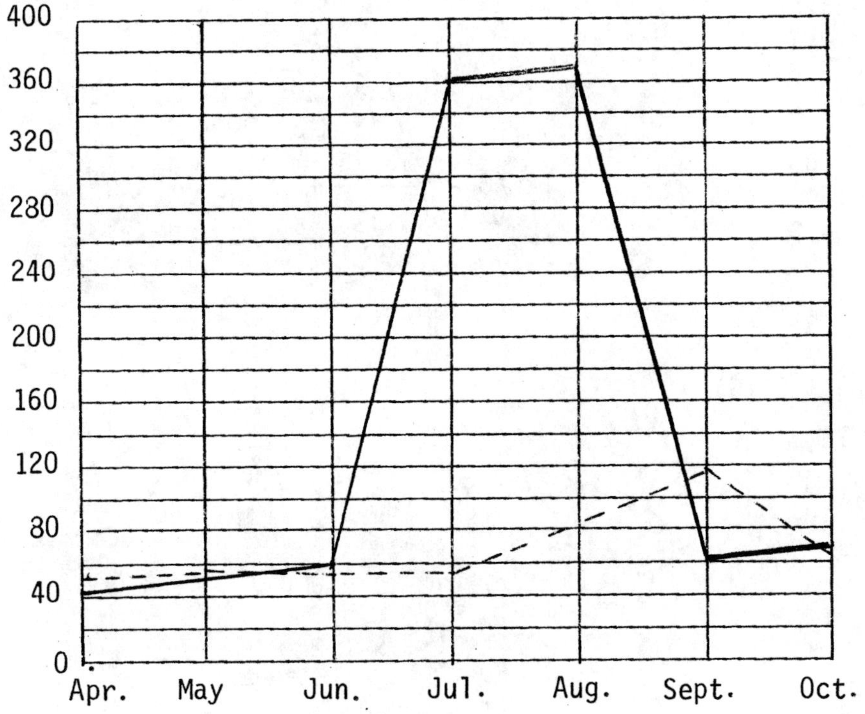

b) By solid line rising much higher than during the rest of the year.

9. (a)

$$\begin{array}{r|l} & a^2 - 2a + 5 \\ a^2 + 4a - 3 & a^4 + 2a^3 - 6a^2 + 26a - 15 \\ & \underline{a^4 + 4a^3 - 3a^2} \\ & \quad -2a^3 - 3a^2 + 26a \\ & \quad \underline{-2a^3 - 8a^2 + 6a} \\ & \qquad 5a^2 + 20a - 15 \\ & \qquad \underline{5a^2 + 20a - 15} \end{array}$$

(b) $a^2 - 2a - 48 = (a - 8)(a + 6)$

$100x^4 - 49y^6 = (10x^2 + 7y^3)(10x^2 - 7y^3)$

$36m^2 + 60mn + 25n^2 = (6m + 5n)^2$

$12c^2 + 7c + 1 = (4c + 1)(3c + 1)$

(c)

$$(8 - \frac{6}{a + 1}) + (8 - \frac{4a - 8}{a^2 - 1}) = \frac{8(a + 1) - 6}{a + 1} + \frac{8(a^2 - 1) - (4a - 8)}{a^2 - 1}$$

$$= \frac{8a + 2}{a + 1}(\frac{a - 1}{a - 1}) + \frac{8a^2 - 4a}{(a + 1)(a - 1)}$$

$$= \frac{8a^2 - 6a - 2 + 8a^2 - 4a}{(a + 1)(a - 1)}$$

$$= \frac{16a^2 - 10a - 2}{(a + 1)(a - 1)}$$

(d)

$$\begin{cases} 6x - y = .9 & (2) \\ x + 2y = .8 \end{cases}$$

$$\begin{array}{rrcl} & 12x - 2y & = & 1.8 \\ (+) & x + 2y & = & .8 \\ \hline & 13x & = & 2.6 \\ & x & = & .2 \end{array}$$

$$\begin{aligned} 6(.2) - y &= .9 \\ 1.2 - y &= .9 \\ -y &= -.3 \\ y &= .3 \end{aligned}$$

Solution (.2; .3)

(e)

$$2\sqrt{108} - 6x\sqrt{5\tfrac{1}{3}} + \sqrt{3(8x - 2)^2}$$

$$= 2\sqrt{36}\sqrt{3} - 6x\sqrt{\frac{16}{3}} + (8x - 2)\sqrt{3}$$

$$= 12\sqrt{3} - 6x(\frac{4}{\sqrt{3}})(\frac{\sqrt{3}}{\sqrt{3}}) + 8x\sqrt{3} - 2\sqrt{3}$$

$$= 12\sqrt{3} - \frac{24x\sqrt{3}}{3} + 8x\sqrt{3} - 2\sqrt{3}$$

$$= 12\sqrt{3} - 8x\sqrt{3} + 8x\sqrt{3} - 2\sqrt{3}$$

$$= 10\sqrt{3}$$

(f) $(2\sqrt{3} - \sqrt{6})(\sqrt{3} + 3\sqrt{6})$

$= 6 + 5\sqrt{18} - 18$

$= -12 + 5(3\sqrt{2})$

$= -12 + 15\sqrt{2}$

(g)

$$\begin{aligned} \frac{3x}{2} &= x + \frac{x + 7}{x - 3} \\ \frac{x}{2} &= \frac{x + 7}{x - 3} \\ x^2 - 3x &= 2x + 14 \\ x^2 - 5x - 14 &= 0 \\ (x - 7)(x + 2) &= 0 \end{aligned}$$

$x - 7 = 0 \qquad x + 2 = 0$

$x = 7 \qquad x = -2$

10. let x = number of single desks $\underline{30}$
y = number of double desks $\underline{6}$

$$(-)\begin{cases} x + y = 36 \\ x + 2y = 42 \end{cases}$$
$$-y = -6$$
$$y = 6$$

$$x + 6 = 36$$
$$x = 30$$

$30 + 6 = 36$ ✓
$30 + 2(6) = 42$ ✓

11. (a)
$$C = \frac{E}{R + r}$$
$$C(R + r) = E$$
$$R + r = \frac{E}{C}$$

(b) $r = \frac{E}{C} - R$ or $\frac{E - RC}{C}$
$$r = \frac{110.7}{15.6} - 4.3$$
$$r = 7.1 - 4.3$$
$$r = 2.8$$

12.
$$x^2 + 2x = \frac{3}{4}$$
$$4x^2 + 8x = 3$$
$$4x^2 + 8x - 3 = 0$$
$$x = \frac{-8 \pm \sqrt{64 - 4(4)(-3)}}{2(4)}$$
$$x = \frac{-8 \pm \sqrt{112}}{8}$$
$$x = \frac{-8 \pm 4\sqrt{7}}{8}$$
$$x = \frac{-2 \pm \sqrt{7}}{2}$$
$$x = \frac{-2 \pm 2.645}{2}$$
$$x = \frac{.645}{2};\ \frac{-4.645}{2}$$
$$x = .3;\ -2.3$$

13. (a) 1) $2\ell h + 2wh$ sq. yd.
2) ℓw sq. yd.
(b) $12(b - c) - d$ in.
(c) $C + \frac{r}{100}C$

14. A circle or bar graph is required.

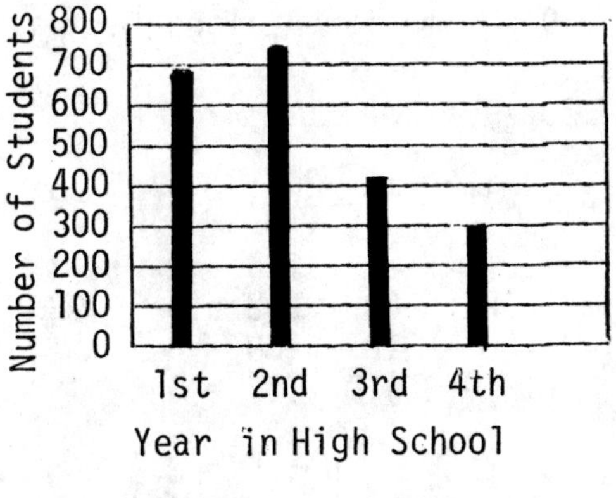

$$\begin{array}{r} 690 \\ 750 \\ 420 \\ \underline{300} \\ 2160 \end{array}$$

$$\frac{690}{2160}(360) = 690\left(\frac{360}{2160}\right) = 690\left(\frac{1}{6}\right) = 115°$$
$$750\left(\frac{1}{6}\right) = 125°$$
$$420\left(\frac{1}{6}\right) = 70°$$
$$300\left(\frac{1}{6}\right) = 50°$$
$$\overline{360°}$$

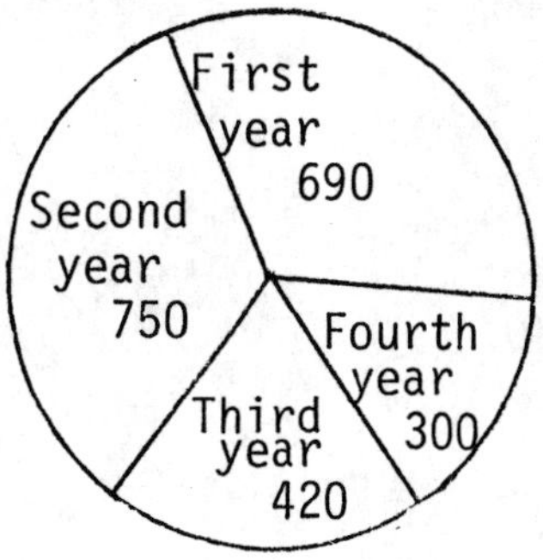

15. let 2x = numerator
3x = denominator

the fraction = $\frac{12}{18}$

$$\frac{2x - 3}{3x - 6} = \frac{3}{4}$$
$$3(3x - 6) = 4(2x - 3)$$
$$9x - 18 = 8x - 12$$
$$x = 6$$
$$2x = 12$$
$$3x = 18$$

$$\frac{12}{18} = \frac{2}{3} \checkmark$$
$$\frac{12 - 3}{18 - 6} = \frac{9}{12} = \frac{3}{4} \checkmark$$

16.
$$3x + 2y = 5$$
$$y + 3 = 6x$$
$$y = 6x - 3$$

$$3x + 2(6x - 3) = 5$$
$$3x + 12x - 6 = 5$$
$$15x = 11$$
$$x = \frac{11}{15}$$

$$y = 6(\tfrac{11}{15}) - 3$$
$$y = \frac{66}{15} - \frac{45}{15}$$
$$y = \frac{21}{15} = \frac{7}{5}$$

Solution $(\frac{11}{15}; \frac{7}{5})$

17.
$$\frac{x}{3} - \frac{x - 3}{3} = 12 - \frac{x + 4}{2} - x$$
$$1 = \frac{24 - x - 4 - 2x}{2}$$
$$1 = \frac{20 - 3x}{2}$$
$$2 = 20 - 3x$$
$$3x = 18$$
$$x = 6$$

18. (a)
$$\sqrt{\frac{3}{4}} + \sqrt{\frac{1}{3}} = \frac{\sqrt{3}}{\sqrt{4}} + \frac{\sqrt{1}}{\sqrt{3}}(\frac{\sqrt{3}}{\sqrt{3}})$$
$$= \frac{\sqrt{3}}{2} + \frac{\sqrt{3}}{3}$$
$$= \frac{3\sqrt{3}}{6} + \frac{2\sqrt{3}}{6}$$
$$= \frac{5\sqrt{3}}{6}$$

(b)
$$(\sqrt{5} - \sqrt{2})(2\sqrt{5} + 3\sqrt{2})$$
$$= 10 + \sqrt{10} - 6$$
$$= 4 + \sqrt{10}$$

19. let A = age of A <u>35</u>
B = age of B <u>15</u>

$$\begin{cases} A + 5 = 2(B + 5) \\ A - 5 = 3(B - 5) \end{cases}$$

$$\begin{cases} A + 5 = 2B + 10 \\ A - 5 = 3B - 15 \end{cases}$$

$$\begin{array}{rl} & A - 2B = 5 \\ (-) & A - 3B = -10 \\ \hline & B = 15 \end{array}$$

$$A + 5 = 2(15 + 5)$$
$$A + 5 = 2(20) = 40$$
$$A = 35$$

35 + 5 = 40	35 - 5 = 30
15 + 5 = 20	15 - 5 = 10
40 is 2(20) ✓	30 is 3(10) ✓

20. let B = time for B alone <u>36 da.</u>
B + 9 = time for A alone <u>45 da.</u>

$$20(\tfrac{1}{B}) + 20(\tfrac{1}{B + 9}) = 1$$
$$B(B + 9)(\tfrac{20}{B} + \tfrac{20}{B + 9}) = B(B + 9)$$
$$20(B + 9) + 20B = B^2 + 9B$$
$$20B + 180 + 20B = B^2 + 9B$$
$$B^2 - 31B - 180 = 0$$
$$(B - 36)(B + 5) = 0$$

B - 36 = 0   B + 5 = 0
B = 36   ~~B = -5~~

$$20(\tfrac{1}{36}) + 20(\tfrac{1}{45}) = \frac{20}{36} + \frac{20}{45} = \frac{5}{9} + \frac{4}{9} = 1$$

21. (a) $x^2 = 2x + 3$

$x^2 - 2x - 3 = 0$

graph $y = x^2 - 2x - 3$

$-[\frac{1}{2}(-2)] = 1$

x	y
1	-4
2	-3
0	-3
3	0
-1	0
4	5
-2	5

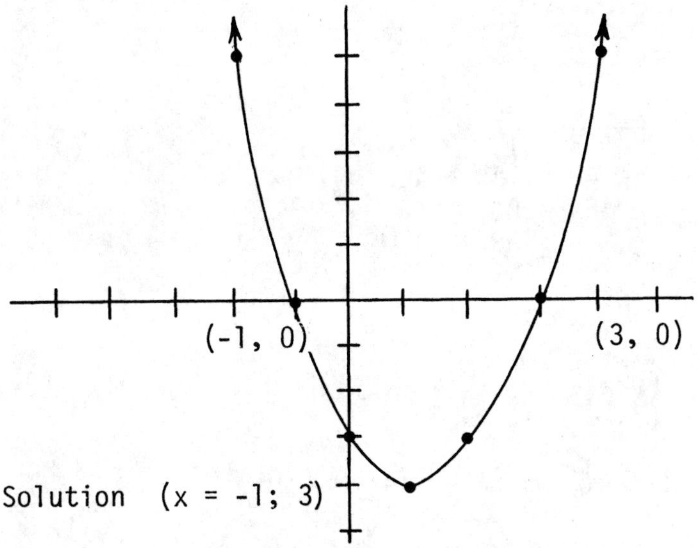

Solution (x = -1; 3)

(b) $x^2 + x + 1 = 0$

$x = \frac{-1 \pm \sqrt{1^2 - 4(1)(1)}}{2(1)}$

$x = \frac{-1 \pm \sqrt{-3}}{2}$

No real solution

22. (a) $2x^2 - 12x + 18 = 2(x^2 - 6x + 9) = 2(x - 3)^2$

(b) $a^2 - 12a - 49b^2 + 36 = (a^2 - 12a + 36) - 49b^2 = (a - 6)^2 - 49b^2$
$= (a - 6 + 7b)(a - 6 - 7b)$
$= (a + 7b - 6)(a - 7b - 6)$

(c) $8 - 18m^2 = 2(4 - 9m^2) = 2(2 + 3m)(2 - 3m)$

23. $\frac{1}{x + 3} + \frac{7}{x^2 - x - 12} + \frac{x + 3}{x - 4} = \frac{1}{x + 3} + \frac{7}{(x - 4)(x + 3)} + \frac{x + 3}{x - 4}$

$= \frac{x - 4}{(x + 3)(x - 4)} + \frac{7}{(x - 4)(x + 3)} + \frac{(x + 3)^2}{(x - 4)(x + 3)}$

$= \frac{x - 4 + 7 + x^2 + 6x + 9}{(x - 4)(x + 3)}$

$= \frac{x^2 + 7x + 12}{(x - 4)(x + 3)} = \frac{\cancel{(x + 3)}(x + 4)}{(x - 4)\cancel{(x + 3)}} = \frac{x + 4}{x - 4}$

24. $\frac{x - 1}{x - 2} + \frac{x^2 - 3}{4 - x^2} + \frac{x}{2 + x}$

$= \frac{x - 1}{x - 2}\left(\frac{x + 2}{x + 2}\right) + \frac{3 - x^2}{(x + 2)(x - 2)} + \frac{x}{x + 2}\left(\frac{x - 2}{x - 2}\right)$

$= \frac{x^2 + x - 2 + 3 - x^2 + x^2 - 2x}{(x + 2)(x - 2)}$

$= \frac{x^2 - x + 1}{(x + 2)(x - 2)}$

25. let w = width <u>27 ft.</u>
$2w + 24$ = length <u>78 ft.</u>

$2w + 2(2w + 24) = 210$
$2w + 4w + 48 = 210$
$6w = 162$
$w = 27$

*26. let $3x$ = one number <u>24</u>
$5x$ = other number <u>40</u>

$\frac{3x - 4}{5x + 8} = \frac{5}{12}$
$36x - 48 = 25x + 40$
$11x = 88$
$x = 8$
$3x = 24$
$5x = 40$

$\frac{24}{40} = \frac{3}{5}$

$\frac{24 - 4}{40 + 8} = \frac{20}{48} = \frac{5}{12}$

If $x < 0$
$5x < 3x$

$\frac{5x - 4}{3x + 8} = \frac{5}{12}$
$60x - 48 = 15x + 40$
$45x = 88$
~~$x = \frac{88}{45}$~~ Reject since $x > 0$.

27. (a) $x^2 + 7x - 18 = (x + 9)(x - 2)$

(b) $(2x - 5y)^2 - (x - 2y)^2 = [(2x - 5y) + (x - 2y)][(2x - 5y) - (x - 2y)]$
$= (3x - 7y)(x - 3y)$

28. $7\sqrt[3]{54} + \sqrt[6]{256} + \sqrt[3]{432} = 7\sqrt[3]{27}\sqrt[3]{2} + \sqrt[6]{64}\sqrt[6]{4} + \sqrt[3]{216}\sqrt[3]{2}$

$= 7(3)\sqrt[3]{2} + 2(2^2)^{\frac{1}{6}} + 6\sqrt[3]{2}$

$= 21\sqrt[3]{2} + 2(2^{\frac{1}{3}}) + 6\sqrt[3]{2}$

$= 21\sqrt[3]{2} + 2\sqrt[3]{2} + 6\sqrt[3]{2} = 29\sqrt[3]{2}$

29. $2x + 3y = 6$

x	y
0	2
3	0
6	-2

$x + y = 3$

x	y
0	3
3	0
2	1

$\begin{cases} 2x + 3y = 6 \\ x + y = 3 \end{cases}$ (3)

$(-)\begin{cases} 2x + 3y = 6 \\ 3x + 3y = 9 \end{cases}$
$-x = -3$
$x = 3$

$3 + y = 3$
$y = 0$ Solution (3, 0)

(continued)

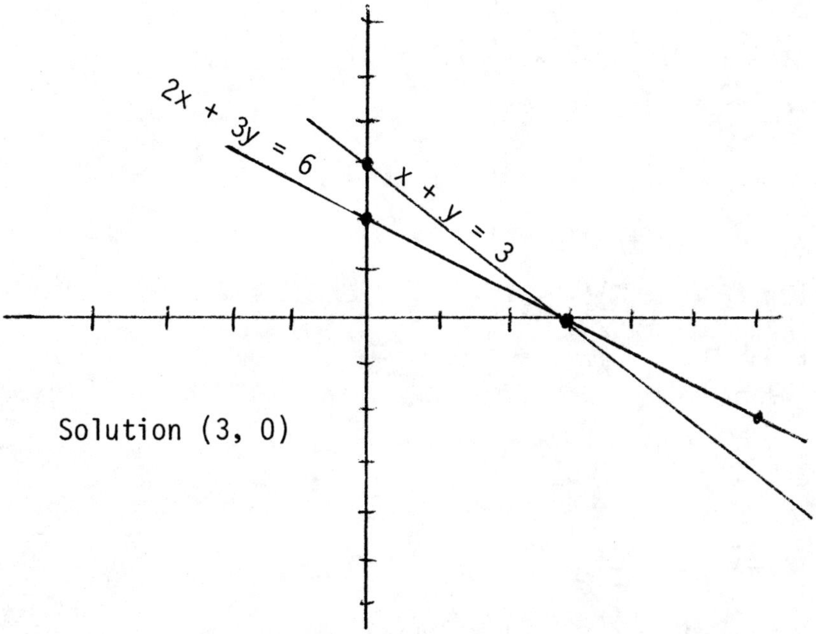

Solution (3, 0)

30. a) $x^2 - 7xy + 10y^2$
$= (x - 5y)(x - 2y)$

b) $98a^2b - 8b^3$
$= 2b(49a^2 - 4b^2)$
$= 2b(7a + 2b)(7a - 2b)$

31. $\sqrt{98x^2} - \sqrt{\frac{9}{8}} - \frac{1}{8}\sqrt{2(4x - 6)^2}$

$= \sqrt{49x^2}\,\sqrt{2} - \frac{3}{\sqrt{4}\,\sqrt{2}} - \frac{1}{8}\sqrt{(4x - 6)^2}\,\sqrt{2}$

$= 7x\sqrt{2} - \frac{3}{2\sqrt{2}}(\frac{\sqrt{2}}{\sqrt{2}}) - (\frac{4x - 6}{8})\sqrt{2}$

$= 7x\sqrt{2} - \frac{3}{4}\sqrt{2} - (\frac{4x - 6}{8})\sqrt{2}$

$= \frac{56x\sqrt{2}}{8} - \frac{6\sqrt{2}}{8} - (\frac{4x - 6}{8})\sqrt{2} = \frac{1}{8}(56x - 6 - 4x + 6)\sqrt{2}$

$= \frac{52x}{8}\sqrt{2} = \frac{13x}{2}\sqrt{2}$

32. (a)

$s = \frac{1}{2}g(2t - 1)$

$2s = g(2g - 1)$

$\frac{2s}{g} = 2t - 1$

$\frac{2s}{g} + 1 = 2t$

$\frac{1}{2}(\frac{2s}{g} + 1) = t$

$t = \frac{s}{g} + \frac{1}{2}$ or $\frac{2s + g}{2g}$

(b) $t = \frac{236.432}{32.16} + .5$

$t = 7.4 + .5$

$t = 7.9$

33. (a) $9a^5 - 36a^3 = 9a^3(a^2 - 4) = 9a^3(a + 2)(a - 2)$

(b) $16x^2 - 120xy + 225y^2 = (4x - 15y)^2$

34.
$$\frac{x}{4} - \frac{x}{x + 4} = \frac{x - 1}{6}$$
$$12(x + 4)\left(\frac{x}{4} - \frac{x}{x + 4}\right) = 12(x + 4)\left(\frac{x - 1}{6}\right)$$
$$3x(x + 4) - 12x = 2(x + 4)(x - 1)$$
$$3x^2 + 12x - 12x = 2x^2 + 6x - 8$$
$$x^2 - 6x + 8 = 0$$
$$(x - 4)(x - 2) = 0$$

$x - 4 = 0$ $\quad$ $x - 2 = 0$

$x = 4$ $\quad$ $x = 2$

35.
$$\left(\frac{2x}{x - 2} - \frac{x}{x - 1}\right) \div \left(\frac{3x}{x - 3} - \frac{2x}{x - 2}\right)$$
$$= \left[\frac{2x(x - 1) - x(x - 2)}{(x - 2)(x - 1)}\right] \div \left[\frac{3x(x - 2) - 2x(x - 3)}{(x - 2)(x - 3)}\right]$$
$$= \frac{x^2}{(x - 2)(x - 1)} \div \frac{x^2}{(x - 2)(x - 3)}$$
$$= \frac{\cancel{x^2}}{\cancel{(x - 2)}(x - 1)} \cdot \frac{\cancel{(x - 2)}(x - 3)}{\cancel{x^2}} = \frac{x - 3}{x - 1}$$

36.
$$\left(\frac{8}{m - x} - \frac{4}{x^2 - m^2}\right) \div \left(\frac{1}{m - x} - \frac{1}{m + x}\right)$$
$$= \left[\left(\frac{8}{m - x}\right)\left(\frac{m + x}{m + x}\right) + \frac{4}{(m + x)(m - x)}\right] \div \frac{m + x - (m - x)}{(m + x)(m - x)}$$
$$= \frac{8m + 8x + 4}{(m + x)(m - x)} \div \frac{2x}{(m + x)(m - x)}$$
$$= \frac{\overset{2}{\cancel{4}}(2m + 2x + 1)}{\cancel{(m + x)}\cancel{(m - x)}} \cdot \frac{\cancel{(m + x)}\cancel{(m - x)}}{\cancel{2}x} = \frac{2(2m + 2x + 1)}{x}$$
$$= \frac{4m + 4x + 2}{2}$$